The Practice of
Gas Chromatography

The Practice of
Gas Chromatography

EDITED BY

Leslie S. Ettre

The Perkin-Elmer Corporation
Norwalk, Connecticut

Albert Zlatkis

The University of Houston
Houston, Texas

INTERSCIENCE PUBLISHERS
A Division of John Wiley & Sons
New York   London   Sydney

We dedicate this book to
Archer J. P. Martin and Anthony T. James
on the fifteenth anniversary of
their first publication on
gas–liquid partition chromatography

Preface

It is often said that gas chromatography is the most widely used analytical technique and that its rapid growth is unparalleled in the history of analytical chemistry. To date, over 12,000 publications have dealt with theoretical and practical aspects of this technique and a fairly large number of books are available discussing various aspects of gas chromatography. It is therefore legitimate to ask: why do we need another book on this subject?

There are three reasons why we think that this book is necessary. First, one should not forget that the basic English textbooks on gas chromatography were written without almost any exemption prior to 1962 and this five-year period represents a significant part of the development of this technique. Secondly, while the existing books are strong in theory, the practical information contained in them is somewhat limited. We are fully aware that no practice can exist without a sufficient knowledge of theory; however, the practical gas chromatographer also needs compilations which handle the practice of the technique in detail. Finally, many special methods and techniques exist which are well documented in the scientific literature, but the large number of publications on the particular subject in many diverse publications make a general understanding of the particular method by the practical gas chromatographer almost impossible. Again, one should not forget that while the origin of all these methods can probably be traced back to the early years of gas chromatography, their real development occurred in the last few years.

To summarize briefly, the intent of this book is to provide a basic guide to the *practice* of gas chromatography for the use of analytical chemists who are now employing or who are contemplating the actual employment of gas chromatographic instruments for the solution of problems in the separation, identification, and measurement of volatile compounds.

As in any technological area (and gas chromatography is principally a *separation process* and not only a simple analytical tool), much of the worker's time and effort is devoted to learning the most efficient procedures which enable him to increase speed, precision, and efficiency. In the area of instrumental analysis, the ability to choose, install, and maintain the instrument, to properly evaluate data, and to perform data reduction processes are basic to sound performance. In years of experience, every intelligent analyst can learn many of the answers to his problems; however, in summarizing the state of the art, we hope to aid our readers in obtaining more rapidly a higher degree of proficiency.

This book consists of ten chapters each of which gives a detailed description of a different part of the gas chromatographic system or of a particular technique and its optimum use for the solution of analytical problems.

Chapter 1 includes descriptive information on the mechanism of the gas chromatographic process and the function and operation of a gas chromatographic instrument. An efficient step-by-step procedure is outlined for placing a chromatograph in operation and optimizing the analysis of an "unknown" sample. The sources of technical information useful to the analyst, such as literature, technical societies, and reference sources, are also compiled.

Chapter 2 considers the nature and effect of the carrier gas in the gas chromatographic process.

Chapter 3 discusses two questions. First it contains a detailed treatment on the various methods used to form certain volatile derivatives prior to actual sample introduction. This was felt necessary since the preparation of these derivatives is usually the task of the practical gas chromatographer. Secondly, this chapter describes the different sample introduction systems.

Chapter 4 discusses, in detail, the theoretical and practical performance aspects of the chromatographic columns.

Chapter 5 includes a systematic survey of the detector systems which have been employed in gas chromatography and the physical characteristics and practical advantages of each.

Chapter 6 discusses the application of digital electronic systems used in gas chromatography for data handling and evaluation.

Chapter 7 elaborates in detail the interpretation of the results of gas chromatographic analyses: the derivation of the qualitative and quantitative composition of the sample determined from the chromatogram.

Chapter 8 summarizes the ancillary techniques used in connection with gas chromatography for the identification of the individual separated sample components.

Chapter 9 gives a summary of the so-called reaction gas chromatography, i.e., the techniques where the sample undergoes a chemical change in the GC system.

Finally, Chapter 10 discusses the application of gas chromatography as an automatic analytical technique for process-control purposes.

Discussion of such a broad subject in such detail is a task which cannot be accomplished by one or two authors. We therefore selected for each chapter individual experienced investigators whose knowledge in that particular field is well known. We are most grateful for the excellent job they have done.

In a book written by over a dozen authors, it is inevitable that some duplication should occur. We tried to avoid this as much as possible; however, our main philosophy was to have each chapter complete even at the expense of some duplication.

Both of us have been involved in gas chromatographic work from the very early stages of its development. We have been concerned with the development and use of chromatographic instruments and methods and with the wide variety of applications and instrumental approaches. In the years which each of us have spent in this field, we have found it most fascinating, challenging, and rewarding. We sincerely hope that, by the publication of this book, many of our fellow chemists will be aided with their research and that their experience will be a pleasant one.

LESLIE S. ETTRE
ALBERT ZLATKIS

March 1, 1967

Acknowledgments

The illustrations and tables in this book, aside from those constructed by the authors, come from a variety of sources. Reproduction of the following material is authorized through the courtesy of the publications and corporations listed below.

Academic Press, New York, N. Y.: Figs. 4-29, 5-20, 5-21, 5-22.

Analytical Chemistry (American Chemical Society, Washington, D.C.): Figs. 3-15, 3-16, 3-17, 3-18, 3-19, 3-23, 4-4, 4-5, 4-17, 4-21, 4-23, 4-25, 5-3, 5-4, 5-5, 5-6, 5-7, 5-14, 5-15, 5-17, 5-18, 5-19, 5-24, 5-25, 5-26, 5-27, 5-28, 5-29, 5-33, 5-34, 5-35, 5-36, 5-37, 5-38, 5-39, 5-40, 5-41, 5-44, 5-45, 5-46, 5-47, 5-48, 5-51, 5-52, 5-53, 5-54, 5-55, 5-56, 5-57, 5-58, 8-12, 8-15; Tables 3-6, 5-1, 5-2, 5-4, 9-2, 9-5.

Annals of the New York Academy of Sciences (The New York Academy of Sciences, New York, N. Y.): Figs. 4-30, 4-35; Table 3-2.

Beckman Instruments, Inc., Fullerton, Calif.: Figs. 10-5, 10-21, 10-22.

Butterworth & Co., Ltd., London, W.C.2, England: Figs. 5-8, 5-9, 5-16, 7-14; Table 5-3.

Carlo Erba S.p.A., Milano, Italy: Fig. 10-9.

Consolidated Electrodynamics Corporation, Pasadena, Calif.: Fig. 10-17.

Foxboro Company, Foxboro, Mass.: Fig. 10-23.

Gow-Mac Instrument Company, Madison, N. J.: Fig. 5-30.

Greenbrier Instrument Division of Bendix Corporation, Roncoverte, W. Va.: Figs. 10-1, 10-19.

Infotronics Corporation, Houston, Tex.: Figs. 6-1 through 6-19; Tables 6-1 through 6-4.

Interscience Publishers Division of John Wiley & Sons, Inc., New York, N. Y.: Fig. 7-9.

ISA Journal and *ISA Proceedings* (Instrument Society of America, Pittsburgh, Pa.): Figs. 10-6, 10-13, 10-15, 10-16.

Jarrell-Ash Company, Waltham, Mass.: Figs. 5-12, 5-13.

Journal of Applied Chemistry (Society of Chemical Industry, London, S.W.1, England): Fig. 4-7.

Journal of the Association of Official Agricultural Chemists (The Association of Official Agricultural Chemists, Washington, D.C.): Fig. 9-3.

Journal of the Chemical Society (The Chemical Society, London, W.1, England): Fig. 4-3.

Journal of Chromatography (Elsevier Publishing Co., Amsterdam, The Netherlands): Figs. 3-20, 3-21, 3-27, 4-26, 4-31, 5-10, 5-11, 5-31, 5-32, 7-13, 7-15, 8-27.

Journal of Gas Chromatography (Preston Technical Abstracts Co., Evanston, Ill.): Figs. 2-1, 2-2, 2-3, 2-4, 2-5, 3-14, 4-8, 4-20, 4-27, 4-33, 5-42, 5-43, 5-49, 5-50, 7-18, 8-1, 8-2, 9-4.

Journal of Lipid Research (The American Institute of Biological Sciences, Washington, D.C.): Table 3-4.

Leeds & Northrup Company, Philadelphia, Pa.: Figs. 10-8, 10-12, 10-14, 10-20, 10-26, 10-27, 10-29, 10-34; Dr. C. W. Ross: Fig. 10-33; Mr. J. V. Eynon: 10-28, 10-32.

The Macmillan Company, New York, N. Y.: Figs. 3-3, 3-4, 3-5, 3-6, 3-7, 3-8, 3-9, 3-10, 3-11, 3-12, 3-13.

Marcel Dekker Inc., New York, N. Y.: Figs. 4-14, 4-18, 4-19.

M.E.C.I., Paris, France: Fig. 10-7.

Mine Safety Appliances Company, Pittsburgh, Pa.: Figs. 10-14, 10-24.

National Instruments Laboratories, Inc., Rockville, Md.: Fig. 5-59.

Nature (Macmillan (Journal) Ltd., London, W.C.2, England): Figs. 3-22, 4-16, 5-23.

N.M.R. Specialties, New Kensington, Pa.: Fig. 8-18.

Oil and Gas Journal (The Petroleum Publishing Co., Tulsa, Okla.): Fig. 1-7.

The Perkin-Elmer Corporation, Norwalk, Conn.: Figs. 1-2, 1-4, 1-5, 5-1, 5-2, 10-11.

Plenum Press, New York, N. Y.: Figs. 10-2, 10-3.

Preston Technical Abstracts Company, Evanston, Ill.: Fig. 1-15.

Proceedings of the American Society of Brewing Chemists (American Society of Brewing Chemists, Madison, Wis.): Figs. 8-14, 8-28.

Reinhold Publishing Company, New York, N. Y.: Table 9-4.

Scientific Reports of the Istituto Superiore di Sanità (Elsevier Publishing Co., Amsterdam, The Netherlands): Fig. 4-24.

Technical Measurements Corporation, New Haven, Conn.: Fig. 8-20.

Varian Aerograph Division of Varian Associates, Walnut Creek, Calif.: Figs. 3-25, 3-26.

Zeitschrift für analytische Chemie (Springer Verlag, Heidelberg, Germany): Figs. 4-15, 8-3, 8-4, 9-4.

Contributors

MORTON BEROZA, Agricultural Research Service, U.S. Department of Agriculture, Beltsville, Maryland

WILLIAM R. BETKER, Chemagro Corporation, Kansas City, Missouri

NATHANIEL BRENNER, The Perkin-Elmer Corporation, Norwalk, Connecticut

JERRY C. CAVAGNOL, Chemagro Corporation, Kansas City, Missouri

RAYLENE A. COAD, P.O. Box 1291, Trone, California

LESLIE S. ETTRE, The Perkin-Elmer Corporation, Norwalk, Connecticut

BENJAMIN J. GUDZINOWICZ, Polaroid Corporation, Cambridge, Massachusetts

CSABA HORVÁTH, Yale University, New Haven, Connecticut

HAL J. JONES, Infotronics Corporation, Houston, Texas

ROBERT E. LUNDIN, Western Regional Research Laboratory, U.S. Department of Agriculture, Albany, California

WILLIAM H. MCFADDEN, International Flavors and Fragrances (U.S.) Union Beach, New Jersey

ROBERT J. OLSON, Shell Oil Company, Deer Park, Texas

JAMES R. SCHERER, Western Regional Research Laboratory, U.S. Department of Agriculture, Albany, California

ROBERT D. SCHWARTZ, United Gas Corporation, Shreveport, Louisiana

EUGENE L. SZONNTAGH, Leeds & Northrup Corporation, North Wales, Pennsylvania

ROY TERANISHI, Western Regional Research Laboratory, U.S. Department of Agriculture, Albany, California

Contents

Contents

CHAPTER 1

Basic Knowledge of Gas Chromatography and Gas Chromatographic Instruments

Nathaniel Brenner, *The Perkin-Elmer Corporation, Norwalk, Connecticut*, and Robert J. Olson, *Shell Oil Company, Deer Park, Texas*

I. Introduction: Principles and Methods

Gas chromatographic instrumentation now makes up part of the equipment of virtually all industrial and academic laboratories engaged in the analysis of organic compounds. This widespread use is remarkable when one considers that in 1955 the gas chromatographic technique was known to but a few workers and the few instruments in use were located in central analytical research facilities of large corporations or universities. The literature at that time consisted of about 40 papers, mainly devoted to descriptions of experimental apparatus, with described applications of the technique limited to fatty acid and light-hydrocarbon analysis. By the close of 1966 over 50,000 gas chromatographs were in operation, and more than 10,000 papers had appeared reporting the application of the technique to virtually every conceivable area of science and technology in which the qualitative or quantitative analysis of volatile materials was of interest. More than 40 commercial firms were engaged in the manufacture and sale of chromatographs, from whom a vast assortment of units of varying design and capabilities were available.

Gas chromatography owes its popularity to several of its inherent advantages to the analyst:

1. The separation of mixtures containing many components, including homologs and isomers, is possible.

2. Results are obtained rapidly.

3. Only small samples are required with minimum sample preparation.

4. The method is applicable to widely divergent sample types.

5. It is distinguished from other instrumental methods by simplicity and reliability of operation of equipment.

6. Relatively high qualitative and quantitative precision is obtainable.

7. It is relatively easy to interpret results.

8. The equipment required has relatively low initial cost, is inexpensive to operate, and has a long, useful life.

The high reliability and precision of gas chromatographs, plus the inherent freedom from chemical interference afforded by quantitative methods which are dependent upon a separation process, has made the technique extremely useful in automatic plant process monitoring and control. Highly specialized, automatically operating plant stream analyzers have been designed and are employed widely in large petroleum and chemical installations.

A. History of Chromatographic Separations

The word "chromatography" (color writing) comes from Tswett (39), who first employed the technique in 1906 for the separation of components of plant pigments. By introducing a solution of the pigment mixture into the top of a column of solid adsorbent and then passing fresh solvent through the column, he found that the sample components traveled down the column at different speeds resulting in discrete bands of colored material. This name remained the accepted term for a group of analytical separation techniques, although the phenomenon of visibly colored bands is not a general characteristic. Keulemans (23) gave the following definition for the various chromatographic methods:

> Chromatography is a physical method of separation in which the components to be separated are distributed between two phases, one of the phases constituting a stationary bed of large surface area, the other being a fluid that percolates through or along the stationary bed.

Following Tswett's original work, the technique fell almost completely into oblivion, and 25 years passed before it was "rediscovered" in 1931 by Kuhn, Winterstein, and Lederer (26).

In this work a liquid was passed through a solid; therefore, this type of chromatography is generally referred to as liquid–solid adsorption chromatography—*liquid–solid chromatography* (LSC).

The technique of liquid–solid chromatography can be divided into three subgroups. The *elution technique* is that used originally by Tswett. The second is *frontal analysis* in which the mixture of the components is fed continuously into a column of adsorbent during the entire course of the process and one component is adsorbed by the column, the others being eluted until the column is saturated. From this moment on, the mixture will flow through without change in concentration. The third form is the *displacement technique*, in which the displacer liquid is more powerfully adsorbed on the column material than the components originally dissolved in the liquid, and therefore it "displaces" them and forces them out of the column. Figure 1-1 illustrates graphically the three techniques.

In these three forms, the moving phase is a liquid and the stationary phase a solid. Similar methods were also developed in which the sample components are in the vapor phase and a gas is used as the moving phase. In the 1930's Schuftan (36) and Eucken et al. (15) described analytical techniques based on gas–solid adsorption chromatography—*gas–solid*

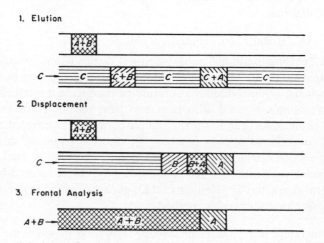

Fig. 1-1. Principles of the three chromatographic techniques. *A* and *B* are the two components to be separated, *C* is the carrier or displacer.

chromatography (GSC)—and numerous workers such as Damköhler et al. (13,14), Turner (40,41), Tiselius (37,38), Claesson (5), Cremer et al. (6–8), Müller (31), Prior (33), and Janák (21,22) contributed to the development of this technique. All three forms of GSC are described in the literature, but only the elution technique is in general use today.

The second group of techniques uses a *liquid* as a stationary phase supported on a solid of larger surface. This method was introduced first in the form of the elution technique of Martin and Synge (29) using a liquid as the moving phase, and was further developed by the authors in a special form called *paper chromatography*. Martin and Synge were awarded the Nobel Prize in 1952 for this work.

Table 1-1 summarizes the different chromatographic techniques. The two gas chromatographic techniques are the subject of this book. Of the two methods, gas–liquid chromatography is the most significant; gas–solid chromatography is used mainly for the separation and analysis of low

TABLE 1-1

Summary of the Different Chromatographic Methods and the First Significant Contributors

	Adsorption chromatography		Partition chromatography	
Stationary phase	Solid		Liquid	
Mobile phase	Liquid (LSC)	Gas (GSC)	Liquid (LLC)	Gas (GLC)
Form of development:				
Elution	Tswett (1906); Kuhn, Winterstein and Lederer (1931)	Damköhler and Thiele (1943); Cremer (1947–1951); Janák (1953–1954)	Paper chromatography; Martin and Synge (1941)	James and Martin (1952); Ray (1954)
Frontal analysis	Tiselius (1940); Claesson (1949)	Phillips (1953–1954)	Phillips (1952)	Phillips (1954)
Displacement	Tiselius (1943); Claesson (1949)	Schuftan (1931); Turner (1943); Claesson (1946); Turkel'taub (1950)	Levi (1949)	

boiling point materials, particularly inorganic gases. Since the instrumental requirements for both methods are practically the same, their
practice can be discussed concurrently.

B. Principles of Gas Chromatography

A schematic diagram of a typical gas chromatograph is shown in Figure
1-2. A suitable source of moving gas phase, or carrier gas, such as a

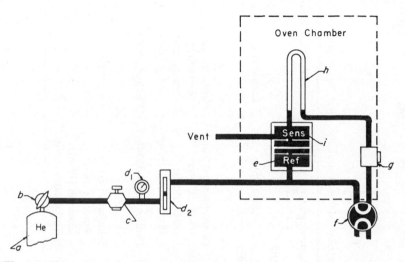

Fig. 1-2. Flow schematic of a typical gas chromatograph: *a*, helium tank; *b*, tank
regulator; *c*, pressure regulator in the gas chromatograph; d_1, pressure gauge; d_2, flow
meter; *e*, reference cell of the thermal conductivity detector; *f*, gas and *g*, liquid sample
injection block; *h*, column; *i*, sensing side of the thermal conductivity detector.

pressurized tank of helium (*a*) is connected via regulators (*b*) and lines to
the instrument, into which the gas flows constantly. There the pressure and
flow of the gas are regulated (*c*) and measured (d_1, d_2), respectively.

In the original paper on what they termed liquid–liquid partition
chromatography, Martin and Synge predicted that

> The mobile phase need not be a liquid, but may be a vapor . . . . Very
> refined separations of volatile substances should . . . be possible in a column
> in which permanent gas is made to flow over gel impregnated with a non-
> volatile solvent in which the substances to be separated approximately obey
> Raoult's law.

In spite of this suggestion, the technique of gas–liquid partition chromatography—also called *gas–liquid chromatography* (GLPC, GLC)—was not
developed until Martin, now associated with James, began to try it himself.

Their work began in 1949 and was first presented in a paper at the Oxford Congress for Analytical Chemistry, in 1952, and described in detail in the four classical publications of the same year (17–20).

The new technique spread rapidly among the English scientists and the scientists working with the Shell Research Laboratory in Amsterdam, Holland. In 1954 Ray (34,35) examined the behavior of a number of hydrocarbons, ethers, and alcohols and introduced many improvements in apparatus. In 1954 Bradford, Harvey, and Chalkley (2) described their analysis of hydrocarbons with the new technique followed by a detailed report on the work of the Dutch group (Keulemans, Kwantes, and Zaal) in 1955 (24,25). These pioneers were then followed by an enormous number of contributors from around the world who helped advance gas chromatography to its present status.

The gas flow then passes the entrance to the reference chamber of a thermal conductivity cell (e).* Within this chamber is a small filament or wire-supported bead which is electrically heated to a temperature somewhat above that of the oven ambient. The filament or bead is made of materials chosen for their high thermal coefficient of resistance; that is, small temperature changes will cause their electrical resistance to change markedly. Though the filament or bead is constantly being heated electrically by an outside source, this excess heat is constantly being dissipated through conductivity to the surrounding carrier gas. The carrier gases usually employed have very high thermal conductivities; helium, hydrogen, and nitrogen are most commonly used. After passing the conductivity cell entrance, the carrier gas flows through a gas sampling area (f) at which point samples which are vapors at normal operating conditions are metered into the system by means of suitable valves. The vapor (gas) sample volume normally required is of the order of 0.1–5 ml.

The gas flow then enters an oven area which is heated to a temperature consistent with the requirement that all sample components must be maintained in the vapor state during the process. Inside the oven, the carrier gas passes through a liquid sample injection area (g) where, in the event that the sample to be analyzed is a liquid under normal conditions, a small volume (0.001–0.010 ml) of material is injected into the stream by means of a hypodermic syringe which passes through a self-sealing rubber septum. The liquid injection area is normally equipped with a separate heating device which raises the temperature somewhat above that of the general

---

* In the first chapter of this book, thermal conductivity detectors will be considered for illustration of general principles. The operation, behavior, and characteristics of other detectors (particularly those of the ionization detectors) will be discussed in subsequent chapters.

oven ambient. This facilitates the rapid vaporization of the liquid sample, a prime requirement for efficient operation.

The sample, mixed with the carrier gas, is now carried to the column entrance (h). The column is commonly a tube, generally 1–4 meters in length and 2–4 mm in diameter, of straight, looped, or coiled metal or glass tubing which has been packed with a granular material upon the surface of which a thin coating of a nonvolatile liquid has been deposited. In some cases this granular material may be a ground crystalline adsorbent, such as silica gel, alumina, or charcoal, without any liquid coating. In this case, the stationary phase is a solid, and an analysis involving gas chromatography with such a column may be termed *gas–solid adsorption chromatography* or, briefly, *gas–solid chromatography*.

In most cases, however, the granular packing consists of inert solids such as diatomaceous earth (Celite or kieselguhr) with a liquid coating. In these cases, the solid or support serves no active purpose in the chromatographic process but merely provides an inert base of high surface area and porosity for the effective distribution of the liquid layer. The liquid material is termed the *stationary phase*, and analysis by gas chromatography involving such a column may be termed *gas–liquid partition chromatography* or *gas–liquid chromatography*.

As the sample and carrier gas mixture enter a partition column, the separation process begins. The sample mixture contains components which will have varying affinities for the stationary phase. The molecules of components which are highly soluble in the partition liquid will tend to dissolve in the liquid more readily than those of less soluble components. Those molecules which are not dissolved are swept further down the column by the moving carrier gas, which may now be termed the *moving phase*. The distribution of molecules of a particular compound between the moving phase and the stationary phase will be governed by the partition coefficient of the compound in the gas–stationary phase system at the column temperature. As molecules of a compound reach a portion of the column, they distribute themselves between gas and liquid phases according to the partition coefficient and move to establish an equilibrium condition. But the molecules which remain in the gas phase are immediately swept by the moving gas to a point farther down the column. New pure gas replaces them in the original portion of the column, causing molecules dissolved in the liquid to reenter the gas phase in order to reestablish equilibrium. It is this constant movement in and out of the liquid and gas phases which is the fundamental mechanism of the gas chromatographic process.

Let us, for example, postulate a mixture of two compounds, one of which is completely insoluble in the liquid phase, and one of which is equally soluble in both liquid and gas. Let us also suppose a column whose liquid volume is equal to the gas volume in the interstitial spaces of the column packing. If we inject the mixture of the two compounds into the column, the carrier gas will propel both through the column. The molecules of the first material always remain in the gas phase and therefore pass through the column at the same rate as the molecules of the carrier gas. On the other hand, the molecules of the second compound will spend approximately equal amounts of time in the liquid and the gas phases. Since they travel down the column only while they are in the gas phase (movement in the liquid phase is relatively small and random in direction), they will require twice as much time to reach the end of the column. The two compounds will emerge from the column at different times and, hence, will be completely separated. The separation of a binary mixture is shown graphically in Figure 1-3. In an actual separation, therefore, the components in a mixture will appear at the end of the column at a time proportional to the solubility of each component in the stationary phase.

Adsorption columns operate in an analogous fashion but with relative adsorption affinities, rather than solubilities, determining the time required for passage of components through the column.

From the column exit, therefore, there is a continuous flow of carrier gas, and at certain time intervals, a component of a sample will appear in a binary mixture with this gas. The carrier and its single dissolved compound proceed through the chamber of a thermal conductivity cell (i) similar in dimension and action to that described previously. However, when a sample component is mixed with the carrier gas, the ability of the gas to conduct heat away from the heated element (thermal conductivity) is changed by a factor porportional to the concentration of that sample component in the carrier gas. The temperature of the cell filament or bead element will therefore change and its resistance will also change. It is this change in resistance, proportional to the concentration of the sample component, which is the source of the electrical signal that is used to detect and measure the output of the chromatograph. After the carrier gas and sample have passed through the thermal conductivity detector, they are vented or passed through a collection system for recovery of the now separated sample components.

Two thermal conductivity cells (e and i) make up a differential detector system as shown in Figure 1-4. The two electrically heated elements make up two arms of a Wheatstone bridge; the other two arms are made up of fixed resistors. Initially, the bridge is balanced before the sample is injected so that only pure carrier gas is contained in both cells. When a sample component reaches the end of the column and enters the cell (e), the

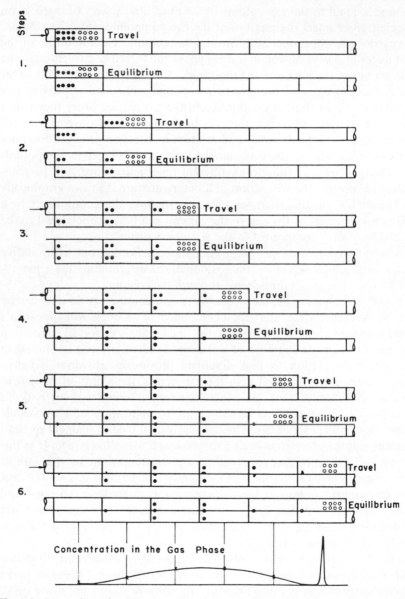

Fig. 1-3. Separation of a binary mixture in a gas chromatographic column: mobile (gas) phase, stationary (liquid) phase.

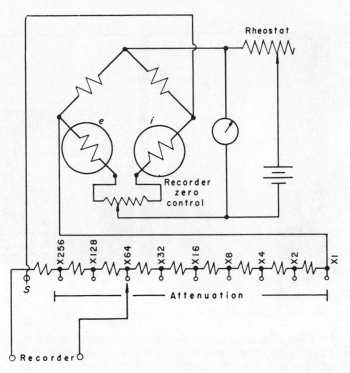

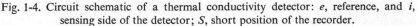

Fig. 1-4. Circuit schematic of a thermal conductivity detector: *e*, reference, and *i*, sensing side of the detector; *S*, short position of the recorder.

resistance change causes an unbalance condition in the bridge and a voltage drop which may be measured across the bridge. This voltage, which is proportional to the amount of sample component in the cell at that moment, is measured by means of a recording potentiometer which amplifies the millivolt-level signal output of the detector to a level sufficient to drive the recorder pen across the chart scale. The amplitude of the pen deflection (which was zero when the bridge was balanced) will again be proportional to the instantaneous sample component concentration in the detector.

The gas chromatograph containing the basic elements described above is generally housed as an integral unit. A typical commercial instrument with its strip-chart potentiometric recorder is shown in Figure 1-5. The letters *A–G* indicate the components already discussed. In addition to these, a set of external controls (*H, I*) and a meter (*J*) are placed on the instrument panel. The controls are heater and thermostat controls, with which the oven and liquid sample injection temperatures may be set and controlled

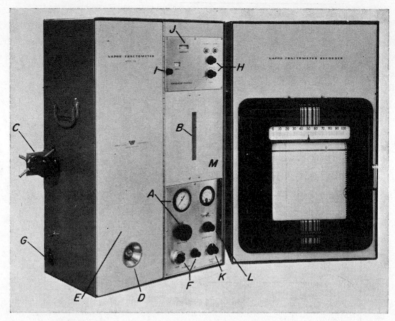

Fig. 1-5. Typical commercial laboratory gas chromatograph: *A*, carrier gas pressure regulator and gauge; *B*, carrier gas flow meter; *C*, gas sampling valve; *D*, liquid sample injection port; *E*, oven chamber (containing column, detector, and heater system); *F*, bridge valance (recorder zero control); *G*, gas outlet port; *H*, oven heater control; *I*, injection block heater control; *J*, oven temperature meter; *K*, rheostat control; *L*, detector bridge voltage control; *M*, detector bridge voltage meter.

by the operator. The temperature range of the ovens of commercial chromatographs are continuously selectable from room temperature to as high as 400°C. Chromatograph ovens may be equipped with facilities to permit operation at subambient temperatures. Thermocouples are usually used for observing the oven temperature.

Control *K* is an output signal step attenuator control. This attenuator serves to divide the output voltage of the detector bridge by preset fixed factors. (The attenuator is shown schematically in the detector circuit diagram in Figure 1-4.) The attenuator serves to reduce the signal fed to the recorder to a level equal to or lower than the rated voltage "span" of the recorder, thereby preventing the movement of the recorder pen above the 100% deflection level on the chart. The individual commercial gas chromatographs use different attenuator steps. The demonstrated detector circuit makes use of steps obtained by multiplication of the previous by two, thus resulting in steps of 1, 2, 4, 8, etc. Other instruments use steps of 1, 3, 10,

30, 100 or 1, 2, 5, 10, etc. The meaning of the attenuation can be illustrated as follows: If using a 5 mV recorder and attenuation ×1, the full-scale deflection of the recorder pen will correspond to 5 mV; at attenuation ×2, it will be 10 mV; at attenuation ×64, it will be 320 mV. Thus, *higher* attenuation always means *lower* recorder sensitivity.

Finally, control *L* regulates the voltage through the detector's hot wire or bead, and the actual voltage can be read on the meter *M*.

C. The Chromatogram

A chromatogram is the recording which results from the pen tracing the output of the chromatographic detector on a moving chart. A representative chromatogram is shown in Figure 1-6. The abscissa is linear with time

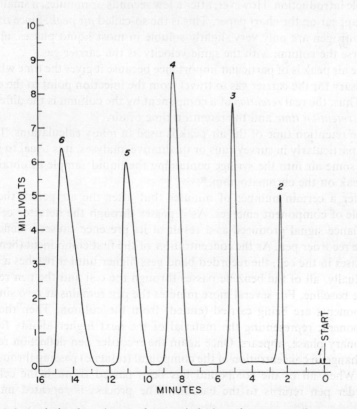

Fig. 1-6. Analysis of a mixture of aromatic hydrocarbons on a column containing picric acid–fluorene as liquid phase. Peaks: *1*, air; *2*, benzene; *3*, toluene; *4*, ethyl benzene; *5*, *m*- and *p*-xylene; *6*, *o*-xylene.

since the recorder chart moves at a constant rate. The ordinate is in millivolts, and, in this case, the full scale is equal to 10 mV (the signal level which, when amplified, will drive the recorder pen to a full-scale deflection).

Prior to injection of the sample, the detector bridge is balanced electrically by adjustment of the recorder zero controls. This consists of setting the pen on the zero deflection line of the recorder. At the start of operation, this pen "baseline" remains at the zero line. When a sample is injected, in this case 5 μl of a liquid mixture of aromatic compounds, a slight pressure disturbance occurs which is registered as a small deflection or "pip" on the recorder. Since this mark coincides with the start of the analysis, it is a convenient marker to designate "time zero" for the run.

Since it requires a finite time for any component to traverse the column, the recorder pen continues to trace a zero baseline for some time after the sample introduction. However, after a few seconds or minutes, a small peak may appear on the chart paper. This is the so-called *air peak*. Since oxygen and nitrogen are only very slightly soluble in most liquid phases, air will traverse the column with the same velocity as the carrier gas.

The air peak is of particular importance because it gives the time which is necessary for the carrier gas to travel from the injection point to the detector. Thus, the real *retention* of a component by the column is the difference of its *retention time* and the retention time of air.

The retention time of the air peak is used in many calculations. Therefore, particularly in survey runs or qualitative analyses, it is usual to introduce some air into the syringe containing the liquid sample to obtain the air peak on the chromatogram.*

After a certain number of minutes (but after the air peak), the first sample of component emerges. As it passes through the detector cell, the unbalance signal produced as a result of its presence causes a deflection of the recorder pen. As the concentration of the first component (benzene) increases in the cell, the recorded band gets higher until it reaches a peak. Gradually, all of the benzene passes through the cell and the pen returns to the baseline. For several more minutes the pen remains at zero since no components are being carried (eluted) from the column. Then the next component, representing the material of the next higher affinity for the stationary phase, appears. Once again the recorder pen deflection reflects the change in concentration of the compound (toluene) passing through the cell. When all of the compound has been passed through the cell, the recorder pen returns to the baseline. The process is repeated until all

---

* Some other (e.g., ionization) detectors do not respond to air. In such cases, other gases, such as methane, which are also only slightly soluble in most liquid phases are used to obtain the "retention time of air."

components have been detected and recorded. Total elapsed time from start (injection of sample) to finish (recording of final peak) is, in the given case, 16 min. Since all of the sample has now passed through the column, the system is ready to run a second sample.

The information derived from the chromatogram is both qualitative and quantitative.

1. The number of bands recorded is the minimum number of components contained in the original sample. Each component yields one band only, but more than one component may be present in a single band.

2. The area included under each band is proportional to the amount of the corresponding component in the original sample. This derives from the fact that recorder pen deflection is proportional to instantaneous concentration of the component in the detector; therefore the summation of all deflection (or area under the band) is proportional to the total concentration of that component.

3. The time required for the appearance of a band, as measured from the time of sample introduction, is a constant for a given compound under specific operating conditions. This time, the retention time (t_R), is measured as distance along the abscissa from the injection pip to the peak of the component band and multiplied by the recorder chart speed. The retention time is the principal number used in the identification of components in general analytical practice.

Examination of the typical chromatogram shows several other characteristic features:

1. Most bands are symmetrical. In gas–liquid chromatography and in many gas–solid systems as well, the small amounts of sample introduced compared to the capacity of the stationary and moving phases will generally result in a condition in which the equilibrium distribution of the component molecules between the two phases will be a constant, regardless of the actual amount of the component. Thus it may be stated in terms of distribution isotherms that these isotherms are linear as shown in Figure 1-7a. In certain cases, the distribution ratio of a component between the two phases will vary with component concentration producing a nonlinear isotherm. If a component is more soluble in the liquid phase at higher component concentrations, then the resultant chromatographic band will appear as shown in Figure 1-7b. Physically this band shape occurs because, as the molecules start to be distributed along the column, those in the lead (at low concentration) tend to be swept down the column rapidly because of their lower solubility in the stationary phase, while those in the center of the original band, since there are more of them, tend to be retarded by their higher solubility in the stationary phase. A "skewed" band results

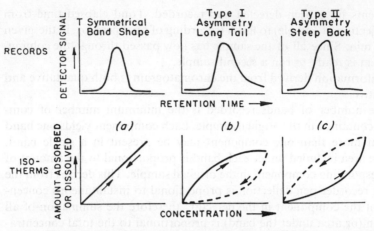

Fig. 1-7. Distribution isotherms. After Hausdorff and Brenner (16).

with the peak retarded relative to the center of the band. The reverse condition is also encountered as shown in Figure 1-7c.

2. The ratio of band height to base width becomes smaller as the retention time increases. This is characteristic of all chromatograms and is readily explained. All components of the sample are injected onto the column in short and equal time. Unless the components are of radically differing concentrations, they will, at any given time, be distributed over a short and almost equal length of the column. But, for reasons described, they move down the column at different rates. A diagram of the position of the components of a mixture at time t after sample introduction inside a column is shown in Figure 1-8.

The benzene band is traveling much more rapidly than the o-xylene peak. Therefore, as the leading edge of the benzene band reaches the detector, the benzene will be rapidly swept off the column and through the detector, causing a fast recording of a band with a high maximum concentration. Later, when the o-xylene band appears, it will travel very slowly off the last section of the column and through the detector. It will take a longer time to record, and, since a larger volume of carrier gas will be

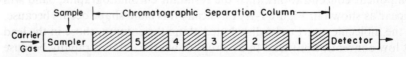

Fig. 1-8. Position of the components of a mixture at time t after sample introduction, inside the column: *1*, Benzene; *2*, toluene; *3*, ethylbenzene; *4*, m- and p-xylene; *5*, o-xylene.

required to sweep it from the end of the column, the concentration of xylene in carrier gas at the detector will never get very high. Therefore, while a narrow (fast) and tall (high concentration) band is recorded for benzene, a wide and short band is recorded for xylene *although their actual component concentrations may have been identical.* If this were indeed the case, the areas under the bands would be similar even though the height–width ratios were markedly different.

II. How to Begin Work with a Gas Chromatograph

Assuming that the instrument and its accessories have been properly selected, installed, and tested by the analyst, he is now ready to start running actual samples. There is a sequence of procedures which, though not basic to the successful operation of the instrument, has been developed by experienced workers to optimize the efficiency of the operation. The basic manipulation of the chromatograph may be quickly derived from the instruction manual which accompanies the equipment, but the following procedures are recommended for their usefulness in saving time and effort in analysis.

A. The Unknown Sample

As in any analytical procedure, it is important to learn as much as possible about the history of the sample and the objectives of the analysis. Questions of interest to the gas chromatographer are:

1. What kind of compounds are in the sample (e.g., hydrocarbons, water, alcohols, inorganic gases, fatty esters)?

2. What is the probable number of components?

3. What is the likely range of component volatility?

4. What is the lowest probable component concentration present or of interest?

5. Are there compounds of known concentration in the mixture?

6. Is the objective of the analysis qualitative identification, quantitative multicomponent analysis, a "purity check" of a high grade material, or a "fingerprint" analysis in which the recorded chromatographic pattern will be compared with previous or subsequent samples for control purposes?

The operating parameters of the analysis will be determined by the information available in answer to the above questions.

B. Operation Parameters and Instrument Setup

1. Selection of the Column

The column for the first attempt at an analysis of an unknown sample should be carefully chosen. It must first contain a substrate suitable for heating to a temperature sufficiently high to accommodate samples of as low volatility as that predicted from the sample history. Always be sure that the column can be heated to any level that may be required. The length of the column required will probably be dependent upon the number and type of components to be separated. Samples in which there are large numbers of compounds or several compounds of similar volatility or chemical formula (isomers) will generally require longer columns than samples with limited numbers of components with differing characteristics The rule for the first survey of an unknown is, however, to use the shortest length of column considered reasonable for the job. In most cases, columns 1–2 m in length are employed for such work.

Selecting the exact substrate (liquid phase) for the accomplishment of the separation is the most difficult task and is discussed in detail in a later chapter. However, if the heating requirement has been satisfied, and, assuming the sample history is not sufficient to indicate a solution from the available literature, some basic procedures may be applied. If the indication is that the sample components are similar in structure but different in volatility, a nonpolar substrate, such as silicone oil or a heavy hydrocarbon (e.g., squalane), is indicated. If the sample components have a close boiling range but are of different functional types, a polar substrate, such as polyglycol or a polyester, is more properly employed.

2. Column Installation and Check Procedure

Once the column type and length have been selected, the column should be installed in the instrument as described in the manufacturer's instructions. At this point, *prior to heating the unit*, a leak check procedure should be followed. The following procedure is applicable to most chromatographs.

1. After installing the column, turn on the carrier gas flow. The flow should be indicated on the flowmeter included in the unit or attached to the entrance line.

The commercial gas chromatographs usually have the flowmeter before the sample port for a practical reason. If rotameter-type flowmeters are installed at the outlet, the higher boiling sample components will often be condensed on the meter float and "glue" it to the inside wall of the rotameter tube. The flowmeter is therefore placed before the sample port. It should not be forgotten that if the flow of the carrier gas is given in connection with the analysis, flow rates measured *at the outlet* are necessary. Therefore, in such cases a flowmeter is usually connected temporarily to the outlet. The flowmeter at the entrance line serves only as a *flow indicator* unless it is accurately calibrated for each operating pressure.

2. Close off the gas vent line from which the gas finally leaves the instrument. If no leaks are present, the flowmeter float should return to zero since no gas is flowing. (This test cannot be performed in cases where special detectors or other components contain other vent paths for the carrier gas.)

3. If a leak exists in the system, the flowmeter will continue to register flow even with the exit line closed off. The location of the leak must then be isolated. There are many gas connections in the chromatograph and because of the continual heating and cooling, plus the changing of columns, these fittings are unfortunately prone to leak. If previous use of the instrument was satisfactory with respect to gas leaks, then it is probable that the source of the new leak is in the column fittings. These should be checked. If this does not solve the problem, then the leak should be located by isolating a section of the gas flow path to localize the source. This is done by closing off the flow of gas at some point close to half the distance from the entrance to exit of the unit. For example, the column may be removed and the column inlet port plugged with a fitting or by finger pressure. Turn the carrier gas on and note the flowmeter. If the float does not return to the zero position then, referring to the schematic in Figure 1-2, the leak must be between the flowmeter and the column entrance port. If the flowmeter does return to zero, the leak is located between the column port and the gas outlet. In the former case, another point for flow stoppage is selected for further localization of the leak. The gas sampling valve may be conveniently turned to a neutral position to block all flow. The flowmeter's behavior will once again determine whether the leak is between the flowmeter and gas valve or between the valve and the column inlet port. This process can be continued until the leak source is definitely associated with a small section. The exact point can then easily be determined by pressurizing the instrument with carrier gas and testing each fitting with a bubble solution. Common nonionic detergents (liquid household detergents or similar solutions sold to children for playing with soap bubbles), when applied to a leaking joint, will form large bubbles.

3. Selection of the Operating Temperature

The temperature of most chromatographic columns is maintained at one point during a run (isothermal operation). Since the time for completion of a run is inversely proportional to the temperature, it may be stated that for the first trial, the highest practical temperature for the analysis should be selected. This temperature is the one which will insure the appearance of the least volatile component expected in the sample mixture in a reasonable time. While high temperature is desirable, it should be remembered that the increased temperature will also cause a loss in separation power of the column. Therefore, this choice must take into account the balance of time required and useful separation expected.

With temperature-programmed column systems, the problem of temperature selection is less critical. Here, the rate at which the column temperature is increased may be set quite high, and a maximum temperature limit set consistent with the given maximum operating temperature of the column substrate. If a programmed temperature unit is available to the analyst, it is highly recommended for precisely this type of survey work.

In the case of liquid samples, the temperature of the sample injection area must be sufficient to instantly vaporize the sample. Since the heat of vaporization of many liquids is high, most chromatographs permit the heating of the sample area to higher levels than the column temperature. This temperature may often be separately controlled by the operator. The choice of temperature must be modified by considerations of sample size, heat of vaporization, and thermal stability of the sample. In general, the temperature of the sample introduction area will be maintained at 50–100°C above the column temperature.

4. Selection of Pressure and Flow

The graphic representation of the van Deemter equation* illustrates that the efficiency of a column decreases only moderately as gas velocities through the column are increased above the optimum value. However, the increase in velocity results in a proportional decrease in analysis time. Therefore, in a survey of an unknown sample, pressure and flow should be set as high as practicable unless distinct objectives (detection of very low concentrations with thermal conductivity cells) dictate otherwise.

5. Control Setting and Stabilization of the Instrument

After the column has been installed and the instrument checked for leaks, the operating conditions selected are set on the control panel in the following sequence:

1. Carrier gas flow is started through the instrument. The pressure is turned up to a preselected operating pressure or to a point where the flowmeter shows sufficient flow. In some cases where high temperature analyses will be run, the carrier gas may be started through at a reduced pressure and flow in order to conserve carrier gas during the relatively long warmup and stabilization period.

* This equation, derived by van Deemter, Zuiderweg, and Klinkenberg relates the efficiency of a column to its construction and operating parameters. (See Chapter 4 for details.)

2. Temperature controllers are set to selected points. The oven temperature is usually set by means of a calibrated dial. In those instruments which permit separate control of the sample injection area and detector, these settings should also be made; the injection system should generally be set above the column oven temperature, the detector control at a temperature equal or close to oven temperature. (In programmed-temperature systems, the anticipated final temperature reached in the program is the basis for detector and sample area heating.) Some instruments permit separate selection of power input to the heaters independent of the thermostat. In this case, equilibration can be speeded up by setting the control so that full power is applied to the system during the heatup period. (The thermostat will prevent overshoot of the selected final temperature.) Where the fastest possible equilibration time in "air bath" systems at high temperatures is desired, the thermostat may be set to a temperature higher than that eventually desired. The oven will then heat to this higher level, resulting in more rapid heating of high-mass components in the oven, such as detector mounts. After a few minutes at the higher level, the oven is cooled to the actual operating temperature desired.

3. The recorder amplifier is turned on. This control is generally independent of the chart drive and pen actuation controls, and the amplifier is warmed before use.

4. The detector power supply is turned on and adjusted to proper operating current or voltage level as given in the instruction manual with the equipment.

5. When the temperature has reached operating level, the carrier gas flow is turned to its desired final flow and the system is leak-checked again by closing off the exit line.

6. The recorder chart and pen drive are turned on.

7. The attenuator control on the chromatograph panel is turned to the "short" position and the recorder checked. At this setting, the chromatograph feeds no signal to the recorder and its pen should therefore read zero deflection.

8. The attenuator is then turned to one of the numbered positions on the switch for a check of baseline stability. The position selected is determined by the analysis to be run. The operator should never spend the time necessary to stabilize the instrument at a sensitivity (attenuator setting) greater than that which he will need in his next run. The time required to stabilize the output of a thermal conductivity cell read at its maximum sensitivity setting is far longer than that required at 1/4 or 1/8 of this sensitivity. Therefore, based upon the anticipated problem, stabilization is accomplished at the lowest practical sensitivity. Only in those cases where trace observation or extreme sample size limitation make the use of the full sensitivity necessary, should the unit be stabilized at this setting. For first-run surveys, settings 8 or 16 (5 or 10 on other attenuator types) are sufficient for good results. The instrument is stabilized sufficiently for useful survey work when the baseline drift is less than 1% of full-scale deflection in 1 min. (Drift is the only instability associated with normal functioning of thermal conductivity cells. Evidence of high frequency noise is indication of a malfunction of some part of the system.)

6. Selection of Sample Size

Based upon the sample history and purpose of the analysis, the analyst will choose a sample with the following facts in mind:

1. Obviously, larger samples produce larger detector output. Therefore, if trace or purity analysis is an objective, relatively high sample sizes and high sensitivities are required.

2. The smaller the sample, the more efficient and accurate the separation. Small samples vaporize faster and pass through the column more ideally, and will therefore appear better separated by the column. They will also prevent any inaccuracies due to exceeding the linear dynamic range of the detector device. Virtually all detectors are linear at low levels; some become nonlinear with high component concentrations.

In general practice, mixtures containing 2–20 components can be surveyed for component concentrations from 0.1 to 100%, conveniently using samples of 0.003–0.010 ml (3–10 μl) of liquid or 0.3–10 ml of gas when thermal conductivity detectors are used at reasonable sensitivities. In the case of solid samples which are dissolved in liquid solvents, the amount of solid sample should be of the order of 3–10 mg dissolved in minimum solvent.

C. The Survey Run

When the instrument has stabilized, the analyst is ready to make the survey run. The objective of this run is to determine the proper conditions and attenuator program for the actual analysis.

1. Carrying Out the Survey Run

To start the run, the following steps are taken:

1. The recorder baseline is set at zero with recorder zero controls.

2. The attenuator is set to the highest stable sensitivity level.

3. The sample is injected quickly. If no injection pip appears on the recorder, a mark should be placed on the chart at the position of the pen at the instant of injection.

4. From this point on the operator watches the recording while holding the attenuator switch. As the first band appears, the pen will start up scale. Unless the band represents a very small component, the pen will rapidly travel full scale and approach the 100% deflection position. As it does so, the operator will quickly switch the attenuator to the next lower sensitivity setting (for example, from 8 to 16), causing the pen to rapidly move around 100 to 50% of scale deflection. The pen may then proceed upward to 100% again, at which time the operator will once again switch to a lower sensitivity setting (16 to 32) and the pen will move again from 100 to 50%. This process may be repeated until the peak of the band is recorded at some sensitivity and at a deflection between 50 and 100% of recorder full scale. After the peak is passed and the recorder pen returns toward the zero line, the attenuator setting at which the peak was recorded should be marked on the chart close to the band. The attenuator is then switched back to the high sensitivity setting originally used and the operation repeated on each band to the end of the survey run. A chromatogram obtained in this manner is shown in Figure 1-9.* The chromatogram shows

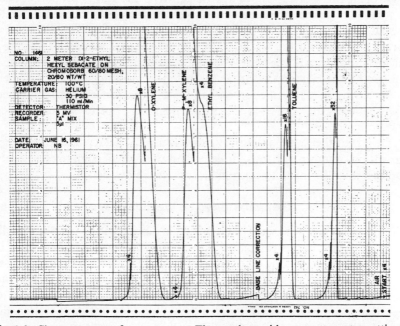

Fig. 1-9. Chromatogram of a survey run. The numbers with x are attenuator settings.

* In the actual survey run, the identification of the individual peaks may not be known. In Figure 1-9, however, the respective components are shown in order to illustrate a properly marked chromatogram.

all bands recorded with the proper attenuator settings for the recording of each band shown adjacent to the band. These markings will serve as an "attenuator program" in subsequent runs on the sample.

2. Interpreting the Survey Run

Based upon sample history information, the survey run is examined to determine whether the column and conditions selected were indeed suitable or, as is more often the case, changes must be made to produce a more satisfactory separation. For example, if in a run of a sample known to contain five components only two bands appear, the analysis must be modified to improve the results. Some of the observations which are made on the survey run are

1. Is the analysis time too long?
2. Are some bands too small for accurate measurement?
3. Are bands insufficiently separated from each other?
4. Are there fewer bands then known components?

If the answers to the above are all negative, the run is probably satisfactory. In this event, the actual analysis of the sample may be immediately started. The attenuator is set at the sensitivity position marked on the survey run chart for the first band. A sample of equal volume to that used for the survey run is injected. When the first band has been recorded and the pen has descended to or near the baseline, the attenuator is switched to the setting noted for the second band. The same procedure is continued with the attenuator preset at the proper position prior to the appearance of each band.

If, on the other hand, the survey run was unsatisfactory because of time, separation, number of bands, or detectability of small components, a second run must be made to attempt to correct the deficiency.

3. Corrections Based on the Survey Run

Prior to making a second run, corrections in operating conditions will be made from the results of the survey run. If the time of analysis is observed to be too long, though the separation was adequate, several corrections can be applied: a shorter length of column can be installed, the pressure and flow of carrier gas can be increased, or the temperature of the column can be increased. Each of these measures will shorten the total time, but the analyst must realize that the time to change pressure and flow and restabilize at the new condition is about 1 min, to change temperature and restabilize may require 10–20 min, and to open the oven, replace the column, reheat the oven, and restabilize may require 20–30 min.

In cases where the sensitivity of the analysis, as indicated by the inadequate size of bands recorded on the survey run, must be corrected in order to perform a complete analysis, the corrections which may be applied are described below:

1. The sample size may be increased provided that component separation is adequate.

2. The detector may be stabilized at a higher sensitivity (lower attenuation range) in order to give higher output for a given sample concentration. Some potentiometric recorders (e.g., the Leeds and Northrup Speedomax "G") are equipped with a span control switch which permits a reduction in the amount of input voltage required to drive the pen to full scale deflection. This feature may be used to increase the sensitivity of the analysis. The sensitivity of the analyses performed on instruments which employ filament-type detectors may also be increased by increasing the filament current.

3. The flow rate may be decreased. Thermal conductivity cells are concentration-measuring devices and, therefore, by decreasing the apparent dilution of the sample components in carrier gas through flow reduction, a greater total response per unit sample is obtained.

4. The temperature may be decreased. In instruments employing thermistor bead-type detectors, the sensitivity of the detector will increase rapidly as the temperature is decreased. In instruments using filament detectors, this effect is negligible. However, the decrease in temperature of operation may permit the operation of the detector at a higher current setting, thereby increasing sensitivity.

5. The column may be replaced by one of decreased length. In many cases, examination of the survey run reveals that the bands which are too small for adequate measurement have very long retention times. Since the height of a band decreases as a retention time increases, these bands are so low as to be barely discernible above the baseline. Decreasing the column length may sharpen the band, facilitating measurement.

6. Other detectors of higher sensitivity may be employed. Throughout this discussion, considerations have been limited to thermal conductivity cells. While these detectors are the most generally used detection devices in gas chromatographs because of their universality of response, simplicity and reliability of operation, and quantitative precision, there are several other types of detectors in reasonably common use. Among these are the ionization gauges which are employed primarily because of their greater sensitivity to organic compounds. Therefore, if the sensitivity of the analysis, as seen with a thermal conductivity cell, is inadequate and the measures described above are insufficient to correct the problem, then the substitution of a detector or instrument containing an ionization gauge may be justified.

4. Improving Separation

The most common and most important corrections made as the result of the survey run are those directed at improving the separation between component bands. In observing the survey run, the analyst must be careful about the conclusions which are drawn as to whether all components in the sample have been separated. In many cases, samples are encountered which are identified as "pure compound *A*" or "a mixture of three compounds" which produce chromatograms which contain literally dozens of bands. This common problem results from the fact that the chromatograph is a far more powerful separator of components and a far more sensitive detector of these components than any of the other methods used by the originator of the sample to obtain his estimate of the sample composition. Therefore, in analyzing a "mixture of three components," the analyst may obtain 3, 13, or 30 bands. He may then be faced with the problem of determining which of the bands are due to the three components or whether even though 30 bands are shown, all of the three components of interest have been separated.

There are also many cases in which it can definitely be seen from the survey run that insufficient separation has been obtained. For example, no separation between meta- and paraxylene in Figure 1-6 is observed. In many other chromatograms, the separations between components is incomplete, and overlapping bands occur as shown in Figure 1-10.

If the survey run is judged to show all components of the sample but to have some inadequate separation (overlap) in some cases, corrections to improve the separation may be considered in the following order.

1. Reducing the flow rate may help to improve the separation. In the original survey, conditions of the flow were set at a deliberately high rate to produce rapid results. Since this rate was probably above the optimum level for the column (see graphs of van Deemter equation in Chapter 4), a reduction in flow rate will improve the separation quality.

2. Decreasing the sample size used will improve the separation in much the same manner as decreasing flow rate. All columns operate at higher resolving power when sample quantities are minimized.

3. Reducing the column temperature will improve separation very markedly in any analysis at the cost of elapsed time and band sharpness. Even a reduction of just a few degrees will increase the difference in retention time between overlapping bands by a significant amount.

4. Increasing the column length will obviously increase the separation between components. The difference between the retention times of two

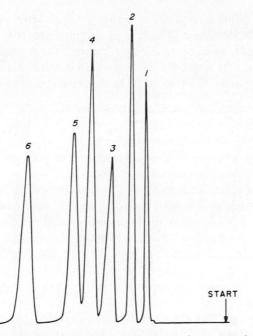

Fig. 1-10. Analysis of C_4-hydrocarbons on a 3-m column containing dimethyl-sulfolane as liquid phase. Peaks: *1*, isobutane; *2*, *n*-butane; *3*, butene-1 and isobutylene; *4*, *trans*-butene-2; *5*, *cis*-butene-2; *6*, butadiene-1,3.

components will in fact be increased by the square root of the ratio of the new length of column to the original. For example, doubling the column length will produce a $2\frac{1}{2}$ increase in separation or 1.4 times the separating efficiency.

5. *Column Interchange*

The corrections described above are recommended for use when the separations shown in the survey run are incomplete. They are easily made, and the results to be expected on the subsequent run are predictable.

A column containing a different stationary phase may also be substituted for that used in the survey run. This change is the most powerful correction available to the gas chromatographer and is, in fact, one of the basic advantages of the technique over comparable analytical separation techniques (distillation). The chromatographic separation obtained is a function of the relative solubilities of sample components in the stationary phase. Changing the chemical nature of the stationary phase results in an entirely new set of relative solubilities in the system; this produces a new outcome in terms of separation between components and often an even distinctly different order of elution of components from the column.

For example, when using a longer column, the separation from that in Figure 1-10 can be improved, but even then it will not demonstrate a complete separation of all components in this mixture of known composition.

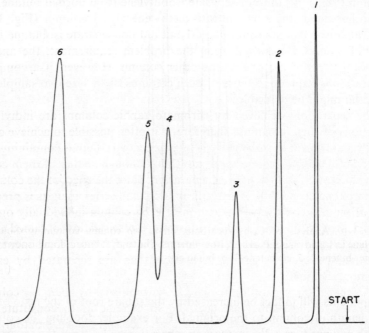

Fig. 1-11. The separation of C_4-hydrocarbons on a column containing diethylene glycol + silver nitrate as stationary phase. After Hausdorff and Brenner (16). Peaks: *1*, isobutane + normal butane; *2*, *trans*-butene-2; *3*, isobutylene; *4*, *cis*-butene-2; *5*, butene-1; *6*, butadiene-1,3.

Two components, isobutylene and butene-1, because of their exactly similar solubility characteristics in the particular stationary phase employed (dimethylsulfolane), appear as one band with no evidence of separation. In a case of this type, the further application of the above-discussed corrections in operation parameters will probably not produce a complete separation of these two components. Proper selection of a new stationary phase can, however, produce a complete separation of the components under conditions which are otherwise identical to those employed in Figure 1-10. Figure 1-11 illustrates this analysis in which only the stationary phase has been changed. In place of dimethylsulfolane, a solution of silver nitrate in diethylene glycol was used in the column. Note that here the isobutylene is clearly separated from the butene-1.

Figures 1-10 and 1-11 also illustrate that there is no universal stationary phase for gas chromatographic work, but that stationary phases—or column substrates, as they are commonly termed—must be selected for the particular problem to be solved. For example, the dimethylsulfolane column (Fig. 1-10) did not separate isobutylene from normal butane. On the other hand, the silver nitrate–diethylene glycol column (Fig. 1-11) separated isobutylene from butene-1 but did not separate isobutane from normal butane. Depending upon the problem requirement, the analyst usually prefers to use one or the other column. However, if a complete separation is required, the use of both columns to analyze two samples of material might be desirable.

The separations achieved by chromatographic columns are individual functions of these columns; therefore, it is often possible to achieve complete separation in a single analysis by placing two columns containing two stationary phases in a series configuration, although neither of them could individually perform the desired separation. Since the effect of the columns is approximately additive, the result of a column series analysis is predictable from a knowledge of the action of each column individually on the subject sample. Figures 1-12a–c illustrate the separation obtained on a particular sample using different columns. Note that more components are separated using the series configuration than are separated by either column individually.

The changes in separation which can be produced by changing column substrates can, in many instances, be so extreme as to constitute the difference between complete failure and success in a chromatography separation. Figure 1-13 shows two chromatograms of the same tar–acid mixture. The conditions of both analyses are identical except for the column substrate employed. In one case, no usable separation results, while in the other, several complete bands and some overlaps bands are resolved.

Because of the very practical use to which the analyst may apply this property of substrate selectivity, it is advisable to have a reasonably large variety of columns of different substrate types available in the laboratory. The particular choice of columns depends largely upon the type of samples which the analyst can anticipate will be run. Guidance as to which substrates are most applicable to particular sample types may be obtained from the literature or from the manufacturer of the chromatograph. A later chapter of this book will discuss this question in detail.

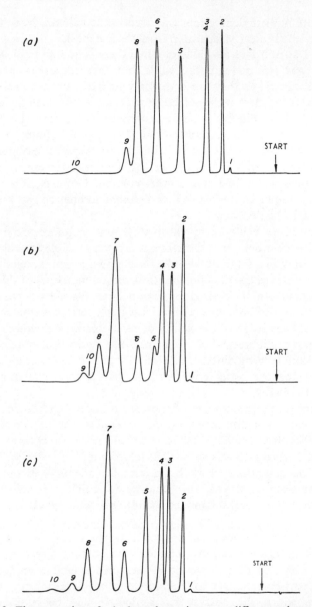

Fig. 1-12. The separation of a hydrocarbon mixture on different columns: (*a*) liquid phase: di(2-ethylhexyl) sebacate; (*b*) liquid phase: dimethylsulfolane; (*c*) the two columns in series. Components: *1*, air; *2*, ethane; *3*, propane; *4*, propylene; *5*, isobutane, *6*, *n*-butane; *7*, isobutylene; *8*, *trans*-butene-2; *9*, *cis*-butene-2; *10*, isopentane.

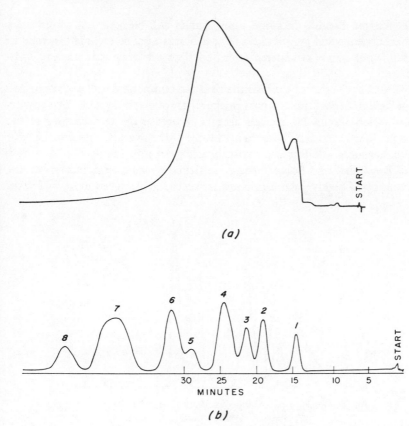

Fig. 1-13. The analysis of a tar acid mixture on two columns with different liquid phase: (*a*) silicone oil; (*b*) diisodecyl phthalate. Peaks: *1*, phenol; *2*, *o*-cresol; *3*, 2,6-xylenol; *4*, *m*- and *p*-cresol; *5*, 2,5-xylenol; *6*, *o*-ethylphenol and 2,4-xylenol; *7*, *m*- and *p*-ethylphenol, 2,3-, and 3,5-xylenol; *8*, 3,4-xylenol.

6. Peak Distortion

Examination of the survey run may also indicate band shape distortion. The desired shape of a chromatographic band is a symmetrical shape conforming to the graphic representation of a Gaussian distribution (normal distribution curve). The area of bands of this type is easy to measure by graphic methods and is also more accurately measured by planimetry or by automatic integration devices. Because these bands are also representative of efficient operating conditions, a chromatogram of a sample which shows symmetrical bands is also more likely to show complete separations between components. Two of the common types of band distortion and recommended corrections can be discussed briefly.

1. Ragged Bands. In some cases, bands will be recorded which have flattened peaks and jagged sides. These bands may be included in runs in which other bands of shorter retention time are quite smooth and symmetrical.

Band shapes of this type indicate that the component was not vaporized in sufficiently short time to pass properly through the system. The corrections which should be applied are: (*1*) increase the temperature of the sample injection area, (*2*) decrease the size of the sample. Either or both of these measures will decrease the sample vaporization time.

2. Band Tailing. Some bands, particularly those resulting from the separation of highly polar compounds (water, alcohols, amines), will show

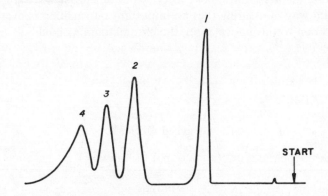

Fig. 1-14. The analysis of an aqueous alcohol mixture. Peaks: *1*, methanol; *2*, ethanol; *3*, isopropanol; *4*, water.

a distorted shape in which the trailing edge (side of the band which appears after the peak) returns to the baseline very slowly. A water peak of this type is shown in Figure 1-14. Corrections to be applied in this case are: (*1*) change to a column which contains a polar substrate material such as one containing hydroxyl, carboxy, or carbonyl structure; (*2*) use a column which has been manufactured specifically for its ability to eliminate tailing of bands. Such columns are available and details of their properties and action are discussed in Chapter 4 of this book.

D. Data Necessary to Characterize a Chromatogram

When corrections resulting from examination of the survey run have been applied, a second run is made and observation of the chromatogram will once again determine whether the result is now satisfactory. If it is not, further corrections are made until a suitable set of conditions for analysis has been developed. The final run is that in which all necessary or possible separations have been performed.

The chromatogram should immediately be marked by the analyst with information necessary for quantitative and qualitative interpretation and to permit duplication of the run at some future time.

The information placed on the chromatogram should include: (1) sample identification (number or type), (2) sample volume, (3) column substrate and concentration, (4) column support and mesh size, (5) column length, (6) column temperature, (7) carrier gas, (8) carrier gas pressure (and/or flow rate), (9) detector type (if several types are in use in the laboratory), (10) date of analysis, and (11) name of operator. A rubber stamp made up for printing the list shown above directly on the chromatogram is a most convenient way of assuring that no important information is overlooked.

In addition to this information, the chromatogram should also contain clearly legible attenuator markings unambiguously placed near the component bands. In the case of analyses involving known mixtures of components, the identification of each component should also be written on or near its corresponding band.

III. Advanced Technology

The basic apparatus and operational technique of gas chromatography as described above have been modified greatly by ingenious devices and techniques developed by scientists and engineers. Some of the more important developments will be introduced here and discussed in greater detail in subsequent chapters.

A. Column Technology

1. Mobile Phase and Sampling

Since the carrier gas provides the means for transporting the sample components through the column, its identity and control are fundamental factors in successful gas chromatographic analysis. Helium and nitrogen are the most widely used carrier gases, helium for its high thermal conductivity, nitrogen for its low cost, and both for their stability. In gas chromatography, as in all chemical analysis, proper sampling techniques are essential. For optimum separation, a gas chromatographic sample should be introduced into the column as a sharp pulse.

2. Open Tubular Columns

Open tubular or capillary columns are long tubes of small diameter having the stationary liquid present as a thin film on the inner walls rather than on a granular packing. Such columns are useful where a high degree of separation is needed to distinguish components of closely similar properties. Compared to packed columns, open tubular columns require smaller samples.

3. Temperature Programming

Samples of wide boiling range are difficult to analyze under isothermal conditions since, at a low temperature the high boiling components yield broad, flat peaks, whereas at a high temperature the peaks for the low boiling components are crowded together. These difficulties can be overcome by programming the column temperature. By starting at a low temperature, the peaks for the lower boiling components can be well separated, and by progressively increasing the column temperature, the higher boiling components can be eluted as sharp, well-defined peaks. For separating gases and low-boiling liquids, subambient temperature programming may be employed (30). The temperature program can be linear or nonlinear depending upon the particular problem. Most manufacturers of gas chromatographic equipment now supply temperature programming accessories which allow precise variation and control of column oven temperatures.

4. Flow Programming

The flow rate of the carrier gas also can be programmed. The effects are similar to those of temperature programming, with the added advantage of instant reset following an analysis (28,43,44).

5. Backflush

Samples frequently contain small amounts of higher boiling materials which are of little interest but which require a lengthy period of time to be eluted in the normal fashion. With such samples, it may be desirable to reverse the direction of carrier gas flow, after the elution of the component of interest, to flush the column free of the heavy components. This technique is also used to regroup components, as in the analysis of a hydrocarbon mixture for hydrocarbon types.

6. Preparative GLC

Preparative GLC provides a convenient means for isolating small amounts of pure materials or concentrates for further study. By equipping the outlet of the column with a refrigerated U-tube or other suitable trapping device, a portion of the eluate can be recovered for examination by infrared, ultraviolet, mass spectrometry, or other techniques. Recently, large-scale preparative GLC's have been developed which permit the injection of 100-ml size quantities for separation of pure materials (4).

B. Detector Technology

Besides the thermal conductivity detector described earlier, a great variety of devices have been used to detect the presence of the separated components in the column effluent. Outstanding among these are the sensitive hydrogen flame ionization detector, which responds to the amount of organic carbon in the sample; the radiation ionization detectors, which offer high sensitivity; and a host of specialized detectors which give enhanced response to particular compound types. Detector technology is covered in detail in Chapter 5.

C. Ancillary Equipment and Technique

While gas chromatography is used primarily for the physical separation of volatile materials, its position as an adjunct to chemistry must always be kept in mind. Difficult samples can be chemically altered before, during, or after introduction to the chromatograph to facilitate their separation and analysis. Nonvolatile compounds or materials of low volatility, such a polymers or biological samples, can be pyrolyzed in specially designed inlet systems and the volatile fragments separated by gas chromatography. By pyrolyzing in the presence of hydrogen, a simplification of chemical structures or of complex mixtures can be obtained. By chemical pretreatment, the volatility of compounds can be increased, or the compounds can be altered to enhance their response to specific detectors. Organic compounds issuing from a chromatographic column can be oxidized to CO_2 to simplify detection and quantitative analysis.

IV. Terms Used in Gas Chromatography

In compilation of this glossary, use was made of the nomenclature recommended by the special group of the International Union of Pure and Applied Chemistry, under the Chairmanship of Dr. Ambrose (32).

adsorbent (*active solid*). Solid, granular material used to pack columns and on the surface of which sample components are held by adsorptive forces.
adsorption chromatography. See *gas–solid chromatography.*
adsorption column. Column used in gas–solid adsorption chromatography. The column material consists of an active solid (adsorbent).

air peak. The peak of a substance which is not retarded by the column material, thus indicating the time necessary for the carrier gas to travel from the injection point to the detector.

attenuator. An electrical element containing a series of resistances which may be selected by a switch to produce the reduction of input voltage to a recorder by a fixed factor.

band. See *peak*.

band area. See *peak area*.

baseline. The line drawn by the recorder pen when no sample is being measured in the detector.

capillary column (open tubular column). Tubing of small diameter, usually 0.25–1.0 mm i.d., in which the inner walls of the tube are used to support the stationary liquid.

carrier gas. The gas, usually inert, which constantly flows from a pressurized source through the chromatograph, impelling the sample through the system.

chromatogram. The graphic recording of the detector response vs. time or volume of carrier gas.

column. A metal or glass tube packed or internally coated with the column material through which the sample and carrier gas flow and in which the chromatographic separation is performed.

column material. The material contained in the column. In adsorption chromatography, the column material is the adsorbent itself; in partition chromatography, the column material consists of a stationary phase distributed on inert solid support or coated on the inside wall of the column.

component. A pure compound contained in the sample mixture.

detector. A measurement device, usually electrical, which emits a signal in the presence of a component which is eluted from a chromatographic column.

elution. The "washing" of a component through and out of the column by the carrier gas.

filament element. A type of thermal conductivity device in which a fine tungsten or similar wire is used as the variable resistance element in the cell chamber.

flow programming. A technique in which the carrier gas flow rate is gradually increased in order to expedite the elution of the higher boiling components.

gas chromatography (GC). Collective noun for all chromatographic methods in which the moving phase is a gas. The "chromatography" itself implies that a stationary phase is present in addition to the moving phase. These methods are also called *vapor-phase chromatography* (VPC).

gas–liquid chromatography (GLC). Chromatographic method in which the stationary phase is a liquid distributed on a solid support. The separation is achieved by partition of the components of a sample between the phases. This method is also called *gas–liquid partition chromatography* (GLPC).

gas–solid chromatography (GSC). Chromatographic method in which the stationary phase is an active solid (adsorbent). The separation is achieved by adsorption of the components of a sample. This method is also called *gas–solid adsorption chromatography*.

integrator. A mechanical or electromechanical device for producing a continuous summation of detector output with respect to time, yielding a measurement of included area of a chromatographic band.

ionization detectors. Chromatographic detectors in which the measurement of a sample is derived from the current produced by the ionization of sample molecules induced by thermal, radioactive, or other excitation sources.

katharometer (catharometer). See *thermal conductivity cell.*

liquid phase. A liquid which is relatively nonvolatile at the column temperature and is sorbed on the solid support where it acts as a solvent for the sample. The separation achieved differs with differences in solubility of the various components of the sample in the liquid phase. This is also called the *stationary phase* or *substrate.*

moving phase (mobile phase). The carrier gas within the column, in which sample component molecules progress down the length of the column.

partition chromatography. See *gas–liquid chromatography.*

peak. The portion of the chromatogram recording the detector response while a single component emerges from the column. (If the separation of a mixed sample is incomplete, two or more components may appear as one peak.)

peak area. The included area formed by the ascending and descending arms of a chromatographic recorded band and the baseline of the chart.

potentiometric recorder. A readout device in which a pen, whose deflection is proportional to the voltage output of the chromatographic detector, writes on a paper chart which is moving at a constant speed.

pyrolysis. A technique in which nonvolatile samples are decomposed in the inlet system and the volatile products admitted to the chromatographic column.

relative retention. The ratio of the retention time of a component to the retention time of a second component chosen as standard.

resolution. The degree of separation between peaks.

retention index. The number of carbon atoms (multiplied by 100) of a hypothetical normal paraffin which under the given conditions would have a retention time identical to that of the substance of interest.

retention volume. The product of the retention time of a component and the volumetric flow rate of the carrier gas.

retention time. The elapsed time from injection of the sample to recording of the peak maximum of a component band.

sample. The gas or liquid mixture injected into the chromatograph for analysis.

sample injector. A device by which a liquid or gaseous sample is introduced into the apparatus. The sample can be introduced directly into the carrier gas stream, or into a chamber temporarily isolated from the system by valves which can be changed so as to instantaneously switch the gas stream through the chamber.

separation. The elapsed time between elution of two successive components, measured on the chromatogram as distance between the recorded bands.

solid support. The first granular material upon which the thin layer of liquid in a partition column is held.

solute. The individual fractions of the sample dissolved in the liquid phase during their travel through the column. This is also used as another term for the sample itself.

solvent. Synonym for the liquid phase.

span of a recorder. The signal level (number of millivolts) required to produce a change in the deflection of the recorder pen from 0 to 100% on the chart scale.

splitter. A T-fitting attached to the column to divert a portion of the flow. An *inlet splitter* allows introduction of very small samples to a capillary column. An *effluent splitter* may be used to permit parallel operation of two detectors.

stationary phase. See *liquid phase.*

substrate. See *liquid phase.*

tailing. A form of band distortion in a chromatogram in which the trailing edge returns to the baseline relatively slowly, producing an asymmetrical band.

temperature programming. A technique in which the column temperature is gradually increased in order to expedite the elution of the higher boiling components.

thermal conductivity. A physical property of materials which is their ability to conduct heat from a warmer to a cooler object.

thermal conductivity cell. A chamber in which an electrically heated element is contained which, by its change in resistance, will reflect changes in thermal conductivity within the chamber atmosphere.

thermistor bead element. A type of thermal conductivity detection device in which a small glass-coated semiconductor sphere is used as the variable resistive element in the cell chamber.

vapor-phase chromatography (VPC). See *gas chromatography.*

V. Literature and Organizations

Gas chromatography is a rapidly growing analytical tool. It is therefore of particular importance that the practical gas chromatographer should know the sources to which he can refer for information: textbooks for detailed studies, journals in which the most important new results are published, reports of scientific meetings where papers on gas chromatography are delivered, societies devoted to gas chromatography, bibliographies and abstracting services, and the technical service departments of instrument manufacturers. The following list was compiled in January, 1967.

A. General Textbooks on Gas Chromatography

The following are books available in the English language, with the most recent listed first. For textbooks in other languages, bibliographic sources should be consulted.

Giddings, J. C., *Dynamics of Chromatography*, Marcel Dekker, New York. Vol. I, 323 pp., 1966; Vols. II–III in preparation. A comprehensive treatment of chromatography as *one* discipline.

Kaiser, Rudolph, *Gas Chromatography*, 199 pp; *Capillary Chromatography*, 120 pp; *Tables for Gas Chromatography*, 162 pp; Butterworths, Washington, 1963. These publications are small handbooks designed as textbooks for college students. The first volume is a general compilation of theory and practice; the second discusses capillary gas chromatography; and the third gives tables and data from the literature.

Dal Nogare, S., and R. S. Juvet, Jr., *Gas–Liquid Chromatography. Theory and Practice*, Interscience, New York, 1962, 450 pp.

Littlewood, A. B., *Gas Chromatography, Principles, Techniques, and Application*, Academic Press, New York, 1962, 514 pp.

Purnell, J. H., *Gas Chromatography*, Wiley, New York, 1962, 441 pp.

Knox, J. H., *Gas Chromatography*, Wiley, New York, 1962, 126 pp. A short monograph.

Ambrose, D., and B. A. Ambrose, *Gas Chromatography*, George Newnes, London, 1961; Van Nostrand, Princeton, N. J., 1962. 220 pp.

Bayer, E., *Gas Chromatography*, American Elsevier, New York, 1961, 240 pp. An English translation of a textbook originally published in German.

Pecsok, R. L. Ed., *Principles and Practices of Gas Chromatography*, Wiley, New York, 1959, 250 pp. A collection of monographs on various aspects of instrumentation and techniques.

Keulemans, A. I. M., *Gas Chromatography*, Reinhold, New York, 1959 (2nd ed.), 250 pp. An older, but excellent, general text with a comprehensive treatment of the theory.

Phillips, C. S. G., *Gas Chromatography*, Butterworths, London, 1956, 98 pp. This earliest text in the field is primarily of historical value but illustrates early apparatus and techniques.

B. Specialized Books of Wide Interest

A few books of the variety available on specialized topics are given below.

Burchfield, H. P., and E. E. Storrs, *Biomedical Applications of Gas Chromatography*, Academic Press, New York, 1962, 680 pp.

Jeffery, P. G., and P. J. Kipping, *Gas Analysis by Gas Chromatography*, Pergamon Press (Macmillan), New York, 1964, 216 pp.

Ettre, L. S., *Open Tubular Columns in Gas Chromatography*, Plenum Press, New York, 1965, 164 pp.

Moshier, R. W., and R. E. Sievers, *Gas Chromatography of Metal Chelates*, Pergamon Press, London, 1965, 163 pp.

Giddings, J. C., and R. A. Keller, Eds., *Advances in Chromatography*, Marcel Dekker, New York, Vol. I, 1966, 392 pp; Vol. II, 1966, 377 pp; Vol. III, 1966, 271 pp. A series of summary articles by contributors to the field of gas chromatography.

Wotiz, H. H., and S. J. Clark, *Gas Chromatography in the Analysis of Steroid Hormones*, Plenum Press, New York, 1966, 288 pp.

Harris, W. E., and H. W. Habgood, *Programmed Temperature Gas Chromatography*, Wiley, New York, 1966, 305 pp.

C. Proceedings of Symposia

Among the most useful sources of reference material for gas chromatography are the published proceedings of important symposia held periodically in the United States and Europe. Many of the outstanding developments in the field were first disclosed at these meetings, particularly in the theoretical and instrumentation areas. Some of these collections are listed below.

1. Symposia of the Gas Chromatography Discussion Group of the Institute of Petroleum

First—London, May, 1956—Desty, D. H., Ed., *Vapour Phase Chromatography*, Butterworths, London and Academic Press, New York, 1957, 436 pp.

Second—Amsterdam, May, 1958—Desty, D. H., Ed., *Gas Chromatography 1958*, Butterworths, London and Academic Press, New York, 1958, 383 pp.

Third—Edinburgh, June, 1960—Scott, R. P. W., Ed., *Gas Chromatography 1960*, Butterworths, Washington, 1960, 466 pp.

Fourth—Hamburg, June, 1962—van Swaay, M., Ed., *Gas Chromatography 1962*, Butterworths, Washington, 1962, 411 pp.

Fifth—Brighton, September, 1964—Goldup, A., Ed., *Gas Chromatography 1964*, Institute of Petroleum, London, 1964, 386 pp.

Sixth—Rome, September, 1966—Littlewood, A. B., Ed., *Gas Chromatography 1966*, Institute of Petroleum, London, 1967, 464 pp.

2. Symposia of the Instrument Society of America, Michigan State University, Lansing, Michigan

First—August, 1947—Coates, V. J., H. J. Noebels, and I. S. Fagerson, Eds., *Gas Chromatography*, Academic Press, New York, 1958, 323 pp.

Second—June, 1959—Noebels, H. J., R. F. Wall, and N. Brenner, Eds., *Gas Chromatography*, Academic Press, New York, 1961, 463 pp.

Third—June, 1961—Brenner, N., J. E. Callen, and M. D. Weiss, Eds., *Gas Chromatography*, Academic Press, New York, 1962, 719 pp.

Fourth—June, 1963—Fowler, L., Ed., *Gas Chromatography*, Academic Press, New York, 1963, 226 pp.

3. Houston Symposia on Advances in Gas Chromatography, Houston, Texas

First—January, 1963—papers published in *Anal. Chem.*, **35,** 426–545 (1963).

Second—March, 1964—papers published in *Anal. Chem.*, **36,** 1410–1565 (1964).

Third—October, 1965—Zlatkis, A., and L. Ettre, Eds., *Advances in Gas Chromatography—1965*, Preston Technical Abstracts Co., Evanston, Ill., 1966, 182 pp.

4. Proceedings of the Canisius College Gas Chromatography Institute, Buffalo, N.Y.

Third—April, 1961—Szymanski, H. A., Ed., *Progress in Industrial Gas Chromatography*, Plenum Press, New York, 1961, 235 pp.

Fourth—April, 1962—Szymanski, H. A., Ed., *Lectures on Gas Chromatography*, Plenum Press, New York, 1963, 282 pp.

Fifth—1963—Szymanski, H. A., Ed., *Biomedical Applications of Gas Chromatography*, Plenum Press, New York, 1964, 324 pp.

Sixth—1964—Mattick, L. R., and H. A. Szymanski, Eds., *Lectures on Gas Chromatography—Agricultural and Biological Applications*, Plenum Press, New York, 1965, 256 pp.

5. Symposium of the New York Academy of Sciences

Williams, E. F., Ed., *The Analysis of Mixtures of Volatile Materials*, in *Ann. N.Y. Acad. Sci.*, **72** (13), 559–785 (March 1959).

6. Symposia of the East German Gas Chromatography Group

First—Leipzig, October, 1958—Angelé, H. P., Ed., *Gas Chromatographie 1958*, Akademie-Verlag, Berlin, 1959, 338 pp.

Second—Böhlen, October, 1959—Kaiser, R. E., and H. G. Struppe, Eds., *Gas Chromatographie 1959*, Akademie-Verlag, Berlin, 1959, 356 pp.

Third—Schkopau, May, 1961—Angelé, H. P., and H. G. Struppe, Eds., *Gas Chromatographie 1961*, Akademie-Verlag, Berlin, 1961 376 pp.

Fourth—Leuna, May, 1963—Angelé, H. P., and H. G. Struppe, Eds., *Gas Chromatographie 1963*, Akademie-Verlag, Berlin, 1963, 421 pp.

Fifth—East Berlin, May, 1965—*Gas Chromatographie 1965*, *I–II*. Struppe, H. G., Ed., Akademie Verlag, Berlin, 1965, 606 + 140 pp.

7. Symposia of the GAMS

First—Paris, June, 1961—Tranchant, J., Ed., *Séparation Immédiate et Chromatographie 1961*, GAMS, Paris, 1961, 350 pp.

Second—Milano, June, 1963—*Atti delle Giornate Italiane della Separatione Immediate e della Chromatographia*, Società Italiana per lo Studio della Sostanze Grasse, Milano, 1964, 153 pp.

Third—Athens, September, 1965—Parissakis, G., Ed., *Chromatographie et Méthodes de Séparation Immédiate*, *I–II*, Union of Greek Chemists, Athens, 1966, 426 and 317 pp.

It is expected that future collections of papers representing proceedings of important technical meetings in gas chromatography will be published periodically. They are of primary use in providing up-to-date information on the most advanced developments in gas chromatography as a field in itself, rather than as a technique to be applied to the solution of analytical problems of interest to workers in other technologies. Generally, the applications papers contained in these collections are present because they are either revolutionary or illustrative of the application of a new instrument or manipulative technique, rather than simply a new solution of a problem in chemical separation per se.

D. Bibliographies

Centralized bibliographical references are invaluable to the practicing gas chromatographer. Through such collections, he can quickly locate original literature references, in spite of the diversity of publications in which gas chromatographic work has appeared. The following bibliographies are particularly useful.

1. Bibliographies in the ISA Proceedings

The proceedings of the first three international symposia organized by the Instrument Society of America (see Section V-3-B) also contained detailed bibliographies. The first bibliography, compiled by S. H. Langer and C. Zahn, lists 490 references and includes work reported through 1957. The second bibliography, compiled by L. S. Ettre, continues the listing through June 1960 and lists 1532 publications. Finally, the third bibliography, compiled by S. T. Preston, Jr., concludes the listing up to about October 1961 and consists of 2362 entries. The organization of these bibliographies is alphabetical, by name of the first listed author of the publication: Authors' names, title, and source of publication are furnished. This series represents the most complete bibliography available for the period up to the end of 1961.

2. Gas Chromatography Abstracts

This collection is published under the auspices of the Informal Discussion Group on Gas Chromatography of the Hydrocarbon Research Group, Institute of Petroleum. It is first published in quarterly issues for members of the Group only; later it is bound in an annual volume for general sale. The volume contains an author index with the listing of the name of every author and an excellent and very detailed subject index. In addition to the completeness of the bibliography, this collection is noteworthy because of the inclusion of brief abstracts of all included papers. It is also the most complete bibliographic work published outside the United States. The books are edited by C. E. M. Knapman. The 1958–1962 volumes were published by Butterworths, London–Washington, D.C.; the volumes since 1963 are published by the Institute of Petroleum and distributed by Elsevier.

———, 1958, 1468 references through 1958.
———, 1959, 717 references.
———, 1960, 875 references.
———, 1961, 833 references.
———, 1962, 763 references.
———, 1963, 1051 references.
———, 1964, 1400 references.
———, 1965, 1100 references.
———, 1966, three issues, 886 references.

3. Bibliographies Published as Separate Books

There are two further books which are devoted entirely to bibliographies.

Preston, S. T., and G. Hyder, *A Comprehensive Bibliography and Index to the Literature on Gas Chromatography*, Preston Technical Abstracts Co., Evanston, Illinois, 1965. This includes 5737 references covering all literature from 1952 through 1962. Literature for subsequent years is available in the Bibliography issue of the *Journal of Gas Chromatography*, usually the December issue. A detailed subject index is included.

Signeur, A. V., *Guide to Gas Chromatography Literature*, Plenum Press, New York, 1964. 7577 references, with detailed author and subject indexes.

4. Other Bibliographies

The general textbooks on gas chromatography also contain detailed bibliographies. *Principles and Practice of Gas Chromatography*, edited by R. L. Pecsok, is noteworthy. It lists 710 publications which are grouped according to the year of publication. It is very useful in searching for early publications; e.g., it lists 80 publications for the period between 1930 and the end of 1953, which, in general, describe archtypes or precursors of the present gas chromatographic techniques.

E. Retention Data

While retention data can be found in practically every book and publication listed here, two specially published volumes compile a large number of data which may be of help to the practical gas chromatographer.

Lewis, J. S., *Compilation of Gas Chromatographic Data*, American Society for Testing and Materials, Philadelphia, Pa., 1963, 625 pp. This large collection of data, chiefly from the literature, affords a rapid means for determining the specific conditions which have been employed for a given analysis, as well as the original reference.

McReynolds, W. O., *Gas Chromatograph Retention Data*, Preston Technical Abstracts Co., Evanston, Ill., 1966. This collection of retention data for 700 compounds on 77 stationary liquids is highly useful for qualitative work.

F. Review Articles

Because gas chromatography is a rapidly growing technique, many journals periodically publish articles which review the publications of a certain period or of a certain field of application. Typical of these review articles are those of Dal Nogare and Juvet (9–12) which have appeared biennially in the annual review issue of *Analytical Chemistry;* subsequent reviews will appear on a biannual basis. Van Rysselberge (42) has reviewed the developments in gas chromatography for the years 1954–1964.

In addition to these basic review articles, many others can be found in various English and foreign language journals. Most of them discuss special fields of gas chromatography, exemplified by the papers of Brooks (3) (steroids), and Bishop (1) (carbohydrates). The bibliographies mentioned above list numerous review articles.

G. Reference Sources

Because of the extremely rapid development of the field, it is both important and difficult for the practical gas chromatographer to keep abreast of the latest developments. Five important sources of summarized current information are available.

Two standard abstracting journals, *Chemical Abstracts* and *Chemisches Zentralblatt*, comprise the first group of sources. These journals are well known, very complete, and generally available. Unfortunately, a relatively long time may elapse between the appearance of a paper and the corresponding abstract.

The second source of current advances in the field is the *Zeitschrift für analytische Chemie* and *Analytical Abstracts*. Both contain abstracts of publications on analytical techniques, among them gas chromatography. The range of the service is worldwide. Both are excellent services but they suffer from the same problem as the big abstracting journals—that the time which elapses between the original publication and the appearance of the abstract is relatively long.

The third source is the weekly journal *Current Contents* published by the Institute for Scientific Information (33 South 17th Street, Philadelphia 3, Pa.) which prints the tables of contents of a large number of chemical, biomedical, and medical journals immediately after publication. Since the tables of contents of overseas journals are sent airmail to the publisher, they sometimes are printed in *Current Contents* earlier than the corresponding issue of the journal actually arrives in the United States. The publishers of *Current Contents* will also supply, upon request, a copy of any paper which was mentioned by title in the regular publication.

The fourth source in continuous information on the most current literature is the Bibliography Section of the *Journal of Chromatography* edited by K. Macek and J. Janák. This bibliography covers all techniques of chromatography (among them, gas chromatography), and it is divided into certain groups corresponding to the subject of the publications. Besides giving the authors' names, the title of the paper, and the reference to the journal where it was published, the subject of the publication is also indicated if it is not evident from its title.

Finally, the most important source of up-to-date information for the practical gas chromatographer is the *Abstracting Service* published by the Preston Technical Abstracts Co., 909 Pitner Avenue, Evanston, Ill. The service regularly abstracts over 400 of the most important journals throughout the world and is also represented at all major meetings in the field. Abstracts are usually received by subscribers within 2–4 weeks of the date of publication or presentation of the work. The abstracts are printed on Unisort punch cards, a typical card being shown in Figure 1-15. Cards,

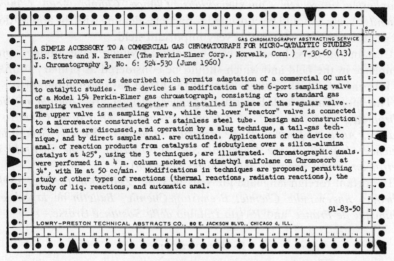

GAS CHROMATOGRAPHY ABSTRACTING SERVICE

A SIMPLE ACCESSORY TO A COMMERCIAL GAS CHROMATOGRAPH FOR MICRO-CATALYTIC STUDIES
L.S. Ettre and N. Brenner (The Perkin-Elmer Corp., Norwalk, Conn.) 7-30-60 (13)
J. Chromatography 3, No. 6: 524-530 (June 1960)

A new microreactor is described which permits adaptation of a commercial GC unit to catalytic studies. The device is a modification of the 6-port sampling valve of a Model 154 Perkin-Elmer gas chromatograph, consisting of two standard gas sampling valves connected together and installed in place of the regular valve. The upper valve is a sampling valve, while the lower "reactor" valve is connected to a microreactor constructed of a stainless steel tube. Design and construction of the unit are discussed, and operation by a slug technique, a tail-gas technique, and by direct sample anal. are outlined. Applications of the device to anal. of reaction products from catalysis of isobutylene over a silica-alumina catalyst at 425°, using the 3 techniques, are illustrated. Chromatographic anals. were performed in a 4 m. column packed with dimethyl sulfolane on Chromosorb at 34°, with He at 50 cc/min. Modifications in techniques are proposed, permitting study of other types of reactions (thermal reactions, radiation reactions), the study of liq. reactions, and automatic anal.

91-83-50

LOWRY—PRESTON TECHNICAL ABSTRACTS CO., 80 E. JACKSON BLVD., CHICAGO 4, ILL.

Fig. 1-15. Abstract card of the Preston Abstracting Service.

as received, are not coded, but the publishers provide a suggested key for this purpose. Over 10,000 abstract cards have appeared to date. A subscription to this service may be obtained from the publishers. The same firm has developed the *Termatrex Index*, an optical coincidence system of retrieval of information, which permits a rapid search of 9809 references by subject matter from 1962 through 1964.

H. Journals

The problem of keeping abreast of current developments in gas chromatography via the published literature is one of increasing difficulty. The number of publications has increased at an unprecedented rate since 1955. The main problem is that there is no single or limited number of journals to which this type of publication is directed, and all the important journals of analytical and organic chemistry publish many articles on solutions to gas chromatographic problems. Further, journals which are related to particular technologies are also very important references for gas chroma-tography articles describing analyses relating to those particular tech-nologies: e.g., the periodicals *Food Technology, Journal of Agricultural and Food Chemistry, Journal of Food Science, Journal of the American Oil Chemists' Society*, represent excellent sources of articles on analysis of food constituents by gas chromatography. Similarly, the various periodicals devoted to biochemistry and clinical chemistry (*Analytical Biochemistry, Biochimica et Biophysica Acta, Biochemical Journal, Biochemical and Biophysical Research Communications, Clinica Chimia Acta, Clinical Chemistry*, etc.) should be consulted for articles dealing with the application of gas chromatography in this very important field.

Certain journals, however, can be selected which have attained pre-eminence in the field and which should be considered as primary sources of information on the current state of the art in gas chromatography.

The most important English language journals are: *Journal of Gas Chromatography, Journal of Chromatography,* Analytical Chemistry, Nature, Analyst, Journal of the American Chemical Society, Separation Science, Journal of the Chemical Society, Journal of the Institute of Petroleum*, and *Chemistry and Industry (London)*.

Important foreign language journals include: *Zeitschrift für analytische Chemie, Angewandte Chemie, Brennstoff-Chemie, Bulletin de la Societé Chimique de France*, and *Rivista Italiana delle Sostanze Grasse*.

I. Organizations

As is the case with journals, the number of technical societies interested in gas chromatographic work is large. Included, essentially, are all societies to which the analysis of volatile compounds is of interest. However, a few groups are intensively concerned with gas chromatography as an instru-mental and analytical technique and are therefore of prime interest to workers in the field. These are enumerated below.

Committee E-19 on Gas Chromatography of the American Society of Testing and Materials. This group is very active in promoting the exchange and dissemination of gas chromatographic information. The Committee organizes every year a symposium discussing various aspects of gas chromatography. Membership in the Committee is arranged by application to the American Society of Testing and Materials, 1916 Race Street, Philadelphia 3, Pa.

Instrument Society of America (ISA), Analysis Instrumentation Division. This organization is active in the United States and Canada. It arranges

---

* Also publishes papers in French or German.

programs in gas chromatography at periodic Society meetings. Membership in the Society is arranged by application to the Instrument Society of America, Penn-Sheraton Hotel, 530 William Penn Place, Pittsburgh, 19, Pa.

American Chemical Society (ACS), Division of Analytical Chemistry and Division of Petroleum Chemistry. These Divisions sponsor excellent programs on gas chromatography on a periodic basis. A large program is also included in the annual Pittsburgh Conference on Analytical Chemistry and Applied Spectroscopy, which is sponsored by the Analytical Chemistry Group of the Society's Pittsburgh Section and the Spectroscopy Society of Pittsburgh. For information regarding the activities of the ACS and its Divisions, the headquarters of the Society (1155 Sixteenth Street N.W., Washington 6, D.C.) should be contacted.

Gas Chromatography Discussion Group, Associated with the Hydrocarbon Research Group of the Institute of Petroleum, London. This group is the leading European organization in the gas chromatography field; its membership, however, is from all over the world and includes many leading American gas chromatographers. In addition to holding several informal meetings each year (of which no printed record is released), the group sponsors the biennial International Symposia and the publication of the *Gas Chromatography Abstracts.* For information regarding membership, the secretariat of the Group, at the Institute of Petroleum (61 New Cavendish Street, London, W.1) should be contacted.

Several other groups can also be mentioned: e.g., the Gulf Coast Spectroscopic Group, the Chicago Gas Chromatography Discussion Group, the Washington Gas Chromatography Discussion Group, and the many other gas chromatography discussion groups in particular areas. Most of the foreign chemical societies also have special groups in their analytical divisions which devote their activity to gas chromatography.

J. Corporate Technical Service Facilities

Several of the larger manufactures of gas chromatographic equipment maintain staffs and equipment for technical service aid to potential and actual customers. Typically these facilities contain extensive reference files of literature, reprints, and abstracts, and are staffed by personnel who are knowledgeable in the area of instrumentation and applications. Useful advice on chromatography problems may be conveniently obtained by writing to these groups. They are usually located at the manufacturing site of the particular company. Some of these manufacturers also publish periodicals which contain information on technical developments in gas chromatography. Such journals are *The Analyzer* (Beckman Scientific and

Process Instrument Division, Fullerton, Calif.), *Facts and Methods for Scientific Research* (F & M Scientific Division of Hewlett-Packard, Avondale, Pa.,), *The Laboratory* (Fisher Scientific Company, Pittsburgh, Pa.), *GC Newsletter* and *Instrument News* (The Perkin-Elmer Corporation, Norwalk, Conn.), *The Column* (W. G. Pye & Co., London), and the *Aerograph Research Notes* and *Petroleum Peaks* (Varian Aerograph, Walnut Creek, Calif.). Complimentary subscriptions to these periodicals may be obtained by writing to the manufacturers.

References

1. C. T. Bishop, *Advan. Carbohydrate Chem.*, **19**, 95 (1964).
2. B. W. Bradford, D. Harvey, and P. E. Chalkey, *J. Inst. Petrol.*, **41**, 80 (1955).
3. C. J. Brooks, *Biochem. J.*, **96**, No. 2, 19P (1965).
4. A. B. Carel and G. Perkins, Jr., *Pittsburgh Conf. Anal. Chem. Appl. Spectry.*, *March 1–5, 1965.*
5. S. Claesson, *Arkiv Kemi, Mineral. Geol.*, **23A**, No. 1, 1 (1946).
6. E. Cremer and R. Müller, *Z. Elektrochem.*, **55**, 217 (1951).
7. E. Cremer and R. Müller, *Mikrochem. Mikrochim. Acta*, **36/37**, 553 (1951).
8. E. Cremer and F. Prior, *Z. Elektrochem.*, **55**, 66 (1951).
9. S. Dal Nogare, *Anal. Chem.*, **32**, 19R (1960).
10. S. Dal Nogare and R. S. Juvet, *Anal. Chem.*, **34**, 35R (1962).
11. S. Dal Nogare and R. S. Juvet, *Anal. Chem.*, **36**, 36R (1964).
12. S. Dal Nogare and R. S. Juvet, *Anal. Chem.*, **38**, 61R (1966).
13. G. Damköhler and H. Thiele, *Angew. Chem.*, **56**, 353 (1943).
14. G. Damköhler and H. Thiele, *Beih. Ver. Deut. Chem.*, No. 49 (1943).
15. A. Eucken and H. Knick, *Brennstoff-Chem.*, **17**, 241 (1936).
16. H. H. Hausdorff and N. Brenner, *Oil Gas J.*, **56**, 73 (June 30); 122 (July 7); 86 (July 21); 89, 93 (August 4), 1958.
17. A. T. James, *Biochem. J.*, **52**, 242 (1952).
18. A. T. James and A. J. P. Martin, *Biochem. J.*, **50**, 679 (1952).
19. A. T. James and A. J. P. Martin, *Analyst*, **77**, 915 (1952).
20. A. T. James, A. J. P. Martin, and G. H. Smith, *Biochem. J.*, **52**, 238 (1952).
21. J. Janák, *Chem. Listy*, **47**, 464 (1953).
22. J. Janák, *Chem. Listy*, **47**, 817 (1953); subsequent papers appeared in the same journal and in German translation in the *Collection Czech. Chem. Commun.*
23. A. I. M. Keulemans, *Gas Chromatography*, 2nd ed., Reinhold, New York, 1959.
24. A. I. M. Keulemans and A. Kwantes, *World Petrol. Congr., Proc. 4th, Rome, 1955.*
25. A. I. M. Keulemans, A. Kwantes, and P. Zaal, *Anal. Chim. Acta*, **13**, 357 (1955).
26. R. Kuhn, A. Winterstein, and E. Lederer, *Hoppe-Seylers Z. Physiol. Chem.*, **197**, 141 (1931).
27. M. Lederer, Ed., *Chromatographic Reviews*, Elsevier, New York, 1965.
28. S. R. Lipsky, R. A. Landowne, and J. E. Lovelock, *Anal. Chem.*, **31**, 852 (1959).
29. A. J. P. Martin and R. L. M. Synge, *Biochem. J.*, **35**, 1358 (1941).
30. C. Merritt, J. T. Walsh, P. Issenberg, and K. J. McCarthy, *J. Gas Chromatog.*, **2**, 314 (1964).
31. R. Müller, Ph.D. thesis, University of Innsbruck, Austria, 1949.

32. "Preliminary Nomenclature Recommendations," in R. P. W. Scott, Ed., *Gas Chromatography 1960*, Butterworths, Washington, D.C., 1960, pp. 423–432.
33. F. Prior, Ph.D. thesis, University of Innsbruck, Austria, 1947.
34. N. H. Ray, *J. Appl. Chem. (London)*, **4**, 21 (1954).
35. N. H. Ray, *J. Appl. Chem. (London)*, **4**, 82 (1954).
36. P. Schuftan, *Die Technische Gasanalyse*, S. Hirzel, Leipzig, 1931.
37. A. Tiselius, *Arkiv. Kemi, Mineral. Geol.*, **14B**, No. 22, 1 (1940).
38. A. Tiselius, *Arkiv. Kemi, Mineral. Geol.*, **16A**, No. 18, 11 (1943).
39. M. Tswett, *Ber. Deut. Botan. Ges.*, **24**, 316, 384 (1906).
40. N. C. Turner, *Natl. Petroleum News*, **35**, 234 (1943).
41. N. C. Turner, *Petrol. Refiner*, **22**, 140 (1943).
42. J. van Rysselberge, *Ind. Chim. Belge*, **29**, 575 (1964).
43. J. M. Vernand, *Bull. Soc. Chim. France*, **1962**, 1914.
44. A. Zlatkis, D. Fenimore, L. S. Ettre, and J. E. Purcell, *J. Gas. Chromatog.*, **3**, 75 (1965).

CHAPTER 2

The Mobile Phase

Robert D. Schwartz,* *Shell Development Co.,*
Houston, Texas

I. Introduction

The practical gas chromatographer is interested in, and concerned with, the mobile phase for a number of important reasons. For analytical, preparative, or theoretical work he must first select a suitable carrier gas. Then, he may find it necessary to purify this gas. Finally, he will wish to select and maintain the proper pressure and flow rate.

The choices made for these factors will often determine to a large degree the overall efficiency of the chromatography system in the resolution obtainable and the time required. The lower limits of detection, for trace analyses, are an important function of the particular combination of

* Present address: United Gas Corporation, Shreveport, Louisiana.

detector and mobile phase. The purity of the mobile phase is critical for low-level analyses. In addition to the above factors, it is important to consider the cost, safety, and convenience of a given carrier gas.

This carrier gas is an important part of systems utilized for gas–liquid or gas–solid chromatography. In gas–liquid chromatography, the carrier gas is considered inert and serves to transport the sample through the separating column and to a detector where the separated components are measured. By contrast, in gas–solid chromatography the carrier gas may compete with sample components for the surface available on the solid, and thus can influence the time of analysis and the separations obtained. In both forms of gas chromatography several factors will influence the choice of carrier gas.

This chapter will include a discussion of the factors to be considered in selecting carrier gases, and of methods and apparatus for supplying, purifying (2), controlling, and measuring the flow of carrier gas. A description of flow programming (1,3,4,6), and its applicability to gas chromatography, will be presented. Finally, we shall include a listing of some new techniques (5) involving variation of the mobile phase.

II. Relationships between Gas Flow and Velocity

Although our basic aim is to provide practical information in utilizing a gas chromatographic system, the definition of a few basic terms is necessary. These are the linear gas velocity (given in cm/sec) and the carrier gas flow rate (given in ml/min).

The linear gas velocity (u) is calculated from the carrier gas flow rate (F) and the free cross section of the column.

$$u = F/\epsilon r^2 \pi \qquad (2\text{-}1)$$

where r is the inside radius of the column tubing and ϵ is the interparticle porosity. $\epsilon = 1$ for open tubular columns.

Because of the compressibility of the mobile phase, the flow rate and the linear velocity are not uniform along the length of a column. Three values of flow rate are of interest.

1. F_a, the flow rate measured at the outlet pressure (p_o) and at ambient temperature (T_a, °K). This measurement is generally made with a soap-film flowmeter.

2. F_c, the corrected flow rate, which is obtained from F_a by correcting it to give the dry gas flow at the column temperature (T_c, °K).

$$F_c = F_a(T_c/T_a)[(p_a - p_w)/p_w] \qquad (2\text{-}2)$$

where p_a is the ambient pressure and p_w is the partial pressure of water at the ambient temperature.

u_o is the linear gas velocity corresponding to F_c.

3. The average linear gas velocity $\bar{u}$ and the average gas flow rate F_c are used to calculate column efficiencies:

$$u = u_o j \tag{2-3}$$

and

$$\bar{F}_c = F_c j \tag{2-4}$$

where j is the compressibility correction factor,

$$j = \frac{3}{2} \frac{(p_i/p_o)^2 - 1}{(p_i/p_o)^3 - 1} \tag{2-5}$$

p_i is the carrier gas inlet pressure and p_o is the carrier gas outlet pressure.

The relationship between the carrier gas pressure drop along the column (Δp) and the average linear gas velocity is the following:

$$\Delta p = (\eta/B_o)L\bar{u} \tag{2-6}$$

where η is the viscosity of the carrier gas and B_o is the specific permeability of the column whose length is L.

B_o is equal to $r^2/8$ for open tubular columns, and is calculated from the Kozeny-Carman equation for packed columns.

When substituted with the values listed above, equation 2-6 becomes

$$\Delta p = \bar{F}_c(\eta/B_o)(L/\epsilon r^2\pi) = F_c j(\eta/B_o)(L/\epsilon r^2\pi) \tag{2-7}$$

Then, using k for the partition ratio of a given component, its retention time (t_R) is given by the following

$$t_R = (L/\bar{u})(1 + k) = (L\epsilon r^2\pi/\bar{F}_c)(1 + k) = (L\epsilon r^2\pi/F_c j)(1 + k) \tag{2-8}$$

III. Selection of the Mobile Phase

The selection of a suitable carrier gas, which carries the sample to the column, through the column, and to a detector, is important for all types of gas chromatographic work. In some cases, the efficiency of the column, the time of analyses, or the sensitivity of a given detector are determined, to a major extent, by the properties of the carrier gas. Among the factors which must be considered in selecting a carrier gas are the following: Availability, cost, effect on the desired separation, effect on the time of analysis, effect on the detection system, and safety considerations.

Hydrogen, helium, argon, nitrogen, and carbon dioxide are the most commonly used carrier gases. In the United States these gases are all readily available, in standard cylinders, in varying grades of purity. In Europe, helium is not easily obtained and is seldom used. For large diameter columns operated at high flow rates, as in preparative gas chromatography, the cost of the carrier gas is often the major consideration. Air is sometimes employed for preparative work, or the carrier gases may be recirculated.

The carrier gas utilized generally does not have a major effect upon the separation obtained with a given column, or upon the time required for an analysis. There are cases involving difficult separations with high-resolution columns (gas–liquid), and some gas–solid separations, where the carrier gas selection is important.

The effectiveness of some detection systems is determined to a major extent by the physical and chemical properties and the purity of the mobile phase. For example, it is necessary to use argon with the ionization detectors developed by Lovelock, which depend upon the formation of metastable argon atoms. In other cases, the sensitivity, noise level, quantitative response factors, and even the useful life of a detector are related to the particular carrier gas which is passed through the system. For trace analyses, the purity of the mobile phase is a very critical factor in allowing sensitive detectors to function properly. The interaction of the carrier gas with the constructional materials of a detector may be important. Hydrogen, for instance, may react with oxides present in certain thermistors and shorten their useful life. If it is necessary to use hydrogen as the mobile phase with a thermal conductivity detector, a hot-wire cell should be utilized.

Use of cylinders of compressed gases to supply the mobile phase requires that certain safety factors be considered. The cylinders should be supported by clamps or chains, and the proper regulators should be employed. For process analyzers, explosion-proof apparatus is often specified. When hydrogen is employed as the mobile phase, the excess gas should be vented through a hood.

Generally, the gases used in gas chromatography are obtained in steel cylinders. The standard cylinders which are supplied contain about 240 cu ft of gas at 2200 psi pressure at 70°F. The cylinders are the property of the gas supplier and are subject to the rules and regulations of the Interstate Commerce Commission. Cylinders used for compressed gases are drawn from a single plate of high-grade steel and are pressure tested every five years by the gas suppliers. The cylinder valves have a safety nut containing a disk of a metal which will burst if too much pressure is developed in the system by an increase in temperature.

IV. Purification of the Mobile Phase

The purity of the mobile phase is important for many reasons. Trace analyses, performed with highly sensitive detectors, require clean carrier gas. The analysis of fractions by spectrometric techniques also places stringent requirements on the carrier gas utilized in certain types of preparative gas chromatography.

The interaction between the carrier gas and some of the sample components must be considered. Thus, it is important to exclude oxygen from systems developed for the analysis or separation of compounds which are readily oxidized. In gas–solid chromatography, where the mobile phase can interact with the active solid, strongly adsorbed impurities in the carrier gas may have important effects upon the retention time and peak shape of sample components. If strongly adsorbed materials are allowed to accumulate on an adsorbent column, the properties of the column will be changed considerably. The adsorbed impurities may even deactivate an adsorbent and thus prevent it from yielding a desired separation.

Certain impurities in carrier gases will cause little or no trouble with an analysis or separation. For example, traces of nitrogen in helium used for a hydrocarbon analysis with a flame ionization detector will not influence the results. Hydrocarbon impurities in the mobile phase are particularly detrimental for the determination of trace hydrocarbons in air. A thorough discussion of the techniques for the preparation of "clean" gases developed by Prescott and Wise (2), and reprinted here with their permission, is presented next.

The purification of air and hydrogen by the methods described gives excellent results. Apparatus for purifying helium to an equivalent cleanliness is not yet commercially available. The methods of purification here presented may not be new, but to our knowledge, the significance of the results has not been previously reported.

A. Apparatus

Clean hydrogen can be produced from inexpensive water-pumped electrolytic hydrogen by using a palladium–silver alloy diffusion purifier, such as the one manufactured by the Milton Roy Company of St. Petersburg, Florida. Hydrogen of comparable cleanliness may be produced by passing the same type of hydrogen through a large liquid-nitrogen cold trap charged with Davison type 912 silica gel. Economic considerations will dictate which system should be used for the particular problem. The large 5-cu ft diffusion purifier will supply five flame ionization detectors, with little or no maintenance, at the cost of 500 W of electrical power and the depreciation of about $1500 worth of instrument. Smaller or larger available models range from 50 ml/min to 200 cu ft. The maintenance cost

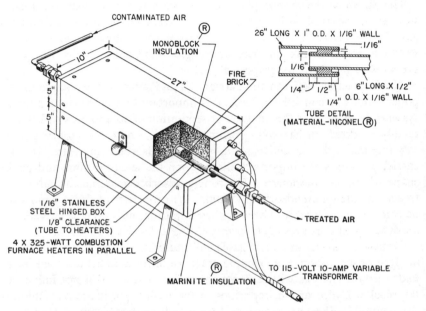

Fig. 2-1. Hydrocarbon/air combustion furnace detail.

of the cold trap is only the cost of about a gallon of liquid nitrogen per 8-hr day per flame. However, there is about $\frac{1}{2}$-hr time lag each morning while the clean hydrogen displaces the contaminated gas which has passed into the system during the night.

Air can be purified by oxidizing the hydrocarbon contaminants in a combustion furnace charged with wire-form cupric oxide. This is not a new technique—the method has been in use for decades in the analyses of hydrogen, carbon monoxide, illuminants, flue gases, etc. Since this process is simple combustion of hydrocarbons in air, no special oxidizer is necessary, and therefore Chromosorb (fire brick) 10–30 mesh is substituted for the cupric oxide charge. The working temperature is 825°C. For safety, the working pressure should not exceed 150 psig at this temperature. Figure 2-1 shows details of such a furnace. The Inconel tube should be radiographed to be certain that there are no weak spots or flaws. Under these conditions, the tube should last more than 100,000 hr before rupture. However, safety dictates that the tube should be changed every two years. "Breathing air," which is scrubbed and tanked for scuba divers, hospitals, safety breathing apparatus, etc., can be used as a starting material. It is passed through a 1- or 2-cu ft surge tank, which in turn supplies the furnace. The output from the furnace is dried by passing the gas through a large stainless steel U-tube charged with Drierite. Air produced by this method is believed to be the cleanest air available and is referred to as "clean air"; the hydrocarbon content is equal to or less than 1 ppb.

B. Performance

Some results of the use of clean gases were predictable, and some are well known; but some have not been previously reported and are quite startling. First, the baseline noise and drift have been reduced sufficiently to allow the chromatographer to operate with a sensitivity which can be increased by one order of magnitude. Second, the buckout current (current needed to place the baseline on the recorder zero) has been reduced to less than 1/10 that used with the cleanest hydrogen and air commercially available. In addition, there is a reduction in cost of tanked gases— "prepurified hydrogen" and "chromatographic air" are much more expensive than water-pumped electrolytic hydrogen and breathing air. Third, and of greatest interest, the development of an understanding of "negative chromatograms" (Fig. 2-3d) explains the occasional "negative" peak at the methane retention time position observed when some low-concentration samples are analyzed.

To explain "negative" or inverse peaks, let us graphically represent the progress of a clean sample through a chromatographic column with a contaminated carrier gas. In Figure 2-2 the contaminating components (C_x, C_y, and C_z) of the carrier gas are shown as though they flowed along individual paths or tubes. Figure 2-2a represents the injection of a plug of clean gas into the stream; b and c represent two stages of the sample's progress through the column; d represents the final stage of the sample's separation just prior to its exit into the detector. The many and various effects which yield a Gaussian-like peak in the normal chromatogram are not considered in this discussion; only the retention times of C_x, C_y, and C_z are considered, and their effect on the signal is discussed.

In the steady-state condition of the system, the contaminated carrier gas is being continuously separated into its chromatographic fractions—that is, each component is being retarded in its progress through the column by its interaction with the partitioning liquid or sorbent. However, since

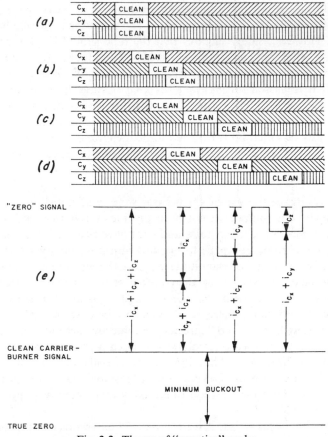

Fig. 2-2. Theory of "negative" peaks.

there is no interruption of flow or change of composition of the gas, there is no change in signal, and no peaks are exhibited. The resulting "zero" signal is the sum of the currents developed by the contaminating components ($i_{C_x} + i_{C_y} + i_{C_z}$ for components C_x, C_y, and C_z, Fig. 2-2e) plus a minimum signal developed by the hydrogen flame.

The introduction of a sample constitutes a change in composition of the gas stream, and a change in signal level can be expected. As a sample of clean gas passes through the column, the interfaces between the carrier and the sample exhibit the chromatographic effect. Thus each region of clean gas into which, and from behind which, a particular contaminant is retarded, travels through the column at a different rate.

In Figure 2-2d, the retention time of each portion of clean gas is

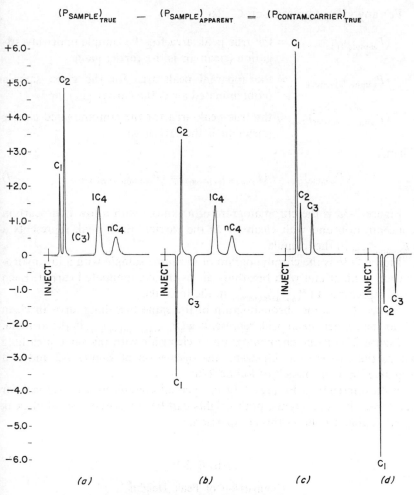

Fig. 2-3. Demonstration of "negative" peaks.

controlled by its respective contaminant in the carrier gas stream. When that portion controlled by C_x leaves the column, the signal is $i_{C_y} + i_{C_z}$. This is less than the original signal by i_{C_x}, the amount of current contributed to the "zero" signal by the contaminant C_x. This loss of i_{C_x} creates a "negative" peak. The same reasoning is followed to obtain "negative" peaks for C_y and C_z, whose signal currents are $i_{C_x} + i_{C_z}$ and $i_{C_x} + i_{C_y}$, respectively.

The above discussion is illustrated in Figure 2-3 with a flame ionization detector and air as the carrier gas.

For any given hydrocarbon C_n, let

$(P_{sample})_{true}$ = the true peak area for the sample under investigation (clean air is the carrier gas),

$(P_{sample})_{apparent}$ = the apparent peak area for the given sample (contaminated air is the carrier gas), and

$(P_{contam.\ carrier})_{true}$ = the true peak area for the contaminated carrier (clean air is the carrier gas).

Then,

$$(P_{sample})_{true} - (P_{sample})_{apparent} = (P_{contam.\ carrier})_{true} \qquad (2\text{-}9)$$

Figure 2-3a is the chromatogram of a sample with a low hydrocarbon concentration and with clean air as the carrier. Each peak represents a $(P_{sample})_{true}$ in the formula.

Figure 2-3b is the chromatogram of the same sample with a low hydrocarbon content and with breathing air as the contaminated carrier. Each peak represents a $(P_{sample})_{apparent}$ in the formula.

Figure 2-3c is the chromatogram of the same breathing air with clean air as the carrier. Each peak represents a $(P_{contam.\ carrier})_{true}$ in the formula.

Figure 2-3d is the chromatogram of clean air with the same breathing air as the carrier; this illustrates the discussion of Figure 2-2 and is a negative "mirror image" of Figure 2-3c.

With reference to Figures 2-3a–c, since all conditions are identical for the three chromatograms, peak heights can be compared instead of peak areas. Table 2-1 shows this comparison.

TABLE 2-1

Comparison of Peak Heights

	C_1	C_2	C_3	iso-C_4	n-C_4
$(P_{sample})_{true}$	+2.37	+4.85	—	+1.42	+0.53
$(P_{sample})_{apparent}$	−3.57	+3.35	−1.20	+1.43	+0.55
Theoretical					
$\quad (P_{contam.\ carrier})_{true}$	+5.94	+1.50	+1.20	−0.01	−0.02
Observed					
$\quad (P_{contam.\ carrier})_{true}$	+5.94	+1.50	+1.21	—	—
Error in					
$\quad (P_{contam.\ carrier})_{true}$	0.00	0.00	+0.01	+0.01	+0.02

It should be carefully noted that in all the chromatograms shown in Figure 2-3, the burned gases (air and hydrogen) were clean. The chromatograms were duplicated for contaminated burning gases with clean air as the carrier or sample in Figures 2-3a, 2-3c, and 2-3d. There was no measurable effect upon peak height. However, the buckout current was about one order of magnitude greater, and the signal-to-noise level was lowered to about 1/50.

Perhaps a less elegant but more forceful way of illustrating the preceding discussion is shown by the "chromatograms" in Figure 2-4. The following discussion refers to points from left to right on the figure.

1. From the beginning to point A the baseline is formed by clean carrier and burner gases. Just prior to A the carrier stream was switched from "clean" air to contaminated air.

2. At A the methane is eluted and raises the signal to the amperage contributed by that contaminant (C_1).

3. In a succession of ascending steps the amperage is increased by the amount contributed by ethane, ethylene, propane, isobutane, and normal butane. The order and spacing are controlled by their respective retention times.

4. At point B a new baseline is established—the "zero" signal for the contaminated carrier, which is the sum of the currents contributed by each contaminant.

5. At point C, a 1.5-ml sample of "clean" air was introduced, and an inverse or "negative" chromatogram was produced.

6. Shortly after the normal butane was eluted, the carrier gas was switched back to "clean" air. Point D marks the start of the descending stairsteps whose order, magnitude, and spacing are the same as those found in the ascending stairsteps: methane, ethane, ethylene, propane, isobutane, and normal butane.

7. Point E marks the return of the "clean" carrier gas, with the baseline the same as that prior to point A.

8. At point F, a 1.5-ml sample of the contaminated carrier gas was introduced, and a normal or "positive" chromatogram was produced. This chromatogram is a perfect inversion of that formed by the injection of "clean" air at point C.

At this writing, no helium purifier is commercially available. The Bell Telephone Laboratories reported success with a helium diffusion purifier; they also implied that a similar argon purifier could be developed. The liquid nitrogen cold trap method of purifying helium will not remove all the methane. There appears to be a level of CH_4 contamination below which all cold trap efforts are to no avail. The higher boiling hydrocarbons

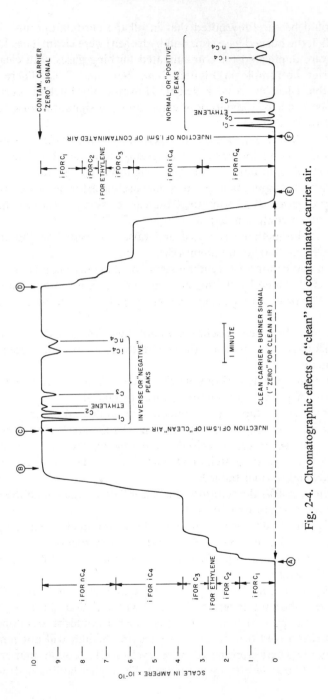

Fig. 2-4. Chromatographic effects of "clean" and contaminated carrier air.

(C$_2$ and up) can be removed by a cold trap to the extent that they are undetectable.

When helium is to be used for concentrating a hydrocarbon sample in a cold trap, it is recommended that a liquid nitrogen cold trap be used in the stream ahead of the extracting and collecting apparatus (Fig. 2-5). This cold trap should be filled with the same sorbent used in the concentrating or collecting cold trap. It should also have a very large capacity and should

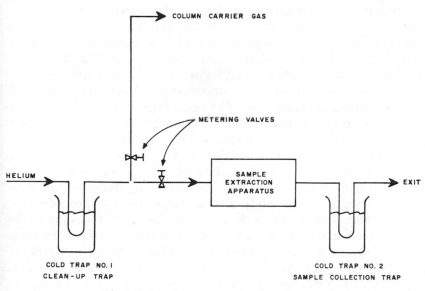

Fig. 2-5. Sample concentration flow diagram.

be changed or allowed to warm up every 8–10 hr. If this procedure is followed, there should be no addition or subtraction from the results of the second, or collecting, cold trap. If care is not used, the first cold trap may become saturated, and thus the sweeping gas can contribute to the collected sample. If the first cold trap is more efficient than the collecting cold trap—for example, Davison type 912 silica gel against Davison type 70 silica gel—there may be a subtraction from the collected sample. In addition, the column carrier gas should be taken from the helium line just after the first cold trap. This will give a carrier gas whose contamination is identical with that of the helium used in collecting the sample in the second trap. Thus there will be minimal falsification of the peaks, such as that demonstrated between Figures 2-3a and b in the earlier discussion of "negative" peaks.

Prescott and Wise (2) concluded:

1. If chromatography and ionization detectors are to deliver the quality of data of which they are capable, clean gases are a necessity.

2. It is more economical to clean the gases to be used than to pay the high cost of "pure" grade gases, which at best are marginal in quality and may be too contaminated for satisfactory quantitative analyses.

3. If the results from a "standard" cannot be duplicated over the long-term operation, or if different instruments give different results, the cleanliness of the gases used should be carefully checked before the differences are ascribed to such things as detector geometry or inlet system. On the other hand, chromatographers should not be lulled into complacency just because they have checked their "standard" or "blank" over a considerable length of time. They may have used carrier gases with the same amount and makeup of contamination and thus have demonstrated a consistent but unknown error. The major error is the "negative" peak effect which cannot be bucked out. It must be remembered that buckout current is the current needed to place the standing current of the detector into the range of the recorder or meter, and it has absolutely no effect on the relative peak heights—only on the position of the base line.

4. Previously reported results may be in error by reason of the carrier gas contamination. However, in most cases this has little effect, since the hydrocarbons which make up the contaminating material may not be the same as those in the sample. In general, the carrier contaminations are in the C_1–C_5 group, whereas most analyses have been in the C_6-and-up range. However, one should not assume that a given tank of gas cannot have higher-boiling components in it. One tank of "chromatographic air" which was analyzed had a spectrum of hydrocarbons through cyclohexane.

5. The trend in detectors is toward greater sensitivity. Clean gases should be used in all cases, even though the "negative" peak effect may have no bearing on the analysis. The quiet, stable baseline will yield more reproducible results and permit better use of electronic integrators.

6. When a hydrocarbon sample is concentrated in a liquid nitrogen cold trap, it is difficult to guarantee that the helium will not contribute to, or subtract from, the collected sample. The column carrier gas should come from the same source as the sweeping gas so that the resulting chromatogram will not have been influenced by differential contamination.

7. The method presented here cannot measure the absolute purity of a gas, but only the relative purity or differential contamination. A close look at Figure 2-3 will show this. If the carrier and the sample have identically the same concentration of a given contaminant, then there would be no peak for that contaminant. Figures 2-3*a* and *c* were made with the cleanest carrier gas available. If a cleaner gas were used, the peaks in Figures 2-3a and c would be larger, but the peaks in Figure 2-3b would remain the same size, and Figure 2-3d would show greater negative peaks.

8. Although this discussion was primarily concerned with the flame ionization detector and low-boiling-point hydrocarbon gases, the basic principles are applicable to any detector and to the chromatographic separation of any material—for example, a helium ionization detector used in a nitrogen–oxygen chromatographic analysis.

Finally, it has been demonstrated that clean gases for sensitive detectors yield better results regardless of the detector or the gas being analyzed.

V. Pressure and Flow Selection and Regulation

When a suitable carrier gas has been chosen, based upon the criteria cited in Section III, the flow rate (linear gas velocity) must then be selected and regulated. For analytical work with high-resolution columns, the flow rate is often important. Since the time of analysis is inversely proportional to the linear gas velocity and the efficiency of separation decreases somewhat with increasing linear gas velocity, a compromise is usually made. The shape of the H (HETP) vs. linear gas velocity curve is a function of the carrier gas and of various column parameters. Van Deemter and his colleagues developed a useful equation for H (height equivalent to a theoretical plate) as a function of the carrier gas velocity. This equation has been written in several forms. For purposes of this discussion it is expressed as:

$$H = A + B/\bar{u} + C\bar{u} \qquad (2\text{-}10)$$

where $\bar{u} = $ the average gas velocity. The meaning of A, B, and C will be discussed in the fourth chapter of this book. In many cases, the plot of H vs. $\bar{u}$ is somewhat flat at high velocities. That is, a two- or threefold increase in velocity does not result in a corresponding increase in H. Therefore, unless very difficult separations must be made, it is advisable to operate at a high velocity and not at the minimum value of H. This will result in obtaining more rapid separations with only a slight decrease in resolution.

A. Flow Rates Utilized with Various Column Types

The flow rates employed for gas chromatographic columns vary from less than 1 ml/min for 0.01 in. i.d. capillary columns to several hundred milliliters per minute for large-diameter columns. These flow rates are generally achieved with pressures of a few pounds per square inch to approximately 100 psig. Consequently, for columns whose outlet pressure is atmospheric, the inlet to outlet pressure ratio will vary from slightly over 1 to approximately 7. As discussed later, with the development of flow-programming procedures, considerably higher pressures may be required.

The identification of sample components by their retention volume requires that the flow rate be measured accurately and that it remain constant from one analysis to another. This requires adequate temperature control as well as the flow control.

B. Apparatus for Control and Measurement of Mobile-Phase Flow Rate

Two-stage regulators, for the carrier gas supply, which contain two independent diaphragms and valve units are utilized to reduce the cylinder pressure to an intermediate pressure and then to the required delivery pressure. A soap film flowmeter is a simple and accurate accessory for measuring the flow of carrier gas. For packed columns, a 50- or 100-ml calibrated buret containing a soap solution is useful. Gas is passed through the solution and the time for a bubble to travel between two of the markings is measured with a stop watch. Smaller burets are desirable for measuring the lower flow rates employed with capillary column systems.

Although the two-stage regulators and gas cylinders are common accessories in most laboratories, it may be advisable here to mention a few items pertaining to their safe and proper utilization. When a new cylinder is put into service it should be supported by a chain or clamp. Open the valve slightly, for an instant, to remove dust which may be on the valve outlet. Unscrew the dust plug from the regulator inlet nut and attach the regulator to the cylinder. Then release the regulator pressure-adjusting screw and open the cylinder valve slowly. This will let the cylinder pressure gauge pointer move up slowly. Next, open the cylinder valve fully. Attach the required tubing to the regulator outlet and then to the gas chromatographic system making sure that the connections are gas-tight.

Soap-film meters are easy to use and provide readings of sufficient accuracy. For theoretical studies, the temperature is also recorded and the flow rates are corrected for the vapor pressure of water. If necessary, the flow rates are also corrected to the column temperature.

With flow-sensitive detection systems, or when it becomes necessary to measure retention volumes very accurately, it is advisable to add a constant differential flow controller and a buffering surge tank, or both, to the system. Flow controllers are usually attached upstream of the injection port and the column. For programmed temperature separations performed with dual-column, dual-detector systems, balancing of the flows and the resultant column "bleed" is difficult. In such cases, it is important to have high-quality regulators in the system.

VI. Principles and Applications of Flow Programming (1,3,4,6)

A. Principles

Ordinarily, the flow of carrier gas is set at some desired value at the beginning of an analysis. For isothermal operation, this flow remains constant during the analysis. If temperature programming is utilized, when the temperature is changed during an analysis the flow rate is altered. It has been shown that flow programming (increasing the flow rate of carrier gas with time) can achieve results similar to those obtained with temperature programming.

The results available at this time indicate that flow programming is applicable to some important analytical problems. A recent publication dealing with flow programming reviews the theoretical reasoning which (6) led to its development and describes a pneumatically controlled system, which permits the column pressure to rise exponentially between preset limits during a predetermined time interval. The analysis of typical samples, with open tubular columns coated with partition liquids and with a packed column containing an adsorbent, by the programmed flow procedure is demonstrated in this publication.

Purnell (3) indicated that programming of the carrier gas flow rate might achieve results similar to those obtained by programmed temperature gas chromatography (PTGC). During the past years, several workers have tried this mode of operation. It appears appropriate to name this procedure *programmed flow gas chromatography* (PFGC).

A concise list of the fundamental equations which relate the carrier gas pressure and the flow and column parameters has been given in the most recent paper pertaining to PFGC (6).

B. Examples of Analyses Performed by PFGC

The methyl esters contained in a complex fish oil, menhaden oil, may be analyzed with an open tubular column coated with butanediol succinate. If this analysis is performed isothermally, at 185°C, the time required is approximately 60 min. Temperature programming, with the same column, from 170 to 205°C, reduces the time of analysis to about 35 min. However, deterioration of the liquid phase produces a rising baseline at the end of the chromatogram. Programmed flow operation, of this system, at 185°C provided a suitable analysis in about 25 min with a minimum of column bleeding.

A group of straight-chain alkylbenzenes, in the C_{15}–C_{20} region, may be analyzed with a DC-550 (phenyl silicone) coated open tubular column. When this analysis is performed by temperature programming from 140 to 170°C, the time required is about 45 min. Programmed flow operation at 145°C provided a more rapid analysis, but the resolution was inferior to that obtained with temperature programming. In this case, a combination of the two types of programming yielded good resolution while further reducing the time requirement.

The same authors demonstrated the PFGC separation of some light gases with a molecular sieve column. The time required for the separation of hydrogen, oxygen, nitrogen, methane, and carbon monoxide was reduced from 9 min to less than 5 min by programming the flow. For this work, two matched columns were connected to a flow-through type of hot wire detector. The applicability of PFGC to thermal conductivity detectors of the thermistor type has been shown by Costa Neto and co-workers.

These examples indicate that PFGC itself and PFGC combined with PTGC provide rapid and useful separations of complex wide-boiling samples. To date, PFGC has not been applied to the analysis of samples containing an extremely wide range of components. For instance, it is not likely that pressures of less than 200 psi will be adequate for the separation of mixtures that ordinarily require temperature increases of 100°C or more for PTGC analyses. For such samples, higher pressures and systems properly designed for their safe and effective utilization will be necessary.

VII. Techniques Involving Variation of the Mobile Phase

A brief listing of some new separation techniques which involve changes in the nature of the mobile phase will be given here because of their novelty and possible interest to practical chromatographers. These techniques were described in a paper by A. A. Zhukovitski (5). These variations are of particular value for process control because they provide for continuous analysis and reduce somewhat the necessity of long-term stability.

A. Vacancy Chromatography

The sample to be analyzed, or the sample diluted with carrier gas, is passed through the column continuously and pure carrier gas is introduced periodically as a plug. The vacancy chromatogram obtained is identical with the elution chromatogram for components whose isotherm is linear. If the isotherm is nonlinear, symmetrical peaks are obtained for small samples. For such cases, the retention volume is a direct function of the solute concentration, and this concentration may be directly determined from the retention time.

B. Differential Chromatography

When a mixture of definite composition is injected, as a plug, to a system with a sample flowing continuously, the vacancies reveal the differences in composition between the two samples. This technique is known as *differential chromatography*. It may be used to compare a process stream (passed continuously through the column) with a specified product (injected intermittently).

C. Iteration Chromatography

In this case, the sample mixture is introduced to the column continuously, and a blend of similar composition is injected intermittently. When the samples have an identical composition, the detector gives no response. For process control, the signal produced may be utilized to adjust the composition of the sample in order to balance the detector.

D. Chromatography without Carrier Gas (CWCG)

Frontal adsorption analysis is a technique which produces a step chromatogram. The mixture to be analyzed is passed continuously through the column. This procedure produces a substantial enrichment of the less strongly adsorbed components.

Frontal desorption analysis is performed by allowing the sample mixture to equilibrate with the column and then eluting it with another gas. This produces an enrichment of the more strongly retained components. The vacancy chromatographic analog is performed by introducing gas of differing composition intermittently.

In all modifications of CWCG the composition of an unknown may be determined from the retention times of zones or from the heights of steps.

References

1. C. Costa Neto, J. T. Koffer, and J. W. de Alencar, *J. Chromatog.*, **15**, 301 (1964).
2. B. Osborne Prescott and H. L. Wise, *J. Gas Chromatog.*, **4**, 80 (1966).
3. J. H. Purnell, *Gas Chromatography*, Wiley, New York, 1962, p. 387.
4. R. P. W. Scott, in *Gas Chromatography 1964*, A. Goldup, Ed., The Institute of Petroleum, London, 1965, p. 25.
5. A. A. Zhukovitski, in *Gas Chromatography 1964*, A. Goldup, Ed. The Institute of Petroleum, London, 1965, p. 161.
6. A. Zlatkis, D. C. Fenimore, L. S. Ettre, and J. E. Purcell, *J. Gas Chromatog.*, **3**, 75 (1965).

CHAPTER 3

Sampling: Preparation of Volatile Derivatives and Sample Introduction

Jerry C. Cavagnol and William R. Betker, *Chemagro Corporation, Kansas City, Missouri*

As a result of their high polarity, low volatility or thermal instability, many samples are not suitable for direct injection into a gas chromatograph. This chapter will cover the conversion of an isolated mixture of organic compounds to derivatives suitable for analysis by gas–liquid chromatography. The mixture may be the end product of an extensive cleanup process or simply a crude extract from a one-step purification. In either case, a subsequent refining step may be necessary before the derivative mixture is injected into the column. Both the techniques and apparatus for handling samples to the point of injection into the column are discussed in the latter part of the chapter.

Derivatives of highly polar compounds are usually prepared in order to reduce the polarity and, concomitantly, to increase the vapor pressure. This is especially important when studying zwitterion structures or compounds in which hydrogen bonding leads to dimerization and a lowering of the vapor pressure. Among the smaller molecules, however, a sharp increase in vapor pressure after derivatization may produce losses if the subsequent concentration step is not carried out with care.

In many cases in which the increase in molecular weight leads to a higher boiling point, the change confers thermal stability on the molecule. Indeed, sometimes the only recourse left the analyst is a drastic reduction in the ratio of the stationary phase to the column packing or the use of a more sensitive detector to offset the low vapor pressure. Finally, the separation of the components in a mixture without overlapping may dictate the choice between two otherwise equally desirable derivatives.

I. Preparation of Derivatives

A. Acids

Except for ions, the carboxylic acids are the most polar organic compounds known. Indeed, this polarity is frequently enhanced by the presence of other groups containing sulfur, nitrogen, and oxygen. As a result of the relatively low volatilities that these groups confer on the molecule of acid, it is necessary to convert carboxylic acids to less polar derivatives in order to realize the combination of thermal stability and increased vapor pressure required for gas–liquid chromatography.

This section will cover the derivatization techniques that include fatty acids and amino, hydroxy, keto, unsaturated, and dicarboxylic acids, as well as aromatic acids, polycyclic acids, and sulfonic acids. As the most widely used derivative of carboxylic acids is the methyl ester, it is appropriate to discuss first the methylation techniques employed.

The classical work on fatty acid gas–liquid chromatography was carried out by James and Martin (51) and James (50). They prepared methyl esters by refluxing the acid with methanolic HCl for 2 hr or treating with diazomethane at 0°:

$$R-\underset{O}{\underset{\|}{C}}-OH + CH_3OH \xrightarrow{HCl} R-\underset{O}{\underset{\|}{C}}-OCH_3 + H_2O$$

$$R-\underset{O}{\underset{\|}{C}}-OH + CH_2 \overset{+}{=} \overset{-}{N}-N \longrightarrow R-\underset{O}{\underset{\|}{C}}-OCH_3 + N_2$$

The 50 fatty acids described in these works are shown in Table 3-1.

Roper and Ma (90) have provided detailed instructions for the preparation and handling of diazomethane. They also describe a diazomethane microgenerator and procedures for converting acids of all kinds to methyl esters. The following acids were used in the study:

succinic	p-nitrobenzoic	benzenephosphonic
oxalic	p-hydroxybenzoic	p-nitrobenzenephosphonic
citric	phthalic	p-methoxybenzenephosphonic
	anisic	phenyl-p-tolylphosphonic

Schlenk and Gellerman (92) accelerated the esterification step by the introduction of gaseous diazomethane into a solution of the acids in ether containing methanol. They prepared methyl stearate, myristate, and linoleate. This same procedure was used by Quin and Hobbs (85) to prepare the methyl esters of malic, furoic, lactic, succinic, glycolic, adipic, citric, heptylic, pimelic, oxalacetic, and α-hydroxyisobutyric acids for GLC studies of cigaret smoke. Two peaks were obtained with glyoxylic acid while maleic and fumaric acids tended to form the nonvolatile pyrazoline. Neither glycine nor nicotinic acid gave chromatographic peaks, and the same was true for tartaric and α-ketoglutaric acids.

Rogozinski (89) showed that carboxylic acids could be converted quickly into methyl esters with no reagent preparation by heating the acid with methanol and sulfuric acid and making a single extraction of the ester with hexane for direct injection into the chromatograph. The methyl

TABLE 3-1

Fatty Acid Methyl Esters Prepared by James (50) and
James and Martin (51)

Formic	n-Tridecanoic
Acetic	cis-Δ^9-Tetradecenoic
Propionic	n-Tetradecanoic
Isobutyric	12-Methyltetradecanoic
n-Butyric	n-Pentadecanoic
2,2-Dimethylpropionic	14-Methylpentadecanoic
2-Methylbutyric	cis-Δ^9-Hexadecenoic
3-Methylbutyric	$trans$-Δ^9-Hexadecenoic
3-Methylpentanoic	n-Hexadecanoic
2-Methylpentanoic	14-Methylhexadecanoic
n-Pentanoic	n-Heptadecanoic
n-Hexanoic	cis-$\Delta^{9,12}$-Octadecadienoic
4-Methylhexanoic	$\Delta^{9,12,15}$-Octodecatrienoic
n-Heptanoic	cis-Δ^9-Octadecenoic
6-Methylheptanoic	$trans$-Δ^9-Octadecenoic
n-Octanoic	cis-Δ^6-Octadecenoic
6-Methyloctanoic	cis-Δ^4-Octadecenoic
n-Nonanoic	$trans$-Δ^4-Octadecenoic
8-Methylnonanoic	n-Octadecanoic
n-Decanoic	$\Delta^{5,8,11,14}$-Eicosatetraenoic
8-Methyldecanoic	Eicosapentaenoic
n-Undecanoic	n-Eicosanoic
10-Methylundecanoic	Docosahexaenoic
n-Dodecanoic	Δ^{13}-Docosaenoic
10-Methyldodecanoic	n-Docosanoic

esters of butyric, caproic, caprylic, and lauric acids were prepared. Application of Lorette and Brown's technique (65) could conceivably eliminate the extraction step, for they methylated acids with anhydrous methanol in the presence of HCl and dimethoxypropane. The latter acted as a water scavenger and yielded acetone and methanol as products with quantitative methylation of propionic, oxalic, and adipic acids. However, some acid-catalyzed polymerization of the acetal occurred. Simmonds and Zlatkis (97) have circumvented this by adding dimethylsulfoxide to the esterification mixture of octanoic, decanoic, and succinic acids; this inhibited completely the formation of polymers.

Downing, Kranz, and Murray (18) precipitated a mixture of fatty acids and hydroxy fatty acids as the calcium salts. The mixture was refluxed with methanol, benzene, and sulfuric acid to form the methyl esters. This mixture was reduced with LiAlH$_4$, and the resulting solution was separated into alcohol and glycol fractions. Both fractions could be converted to iodides with red phosphorus and iodine, then reduced to hydrocarbons with LiAlH$_4$. However, pure reference acids were not put through the same process.

Vorbeck, Mattick, Lee, and Pederson (116) compared four methylation methods on a quantitative basis: (1) diazomethane, (2) methanol–HCl with sublimation, (3) methanol–HCl on ion-exchange resin, and (4) methanol–boron trifluoride. Based on the better recoveries of the following high and low molecular weight acids obtained, they recommended diazomethane for quantitative work:

hexadecenoic	butyric
hexadecadienoic	valeric
octadecenoic	caproic
octadecadienoic	caprylic
octadecatrienoic	myristic
octadecatetraenoic	palmitic
eicosatetraenoic	stearic
eicosapentaenoic	oleic
docosapentaenoic	linoleic
docosahexaenoic	

Both micro- and macroquantitative methylation methods were reported by Gehrke and Goerlitz (31). They converted the fatty acids to the potassium salts, then precipitated and dried the corresponding silver salts. The solid mixture, suspended in pentane, was treated with methyl iodide in an inert atmosphere:

$$R\!-\!\underset{\underset{O}{\|}}{C}\!-\!OR' + KOH \rightarrow R\!-\!\underset{\underset{O}{\|}}{C}\!-\!OK + R'OH$$

$$R\!-\!\underset{\underset{O}{\|}}{C}\!-\!OK + AgNO_3 \rightarrow R\!-\!\underset{\underset{O}{\|}}{C}\!-\!OAg + KNO_3$$

$$R\!-\!\underset{\underset{O}{\|}}{C}\!-\!OAg + CH_3I \rightarrow R\!-\!\underset{\underset{O}{\|}}{C}\!-\!OCH_3 + AgI$$

The esters in pentane could then be chromatographed directly. Manipulative losses were minimized or eliminated and the conversions were found to be quantitative for butyric, caproic, lauric, myristic, palmitic, and oleic acids.

Ralls (86) investigated the flash reaction (transesterification) between potassium ethyl sulfate and the potassium salts of formic, acetic, propionic, butyric, valeric, caproic, isobutyric, isovaleric, isocaproic, pivalic, acrylic, methacrylic, crotonic, and dimethylacrylic acids, which formed the ethyl esters:

$$R—\underset{\underset{O}{\|}}{C}—OK + C_2H_5OSO_3K \rightarrow R—\underset{\underset{O}{\|}}{C}—OC_2H_5 + K_2SO_4$$

Solvents and extractions were eliminated but conversions were only about 32%.

Preparation of the 2-chloroethanol fatty acid esters was achieved by Oette and Ahrens (80) using either HCl or BF$_3$ as catalysts:

$$R—\underset{\underset{O}{\|}}{C}—OH + HO—CH_2CH_2Cl \xrightarrow{\text{HCl or BF}_3} R—\underset{\underset{O}{\|}}{C}—OCH_2CH_2Cl + H_2O$$

The C$_3$–C$_9$ esters were formed and recovered by GLC quantitatively, but variable results were obtained with formic and acetic esters.

Clement and Bezard (13) prepared the butyl esters of C$_4$–C$_{20}$ acids by transesterification of esters in the presence of sodium butylate or by esterification of the free acids with n-butanol in the presence of sulfuric acid.

Langner (63) prepared the n-amyl esters of C$_1$–C$_5$ acids in quantitative yield by treating the acids with n-pentanol and boron trifluoride in ethyl ether. After removal of BF$_3$, the solution was ready for injection.

Craig, Tulloch, and Murty (15) studied the butyl, phenacyl, and decyl esters of C$_3$–C$_9$ fatty acids and C$_4$–C$_{10}$ dicarboxylic acids. Butylation was accomplished by heating acids with diazobutane in ether, followed by removal of volatiles:

$$CH_3CH_2CH_2CH=\overset{+}{N}=\overset{-}{N} + R—\underset{\underset{O}{\|}}{C}—OH \rightarrow R—\underset{\underset{O}{\|}}{C}—OCH_2CH_2CH_2CH_3 + N_2$$

The phenacyl esters were made by reacting the potassium salts of fatty acids with α-bromoacetophenone:

$$\langle\bigcirc\rangle—\underset{\underset{O}{\|}}{C}—CH_2Br + R—\underset{\underset{O}{\|}}{C}—OK \rightarrow \langle\bigcirc\rangle—\underset{\underset{O}{\|}}{C}—CH_2O—\underset{\underset{O}{\|}}{C}—R + KBr$$

Excess reagent was precipitated with pyridine and the esters extracted with ether. Decylation was carried out by treating the potassium salts with decyl alcohol and hydrogen chloride:

$$CH_3(CH_2)_8CH_2OH + R—\underset{\underset{O}{\|}}{C}—OK \xrightarrow{\text{HCl}} CH_3(CH_2)_8CH_2O—\underset{\underset{O}{\|}}{C}—R + KCl$$

Salts were removed with water, but it was necessary to chromatograph the mixture through an aluminum oxide column to remove excess decanol before separation on the GLC column could be effected.

The esterification of nonvolatile acids with methanol–HCl and thionyl chloride was studied by Gee (30). An optimum esterification time of 10 min under reflux was used to prepare methyl pyruvate, lactate, glycolate, levulinate, and pyrrolidone carboxylate, and dimethyl oxalate, malonate, fumarate, maleate, malate, and tartrate as well as trimethyl citrate. James and Webb (52) presented data on the separation of the C_4–C_{11} dicarboxylic acid methyl esters prepared with diazomethane in ether. McKeown and Read (74) prepared the methyl esters of di- and tricarboxylic acids with both diazomethane and methanol–sulfuric acid and achieved good separations.

Gutenmann and Lisk (38) took advantage of the sensitivity of the electron affinity detector to halogen by esterifying 4-chloro-2-methylphenoxy-acetic acid with 2-chloroethanol. The sensitivity gained by the addition of another halogen permitted detection at much lower levels.

A number of sulfonic acids and salts were converted into derivatives suitable for GLC by Kirkland (57). The free sulfonic acids or sodium salts were made into the corresponding sulfonyl chlorides by heating with thionyl chloride or phosgene in dimethylformamide:

$$R—SO_3H + SOCl_2 \rightarrow R—SO_2Cl + SO_2 + HCl$$

$$R—SO_3H + Cl_2CO \rightarrow R—SO_2Cl + CO_2 + HCl$$

Similarly, the free sulfonic acids were converted into esters at low temperature by treatment with diazomethane in ether:

$$RSO_3H + CH_2{=}\overset{+}{N}{=}\overset{-}{N} \rightarrow RSO_3CH_3 + N_2$$

For all workups, the volatiles were removed under vacuum and the residue was dissolved in a suitable solvent for GLC. Using these procedures they converted 1-butanesulfonic acid, 3-methyl-1-butanesulfonic acid, benzene-sulfonic acid, p-toluenesulfonic acid, 2,5-dimethylbenzenesulfonic acid, 2-naphthalenesulfonic acid, p-n-butylbenzenesulfonic acid, and n-dodecyl-sulfonic acid into the corresponding sulfonyl chlorides. The methyl esters of p-toluenesulfonic acid and 2,5-dimethylbenzenesulfonic acid were also prepared. Derivatives of phosphoric acids were cited earlier (90).

Williams (124) prepared the methyl dimethoxybenzoates of the six isomeric dihydroxybenzoic acids (2,3; 2,4; 2,5; 2,6; 3,4; and 3,5) by reacting an alcoholic solution of the acids with diazomethane for 16 hr. Attempts to prepare O,O'-diacetoxy esters, dihydroxy esters, O,O'-trimethylsilyloxy esters or O,O'-trifluoroacetoxy esters were not successful as incomplete reactions gave rise to multiple products for some acids and no product for others.

Kirkland (58) was unable to esterify all polychlorinated benzoic acids with methanol–HCl or methanol–BF_3. However, quantitative methylation was obtained for 2,5-di-, 3,4-di-, 2,4,6-tri-, 2,3,6-tri-, 2,3,5-tri-, 2,4,5-tri-, 3,4,5-tri-, 2,3,4-tri-, 2,3,5,6-tetra-, 2,3,4,6-tetra-, 2,3,4,5-tetra-, and pentachlorobenzoic acids with diazomethane in ether.

A number of resin acid esters (alkylated hydrophenanthrene carboxylates) were subjected to GLC study by Hudy (48). The methylation of neoabietic, levopimaric, abietic, dihydroabietic, Δ8a,8-isopimaric, palustric, dihydroisopimaric, dihydropalustric, tetrahydroabietic, dihydroabietic, tetrahydroisopimaric, pimaric, tetrahydropimaric, dihydropimaric, and Δ4b,8a-isopimaric acids was carried out with diazomethane.

B. Amino Acids

The two functional groups of amino acids permit the exploration of a variety of mono- and difunctional derivatives. Acylation, alkylation, and esterification and combinations thereof are most widely cited because conversions are generally rapid and quantitative and lead to a significant decrease in polarity. When an increase in molecular weight is undesirable or must be minimized, deamination, decarboxylation, and dehydration techniques can yield less polar derivatives. In the earliest report on gas–liquid chromatography of amino acid derivatives, Hunter et al. (49) converted a mixture of leucine and isoleucine quantitatively into the corresponding butanals but they obtained only partial resolution of the peaks.

1. Oxidation to Aldehydes

Zlatkis, Oro, and Kimball (127,128) converted aqueous solutions of mixed amino acids and ninhydrin into aldehydes and carbon dioxide by injecting a sample into a special microreactor at 140°C. The reactor, part of a continuous flow system attached to the GLC column, contained ninhydrin on diatomaceous earth. In this way the derivative formed was carried directly into the GLC column in one operation. Mixtures of alanine, α-amino-n-butyric acid, valine, norvaline, leucine, isoleucine, and norleucine yielded volatile aldehydes. Glycine formed formaldehyde which polymerized. The aldehydes from phenylalanine and methionine required a higher temperature because of the decrease in volatility.

2. Decarboxylation

Bier and Teitelbaum (6) discussed the decarboxylation of amino acids followed by gas chromatographic analysis of the liberated amines:

$$R-CH-\overset{\overset{\displaystyle O}{\|}}{C}-OH \xrightarrow{\Delta} R-CH_2-NH_2 + CO_2$$
$$\underset{\displaystyle NH_2}{|}$$

They carried out decarboxylation experiments using both p-dimethylaminobenzaldehyde and diphenylmethane as solvents at elevated temperatures. Their data on yield are summarized in Table 3-2.

TABLE 3-2

Yield of Amines Obtainable by Decarboxylation of Amino Acids

| | Decarboxylation with | | | |
| | Diphenylmethane | | p-Dimethylaminobenzaldehyde | |
Amino acid	Percentage yield	Temperature, °C	Percentage yield	Temperature, °C
Alanine	78	240	48	180
Glycine	29	235	71	180
Leucine	84	235	78	190
Lysine	10	260	80	210
Methionine	77	240	48	190
Phenylalanine	88	225	36	175
Proline	70	235	40	180
Serine	32	245	66	195
Threonine	44	250	78	180
Valine	83	240	80	190
2-Aminovaleric acid	85	235	72	180

It is apparent that this technique leaves something to be desired until better conversions are achieved.

3. Oxidation to Acids

As a sequel to the early work of Hunter, Dimick, and Corse (49) on the conversion of amino acids to aldehydes with ninhydrin, Baraud (1) extended the reaction by converting the aldehydes from alanine, valine, norvaline, leucine + isoleucine, norleucine, and phenylalanine into acids by oxidation in alkaline permanganate. After destruction of excess permanganate followed by acidification, the volatile acids were steam distilled and titrated with standard base. The acids were extracted into ether after acidification and injected directly into the column.

α-Chloro Methyl Esters. A mixture of glycocoll, alanine, α-amino-butyric acid, valine, norvaline, leucine, isoleucine, and norleucine α-chloro methyl esters was prepared by Melamed and Renard (75) by first reacting the amino acids with a mixture of concentrated nitric and hydrochloric acids. The α-chloro acids formed were extracted into ether. Conversion to the esters was achieved with diazomethane in ether and the final solution was injected into the GLC column without further separation or isolation:

$$R\text{—}CH\text{—}\underset{\|}{\overset{O}{C}}\text{—}OH + HCl + HNO_3 \rightarrow R\text{—}CH\text{—}\underset{\|}{\overset{O}{C}}\text{—}OH + 2H_2O + N_2O$$
$$\underset{NH_2}{|} \qquad\qquad\qquad\qquad \underset{Cl}{|}$$

$$R\text{—}CH\text{—}\underset{\|}{\overset{O}{C}}\text{—}OH + CH_2N_2 \rightarrow R\text{—}CH\text{—}\underset{\|}{\overset{O}{C}}\text{—}OCH_3 + N_2$$
$$\underset{Cl}{|} \qquad\qquad\qquad\qquad \underset{Cl}{|}$$

α-Hydroxy Methyl Esters. Wagner and Rausch (117) converted valine, leucine, isoleucine, threonine, methionine, phenylalanine, histidine, lysine, and arginine to the corresponding α-hydroxy acids by treatment with sulfuric acid and sodium nitrite. The deaminated acids were extracted with ether and dried, and the solvent was removed. Yields varied from 20 to 80% but good reproducibility was possible under the experimental conditions described. The deamination of lysine resulted in the formation of the lactide. Because the polarity of these compounds was too high for easy GLC separation, they were transformed into the methyl esters with diazomethane (no experimental details given).

4. Free Base and Methyl Ester Salts

Von Brenner and Huber (113) described the esterification of L-leucine and L-methionine with methanol and thionyl chloride:

$$R\text{—}CH\text{—}\underset{\|}{\overset{O}{C}}\text{—}OH + CH_3OH + SOCl_2 \rightarrow R\text{—}CH\text{—}\underset{\|}{\overset{O}{C}}\text{—}OCH_3 + SO_2 + HCl$$
$$\underset{NH_2}{|} \qquad\qquad\qquad\qquad \underset{\overset{+}{N}H_3\overset{-}{Cl}}{|}$$

No free water was formed, and the ester hydrochloride could be isolated after driving off the sulfur dioxide and hydrogen chloride.

The following amino acid methyl esters were studied by Nicholls, Makisumi, and Saroff (79) as the free bases, acetate salts, and hydrochloride salts:

leucine	arginine
proline	alanine
serine	valine
aspartic acid	isoleucine
phenylalanine	threonine
hydroxyproline	glutamic acid
cysteine	methionine
cystine	glycine
lysine	histidine
tyrosine	tryptophan

The starting derivatives were the methyl ester hydrochlorides in anhydrous methanol; these were converted to the free base on a dehydrated Dowex-1 resin in the hydroxide form. The acetates were prepared similarly by using anhydrous Dowex-1 in the acetate form.

5. Methyl N-Formyl Esters

Losse, Losse, and Stoeck (66) converted amino acids to the N-formyl derivatives with a mixture of formic acid and acetic anhydride. The mixture was then esterified with diazomethane in methanol–ether. The overall conversion was nearly quantitative for the 10 amino acids studied: glycine, alanine, valine, leucine, norvaline, proline, asparaginic acid, glutaminic acid, methionine, and phenylalanine. During the GLC separation process, the dimethyl N-formyl glutaminic ester was transformed into methyl pyrrolidonecarboxylate above 100°C and eluted as such.

6. N-Acetyl n-Propyl Esters

Graff, Wein, and Winitz (32) prepared the N-acetyl n-propyl derivatives of the following amino acids (119):

glycine	d-α-aminoundecanoic acid
alanine	d-α-aminododecanoic acid
dl-α-amino-n-butyric acid	l-phenylalanine
dl-valine	l-methionine
dl-norvaline	l-proline
l-leucine	l-tyrosine
l-isoleucine	dl-α-aminophenylacetic acid
l-alloisoleucine	γ-amino-n-butyric acid
dl-norleucine	β-alanine
dl-α-aminocaprylic acid	dl-isovaline
l-α-aminoheptanoic acid	dl-α-aminoisobutyric acid
l-α-aminononylic acid	dl-α-aminostearic acid
l-α-aminodecanoic acid	dl-cyclohexylalanine

Esterification was accomplished with *n*-propanol and an acidic catalyst and benzene was used to remove water azeotropically. The esters were then acylated with acetic anhydride and the final derivatives were extracted and diluted for gas chromatography:

$$
\underset{\underset{NH_2}{|}}{R-CH}-\overset{\overset{O}{\|}}{C}-OH + C_3H_7OH \xrightarrow{H^+} \underset{\underset{NH_2}{|}}{R-CH}-\overset{\overset{O}{\|}}{C}-OC_3H_7 \xrightarrow{(CH_3CO)_2O}
$$

$$
\underset{\underset{NH-\overset{\|}{C}-CH_3}{|}}{R-CH}-\overset{\overset{O}{\|}}{C}-OC_3H_7 + CH_3COOH
$$

Reactions were effected in a single glass apparatus designed to obviate all transfers. Exactly the same derivatives were obtained by carrying out the reactions in the reverse order.

7. N-Acetyl n-Butyl Esters

The *N*-acetyl *n*-butyl esters of glycine, alanine, valine, leucine, isoleucine, and proline were prepared by Youngs (125). The acid mixture was heated with *n*-butanol and HCl so that the butanol–water azeotrope distilled. After removing excess solvent, the mixture was acetylated with acetic anhydride at room temperature. Volatiles were removed under vacuum and the residual oil was injected into the column.

8. N-Acetyl n-Amyl Esters

The *N*-acetyl *n*-amyl esters of the following amino acids were prepared by Johnson, Scott, and Meister (55):

α-alanine	α-aminobutyric acid	isoleucine
valine	β-aminoisobutyric acid	norvaline
leucine	β-aminobutyric acid	norleucine
glycine	γ-aminobutyric acid	alloisoleucine
proline	α-aminoadipic acid	ornithine
serine	aspartic acid	threonine
lysine	glutamic acid	tryptophan
cystine	pipecolic acid	methionine
arginine	allothreonine	ethionine
histidine	S-methylcysteine	phenylalanine
cysteine	allohydroxyproline	tyrosine
β-alanine	hydroxyproline	

The esterification step was performed by passing anhydrous hydrogen bromide into a suspension of the amino acid(s) in *n*-amyl alcohol. Excess solvent was removed under vacuum and the residual hydrobromide mixture was mixed with acetic anhydride and allowed to stand. The solution was evaporated under vacuum to a syrup which was taken up in *n*-amyl alcohol or benzene for column injection. Conversion to the derivatives was conservatively estimated to be about 85% based on a comparison of the responses of pure derivatives with converted amino acids by the above procedure. Radioactive tracers were also utilized in determining the percent conversion of amino acid to derivative.

Acetylation of the hydroxyl groups of serine, threonine, tyrosine and hydroxyproline could be confirmed by elemental analyses of the derivatives. Also, both carboxyl groups in dicarboxylic acids were esterified. The esterification step for methionine gave rise to oxidation to the sulfoxide derivative. Cystine and tryptophan did not form stable derivatives, and histidine and arginine were esterified in poor yields. Acetylation of the latter two amino acids was unsatisfactory. The authors suggested converting arginine to ornithine so that a stable derivative could be prepared and evaluated.

9. N-Trifluoroacetyl Methyl Esters

Cruickshank and Sheehan (16) converted alanine, arginine, aspartic acid, cysteine, cystine, glutamic acid, glycine, histidine, hydroxyproline, isoleucine, leucine, lysine, methionine, ornithine, phenylalanine, proline, serine, threonine, tryptophan, tyrosine, and valine into *N*-TFA methyl esters by two routes, (*1*) direct acylation with trifluoroacetic anhydride in trifluoroacetic acid, followed by methylation with diazomethane in methanol,

$$R\text{—}\underset{\underset{COOH}{|}}{CH}\text{—}NH_2 + (CF_3\overset{\overset{O}{\|}}{C})_2O \rightarrow R\text{—}\underset{\underset{COOH}{|}}{CH}\text{—}NH\text{—}\overset{\overset{O}{\|}}{C}\text{—}CF_3 + CF_3\overset{\overset{O}{\|}}{C}\text{—}OH$$

$$R\text{—}\underset{\underset{COOH}{|}}{CH}\text{—}NH\text{—}\overset{\overset{O}{\|}}{C}\text{—}CF_3 + CH_2N_2 \rightarrow R\text{—}\underset{\underset{COOCH_3}{|}}{CH}\text{—}NH\text{—}\overset{\overset{O}{\|}}{C}\text{—}CF_3 + N_2$$

and (*2*) esterification with dimethyl sulfite in methanol–hydrochloric acid followed by trifluoroacetylation:

$$2R\text{—}\underset{\underset{NH_2}{|}}{CH}\text{—}\overset{\overset{O}{\|}}{C}\text{—}OH + (CH_3O)_2SO \rightarrow 2R\text{—}\underset{\underset{NH_2}{|}}{CH}\text{—}\overset{\overset{O}{\|}}{C}\text{—}OCH_3 + H_2SO_3$$

$$R\text{—}\underset{\underset{NH_2}{|}}{CH}\text{—}\overset{\overset{O}{\|}}{C}\text{—}OCH_3 + (CF_3\overset{\overset{O}{\|}}{C})_2O \rightarrow R\text{—}\underset{\underset{NH\text{—}\underset{\underset{O}{\|}}{C}CF_3}{|}}{CH}\text{—}\overset{\overset{O}{\|}}{C}\text{—}OCH_3 + CF_3\text{—}\overset{\overset{O}{\|}}{C}\text{—}OH$$

Only valine, isoleucine, threonine, and lysine showed traces of incomplete esterification. The hydroxy–amino acid derivatives (threonine, serine, hydroxyproline, tyrosine) contained free hydroxyl groups when acylation preceded esterification, and when the sequence was reversed the N,O-bis(trifluoroacetyl) derivatives were formed.

Makisumi and Saroff (68) prepared the same derivatives of amino acids by methylation with methanol–HCl, then acylation with trifluoroacetic anhydride alone or with ethyl acetate. These authors identified the triacyl derivative of arginine and the diacyl derivatives of cysteine, histidine, ornithine, lysine, and tryptophan in addition to the four found by Cruickshank and Sheehan (16). It was necessary to maintain the derivatives under rigorously anhydrous conditions in order to prevent hydrolysis before GLC.

10. N-Trifluoroacetyl n-Butyl Esters

The derivatives of a mixture of alanine, valine, isoleucine, glycine, threonine, leucine, proline, serine, cysteine, hydroxyproline, methionine, aspartic acid, phenylalanine, glutamic acid, tyrosine, lysine, arginine, histidine, tryptophan, and cystine were prepared by Lamkin and Gehrke (61) in quantitative yield. Esterification was carried out in methanol–HCl, and the product was then interesterified with n-butanol–HCl. Trifluoroacetylation was accomplished with trifluoroacetic anhydride in the presence of methylene chloride:

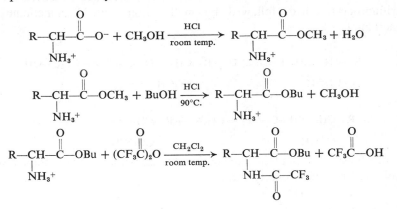

Tryptophan and arginine formed both monoacyl and diacyl derivatives. Subsequent papers from Gehrke's group (31a,31b,98a) described their techniques in more detail.

Zomzely, Marco, and Emery (129) prepared a similar group of derivatives, hydroxyproline excepted, but with sarcosine and ornithine added. They esterified the acids directly with n-butanol and HCl in dimethyl formamide using dibutoxypropane as a water scavenger. After extraction and drying, the salt-free esters were acylated with trifluoroacetic anhydride in a methylene chloride–dimethylformamide solvent mixture. Excess reagents were removed under vacuum, and the residue was dissolved in acetone for GLC.

The hydrochlorides of proline, alanine, glycine, valine, methionine, threonine, leucine, isoleucine, glutamic acid, phenylalanine, and aspartic acid were esterified by Marcucci, Mussini, Poy, and Gagliardi (70) in n-butanol using Dowex 50W-X4 resin as a catalyst. The esters were eluted with citrate buffer, extracted with methylene chloride and concentrated under vacuum. Acylation was carried out with trifluoroacetic anhydride in methylene chloride, and excess reagents were removed under vacuum before the derivatives were injected into the GLC.

11. N-TFA-DL-sec-Butyl Esters

Pollock, Oyama, and Johnson (84), in their study on the separation of racemic amino acids, prepared the N-TFA sec-butyl esters of alanine, α-aminobutyric acid, norvaline, valine, isoleucine, alloisoleucine, norleucine, leucine, threonine, serine, methionine, aspartic acid, and phenylalanine. The syntheses were achieved by bubbling dry hydrogen chloride into the mixture of amino acid and sec-butyl alcohol at 0° for 30–60 min, then refluxing for 2 hr. After conversion to the free base with triethylamine, the ester was acylated with methyl trifluoroacetate for 2–16 hr, dissolved in ethyl acetate, washed, concentrated and dried. Ten of the 13 N-TFA-DL-amino acid–DL-sec-butyl esters were resolved into their antipodes by GLC.

12. N-TFA n-Amyl Esters

Darbre and Blau (17) prepared the N-TFA amino acid n-amyl esters of alanine, glycine, valine, leucine, isoleucine, and threonine by passing HCl gas through an n-pentanol solution of the amino acid mixture at 108°C for 25 min, then treating with TFA anhydride for 1 hr. Volatiles were removed under vacuum at room temperature between treatments. A solution of the residue in nitromethane or methyl ethyl ketone was injected into the GLC column.

Although no studies were carried out on other derivatives, the ethyl, propyl, and butyl esters were made as in the first method described above for the amyl ester, except that the esterification temperature was 80° instead of 108°. The preferred method for methyl esters was one in which the amino acids were first converted to the N-TFA derivative, then methylated with diazomethane. Volatile materials were evaporated under vacuum between treatments as above. Benzyl esters were prepared by using phenyldiazomethane followed by treatment with TFA anhydride as above. Teuwissen, Lenain, Dorlet, and Leonis (102) prepared the same derivative of valine, α-alanine, isoleucine, leucine, glycine, β-alanine, proline, glutamic acid, threonine, methionine, aspartic acid, phenylalanine, serine, lysine, and tyrosine by a slightly different process. They suspended the amino acids in the alcohol and saturated the mixture with hydrogen bromide, as described by Johnson, Scott, and Meister (55).

13. Butyl Ester Hydrochlorides

Saroff, Karmen, and Healy (91) injected alcoholic solutions of butyl and ethyl ester hydrochlorides of alanine, valine, glycine, isoleucine, leucine, proline, aspartic acid, threonine, methionine, serine, glutamic acid, phenylalanine, lysine, and hydroxyproline into a polyethyleneglycol adipate column at 131°C. They obtained no separation when they used nitrogen alone as a carrier gas, but addition of ammonia to the gas stream produced well-defined peaks. They were unable to achieve separation of the valine–glycine and isoleucine–leucine derivative pairs.

14. 2,4-Dinitrophenyl Methyl Esters

Pisano, VandenHeuvel, and Horning (83) prepared the 2,4-dinitrophenyl methyl esters of alanine, glycine, proline, valine, leucine, isoleucine, aspartic acid, glutamic acid, serine, threonine, glutamine, asparagine, methionine, phenylalanine, tyrosine, histidine, and tryptophan by preparing the DNP, then esterifying with diazomethane.

15. Phenylthiohydantoins

Pisano, VandenHeuvel, and Horning (83) studied the separation of a mixture of pure 3-phenyl-2-thiohydantoins of alanine, glycine, proline, valine, leucine, isoleucine, aspartic acid, glutamic acid, serine, threonine, glutamine, asparagine, methionine, phenylalanine, tyrosine, histidine, and tryptophan. The compounds were prepared according to Sjöquist (98) in which amino acids were treated with phenylisothiocyanate in acetone. The mixture of thiocarbamates was evaporated to dryness, treated with acetic and hydrochloric acids and again evaporated to dryness:

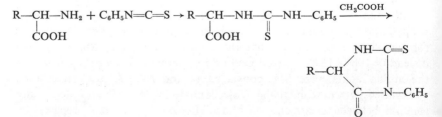

It was necessary to oxidize cystine and cysteine to cysteic acid before coupling with phenylisothiocyanate.

16. Silylated Amino Acids

Von Rühlmann and Giesecke (115) converted alanine, glycine, leucine, isoleucine, valine, glutamic acid and phenylalanine into the N-trimethyl-silyl amino acid trimethylsilyl ester by treating the amino acid salt with trimethylchlorosilane. The same conversion could be accomplished by treating the amino acid with trimethylsilyldialkylamines. Yields were nearly quantitative and the reactions proceeded quickly and smoothly.

17. Nitriles

The conversion of alanine, α-amino-n-butyric acid, norvaline, valine, leucine and phenylalanine to the corresponding nitriles with one less car-bon atom was reported by Stevenson and Luck (99). The amino acid and powdered N-bromosuccinimide were mixed well, water was added, and the reaction allowed to proceed for one hour. Excess N-bromosuccinimide was destroyed with thiosulfate and the nitrile was extracted with o-xylene which was injected into the gas chromatograph:

$$R{-}\underset{\underset{NH_2}{|}}{CH}{-}COOH + NBS \longrightarrow R{-}\underset{\underset{NH_2}{|}}{CHBr} + CO_2$$

$$R{-}\underset{\underset{NH_2}{|}}{CH}{-}Br + NBS \longrightarrow RCN + 2HBr$$

$$R{-}\underset{\underset{NH_2}{|}}{CH}{-}Br + H_2O \xrightarrow{\;H^+\;} R{-}\underset{\underset{O}{\|}}{CH} + NH_4Br$$

Yields of cyanides varied from 38 to 51 %, and the formation of aldehydes as a side reaction was in the range of 3–30%. No ammonia was produced as this was immediately oxidized to nitrogen with the NBS reagent.

18. Reduction of Peptides

As an extension of their previous work on reduction of small peptides with lithium aluminum hydride, Biemann and Vetter (5) reduced the ester groups in N-acetyl peptide ethyl esters to alcohols with lithium aluminum deuteride (LiAlD$_4$). The reduction was carried out overnight with an excess of LiAlD$_4$ in tetrahydrofuran. After the mixture had been decom-posed with water, the polyacetamido alcohols were extracted with ether–methanol, and were dried, evaporated, and injected into a GLC column.

In this way polyamino alcohols were prepared from the derivatives of leucyl-alanyl-proline, glycyl-phenylalanine, phenylalanyl-glycine, leucyl-alanine, and leucyl-alanyl-glycyl-leucine.

If hydroxy or two ester groups in an *N*-acetyl peptide ethyl ester were reduced, however, the resulting dihydroxypolyacetamide was too polar for rapid GLC work. This problem was circumvented by converting the

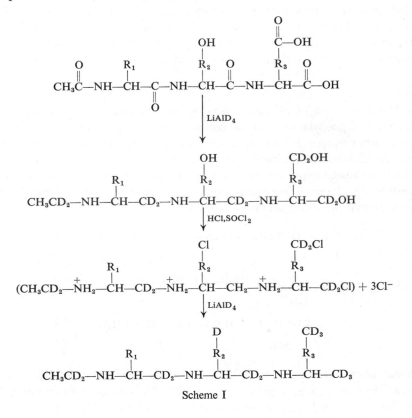

Scheme I

alcoholic groups to chloro derivatives with thionyl chloride in chloroform. The residue obtained after evaporation was reduced with $LiAlD_4$ in tetrahydrofuran which converted the chloromethyl groups to deuterated methyl derivatives (Scheme I). The resulting sharp reduction in polarity facilitated the subsequent GLC work. Peptides subjected to the additional reduction step were leucyl-phenylalanine, phenylalanyl-asparagine, leucyl-threonine, leucyl-alanyl-glycyl-leucine, and leucyl-alanyl-glutamic acid. Some of the latter peptide cyclized before reduction to form a pyrrolidine ring.

19. Dipeptides

Weygand, Kolb, Prox, Tilak, and Tomida (122) synthesized 27 N-TFA dipeptide methyl esters. The pure compounds were prepared by reaction of an N-TFA amino acid thiophenyl ester with an amino acid to form the N-TFA dipeptide acid, which was then methylated with diazomethane. This preparative scheme was later extended to a total of 45 dipeptide derivatives (Table 3-3) by Weygand, Kolb, and Kirchner (121).

TABLE 3-3

N-TFA Dipeptide Methyl Esters Prepared by Weygand, Kolb, and Kirchner (121)

L-Ala.L-Ala	L-Ileu.L-Ala	L-Pro.Gly
L-Ala.Gly	L-Ileu.L.Val	L-Pro.L-Leu
L-Ala.L-Val	L-Ileu.L-Leu	
L-Ala.L-Leu	L-Ileu.L-Ileu	
L-Ala.L-Phe	L-Ileu.L-Met	
Gly.L-Ala	L-Glu-α.L-Ala	L-Leu.L-Ala
Gly.Gly	L-Glu-α.L-Leu	L-Leu.Gly
Gly.L-Val	L-Glu-α.L-Phe	L-Leu.L-Val
Gly.L-Leu	L-Glu-γ.L-Ala	L-Leu.L-Leu
Gly.L-Ileu	L-Glu-γ.L-Leu	L-Leu.L-Ileu
Gly.L-Pro	L-Glu-γ.L-Phe	L-Leu.L-Pro
Gly.L-Phe		L-Leu.L-Met
	L-Phe.L-Ala	L-Leu.L-Phe
L-Val.L-Ala	L-Phe.Gly	
L-Val.Gly	L-Phe.L-Leu	
L-Val.L-Val	L-Phe.L-Met	
L-Val.L-Leu	L-Phe.L-Phe	
L-Val.L-Ileu		
L-Val.L-Met		
L-Val.L-Phe		

C. Alcohols

The majority of lower alcohols can be chromatographed directly except when they are in dilute solutions. Under conditions where concentration, extraction or distillation is impractical, the conversion to nonpolar derivatives could provide the necessary means for the separation from water for subsequent GLC analysis.

Zahn, Sharkey, and Wender (126) prepared the trimethylsilyl ethers of 23 alcohols ranging from C_1 to C_{12}, and two glycols:

methanol	3-methylpentanol
ethanol	2-ethylbutanol
n-propanol	n-heptanol
n-butanol	3-heptanol
2-methylpropanol	n-octanol
n-pentanol	2-ethylhexanol
2-methylbutanol	n-nonanol
2-methyl-2-butanol	n-decanol
3-methylbutanol	n-undecanol
2,2-dimethylpropanol	n-dodecanol
n-hexanol	ethylene glycol
2-hexanol	propylene glycol
2-methylpentanol	

The authors employed four methods for the preparation of the ethers: (1) conversion of the alcohol to the alkoxide with sodium hydride followed by reaction with trimethylchlorosilane,

$$NaH + ROH \rightarrow NaOR + H_2$$

$$(CH_3)_3SiCl + NaOR \rightarrow NaCl + (CH_3)_3SiOR$$

(2) treatment of the alcohol with trimethylchlorosilane in the presence of an amine to scavenge the acid formed,

$$(CH_3)_3SiCl + ROH + amine \rightarrow (CH_3)_3SiOR + amine—HCl$$

(3) reaction between the alcohol and hexamethyldisilazane with a trace of acid as a catalyst,

$$(CH_3)_3SiNHSi(CH_3)_3 + 2ROH \rightarrow 2ROSi(CH_3)_3 + NH_3$$

and (4) the reaction of the alcohol, trimethylchlorosilane, and hexamethyl-disilazane:

$$3ROH + (CH_3)_3SiCl + (CH_3)_3SiNHSi(CH_3)_3 \rightarrow 3ROSi(CH_3)_3 + NH_4Cl$$

Method (4) was found to be the most generally applicable.

The acetate derivatives of fatty alcohols and polyhydric alcohols have been prepared by refluxing them with acetic anhydride and then isolating the acetylated products from water after hydrolysis of excess reagent. Esposito and Swann (21) prepared the esters of ethylene glycol, propylene glycol, diethylene glycol, glycerol, trimethylolethane, trimethylolpropane, pentaerythritol, mannitol, and sorbitol. The same esterification of stearyl alcohol, oleyl alcohol, linoleyl alcohol, and linolenyl alcohol was reported by Link, Hickman, and Morrissette (64).

Von Drawert, Felgenhauer, and Kupfer (114) chromatographed the nitrite esters and olefins derived from the following alcohols:

methanol	2-methylpropanol	1-pentanol	1-hexanol
ethanol	2-methyl-2-propanol	isoamyl alcohol	1-heptanol
n-propanol	n-butanol	2-pentanol	1-octanol
2-propanol	2-butanol	2-methyl-2-butanol	1-nonanol
			1-decanol

The nitrite esters were prepared from a mixture of sodium nitrite and tartaric acid:

$$ROH + HONO \rightarrow RONO + H_2O$$

The olefins were formed after the alcohol solution had been dehydrated over a support containing phosphoric acid. In each case the support was contained in a reaction tube that was part of the injection port leading to the column.

Hallgren and Larsson (40) carried out GLC studies on glyceryl ethers, $HOCH_2$—$CHOH$—CH_2OR, where R varied from C_{14} to C_{22}. They prepared the dimethoxy derivatives by treating the glyceryl ethers with diazomethane in the presence of boron trifluoride.

Downing, Kranz, and Murray (18) separated monohydric alcohols from glycols and converted each of the mixtures to hydrocarbons. The conversions were effected by heating each mixture with iodine and red phosphorus to form the iodides. The latter were then reduced to the corresponding hydrocarbons with lithium aluminum hydride in ether. Mixtures subjected to GLC covered the range of C_{12}–C_{33} alcohols.

The 3,5 dinitrobenzoates of the following alcohols were prepared by Galetto, Kepner, and Webb (29):

methyl	2-pentyl	2-hexyl	n-heptyl
ethyl	3-methyl-2-butyl	n-amyl	n-octyl
isopropyl	n-butyl	cis-3-hexenyl	benzyl
n-propyl	d-2-methyl-n-	2-heptyl	n-nonyl
sec-butyl	butyl	n-hexyl	2-phenethyl
isobutyl	isoamyl	isoheptyl	n-decyl

The alcohol derivatives were prepared by shaking aqueous alcohol solutions with 3,5-dinitrobenzoyl chloride in benzene and injecting the benzene phase into the GLC column:

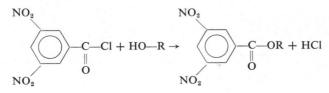

By proper choice of reaction conditions, tertiary alcohols were converted into stable trimethylsiloxy derivatives. Friedman and Kaufman (27) effected these conversions quantitatively with 2-methyl-2-butanol, 3-ethyl-3-pentanol, and 2,4-dimethyl-2-heptanol by reaction of the alcohol with hexamethyldisilazane in either dimethylformamide or dimethylsulfoxide.

D. Aldehydes and Ketones

It has been shown (see Section I-E) that ketones may be used to form volatile derivatives of amines which are less polar than the parent compound. Similarly, VandenHeuvel, Gardiner, and Horning (111) prepared eneamines (Schiff bases) of di-n-hexyl and di-n-heptyl ketones by treating them with N-aminopiperidine, N-aminohomopiperidine, pentafluorophenylhydrazine, and phenylhydrazine:

$$R—\underset{\underset{O}{\|}}{C}—R + R'—NH \rightarrow R—\underset{\underset{N—R'}{\|}}{C}—R + H_2O$$

The condensations were carried out in ethyl acetate solvent with an acetic acid catalyst.

Schogt, Begemann, and Recourt (93) converted higher aliphatic aldehydes to the acids with silver oxide, which were then esterified with diazomethane:

$$R—CHO + Ag_2O \rightarrow R—\underset{\underset{O}{\|}}{C}—OH \xrightarrow{CH_2N_2} R—\underset{\underset{O}{\|}}{C}—OCH_3$$

A portion of the ester mixture was hydrogenated over Adams' PtO$_2$ catalyst, and GLC of both portions gave clear separations which permitted differentiation of saturated from unsaturated members.

Gray (33) synthesized dimethyl acetals by refluxing aldehydes with methanolic HCl; the conversion was $>95\%$.

$$R—CHO + 2CH_3OH \xrightarrow{HCl} R—CH(OCH_3)_2 + H_2O$$

The acetals were extracted with petroleum ether, then purified by caustic hydrolysis and vacuum distillation. Bromination as a means of detecting unsaturation was unsuccessful as only nonvolatile products were formed. Gray (34) also oxidized the acetals to acids with chromium trioxide in glacial acetic acid, then methylated the acids with methanolic HCl.

Farquhar (23) prepared acetals and acids from fatty aldehydes, and showed that both derivatives could be reduced to alcohols with lithium aluminum hydride. The fatty alcohols were acetylated with acetic anhydride and isolated with petroleum ether. His study covered derivative and GLC interrelationships among the acids, acetates, alcohols, and aldehydes shown in Table 3-4.

Ralls (86) demonstrated that the accompanying aldehydes and ketones present in dilute solution could be derivatized and measured by GLC:

Aldehydes	Ketones
formaldehyde	acetone
acetaldehyde	butanone
propionaldehyde	2-pentanone
isobutyraldehyde	3-pentanone
n-butyraldehyde	3-methyl-2-butanone
isovaleraldehyde	2-hexanone
n-valeraldehyde	4-methyl-3-penten-2-one
2-methyl-1-butanal	cyclohexanone
acrolein	biacetyl(bis)
crotonaldehyde	
2,4-pentadienal	
2-hexenal	
methional	
benzaldehyde	

Mixtures were converted to 2,4-dinitrophenylhydrazones in acid. The dry solid derivative and α-ketoglutaric acid were mixed well and placed in a capillary for injection into the GLC apparatus. A flash exchange regenerated the aldehydes and ketones *in situ*; these were separated on the column. Regeneration of unsaturated aldehydes and ketones was less efficient than of the saturated compounds. Aromatic aldehydes and polycarbonyl compounds gave no response.

E. Amines, Amino Alcohols, and Amino Phenols

Morrissette and Link (77) prepared the trifluoroacetyl derivatives of saturated (C_8, C_{10}, C_{14}, C_{16}, C_{18}, C_{22}) and unsaturated (C_{18}-2H, C_{18}-4H) fatty amines. They allowed trifluoroacetic anhydride and amine to react at room temperature in chloroform. Excess anhydride was destroyed with water or butanol, and the lower layer was chromatographed directly.

Brooks and Horning (11), Horning, Horning, VandenHeuvel, Knox, Holmstedt, and Brooks (44), and Miles and Fales (76) studied the trimethylsilyloxy, acetyl, propionyl, pentafluoropropionyl, and eneamine

TABLE 3-4

Fatty Aldehyde Derivative Interrelationships by Farquhar (23)

Acids	Acetates	Alcohols	Aldehydes[a]
—	—	—	Nonanal
		—	Undecanal
Tetradecanoic (myristic)	Tetradecanoate	Tetradecanol	Tetradecanal
13-Methyltetradecanoic	—	13-Methyltetradecanol	—
Pentadecanoic	Pentadecanoate	Pentadecanol	—
13,13-Dimethyltetradecanoic	—	—	—
15-Methylpentadecanoic	15-Methylpentadecanoate	—	—
cis-Hexadeca-9-enoic (palmitoleic)	cis-Hexadeca-9-enoate	cis-Hexadeca-9-enol	—
Hexadecanoic (palmitic)	Hexadecanoate	Hexadecanol	Hexadecanal
15-Methylhexadecanoic	15-Methylhexadecanoate	15-Methylhexadecanol	—
Heptadecanoic	Heptadecanoate	Heptadecanol	—
15,15-Dimethylhexadecanoic	15,15-Dimethylhexadeca-noate	—	—
17-Methylheptadecanoic	—	—	—
cis,cis-Octadeca-9,12-dienoic (linoleic)	cis,cis-Octadeca-9,12-dienoate	cis,cis-Octadeca-9,12-dienol	—
cis-Octadeca-9-enoic (oleic)	cis-Octadeca-9-enoate	cis-Octadeca-9-enol	—
trans-Octadeca-9-enoic (elaidic)	—	trans-Octadeca-9-enol	—
cis-Octadeca-6-enoic (petrosolinic)	—	cis-Octadeca-6-enol	—
trans-Octadeca-6-enoic (petroselaidic)	—	trans-Octadeca-6-enol	—
trans-Octadeca-11-enoic (vaccenic)	—	trans-Octadeca-11-enol	—
cis-Octadeca-12-enoic	—	cis-Octadeca-12-enol	—
Octadecanoic (stearic)	Octadecanoate	Octadecanol	Octadecanal
17-Methyloctadecanoic	—	—	—
Nonadecanoic	—	Nonadecanol	—

[a] Includes all corresponding dimethyl acetal derivatives.

derivatives of nucleosides, catecholamines, phenylalkylamines, imidazole, and indole types, and other hydroxyamine metabolites. In many cases the acylation of both amino and hydroxy groups permitted facile passage through the column with good resolution. Also, when an acetone solution of a hydroxyamine was treated with hexamethyldisilazane, the eneamine of the trimethylsilyloxy derivatives was formed. In addition to the derivatives shown in Table 3-5, the acetyl and propionyl derivatives of normetanephrine, metanephrine, noradrenaline, and adrenaline, and the pentafluoropropionyl derivatives of adrenaline and noradrenaline were prepared and chromatographed.

Sen and McGeer (94) converted dopamine, epinephrine, norepinephrine, *dl*-metanephrine, *dl*-normetanephrine, and 3-methoxytyramine to the trimethylsilyl derivatives by treating them with hexamethyldisilazane in the presence of pyridine. For very low levels of biological amines, the sensitivity to electron capture detection was increased by acylation with pentafluoropropionic anhydride or heptafluorobutyric anhydride. Brochmann-Hanssen and Svendsen (9) prepared the acetone and butanone eneamines of amphetamine, ephedrine, phenylpropanolamine, pseudoephedrine, tuaminoheptane, hydroxyamphetamine, metaraminol, phenylephrine, and mephentermine by allowing a solution of the amine in the ketone to stand for several hours and injecting it. They observed that the introduction of two acetyl and one trimethylsilyl groups into epinephrine and levarterenol conferred greater stability than preparing the triacetyl derivative, as the latter gave three GLC peaks.

Sweeley and Moscatelli (100) oxidized sphingolipid bases to aldehydes with aqueous sodium periodate at room temperature, then extracted the solution with methylene chloride. The resulting aldehydes were chromatographed before and after catalytic reduction to distinguish unsaturated from saturated members.

VandenHeuvel, Gardiner, and Horning (110) carried out a comprehensive study of the GLC behavior of nearly all 14 derivatives of 11 primary and secondary aliphatic and aromatic amines. The eneamines in Table 3-6 were prepared by dissolving the amine in the ketone, while the other derivatives were formed when the amine was treated with the appropriate reagent in ethyl acetate and pyridine.

F. Carbohydrates

The conversion of all varieties of carbohydrates to suitable derivatives for GLC has been the subject of extensive reviews by Bishop (7) and Wells, Sweeley, and Bentley (120). Detailed procedures are given for the preparation of acetals, ketals, alkyl, thioalkyl, dimethylsilyl, and trimethylsilyl

TABLE 3-5

Hydroxyamine Prepared by Brooks et al. (11), Horning et al. (44), and Miles et al. (76).

Nucleoside derivatives	Acetone eneamines	Acetylated amines
Uridine 2′,3′,5′-triacetate	β-Phenylethyl-amine	β-Phenylethyl-amine
3-Methyluridine 2′,3′,5′-tri-acetate	β-Hydroxyphenyl-ethylamine	β-Hydroxyphenyl-amine
2′,3′-O-Isopropyl-ideneuridine	Tyramine	Tyramine
2′-Deoxyuridine 3′,5′-diacetate	Octopamine	Octopamine
Thymidine 3′,5′-diacetate	Homovanillyl-amine	Homovanillyl-amine
3-Methylthymidine 3′,5′-diacetate	Normetanephrine	Normetanephrine
1-β-D-Glucopyrano-syluracil 2′,3′,-4′,6′-tetraace-tate	Amphetamine	Dopamine
	Tryptamine	Norepinephrine
	5-Methoxytrypt-amine	Homoveratrylamine
	5-Trimethyl-siloxytrypta-mine	Methanephrine
1-β-D-Glucopyrano-syl-3-methylur-acil 2′,3′,4′,6-tetraacetate	N,N-D-methyl-tryptamine	Epinephrine
	Serotonin	Amphetamine
		Norephedrine
		Vanillylamine
		Mescaline
1-β-D-Glucopyrano-syl-4-methoxy-2(1H)-pyrimi-done 2′,3′,4′,-6′-tetraacetate		3,4-Dihydroxynor-ephedrine
		Deoxyephedrine
		Ephedrine
		Synephrine
		Phenylephrine
	2′,3′-O-Isopropyl-idineadenosine	Hordenine
1-β-D-Glucopyrano-sylthymine 2′,3′,-4′,6′-tetraace-tate	2′-Deoxyadenosine 3′,5′-diacetate	4-Methoxy-β-phenyl-ethylamine
	N-Acetyl-2′-deoxy-adenosine 3′,5′-diacetate	Tryptamine
		N-Methyltryptamine
1-β-D-Glucopyrano-syl-3-methylthy-mine 2′,3′,4′,6′-tetraacetate	1-Methylinosine 2′,3′,5′-tri-acetate	Serotonin
		N,N-Dimethyltrypt-amine
Adenosine 2′,3′,5′-triacetate	6-Methoxy-9-β-D-ribofurano-sylpurine 2′,3′,5′-triacetate	5-Methoxytryptamine
N-Acetyladenosine 2′,3′,5′-triacetate		N-Methylhistamine
		Histamine

(continued)

TABLE 3-5 (*continued*)

Trimethylsilyloxy derivatives	Acetyl and propionyl derivatives	Pentafluoropropionyl derivatives
4-Hydroxy-*N,H*-di-methyltryptamine	Normetanephrine	Adrenaline
5-Hydroxy-*N,H*-di-methyltryptamine	Metanephrine	Noradrenaline
6-Hydroxy-*N,H*-di-methyltryptamine	Noradrenaline	Noradrenaline
7-Hydroxy-*N,H*-di-methyltryptamine	Adrenaline	
5-Hydroxy-*N,N*-diethyltrypta-mine		
Serotonin eneamine		

ethers as well as alkylidene, acyl, aroyl, sulfonyl, and combinations of these derivatives.

G. Esters

Unlike other fatty acid esters, the lipids and glycerides must be transformed into lower molecular weight derivatives in order to survive the GLC column. For most cases saponification and esterification, ester interchange, and alcoholysis (60) are usually employed. In those situations where saponification is desirable or a necessary part of the isolation or cleanup technique, a host of derivatives are available (see Section I-A) for the fatty acids formed.

Luddy, Barford, and Riemenschneider (67) transesterified lipids with methanol in the presence of sodium methoxide and obtained quantitative yields, but the individual esters were not cited. Kaufmann and Mankel (56) obtained the fatty acid esters by both ester exchange and saponification plus esterification using diazomethane, BF_3, and HCl. Identical results were obtained with all methods for long-chain acids, but those containing less than 10 carbon atoms were esterified quantitatively only when a saturated solution of docosane in petroleum ether was used as an extractant. Peterson, deSchmertzing, and Abel (82) compared the relative efficacies of BF_3 and BCl_3 as catalysts for transesterification of lipids with methanol. They found that BCl_3 provided faster rates and reacted with the water formed which maintained anhydrous conditions. Mason and Waller (71) devised a simple, mild procedure for transesterifying glycerides containing C_6–C_{18} acids. A mixture of fat, benzene, methanol–HCl, and dimethoxypropane (DMP) was allowed to stand overnight for complete

TABLE 3-6

Amine Derivatives Prepared by VandenHeuvel et al. (110)

	Carbamyl	Thiocarbamyl	Pentafluoropropionyl	Heptafluorobutyryl	Methanesulfonyl	Trifluoroacetyl	Acetyl	Propionyl	Butyryl	Trifluoroacetone eneamine	Cyclopentanone eneamine	Cyclohexanone eneamine	Cycloheptanone eneamine	Acetone eneamine
n-Dodecylamine	×	×	×	×	×	×	×	×	×	×	×	×	×	×
n-Tetradecylamine	×	×	×	×	×	×	×	×	×	×	×	×	×	×
n-Hexadecylamine	×	×	×	×	×	×	×	×	×	×	×	×	×	×
Cyclododecylamine	×	×	×	×	×	×	×	×	×	×	×	×	×	×
1,4-Diaminobutane			×	×		×	×	×	×		×	×	×	
1,5-Diaminopentane			×	×		×	×	×	×		×	×	×	
Benzylamine	×	×	×				×					×		×
Benzylmethylamine	×	×	×				×					×		×
α-Methylbenzylamine	×	×	×				×					×		×
4-Methylbenzylamine	×	×	×				×					×		×
Amphetamine	×	×	×	×	×	×	×	×	×	×	×	×	×	×

transesterification. After neutralization, a sample was injected directly into the column. The DMP acted as a water scavenger and also converted the glycerol formed into isopropylidene glycerol, which passed through the GLC column. The simultaneous determination of glycerol and fatty acids in glycerides was also studied by Horrocks and Cornwell (47). They reduced mono-, di-, and triglycerides to fatty alcohols and glycerol with lithium aluminum hydride, then acetylated all products with acetic anhydride (Scheme II). Quantitative results were obtained for tetradecanyl, hexadecanyl, hexadecenyl, glyceryl, octadecanyl, octadecenyl, and octade-cadienyl acetates.

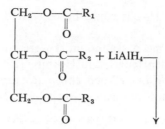

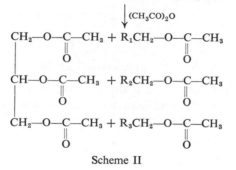

HOCH₂—CHOH—CH₂OH + R₁CH₂OH + R₂CH₂OH + R₃CH₂OH

Scheme II

McInnes, Tattrie, and Kates (73) developed a procedure for the quantitative determination of α- and β-monoglycerides by derivatization of the associated fatty acids. The monoglycerides were converted into the bis-methylsulfonyl derivatives with methylsulfonyl chloride in pyridine, then into the allyl fatty acid esters (C_4–C_{18}) with acetone and sodium iodide (Scheme III). Also, α-monoglycerides were distinguished from the β-forms

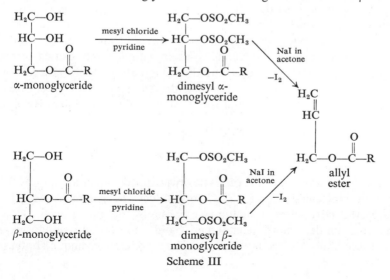

Scheme III

because the vicinal hydroxyls could be converted to the isopropylidene derivatives.

Thiol esters (coenzyme A compounds) were converted to hydroxamic acids by Vagelos, VandenHeuvel, and Horning (108), then acetylated with acetic anhydride in pyridine. When chromatographed, the hydroxamate esters were converted to isocyanates which were readily separated:

$$R—CO—SCoA + NH_2OH \rightarrow R—CO—NHOH + CoASH$$

$$R—CO—NHOH + CH_3CO—O—COCH_3 \rightarrow$$

$$CH_3COOH + R—CO—NH—O—COCH_3$$

$$R—CO—NH—O—COCH_3 \rightarrow R—N{=}C{=}O + CH_3COOH$$

H. Miscellaneous

The melting point of maleic hydrazide was reduced substantially by treatment with alkylchlorocarbonates which converted it into alkyl carbonates. Fishbein and Zielinski (25) prepared the methyl, ethyl, propyl, butyl, amyl, and 3-chloropropyl carbonates which were readily separated by GLC.

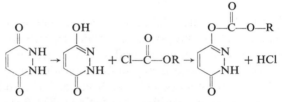

A new approach to derivatization was made by Bassette, Özeris, and Whitnah (2) in which a mixture of sulfides, carbonyls, esters, and alcohols was studied by selective removal of peaks. Carbonyl peaks could be removed with acid hydroxylamine solution, sulfides were caused to react with mercuric chloride solution, and the combination of ester and carbonyl compounds was eliminated with basic hydroxylamine. In the latter case the alcohol peaks were enhanced by formation of alcohol from ester hydrolysis:

$$R_1R_2C{=}O + NH_2OH \rightarrow R_1R_2C{=}NHOH$$

$$2RSH + HgCl_2 \rightarrow RS—Hg—SR + 2HCl$$

Beroza and Sarmiento (4) catalytically stripped functional groups from aliphatic molecules prior to GLC to produce the parent hydrocarbons and/or the next lower homolog. Compounds containing acid, alcohol, aldehyde, amide, amine, ester, ether, halide, nitrile, and sulfide groups were successfully analyzed in this manner. In a related technique Thompson et al. (103–107) studied the vapor-phase hydrogenation and GLC of complex organic molecules. These included aromatic, heterocyclic, metallo–organic, heteroaromatic, bicyclic, and alkyl–aryl systems containing antimony, arsenic, bismuth, halogen, iron, nickel, nitrogen, oxygen, phosphorus, sulfur, and tin. All compounds were converted to the reduced hydrocarbon skeleton just prior to GLC. Warrington (118) also utilized hydrogenation in studying the homologs of mixed alkyl–benzyldimethyl-ammonium chlorides. The quaternary salts were hydrogenated in a Parr apparatus and the debenzylated alkyldimethylamines (C_8–C_{18}) separated by GLC:

$$\text{C}_6\text{H}_5\text{—CH}\overset{+}{\text{N}}(\text{CH}_3)_2\text{R} + \text{H}_2 \rightarrow \text{C}_6\text{H}_5\text{—CH}_3 + (\text{CH}_3)_2\text{NHR}^+$$

In an allied study Setzkorn and Carel (95) desulfonated alkylarylsulfonates by heating them at 220°C with phosphoric acid. They showed that the phenyl C_{10}–C_{15} compounds were converted into the corresponding hydrocarbons which were readily chromatographed. The reaction may be depicted as occurring as follows:

$$2C_6H_5(CH_2)_nCH_2SO_3Na + 2H_2O \xrightarrow[\text{H}_3\text{PO}_4]{\Delta} 2C_6H_5(CH_2)_nCH_3 + 2NaHSO_4$$

Dutton and Mounts (19) used mild conditions to reduce the three unsaturated esters—methyl oleate, methyl linoleate, and 9,15-octadecadienoate—to methyl stearate without affecting the ester group. The ester function in plasticizers and polymers was studied by Jankowski and Garner (53). They transesterified polymers, made up of aliphatic and aromatic dicarboxylic acid esters, into methyl esters by refluxing with sodium methoxide in methanol and methyl acetate. This was followed by extraction with benzene, and the resulting solutions were then chromatographed. Reference dimethyl esters of succinic, glutaric, adipic, pimilic, suberic, azelic, sebacic, terephthalic, isophthalic, and phthalic acids were cited.

Hancock and Coleman (42) recently showed that trimethylsilylation of the following purine and pyrimidine nucleosides with trimethylchlorosilane and hexamethyldisilazane yields derivatives that are separable by GLC:

adenosine	cytidine	deoxyguanosine
guanosine	uridine	deoxyuridine
inosine	5-fluorouridine	thymidine
xanthosine	deoxyadenosine	5-fluorodeoxyuridine

Cook, Riley, Nunn, and Budgen (14) prepared the N,N'-dimethyl derivatives of 5,5-disubstituted barbituric acids by treatment with diazomethane in ether and separated the viscous oily derivatives by GLC. The barbiturates included in this study were:

barbitone	pentobarbitone	phenyl-methyl-
allobarbitone	quinalbarbitone	barbituric acid
butobarbitone	hexobarbitone	phenobarbitone
amylobarbitone	cyclobarbitone	thiopentone

I. Pesticides

Gutenmann and Lisk (35–37,39) have studied the bromination of pesticides and their hydrolysis products as a means of gaining sufficient sensitivity with electron capture detectors.

Diphenylamine (36) was brominated in the presence of iodine dissolved in carbon tetrachloride. The mixture was evaporated to dryness and the residue dissolved in hexane and injected. CIPC [isopropyl N-(3-chlorophenyl) carbamate], Monuron (3-p-chlorophenyl-1,1-dimethylurea), and Diuron [3-(3,4-dichlorophenyl)-1,1-dimethylurea] were brominated and then hydrolyzed (39) to the corresponding 2,4,6-tribromo-3-chloroaniline, 2,6-dibromo-4-chloroaniline, and 2,6-dibromo-3,4-dichloroaniline, respectively.

Similarly (35), the bromination of diphenyl proceeded smoothly (p,p'-dibromo?) to yield a product for low level electron affinity detection. Guthion [O,O-dimethyl-S-4-oxo-1,2,3-benzotriazin-3(4H)-ylmethyl phosphorodithioate] was hydrolyzed in alkali and the resulting o-aminobenzoic acid was brominated and methylated to yield methyl 2-amino-3,5-dibromobenzoate. Both MCP (2-methyl-4-chlorophenoxyacetic acid) and MCPB (2-methyl-4-chlorophenoxybutyric acid) were brominated and esterified to form derivatives amenable to GLC.

Gutenmann and Lisk (37) determined Ethion (O,O,O',O'-tetraethyl S,S'-methylene-bisphosphorodithioate) and Malathion [O,O-dimethyl S-(1,2-dicarbethoxyethyl)-phosphorodithioate] by heating the organophosphate ester with HI to convert the Ethion to ethyl iodide and the Malathion to methyl iodide. Injection of the headspace gas from these solutions yielded linear data.

Van Middelem, Norwood, and Waites (109) prepared derivatives of Sevin (1-naphthyl-N-methylcarbamate), Bayer 37344 [4-(methylthio)-3,5-xylyl-N-methylcarbamate], and UC 10854 (3-isopropylphenyl-N-methylcarbamate). These compounds were hydrolyzed in methanolic KOH, then extracted with ether after acidification. The resulting phenols were brominated with bromine and iodine, and evaporative losses were minimized by adding polyethylene glycol prior to removal of solvent. The resulting brominated phenols gave a 1000-fold enhancement of sensitivity to electron affinity detection over the parent compounds. They could not detect either Zectran [4-dimethylamino-3,5-xylyl-methylcarbamate] or Bayer 44646, Matacil (4-dimethylamino-*m*-tolyl methylcarbamate) by this method.

J. Phenols

The problem of reducing the polarity of phenols by suitable derivatization has its counterpart in alcohols.

Shulgin (96) reported the trifluoroacetylation of phenols for the first time. He heated them in trifluoroacetic anhydride with a trace of NaOH solution:

$$\langle R \rangle—OH + (CF_3CO)_2O \rightarrow \langle R \rangle—O—\overset{\displaystyle O}{\underset{\displaystyle \|}{C}}—CF_3 + CF_3\overset{\displaystyle O}{\underset{\displaystyle \|}{C}}—OH$$

After the volatiles were removed the ester was purified by distillation under vacuum. The following phenolic trifluoroacetates were prepared and chromatographed:

phenol	2,4,6-trimethylphenol
o-cresol	2,3,6-trimethylphenol
m-cresol	2,3,5-trimethylphenol
p-cresol	2,4,5-trimethylphenol
2,6-xylenol	2,3,4-trimethylphenol
2,5-xylenol	3,4,5-trimethylphenol
2,4-xylenol	2,3,5,6-tetramethylphenol
3,5-xylenol	2,3,4,6-tetramethylphenol
2,3-xylenol	2,3,4,5-tetramethylphenol
3,4-xylenol	pentamethylphenol

The pairs 2,4-xylenol-3,5-xylenol and 2,3,5-trimethylphenol-2,4,5-trimethylphenol were not resolved.

Higginbottom, Culbertson, and Woodbrey (43) converted phenol, mono-, di-, and trihydroxymethylphenols, dihydroxydiphenylmethanes, and dihydroxydibenzyl ethers to acetates with acetic anhydride and pyridine. The mixture was treated with water, extracted with ether, and the solvent removed. Solutions of the esters in acetone were used for GLC. The authors also prepared the trifluoroacetates and trimethylsilyl ethers but found them more difficult to handle and to isolate in pure form.

The quantitative conversion of phenols to the trimethylsilyl derivatives was accomplished by Freedman and Croitoru (26). They heated a mixture of phenol, *o*-cresol, *m*-cresol, *p*-cresol, 2,5-xylenol, 2,4-xylenol, and 2,6-xylenol in hexamethyldisiliazane with a number of acidic oxide catalysts.

$$(CH_3)_3Si\underset{\displaystyle H}{N}Si(CH_3)_3 + 2 \langle R \rangle—OH \rightarrow 2(CH_3)_3Si—O—\langle R \rangle + NH_3$$

Furuya (28) prepared the same derivatives of 22 flavonoids and related compounds with a mixture of hexamethyldisilazane and trimethylchlorosilane in pyridine. After centrifuging, the supernatant layer was injected into the GLC apparatus. The following compounds were used in the study:

flavone	quercetin	eriodictyol
wogonin	morin	fustin
baicalein	robinetin	isoliquiritigenin
luteolin	myricetin	gleditsin
kaempferol	quercetagetin	formononetin
fisetin	liquiritigenin	daidzein
isorhamnetin	sakuranetin	
nor-icaritin	naringenin	

Reduction of fisetin, fustin, and gleditsen occurred during GLC.

K. Steroids

Horning, Luukkainen, Haahti, Creech, and VandenHeuvel (45) and Horning, VandenHeuvel, and Creech (46) have presented comprehensive reviews on methods for preparing trifluoroacetates, acetates, and trimethylsilyl and methyl ethers as hydroxyl derivatives, and N,N-dimethylhydrazones for ketones. A recent monograph by Wotiz and Clark (124a) also discusses in detail the various sample preparation methods.

The GLC behavior of the chloroacetates and acetates of corticosterone, 11-dehydrocorticosterone, 11-deoxycorticosterone, 17α-hydroxycorticosterone, 17α-hydroxy-11-dehydrocorticosterone, 17α-hydroxy-11-deoxycorticosterone, aldosterone, and testosterone were compared by Rapp and Eik-Nes (87). They concluded that the acetates were more useful derivatives than their chlorinated counterparts. Fales and Luukkainen (22) converted the following ketosteroids and trimethylsiloxy derivatives to O-methyloxines by treatment with methoxyamine:

androstane-17-one	testosterone acetate
androstane-3,17-dione	estrone
	estrone-3-TMSi
Δ4-androstene-3,17-dione	6-ketoestradiol-3,17-di-TMSi
pregnane-3,20-dione	16-ketoestradiol-3,17-di-TMSi
allopregnane-3,20-dione	etiocholanolone
allopregnane-3,11,20-trione	11-ketoeticholanolone
allopregnane-3β-ol-20-one	equilenin
allopregnane-3β-ol-20-one-3-TMSi	cholestanone
androsterone	cortisone (as adrenosterone)
androsterone-3-TMSi	
dehydroepiandrosterone	hydrocortisone (as Δ4-androstene-
dehydroepiandrosterone-3-TMSi	11-ol-3,17-dione)
testosterone	
testosterone-17-TMSi	Menadione (vitamin K_3)

The 3-, 6-, 16-, 17- and 20-O-methyloxines were formed readily but the 11-position was found to be unreactive.

Brooks (10) has reported on an extensive GLC study of the acetates of the following steroids:

11β-hydroxyprogesterone

17α-hydroxyprogesterone

Substance S

Substance S-21-acetate

deoxycorticosterone

corticosterone

cortisol

3β-hydroxy-5α-pregnan-20-one

3α-hydroxy-5β-pregnan-20-one

3β-acetoxy-17α-hydroxypregn-5-en-20-one

11-deoxycorticosterone

3β-acetoxypregn-5-en-20-one

cortisone

corticosterone-21-acetate

cortisone-21-acetate

cortisone diacetate

cortesol-21-acetate

11β-acetoxyprogesterone

3β-hydroxy-5α-pregnane-11,20-dione

Acetylations were carried out in good yield by heating the steroid with acetic anhydride containing p-toluenesulfonic acid, evaporating to dryness, and extracting the derivatives with chloroform.

After studying the decomposition product of sterol methanesulfonates and -p-toluenesulfonates, VandenHeuvel, Stillwell, Gardiner, Wikstrom, and Horning (112) showed that the following were unsuitable as sterol derivatives for GLC studies:

cholestanyl methanesulfonate

cholestanyl p-toluenesulfonate

epicholestanyl methanesulfonate

cholesteryl p-toluenesulfonate

cholesteryl methanesulfonate

epicholesteryl p-toluenesulfonate

5α-pregnane-20β-methanesulfonate-3-one

estrone methanesulfonate

Landowne and Lipsky (62) prepared a series of cholesteryl haloacetates and compared their electron-capture capabilities. The unexpected order of sensitivities was found to be mono-Cl $>$ di-Cl $>$ mono-Br $>$ tri-Cl $>$ tri-F.

Makita and Wells (69) prepared derivatives of 20 fecal bile acids by methylating the acids with diazomethane in methanol and ether followed by trimethylsilylation in pyridine with hexamethyldisilizane. The methylcholanyl trimethylsilyl ethers prepared in this study were:

methyl cholanate

3α-hydroxy

3β-hydroxy

3α,6α-dihydroxy

3α,7α-dihydroxy

3α,7β-dihydroxy

3α,12α-dihydroxy

3α,6α,7α-trihydroxy

3α,6α,7β-trihydroxy

3α,6β,7α-trihydroxy

3α,6β,7β-trihydroxy

3α,7α,12α-trihydroxy

3-keto

3α-hydroxy-7-keto

3α-hydroxy-12-keto

3α,7α-dihydroxy-12-keto

3α,12α-dihydroxy-7-keto

3α-hydroxy-7,12-diketo

3,7-diketo

3,12-diketo

Kirschner and Fales (59) showed that the 20,21-side chain of 10,17-hydroxycorticosteroids could be stabilized for GLC through formation of the bismethylenedioxy derivatives. The following compounds were prepared by treating the steroid with formalin in hydrochloric acid and chloroform, washing with caustic, drying and filtering the solution which was applied directly to the column:

17,20;20,21-bismethylenedioxy-4-pregnene-3,11-dione (Cortisone-BMD)

17,20;20,21-bis-methylenedioxy-4-pregnene-11β-ol-3-one (Cortisol-BMD)

17,20;20,21-bismethylenedioxy-4-pregnene-3-one (Desoxycortisol-BMD, Substance S BMD)

17,20;20,21-bismethylenedioxy-5β-pregnane-3α-ol-11-one (Tetrahydrocortisone-BMD)

17,20;20,21-bismethylenedioxy-2α-methyl-4-pregnene, 3,11-dione (2α-methyl cortisone BMD)

17,20;20,21-bismethylenedioxy-16α-methyl-4-pregnene-3,11-dione (16α-methyl cortisone BMD)

17,20;20,21-bismethylenedioxy-16α-methyl-4-pregnene-11β-3-one (16α-methyl hydrocortisone BMD)

17,20;20,21-bismethylelenedioxy-3-ethylenedioxy-5α-pregnene-6,11 dione

17,20;20,21-bismethylenedioxy-6-methyl-5-pregnene-11β-ol

17,20;20,21-bismethylenedioxy-11α-methyl-5-pregnene-11β-ol

II. Sampling and Sample Transfer

Under ideal sample transfer conditions a compound or mixture is injected quantitatively into a carrier gas stream. It should vaporize immediately without decomposition and move into the column as a homogeneous plug so that its volume is a minimum under the existing condition of pressure and temperature and peak broadening is avoided. Vaporization of liquid and solid samples disturbs the gas flow and produces a temperature drop resulting from the absorption of the heat of vaporization from the injection block. Consideration must be given to minimizing these effects while preserving the plug of vaporized sample in intact form.

Numerous devices have been developed for the purpose of introducing gaseous, liquid, and solid samples into the GLC apparatus. The major applications involve liquid samples that are injected directly into the column or into a heater block just preceding the column. The hypodermic-type devices may be simple glass barrels graduated in microliters with plungers of metal or polymer-coated metals for special requirements. For high pressure work, barrels have been made of brass, stainless steel, or Monel metal. If cooling or heating is required to maintain the sample in a condition suitable for injection, the barrel of the syringe can be fitted with a jacket for circulating the cooling or heating liquids. Various needles have been designed to penetrate cork and metal covers for head space analysis. Special injection devices have been made for sampling gases from liquid systems, from high and low pressure sources, and those made up of corrosive constituents.

A. Gases

In Figures 3-1 and 3-2 are illustrated schematic diagrams of simple systems for removing gaseous samples from sources under reduced pressure. Figure 3-1 is a multiport metal valve constructed along the same lines as the two-loop gas sampling valve shown in Figure 3-14 (41). When the plunger is full in and the stop is turned to the top of the cylinder, helium flows through port 6 only to the column. No sample flows and the inlet terminates at port 4. Ports 2, 3, and 5 are evacuated to a pressure significantly lower than the pressure in the sample line. Turning the plunger handle until the stop is at the bottom of the cylinder (center sketch) shuts off the vacuum system and permits sample to flow into the evacuated ports.

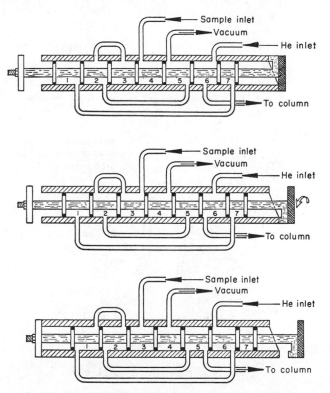

Fig. 3-1. Metal sampling valve for samples under vacuum.

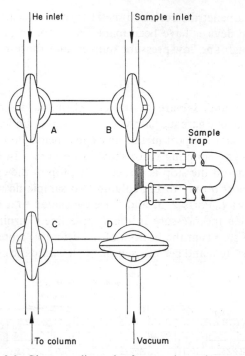

He inlet   Sample inlet

A   B

Sample
trap

C   D

To column   Vacuum

Fig. 3-2. Glass sampling valve for samples under vacuum.

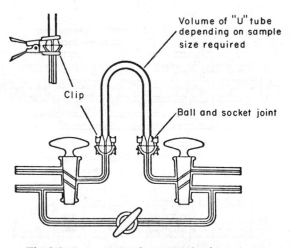

Volume of "U" tube
depending on sample
size required

Clip

Ball and socket joint

Fig. 3-3. A constant-volume sample pipet.

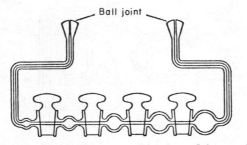

Fig. 3-4. A calibration pipet. This pipet, used in place of the sample loop in Figure 3-2, is used to isolate and inject any of a small number of fixed volumes of sample gas into the carrier gas stream.

Helium continues to flow directly to the column. When the plunger is pulled full out, the helium flow is diverted into port *6*, whence it flows sequentially into ports *1*, *2*, *5*, and the column. The samples remaining in ports *3* and *7* are not used but are removed during the next evacuation and filling cycle.

The all-glass apparatus shown in Figure 3-2 can be used to carry out the same sequence of operations illustrated in Figure 3-1. The sample trap, consisting of a U-tube fitted with ground joints, can be fabricated in a variety of sizes to provide any number of sample capacities when attached to the male ground joints in leg *BD* of the apparatus. By manipulation of the stopcocks, the sample leg of the system can be evacuated while maintaining helium flow to the column. The vacuum and sample inlets are then closed and the helium is routed through stopcocks *B* and *D* to carry the sample into the column.

Jeffrey and Kipping (54) reviewed gas sample transfer systems for GLC. They described various by-pass sample loops that were used as constant volume (Fig. 3-3) and calibration pipets (Fig. 3-4). Four-way stopcocks (Fig. 3-5), a six-way stopcock (Fig. 3-6), a multiport sample valve (Fig. 3-7), and by-pass sample valves (Figs. 3-8 and 3-9) were shown to be useful in specific applications. For trapping and transferring condensable gases, the

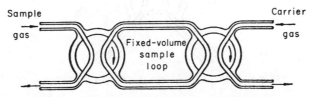

Fig. 3-5. Four-way taps used for sample injection.

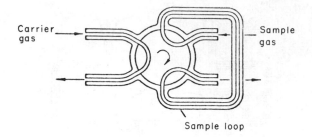

Fig. 3-6. A six-way tap for sample injection.

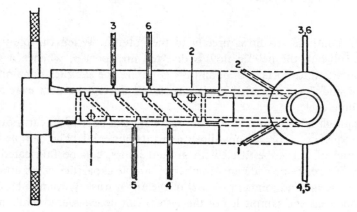

Fig. 3-7. A multiport sample valve. (1) vacuum; (2) reaction vessel; (3, 4) sample volume; (5) carrier gas supply; (6) chromatographic column.

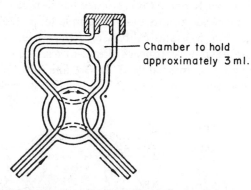

Fig. 3-8. A by-pass sample valve for syringe injection.

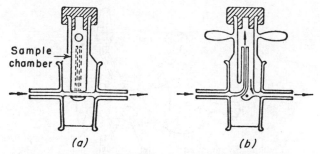

Fig. 3-9. An improved by-pass sample valve for syringe injection. (*a*) By-pass position.
(*b*) Sample injection position.

same authors described a trap (Fig. 3-10) and cells (Figs. 3-11 and 3-12)
patterned on the by-pass principle that permitted rapid switching from
carrier gas flow to sample injection and back again. One interesting system
they described (Fig. 3-13) was used to transfer as little as 10^{-5} ml of gas
for use with very sensitive detectors.

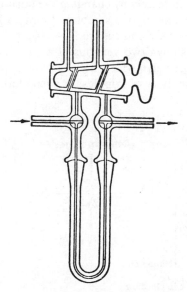

Fig. 3-10. Liquid nitrogen trap.

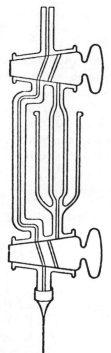

Fig. 3-11. Sample transfer cell
with liquid nitrogen trap.

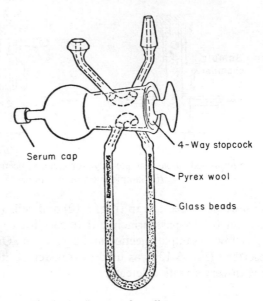

Fig. 3-12. Gas transfer cell.

Hamilton (41) modified the multiport valve apparatus so that either small or large samples may be introduced merely by changing the position of the valve stem which permits either one or two sampling loops to be connected into the carrier gas stream as shown in Figure 3-14.

In Figures 3-15 and 3-16 there are shown two versions of a constant-volume trap combined with a multiport valve which Bellar, Brown, and Sigsby (3) used to carry out repetitive analyses of samples for air pollution work.

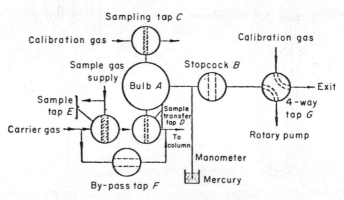

Fig. 3-13. Gas handling system for the transfer of small amounts of sample material.

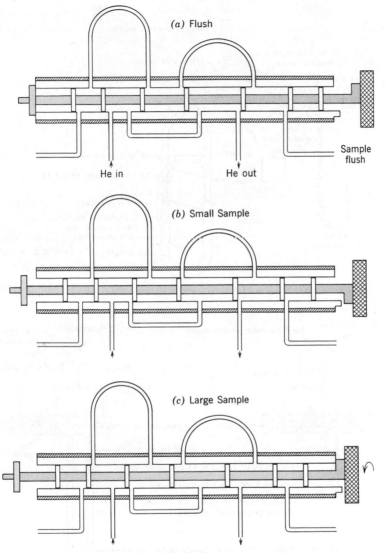

(a) Flush

He in   He out

Sample
flush

(b) Small Sample

(c) Large Sample

Fig. 3-14. Stem positions for a two-loop gas sampling valve.

Swinnerton, Linnenbom, and Cheek (101) stripped dissolved gases from a solution by passing carrier gas through a glass frit to form fine bubbles which passed through the liquid. In Figure 3-17 is shown the arrangement of sample loops and degassing chamber connected to the GLC apparatus.

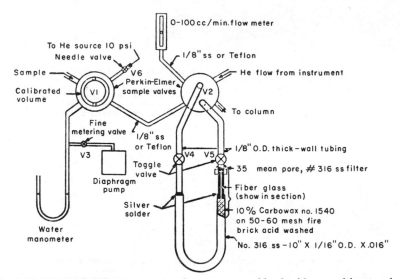

Fig. 3-15. Schematic of a constant volume trap combined with a multiport valve.

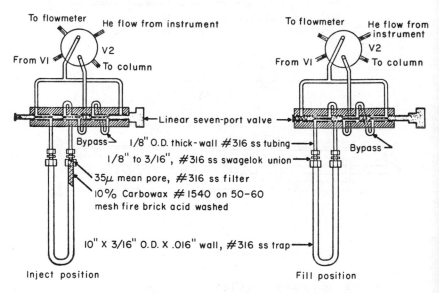

Fig. 3-16. Modification of the system shown in Figure 3-15.

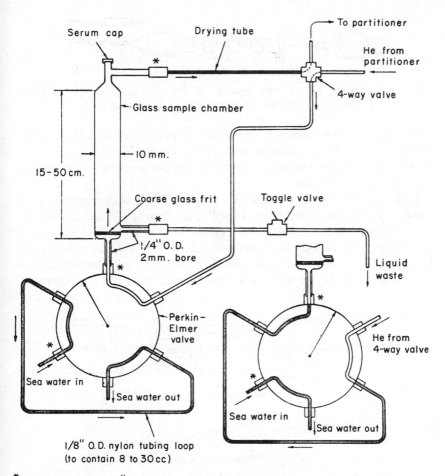

Serum cap   Drying tube   → To partitioner

                                                       He from
                                                       partitioner

                                                       4-way valve

←Glass sample chamber

←10 mm.

15–50 cm.

Coarse glass frit   Toggle valve

!/4" O. D.   Liquid
2mm. bore   waste

←Perkin–
  Elmer
  valve   He from
                                                       4-way valve

Sea water in

↓Sea water out   Sea water in
                                         ↓Sea water out

1/8" O.D. nylon tubing loop
(to contain 8 to 30 cc)

*Swagelok unions 1/4", all other   Perkin–Elmer valve in position for He
connections are made with Perkin–   to force water from loop into chamber
Elmer fittings

Position #1   Position #2
Sample loop filling position

Fig. 3-17. Liquid sampling valve assembly and glass purging chamber.

B. Solids and Liquids

Solid samples are usually dissolved in a suitable solvent, and an aliquot
of this solution is injected into a gas chromatograph. A solvent should be
chosen that boils much lower than the material being analyzed, so that it is
completely eluted before any of the sample components appear. It is also

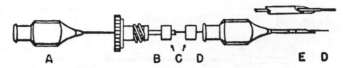

A   B C D   E D

Fig. 3-18. Exploded view of solid injector. *A*, Plunger; *B*, sampling-wire guide; *C*, silicone rubber discs; *D*, sampling wire; *E*, injection needle.

desirable to use a solvent that gives little or no response with the detector being used. In a flame ionization detector, carbon disulfide is not detectable. In an electron capture detector, aliphatics give the least response, followed by benzene and dioxane.

If the solid sample is difficultly soluble, or if it is undesirable to use a solvent, a solid sampling device is applicable. One of the simplest devices for introducing solid samples into a GLC column, shown in Figure 3-18, was constructed by Parker, Fontan, and Kirk (81). It consists of a solid sample carrier made from a wire used for cleaning hypodermic needles. Solutions of solids are applied to the tip and the solvent evaporated.

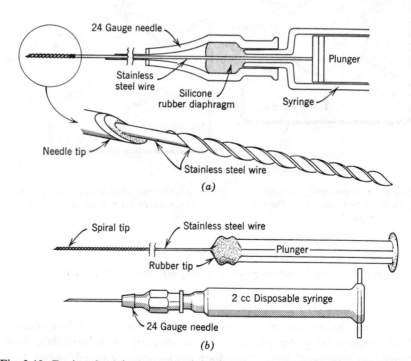

Fig. 3-19. Devices for injecting solids (*a*) with silicone rubber diaphragm in hub of needle (*b*) using syringe with a gas-tight plunger.

Volatile amines are converted to salts with hydrochloric acid by applying a drop of each to the wire. The sample is injected by retracting the wire, inserting the needle through the diaphragm, and extending the wire which extrudes the sample into the heated zone.

A similar device (Fig. 3-19), constructed by McComas and Goldfien (72), utilizes a sample wire tip ground square, then twisted into a spiral. This design permits only a minimum surface of wire to contact the inside of the needle when it is drawn inward and also accommodates larger samples.

Renshaw and Biran (88) constructed a sample introduction apparatus (Fig. 3-20) that contains a metal rod having a trough (spoon) at one end capable of holding 0.1–0.2 ml of liquid and a soft iron cylinder at the other end. The rod fits into a T-tube which is an extension of the top of the GLC column and provisions are made for vertical introduction of the spoon and exclusion of air. All operations are effected without interrupting the carrier gas flow and the sample is vaporized after lowering the sample rod by manipulating an external circular magnet.

Cagnazzo, Ros, and Bignardi (12) described a similar device (shown in Fig. 3-21) of somewhat simpler construction, which utilizes a silver spiral to hold the sample in a horizontal tube connected to the GLC inlet.

Other sampling devices which accommodate glass capillary sample tubes coupled with the inlet system of the gas chromatograph are available commercially. Bowman and Karmen (8) constructed the apparatus shown in Figure 3-22 in which a notch is cut into the barrel of the plunger so that the sample can be introduced with little, if any, air. By retracting the plunger almost the full travel the notch is exposed. This serves to carry a glass sample capillary tube into the chamber above the column containing a slotted plate on which the sample tube is crushed, releasing the sample.

Ellis (20) has described a method of introducing and manipulating moisture-sensitive samples under anhydrous conditions. He transferred small samples of niobium(V) and tantalum(V) chlorides from a sample tube with a spoon into a crucible in a glass apparatus of special design. The construction is shown in Figure 3-23, and the original article should be consulted for manipulation details.

Nerheim (78) patented an apparatus (Fig. 3-24) which accommodates encapsulated samples (S) in an indium capillary, where the ends are closed by crimping. When the metal sample tube is inserted through a flexible air lock (A) into the hot zone of the GLC the metal melts and the sample is released instantaneously. Molten indium can be removed through a second air lock (B).

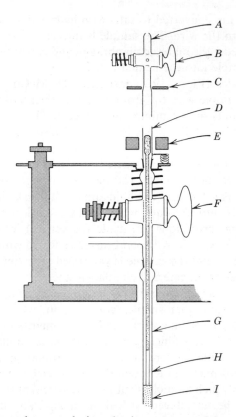

Fig. 3-20. The complete sample introduction apparatus as used with the "Pye" argon chromatograph. The apparatus is drawn in the position in which the sample is discharged into the column, with the trough of the "spoon" touching the packing phase. A, capillary gas leak; B, stopcock leading to the leak; C, soft iron ring; D, the holder of the "spoon"; E, circular magnet; F, wide bore stopcock with side arm; G, the sample introduction device (the "spoon"); H, the trough at the end of the "spoon"; I, gas chromatographic column. The figure is approximately 1/4 scale. The dimensions of the "spoon" (G) are: length 28 cm, length of trough (H) 3.5 cm, diameter 3 mm. The length of the holder between the soft iron ring (C) and the ground glass joint is 28.5 cm.

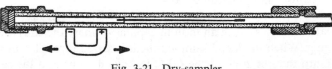

Fig. 3-21. Dry-sampler.

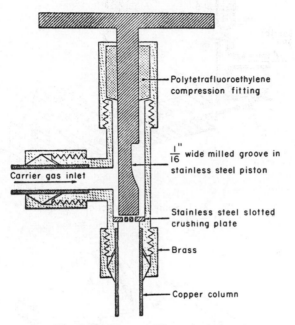

Fig. 3-22. Glass capillary sampler.

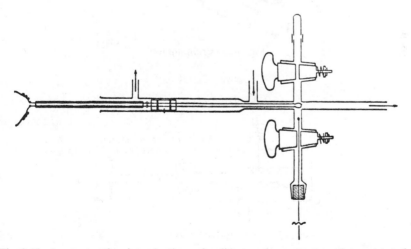

Fig. 3-23. Apparatus for introduction of solid samples onto gas chromatography columns.

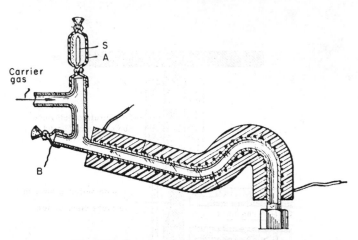

Fig. 3-24. Sample introduction system.

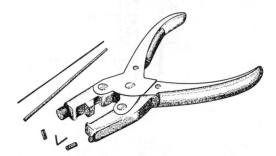

Fig. 3-25. Crimping tool.

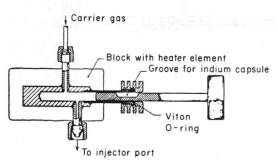

Fig. 3-26. Capsule introduction system.

The crimping tool, shown in Figure 3-25 (123), which is available commercially, is used to seal the ends of the indium capillary containing the sample. A capsule introduction system, patterned after the design by Bowman and Karmen (8), shown in Figure 3-22, is available commercially (123) and is illustrated in Figure 3-26.

C. Split Stream Injectors

With the previously described devices, one is injecting the whole sample in the device into the carrier gas stream, and one is assuming that this sample amount does not exceed the maximum permissible sample size of the gas chromatographic system (column and detector). There is, however, a very important column group where the permissible sample size of the system is very small and the direct introduction of such small samples with the conventional sampling system is impractical or even impossible. These are columns with small diameter or capillary columns* the sample capacity of which may be in the order of $10^{-3} \mu l$.

For these columns, an indirect procedure is generally utilized (13a,17a, 39b,126a). A relatively large (0.5–2 μl) liquid sample is introduced into the sample introduction port and evaporated, and either the sample vapor or its homogeneous mixture with the carrier gas is split into two highly unequal parts, the smaller of which is introduced by the carrier gas flow into the column while the latter is discarded. In this way, the actual sample entering the column will be only a fraction of the originally injected volume.

There is a second case when sample splitting is recommended. There are certain columns—e.g., support-coated open tubular columns—which would have adequate sample capacity to permit direct sample injection with standard syringes; however, the flow rates used with these columns are usually below 5 ml/min. Practically all conventional injection blocks are designed for flow rates of at least 20 ml/min and with lower flow rates, band spreading will definitely occur. Therefore, one rather favors a low splitting injection.

1. Static Splitting

In this type of split system, the sample is first evaporated in a closed volume; a small part of its homogeneous vapor is introduced into the carrier gas flowing toward the column. A typical system described by

* In this discussion, the term "capillary column" is used in the correct way, i.e., by describing the dimension of column diameter without restricting this term to any particular type of column. "Capillary columns" consist of two categories: *packed* capillary columns and *open tubular* columns with small diameter. It should be emphasized that the latter are not restricted to capillary dimensions (21a).

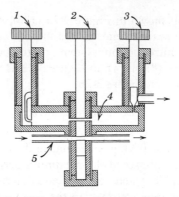

Fig. 3-27. Static split system (24).

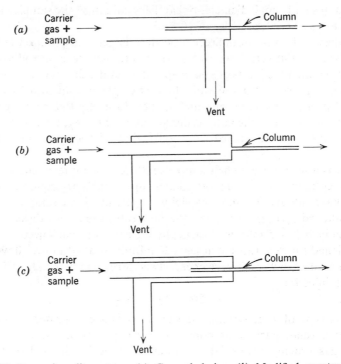

Fig. 3-28. Dynamic split systems. (*a*) General design. (*b*) Modified construction of Halász and Schneider (39*a*). (*c*) Modified construction of Clarke (12*a*).

Fejes et al. (24) is illustrated in Figure 3-27. In this system, micropipet *1* is filled with the liquid sample and then pushed halfway down in a channel. The vaporization chamber *4* of known volume is evacuated through needle valve *3* which is then closed. Consequently, the micropipet is pushed down; the liquid evaporates and fills the vaporization chamber. By pushing down rod *2*, the vapor in the sample volume of this rod (which is a fraction of the volume of the whole chamber) is introduced into the carrier gas line *5*.

Conventional gas chromatographs do not generally use static split systems.

2. Dynamic Splitting

In this case, a homogenous mixture of the sample vapor and carrier gas moves through the split system where it is split into two highly unequal parts, the smaller being introduced into the column itself while the larger is vented. If the sample and carrier gas are truly homogeneously mixed prior to splitting, the sample will be split in the ratio determined by the two flow rates.

The question concerning the problems of sample splitting and the criteria for representative (so-called "linear") splitting are discussed in detail by Ettre et al. (8a,21a–d).

Today, practically all dynamic split systems consist of two concentric tubes (Fig. 3-28a). Halász and Schneider (39a) and Clarke (12a) described modifications of this basic system. (Figs. 3-28b, c.) In all these systems, a pneumatic restrictor is placed in the vent line. In order to obtain a constant split ratio, the pneumatic resistance of the restrictor in the vent line must be extremely constant during operation. Both needle valves and (interchangeable) capillary tubes of various diameters have been used, the latter are considered somewhat superior with respect to constancy and reproducibility.

References

1. M. J. Baraud, *Bull. Soc. Chim. France*, **1960**, 785.
2. R. Bassette, S. Özeris, and C. H. Whitnah, *Anal. Chem.*, **34,** 1540 (1962).
3. T. A. Bellar, M. F. Brown, and J. E. Sigsby, Jr., *Anal. Chem.*, **35,** 1924 (1963).
4. M. Beroza and R. Sarmiento, *Anal. Chem.*, **37,** 1040 (1965).
5. K. Biemann and W. Vetter, *Biochem. Biophys. Res. Commun.*, **3,** 578 (1960).
6. M. Bier and P. Teitelbaum, *Ann. N.Y. Acad. Sci.*, **72,** 641 (1959).
7. C. T. Bishop, in *Methods of Biochemical Analysis*, Vol. 10, D. Glick, Ed., Interscience, New York, 1962, pp. 14–22.
8. R. L. Bowman and A. Karmen, *Nature*, **182,** 1233 (1958).
8a. N. Brenner and L. S. Ettre, *Acta Chim. Acad. Sci. Hung.*, **27,** 205 (1961).
9. E. Brochmann-Hanssen and A. B. Svendsen, *J. Pharm. Sci.*, **51,** 938 (1962).
10. C. J. W. Brooks, *Anal. Chem.*, **37,** 636 (1965).
11. C. J. W. Brooks and E. C. Horning, *Anal. Chem.*, **36,** 1540 (1964).

12. G. Cagnazzo, A. Ros, and G. Bignardi, *J. Chromatog.*, **19**, 185 (1965).
12*a*. D. R. Clarke, *Nature*, **198**, 681 (1963).
13. G. Clement and J. Bezard, *Compt. Rend.*, **253**, 564 (1961).
13*a*. R. D. Condon, *Anal. Chem.*, **31**, 1717 (1959).
14. J. G. H. Cook, C. Riley, R. F. Nunn, and D. E. Budgen, *J. Chromatog.*, **6**, 182 (1961).
15. B. M. Craig, A. P. Tulloch, and N. L. Murty, *J. Am. Oil Chemists' Soc.*, **40**, 61 (1963).
16. P. A. Cruickshank and J. C. Sheehan, *Anal. Chem.*, **36**, 1191 (1964).
17. A. Darbre and K. Blau, *J. Chromatog.*, **17**, 31 (1965).
17*a*. D. H. Desty, A. Goldup, and B. H. F. Whyman, *J. Inst. Petrol.*, **45**, 287 (1959).
18. D. T. Downing, Z. H. Kranz, and K. E. Murray, *Australian J. Chem.*, **13**, 80 (1960).
19. H. J. Dutton and T. L. Mounts, *J. Catalysis*, **3**, 363 (1964).
20. C. P. Ellis, *Anal. Chem.*, **35**, 1327 (1963).
21. G. G. Esposito and M. H. Swann, *Anal. Chem.*, **33**, 1854 (1961).
21*a*. L. S. Ettre, *Open Tubular Columns in Gas Chromatography*, Plenum Press, New York, 1965.
21*b*. L. S. Ettre and W. Averill, *Anal. Chem.*, **33**, 680 (1961).
21*c*. L. S. Ettre, E. W. Cieplinski, and N. Brenner, *ISA Trans.*, **2**, 134 (1963).
21*d*. L. S. Ettre and F. J. Kabot, *Anal. Chem.*, **34**, 1431 (1962).
22. H. M. Fales and T. Luukkainen, *Anal. Chem.*, **37**, 955 (1965).
23. J. W. Farquhar, *J. Lipid Res.*, **3**, 21 (1962).
24. P. Fejes, J. Engelhardt, and G. Schay, *J. Chromatog.*, **11**, 151 (1963).
25. L. Fishbein and W. L. Zielinski, Jr., *J. Chromatog.*, **18**, 581 (1965).
26. R. W. Freedman and P. P. Croitoru, *Anal. Chem.*, **36**, 1389 (1964).
27. S. Friedman and M. L. Kaufman, *Anal. Chem.*, **38**, 144 (1966).
28. T. Furuya, *J. Chromatog.*, **19**, 607 (1965).
29. W. G. Galetto, R. E. Kepner, and A. D. Webb, *Anal. Chem.*, **38**, 34 (1966).
30. M. Gee, *Anal. Chem.*, **37**, 926 (1965).
31. C. W. Gehrke and D. F. Goerlitz, *Anal. Chem.*, **35**, 76 (1963).
31*a*. C. W. Gehrke, W. M. Lamkin, D. L. Stalling, and F. Shahrokhi, *Biochem. Biophys. Res. Commun.*, **19**, 328 (1965).
31*b*. C. W. Gehrke and F. Shahrokhi, *Anal. Biochem.*, **15**, 97 (1966).
32. J. Graff, J. P. Wein, and M. Winitz, *Federation Proc.*, **22**, 244 (1963).
33. G. M. Gray, *J. Chromatog.*, **4**, 52 (1960).
34. G. M. Gray, *J. Chromatog.*, **6**, 236 (1961).
35. W. H. Gutenmann and D. J. Lisk, *J. Assoc. Offic. Agr. Chemists*, **46**, 859 (1963).
36. W. H. Gutenmann and D. J. Lisk, *J. Agr. Food Chem.*, **11**, 468 (1963).
37. W. H. Gutenmann and D. J. Lisk, *J. Agr. Food Chem.*, **11**, 470 (1963).
38. W. H. Gutenmann and D. J. Lisk, *J. Assoc. Offic. Agr. Chemists*, **47**, 353 (1964).
39. W. H. Gutenmann and D. J. Lisk, *J. Agr. Food Chem.*, **12**, 46 (1964).
39*a*. I. Halász and W. Schneider, in *Gas Chromatography*, N. Brenner, J. E. Callen, and M. D. Weiss, Eds., Academic Press, New York, 1962, pp. 287–306.
39*b*. I. Halász and G. Schreyer, *Chem.-Ingr.-Tech.*, **32**, 675 (1960).
40. B. Hallgren and S. Larsson, *J. Lipid Res.*, **3**, 31 (1962).
41. L. H. Hamilton, *J. Gas Chromatog.*, **2**, 302 (1964).
42. R. L. Hancock and D. L. Coleman, *Anal. Biochem.*, **10**, 365 (1965).
43. H. P. Higginbottom, H. M. Culbertson, and J. C. Woodbrey, *Anal. Chem.*, **37**, 1021 (1965).

44. E. C. Horning, M. G. Horning, W. J. A. VandenHeuvel, K. L. Knox, B. Holmstedt, and J. W. Brooks, *Anal. Chem.*, **36**, 1546 (1964).
45. E. C. Horning, T. Luukkainen, E. O. A. Haahti, B. G. Creech, and W. J. A. VandenHeuvel, in *Recent Progress in Hormone Research*, Vol. 19, G. Pincus, Ed., Academic Press, New York, 1963, pp. 57–92.
46. E. C. Horning, W. J. A. VandenHeuvel, and B. G. Creech, in *Methods of Biochemical Analysis*, Vol. 11, D. Glick, Ed., Interscience, New York, 1963, pp. 69–147.
47. L. A. Horrocks and D. G. Cornwell, *J. Lipid Res.*, **3**, 165 (1962).
48. J. A. Hudy, *Anal. Chem.*, **31**, 1754 (1959).
49. I. R. Hunter, K. P. Dimick, and J. W. Corse, *Chem. Ind.* (*London*), **1956**, 294.
50. A. T. James, *J. Chromatog.*, **2**, 552 (1959).
51. A. T. James and A. J. P. Martin, *Biochem. J.*, **63**, 144 (1956).
52. A. T. James and J. Webb, *Biochem. J.*, **66**, 515 (1957).
53. S. J. Jankowski and P. Garner, *Anal. Chem.*, **37**, 1709 (1965).
54. P. G. Jeffrey and P. J. Kipping, *Sample Transfer Systems*, Macmillan, New York, 1964, pp. 8–22.
55. D. E. Johnson, S. J. Scott, and A. Meister, *Anal. Chem.*, **33**, 669 (1961).
56. H. P. Kaufmann and G. Mankel, *Fette, Seifen, Anstrichmittel*, **65**, 179 (1963).
57. J. J. Kirkland, *Anal. Chem.*, **32**, 1388 (1960).
58. J. J. Kirkland, *Anal. Chem.*, **33**, 1520 (1961).
59. M. A. Kirschner and H. M. Fales, *Anal. Chem.*, **34**, 1548 (1962).
60. H. Kurz, *Fette Seifen*, **44**, 144 (1937).
61. W. M. Lamkin and C. W. Gehrke, *Anal. Chem.*, **37**, 383 (1965).
62. R. A. Landowne and S. R. Lipsky, *Anal. Chem.*, **35**, 532 (1963).
63. H. J. Langner, *Angew. Chem. Intern. Ed. Engl.*, **4**, 71 (1965).
64. W. E. Link, H. M. Hickman, and R. A. Morrissette, *J. Am. Oil Chemists' Soc.*, **36**, 300 (1959).
65. N. B. Lorette and J. H. Brown, *J. Org. Chem.*, **24**, 261 (1959).
66. G. Losse, A. Losse, and J. Stoeck, *Z. Naturforsch.*, **17b**, 785 (1962).
67. F. E. Luddy, R. A. Barford, and R. W. Riemenschneider, *J. Am. Oil Chemists' Soc.*, **37**, 447 (1960).
68. S. Makisumi and H. A. Saroff, *J. Gas Chromatog.*, **3**, 21 (1965).
69. M. Makita and W. W. Wells, *Anal. Biochem.*, **5**, 523 (1963).
70. F. Marcucci, E. Mussini, F. Poy, and P. Gagliardi, *J. Chromatog.*, **18**, 487 (1965).
71. M. E. Mason and G. R. Waller, *Anal. Chem.*, **36**, 583 (1964).
72. D. B. McComas and A. Goldfien, *Anal. Chem.*, **35**, 263 (1963).
73. A. G. McInnes, N. H. Tattrie, and M. Kates, *J. Am. Oil Chemists' Soc.*, **37**, 7 (1960).
74. G. G. McKeown and S. I. Read, *Anal. Chem.*, **37**, 1780 (1964).
75. N. Melamed and M. Renard, *J. Chromatog.*, **4**, 339 (1960).
76. H. T. Miles and H. M. Fales, *Anal. Chem.*, **34**, 860 (1962).
77. R. A. Morrissette and W. E. Link, *J. Gas Chromatog.*, **3**, 67 (1965).
78. A. G. Nerheim, U.S. Pat. 3,063,286 (Nov. 13, 1962).
79. C. H. Nicholls, S. Makisumi, and H. A. Saroff, *J. Chromatog.*, **11**, 327 (1963).
80. K. Oette and E. H. Ahrens, Jr., *Anal. Chem.*, **33**, 1847 (1961).
81. K. D. Parker, C. R. Fontan, and P. L. Kirk, *Anal. Chem.*, **35**, 356 (1963).
82. J. I. Peterson, H. deSchmertzing, and K. Abel, *J. Gas Chromatog.*, **3**, 126 (1965).
83. J. J. Pisano, W. J. A. VandenHeuvel, and E. C. Horning, *Biochem. Biophys. Res. Commun.*, **7**, 82 (1962).

84. G. E. Pollock, V. I. Oyama, and R. D. Johnson, *J. Gas Chromatog.*, 3, 174 (1965).
85. L. D. Quin and M. E. Hobbs, *Anal. Chem.*, 30, 1400 (1958).
86. J. W. Ralls, *Anal. Chem.*, 32, 332 (1960).
87. J. P. Rapp and K. B. Eik-Nes, *J. Gas Chromatog.*, 3, 235 (1965).
88. A. Renshaw and L. A. Biran, *J. Chromatog.*, 8, 343 (1962).
89. M. Rogozinski, *J. Gas Chromatog.*, 2, 136 (1964).
90. R. Roper and T. S. Ma, *Microchem. J.*, 1, 245 (1957).
91. H. A. Saroff, A. Karmen, and J. W. Healy, *J. Chromatog.*, 9, 122 (1962).
92. H. Schlenk and J. L. Gellerman, *Anal. Chem.*, 32, 1412 (1960).
93. J. C. M. Schogt, P. H. Begemann, and J. H. Recourt, *J. Lipid Res.*, 2, 142 (1961).
94. N. P. Sen and P. L. McGeer, *Biochem. Biophys. Res. Commun.*, 13, 390 (1963).
95. E. A. Setzkorn and A. B. Carel, *J. Am. Oil Chemists' Soc.*, 40, 57 (1963).
96. A. T. Shulgin, *Anal. Chem.*, 36, 920 (1964).
97. P. G. Simmonds and A. Zlatkis, *Anal. Chem.*, 37, 302 (1965).
98. J. Sjöquist, *Biochim. Biophys. Acta*, 41, 20 (1960).
98a. D. L. Stalling and C. W. Gehrke, *Biochem. Biophys. Res. Commun.*, 22, 329 (1966).
99. G. W. Stevenson and J. M. Luck, *J. Biol. Chem.*, 236, 715 (1961).
100. C. C. Sweeley and E. A. Moscatelli, *J. Lipid Res.*, 1, 40 (1959).
101. J. W. Swinnerton, V. J. Linnenbom, and C. H. Cheek, *Anal. Chem.*, 34, 1509 (1962).
102. B. Teuwissen, C. Lenain, C. Dorlet, and J. Leonis, *J. Pharm. Belg.*, 81, 413 (1663).
103. C. J. Thompson, H. J. Coleman, R. L. Hopkins, C. C. Ward, and H. T. Rall, *Anal. Chem.*, 32, 1762 (1960).
104. C. J. Thompson, H. J. Coleman, R. L. Hopkins, and H. T. Rall, *Anal. Chem.*, 37, 1042 (1965).
105. C. J. Thompson, H. J. Coleman, C. C. Ward, and H. T. Rall, *Anal. Chem.*, 32, 424 (1960).
106. C. J. Thompson, H. J. Coleman, C. C. Ward, and H. T. Rall, *Anal. Chem.*, 34, 151 (1962).
107. C. J. Thompson, H. J. Coleman, C. C. Ward, and H. T. Rall, *Anal. Chem.*, 34, 154 (1962).
108. P. R. Vagelos, W. J. A. VandenHeuvel, and M. G. Horning, *Anal. Biochem.*, 2, 50 (1961).
109. C. H. Van Middelem, T. L. Norwood, and R. E. Waites, *J. Gas Chromatog.*, 3, 310 (1965).
110. W. J. A. VandenHeuvel, W. L. Gardiner, and E. C. Horning, *Anal. Chem.*, 36, 1550 (1964).
111. W. J. A. VandenHeuvel, W. L. Gardiner, and E. C. Horning, *J. Chromatog.*, 18, 391 (1965).
112. W. J. A. VandenHeuvel, R. N. Stillwell, W. L. Gardiner, S. Wikstrom, and E. C. Horning, *J. Chromatog.*, 19, 22 (1965).
113. M. von Brenner and W. Huber, *Helv. Chim. Acta*, 36, 1109 (1953).
114. F. von Drawert, R. Felgenhauer, and G. Kupfer, *Angew. Chem.*, 72, 555 (1960).
115. K. von Rühlmann and W. Giesecke, *Angew. Chem.*, 73, 113 (1961).
116. M. L. Vorbeck, L. R. Mattick, F. A. Lee, and C. S. Pederson, *Anal. Chem.*, 33, 1512 (1961).
117. J. Wagner and G. Rausch, *Z. Anal. Chem.*, 194, 350 (1963).
118. H. P. Warrington, Jr., *Anal. Chem.*, 33, 1898 (1961).
119. J. P. Wein, private communication.

120. W. W. Wells, C. C. Sweeley, and R. Bentley, in *Biomedical Applications of Gas Chromatography*, H. A. Szymanski, Ed., Plenum Press, New York, 1964, pp. 169–223.

121. F. Weygand, B. Kolb, and P. Kirchner, *Z. Anal. Chem.*, **181**, 396 (1961).

122. F. Weygand, B. Kolb, A. Prox, M. A. Tilak, and I. Tomida, *Z. Physiol. Chem.*, **322**, 38 (1960).

123. Varian Aerograph, Division of Varian Associates, Walnut Creek, Calif.

124. C. M. Williams, *Anal. Biochem.*, **11**, 224 (1965).

124a. H. H. Wotiz and S. J. Clark, *Gas Chromatography in the Analysis of Steroid Hormones*, Plenum Press, New York, 1966.

125. C. G. Youngs, *Anal. Chem.*, **31**, 1019 (1959).

126. C. Zahn, A. G. Sharkey, Jr., and I. Wender, *Bur. Mines, Rept. Invest.*, **5976**, 1 (1962).

126a. A. Zlatkis and J. E. Lovelock, *Anal. Chem.*, **31** 620 (1959).

127. A. Zlatkis and J. F. Oro, *Anal. Chem.*, **30**, 1156 (1958).

128. A. Zlatkis, J. F. Oro, and A. P. Kimball, *Anal. Chem.*, **32**, 162 (1960).

129. C. Zomzely, G. Marco, and E. Emery, *Anal. Chem.*, **34**, 1414 (1962).

CHAPTER 4

Columns in Gas Chromatography

Csaba Horváth, *Yale University, New Haven, Connecticut*

I. Introduction

The column in which the separation of the sample components takes place is the core of gas chromatography. While instrumentation has been taken over largely by the manufacturers, the selection and also often the preparation of the column is still a task of the analyst, who has to make up for his particular analytical problem.

This chapter is written with particular regard to the practical analytical work. In this respect, the discussion of column parameters which determine efficiency, basic column technology, and techniques increasing column efficiency are considered to be more important than the theoretical aspects of gas chromatography. The reader interested in the theory of gas chromatography is referred to the excellent books of Dal Nogare and Juvet (1), Littlewood (2), Purnell (3), and Giddings (4), as well as to the original papers.

The column is a tube which holds the stationary phase fixed in a finely dispersed form, thus providing a large interfacing surface area with the mobile phase, that is, the carrier gas, in which the sample components move down the column.

In *elution gas chromatography*, which is discussed here, the vaporous sample is always applied as a "plug" into the carrier gas stream at one end of the column. Its components, described as solutes, will be distributed between the mobile and stationary phases; they emerge as more or less separated bands at the other end of the column and are recorded as peaks on the chromatogram. Gas chromatography in general, and thus the columns also, are divided into the following three major categories by the nature of the stationary phase:

Gas–Solid Chromatography (GSC). The stationary phase is a solid with a high specific surface area, like silica gel, alumina, molecular sieve, organic polymers, etc. At the beginning of gas chromatography, GSC was regarded to be limited to the separation of highly volatile and nonpolar samples only. Recent developments, however, show that less volatile and even polar samples can be separated with the use of specially prepared adsorbents, novel column types, and highly sensitive detectors. This technique is also called *gas adsorption chromatography* and the columns referred to as adsorption columns.

Gas–Liquid Chromatography (GLC). The stationary phase in this technique is a liquid distributed on an inert support. This technique is generally applicable and is mainly responsible for the tremendous development of gas chromatography. For this reason, GLC has often been referred to as *the* gas chromatography. This technique is also frequently called *gas–liquid partition chromatography* and the columns as partition columns. The overwhelming majority of the gas chromatographic analyses has been done by using liquid stationary phases.

Gas–Solid–Liquid Chromatography (GSLC). The stationary phase is a synergetic combination of an adsorbent and a liquid. Either the surface of an adsorbent is impregnated with a liquid or a liquid is compounded with a colloidal solid. This technique may be considered as GSC with a modified adsorbent or GLC with a liquid altered by an active solid. In any case the combination results in a new kind of stationary phase. So far, such columns have been only infrequently used purposely. However, the unintentional use of such stationary phases is more common than assumed because of support activity in GLC or contamination of the adsorbent surface in GSC.

Gas chromatography is best understood, and the study of column parameters is least complicated, if the column is operated isothermally at constant inlet pressure. This mode of operation is most common in practice and forms the basis of most discussions in the present chapter. However, if samples must be analyzed which have components with a wide boiling-point range, the employment of programming or grouping techniques— i.e., programmed temperature gas chromatography, back-flushing, etc.—may be of great practical advantage. These techniques are described at the end of this chapter.

II. Column Types According to Their Construction

In order to exploit the potentialities of gas chromatography many column types have been developed, and the design as well as the preparation of columns has been a major section of gas chromatography, described as column technology. It involves finding the proper combination of the stationary phase and column construction for solving a particular separation problem. In the term "construction" we include the length and principally all features of the cross section of the column except the nature of the stationary phase, e.g., tube diameter, structure of the support, the volume ratio of the stationary phase to the mobile phase, etc. Based on their construction, columns are divided into two major groups: packed and open tubular columns.

A. Packed Columns

A packed column is essentially a packed bed in a tubular envelope. The tube is filled with a granular *column material*, and the carrier gas is forced through the interstitial channel system (Fig. 4-1) of the packing. Generally, the wider the diameter of the tube and the higher the amount of stationary phase per unit column length, the larger the maximum tolerable sample size. Therefore, if sample components are to be recovered or the sensitivity of the detector is low, relatively large diameter columns and heavy loadings are used. On the other hand, high column performance can be obtained with small diameter columns and light stationary phase loading, and such columns are preferred for analytical work with sensitive

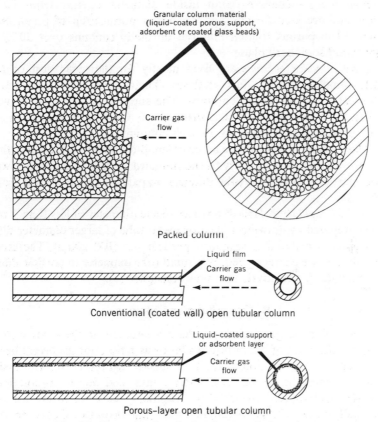

Fig. 4-1. Structure of packed and open tubular columns.

detectors. The column material may be the adsorbent itself (GSC), or an inactive granular support impregnated with the liquid stationary phase (GLC). The support is either a porous material such as diatomaceous earth or a compact material such as glass microbeads. The length of packed columns is usually 1–3 m, but lengths up to 30 m or even higher have also been reported.

1. Standard packed columns are constructed of metal or glass tubing and have 2–9-mm inside diameter. The tube is packed with a granular porous column material impregnated with 5–30% by weight liquid stationary phase or with a granular adsorbent. The particle size of the column material is most commonly between 100 and 600 μ. At least 80% of the gas chromatographic work is done with such columns at the present time.

2. Preparative columns have an inside diameter ranging from 10 to 300 mm and are used for the separation and purification of preparative amounts. The porous column material normally contains over 20% by weight liquid stationary phase.

3. Lightly loaded columns are used mostly for the separation of less volatile samples and for fast analyses. Their dimensions are similar to those of standard packed columns. The support is impregnated with less than 5% by weight liquid stationary phase. Glass microbeads are frequently used as support material in such columns.

*4. Micro packed columns** are made of small-diameter tube, i.d. less than 1 mm, which is packed similarly to the standard packed columns, but with smaller particles so that the tube diameter to particle diameter ratio is also similar (5).

*5. Packed capillary columns** have an inside diameter of less than 1 mm and are prepared by drawing a glass or metal tube of larger diameter filled with a column material of standard particle size (100–200 μ). Therefore, these columns are characterized by a small tube diameter to particle diameter ratio and by a relatively low flow resistance (6).

B. Open Tubular Columns

In these columns, the stationary phase is situated on the inner wall of the tube in the form of a thin liquid film or as a thin porous layer; hence the carrier gas flow is unobstructed, as shown in Figure 4-1. The inside diameter of the tube is generally under 1 mm, and due to its smallness these columns are often described as "capillary" columns. They are also occasionally named Golay columns, after their inventor. Golay pointed out (7) that not the smallness but the openness is the characteristic feature of this column type, and actually a long, empty pipeline whose inner wall is coated with an oil could be compared to and used as an open tubular column. In earlier stages of gas chromatography, however, the small inner diameter, which required handling of small samples and highly sensitive detectors, was considered the most distinguishing attribute of these columns.

1. Standard open tubular columns have a thin liquid film on the inner wall and usually 0.25–0.50-mm (0.010–0.020 in.) inside diameter. Columns having smaller bore (i.d. 0.1 mm) may be used for fast analyses of very

---

* This nomenclature is, of course, relative. By the selection of these terms, the original authors tried to indicate that columns of the first category are close to "packed" columns while the columns of the second category have a performance closer to that of the "capillary" columns.

small samples (8), while larger bore columns (i.d. up to 2 mm) are used with less sensitive detectors or for semipreparative work (9).

2. Porous layer open tubular columns have a similar inner diameter. The porous layer on the inner wall can be rendered by chemical treatment or deposited from a supension. The stationary phase is either the solid itself (GSC) or the layer is impregnated with a liquid phase (GLC).

Open tubular columns have a low flow resistance which permits the use of very long columns with high resolution. In practice, column length varies from 15 to 100 m (50–300 ft). The sample capacity of standard columns is very low, in the order of 10^{-6} g, due to the small amount of stationary phase per unit column length. Porous layer open tubular columns contain a relatively larger amount of stationary phase in a given column segment and therefore have a significantly higher sample capacity than standard open tubular columns.

For details on open tubular columns, the reader is referred to the treatise of Ettre (10).

III. Retention of a Single Solute

A. Measurement of Retention

1. Retention Times

Figure 4-2 illustrates the chromatogram of a single solute. A sample consisting of the solute and some inert gas enters the column at time *0*, the starting point of the chromatogram. The inert gas does not interact with the stationary phase and emerges at point *A* with the carrier gas, which entered the column with the sample. Consequently, time t_A measured

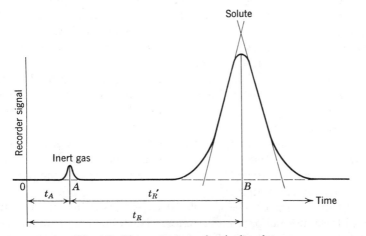

Fig. 4-2. Chromatogram of a single solute.

from the starting point 0 to the inert gas peak maximum A is equal to the time needed by the carrier gas to move from one end of the column to the other and is called *retention time of an unsorbed gas* or *retention time of the unretained solute*. Since air is used most conveniently for the determination of t_A, the inert gas peak is often called the *air peak* and t_A described as the *air peak time*.

The solute is retarded by the stationary phase and emerges later than the inert gas; this shows as a peak which is, in the ideal case, Gaussian in shape. The maximum of the solute peak is at point B on the time scale. The position of this peak on the chromatogram is defined by the following two parameters:

Retention time of the solute, t_R, is the time that elapses between the injection of the sample and the recording of the peak maximum. It is equal to the distance $0B$ in Figure 4-2. The retention time is a fundamental value and has great practical importance as the expression for the analysis time of the solute.

Adjusted retention time of the solute, t'_R, is the time that elapses between the emergence of the inert gas and the solute peak maxima. It is equal to the distance AB. Thus

$$t'_R = t_R - t_A \qquad (4\text{-}1)$$

and

$$t_R = t_A + t'_R \qquad (4\text{-}2)$$

Equation 4-2 expresses the fact that the retention time of a solute, i.e., the time required for the solute to pass through the column, is the sum of the time spent by the solute in the gas phase, t_A, and the time during which the solute is sorbed by the stationary phase, t'_R. Hence, t_A is often described as the *gas holdup time* and t'_R as the *liquid holdup time* when liquid stationary phase is used. In practice it is usually sufficient to compare retention times on the same chromatogram and to use the corresponding *retention distances* on the chart paper.

Retention time of the unretained solute is usually measured by injecting some air or inert gas with the sample or in a different run. Some detectors do not respond to air (e.g., flame ionization detector); in such cases methane is often used as a substitute with tolerable error in practical work, at least in GLC at higher temperatures. With a large inert gas sample, particularly when hydrogen is used as carrier gas, the flame ionization detector also gives a signal (11). In GSC or GSLC, neither methane nor air can be considered as an inert gas.

Gas holdup time can be calculated by extrapolation of the retention time of lower normal paraffin homologs. The following procedure is given by Peterson and Hirsch (12). Peaks of three homologs the carbon numbers of which satisfy the relation $z_2 - z_1 = z_3 - z_2$ have to appear on the chromatogram. The distances from an arbitrary point to their peak maxima (x_1, x_2, x_3) are measured, and the point corresponding to the "air peak" is obtained by its distance from the arbitrary point, y, which is calculated by the following equation:

$$y = (x_2{}^2 - x_3 x_1)/(x_3 + x_1 - 2x_2) \qquad (4\text{-}3)$$

A similar method described by Gold (13) permits the use of any three homologs.

Retention time of the solute varies with the sample size above a critical amount. Generally, t_R decreases with the increase of the sample amount, and for accurate measurement correction must be made by the extrapolation of t_R to zero sample size. The critical sample amount depends largely on the column construction and operating conditions.

So far, it has been assumed that t_A and t_R were retention times attributed only to the column. However, these values as obtained from the chromatogram are larger, due to holdup by the volume of the sampling device, detector, and other extracolumn volumes, V_D, also termed the *dead volume* of the chromatographic systems. When the apparatus is properly designed, the error is usually small and may be neglected in practical work. For calculation of the adjusted retention time, t'_R, no correction for *extra column holdup time*, t_D, is necessary, since

$$t'_R = t_R - t_A = (t_R + t_D) - (t_A + t_D) \qquad (4\text{-}4)$$

where t_A and t_R are the retention times due to the column only.

2. Retention Volumes

The volume of the carrier gas which flows through the column during the retention time is described as the retention volume. In practical work, the use of retention times is mostly adequate. However, the employment of corrected retention volumes is necessary when gas chromatographic data should be connected to physicochemical quantities.

Retention volumes are calculated from the corresponding retention times and from the flow rate of the carrier gas. Due to the pressure drop across the column and the compressibility of the carrier gas, the actual flow rate varies from point to point in the column and it is smaller than the outlet flow rate at column temperature F_c. In order to obtain the true gas volume which flows through the column in a given time, F_c must be corrected to zero pressure drop with the gas compressibility correction factor, j; this is discussed in the Chapter 2. Retention volumes are also calculated without correction for gas compressibility and are often used in practice.

These uncorrected retention volumes, described simply as retention volumes in the literature, designate that gas volume at column temperature which emerges from the column at outlet pressure in the retention time.

The following terms are used most frequently:

Retention volume of the inert gas, V_A, is described as the gas holdup of the column and calculated as

$$V_A = t_A F_c \qquad (4\text{-}5)$$

Corrected retention volume of the inert gas, V_M, is equal to the free space in the column and given by

$$V_M = V_A j = t_A F_c j \qquad (4\text{-}6)$$

Retention volume of the solute, V_R, is expressed as

$$V_R = t_R F_c \qquad (4\text{-}7)$$

Corrected retention volume of the solute, V_R^o, is obtained by conversion of V_R by application of the compressibility correction:

$$V_R^o = V_R j = t_R F_c j \qquad (4\text{-}8)$$

Adjusted retention volume, V_R', is calculated from the adjusted retention time as

$$V_R' = t_R' F_c = (t_R - t_A) F_c \qquad (4\text{-}9)$$

thus

$$V_R' = V_R - V_A \qquad (4\text{-}10)$$

Net retention volume, V_N, is the corrected adjusted retention volume

$$V_N = V_R' j = V_R^o - V_M = (t_R - t_A) F_c j = t_R' F_c j \qquad (4\text{-}11)$$

Retention volumes cannot be calculated in this simple manner when flow or temperature-programmed techniques are used, since the flow rate or the inlet pressure usually varies during elution.

B. Factors Determining Retention

1. Equilibrium Constant

The solute entering the column in the carrier gas is partly sorbed by the stationary phase to achieve equilibrium where the free energy of the solute molecules is the same in both phases. As a result of the gas flow, the solute band moves with a velocity determined by the carrier gas velocity and by the ratio of the nonsorbed fraction to the whole amount of solute.

Due to the dynamic nature of the chromatographic process this equilibrium is not established in any microscopical part of the column, and the nonequilibrium is the major cause of band broadening. However, the position of the peak maximum is related to the equilibrium, which would be complete if the flow ceased, so that solute retention is connected to a constant characteristic for the equilibrium.

In the practice of gas chromatography, this equilibrium constant is defined as the ratio of the solute concentration in or on the stationary phase to the solute concentration in the carrier gas at a given temperature. The quantity is independent of the solute concentration in the concentration range where the sorption isotherm is linear. For an unretained component, the equilibrium constant is evidently equal to zero.

There are many possible ways to express concentration and several expressions have been introduced to characterize the equilibrium between the solute sorbed by the stationary phase and its vapor. These are physicochemical constants related to the net retention volume under isotherm conditions. The most fundamental form is the dimensionless *partition coefficient*, K, which is used in GLC. By definition

$$K = \frac{\text{amount of solute per volume of stationary phase}}{\text{amount of solute per volume of mobile phase}}$$

and may be calculated from gas the chromatographic data according to the following equation:

$$K = V_N/V_L = V_N \rho_S/W_S \qquad (4\text{-}12)$$

where V_N is the net retention volume, V_L is the volume, W_S is the weight of liquid stationary phase present in the column, and ρ_S is the density of the stationary phase at the reference temperature.

Another more practical expression is the *specific retention volume*, V_g, defined as

$$V_g = \frac{\text{amount of solute per gram of stationary phase}}{\text{amount of solute per milliliter of gas at } 0°C}$$

and has the dimension of milliliter per gram. It is called the specific retention volume because this quantity is equal to the net retention volume, corrected to 0°C as reference temperature, per gram of liquid stationary phase in the column:

$$V_g = (V_N/W_S)(273/T) \qquad (4\text{-}13)$$

where T is the absolute temperature of the column.

This parameter is widely used, because the often burdensome determination of the density of the stationary phase is not necessary for its calculation, in contrast to that of the partition coefficient. However, the determination of the exact amount of stationary phase in the column may give rise to some difficulties. Partition coefficient and specific retention volume are related by the following equation:

$$K = V_g \rho_S T / 273 \qquad (4\text{-}14)$$

The following expression has been suggested for the equilibrium constant in GSC (14):

$$U_a = \frac{\text{amount of solute per gram of stationary phase}}{\text{amount of solute per milliliter gas at column temperature}}$$

which has the same dimension as the specific retention volume and is calculated as

$$U_g = V_N / W_S \qquad (4\text{-}15)$$

where W_S is the weight of adsorbent in the column.

When adsorption takes place, the equilibrium concentrations of the solute are determined rather by the surface area than by the volume or weight of the adsorbent, and it is more meaningful to define the equilibrium by

$$K_a = \frac{\text{amount of solute per square meter of adsorbent surface}}{\text{amount of solute per milliliter of gas}}$$

This constant corresponds to the net retention volume per unit surface area of the stationary phase and has the dimension milliliters per square meter. Thus

$$K_a = V_N / A_S = V_N / W_S \delta_S = U_g / \delta_S \qquad (4\text{-}16)$$

where A_S is the adsorbent surface area present in the column in square centimeters and δ_S is the specific surface area of the stationary phase in square centimeters per gram. A_S is calculated from W_S and δ_S. The latter may be obtained by the procedure described by Eggertsen and Nelsen (15). For adsorbents with homogeneous surface, such as graphitized carbon black and specially treated silica gel, Kiselev et al. have found K_a to be independent of δ_S (16).

Thus, the net retention volume is related to the various expressions of the equilibrium constant by

$$V_N = K V_L = K W_S \rho_S = V_g W_S (273/T) = U_g W_S = K_a A_S \quad (4\text{-}17)$$

When absorption and adsorption are concurring in establishing equilibrium, the net retention volume of a solute may be written as

$$V_N = K V_L + K_a A_L \qquad (4\text{-}18)$$

where A_L is the surface area of the liquid phase.

In GLC, when the surface tension of the liquid phase decreases with adsorption of solute on the liquid surface, K_a becomes significant and, according to the suggestion of Martin (17), equation 4-18 has to be used.

Such separation of distribution coefficients is also justified when an adsorbent and liquid independently contribute to the equilibrium, that is, the individual distribution coefficients are not affected by interaction between the solid and liquid. Bruner and Cartoni (19) reported that on etched glass open tubular columns coated with different amounts of squalane, the contribution of adsorption and absorption could be treated separately except at very low loading.

When column temperature varies during a chromatographic run, as in temperature-programmed gas chromatography, there is no such simple relationship between the net retention volume and the equilibrium constant, since the latter varies with the temperature.

The temperature dependence of the equilibrium constant is given by the Clausius–Clapeyron equation from which it follows, by simplifying assumptions, for a relatively small temperature interval that

$$\log V_g = -\Delta H/2.3RT + c \qquad (4\text{-}19)$$

where ΔH is the heat of solution or heat of adsorption, T is the absolute temperature, and R and c are constant.

Correlation plots of $\log V_g$ or $\log K_a$ against the reciprocal absolute temperature of the column usually give a straight line as shown in Figures 4-3 and 4-4, and may be used for the determination of ΔH or for estimation of V_g at other temperatures.

The phase equilibrium is related to various thermodynamic quantities, and the exact measurement of the equilibrium constant has become important in the nonanalytical application of gas chromatography for obtaining such physical data as vapor pressure, activity coefficients, free energy, entropy, etc. Nevertheless, such measurements require carefully selected conditions usually not present in practical analytical work.

Retention Plots. There is often a linear relationship between some physicochemical properties (heat of evaporation, boiling point, etc.) and the number of carbon atoms or other structural units in members of homologous series. Frequently the logarithm of the equilibrium constant also changes linearly with the number of fundamental structural units. In such cases straight lines are obtained by plotting the logarithm of isothermal adjusted retention volumes or times against the number of structural units, as shown in Figure 4-5.

In qualitative analysis, such retention plots have great practical importance for the estimation of retention values or for the tentative identification

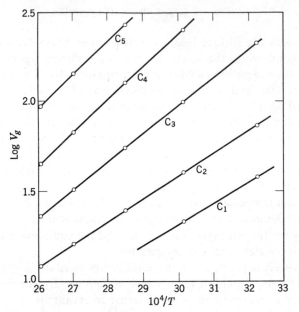

Fig. 4-3. Plots of log V_g against reciprocal absolute temperature. Samples: normal alkyl alcohols. Stationary phase: silicone oil 702. Temperature range: 30–110°C (18).

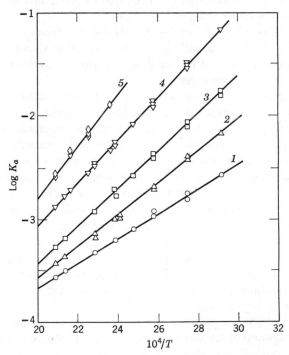

Fig. 4-4. Plot of log K_a against reciprocal absolute temperature for alkanols on graphitized carbon black. *1*, methanol; *2*, ethanol; *3*, n-propanol; *4*, n-butanol; *5*, n-pentanol (20).

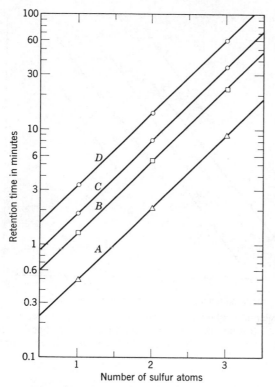

Fig. 4-5. Log retention time vs. number of sulfur atoms for mono-, di-, and tri-
sulfides (21). *A*, Dimethyl; *B*, allyl methyl; *C*, di-*n*-propyl; *D*, diallyl.

of peaks. The Kováts' retention-index system is also based on the good
linear relation between the logarithms of adjusted retention volumes and
the carbon numbers of normal alkanes.

A refinement of the retention data plots is to measure the retention
values on two columns having different polarity and plot their logarithms
against each other. Figure 4-6 shows that for homologous series straight
lines are obtained. By using such two-column plots, valuable information
can be obtained on homologous series in a given sample.

2. Partition Ratio and Phase Ratio

The distribution of the solute by quantity between the stationary and
mobile phases is expressed by the dimensionless *partition ratio, k*. It is defined as

$$k = \frac{\text{amount of solute in the stationary phase}}{\text{amount of solute in the mobile phase}}$$

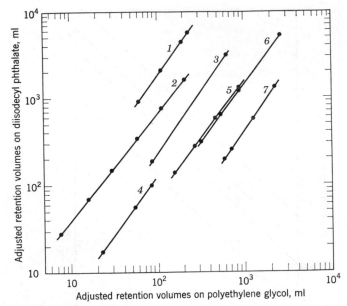

Fig. 4-6. Log retention volumes on diisodecyl phthalate vs. log retention volumes on polyethylene glycol (Carbowax 1500) measured at 100°C. *1*, Benzene homologs; *2*, normal paraffins; *3*, ethers; *4*, acetylenes; *5*, aldehydes; *6*, ketones; *7*, normal primary alcohols.

and is measured by the ratio of the net retention volume, V_N, to the gas volume of the column, V_M,

$$k = V_N/V_M \tag{4-20}$$

Comparison of equations 4-12 and 4-20 shows that in GLC

$$k = KV_L/V_M \tag{4-21}$$

i.e., the partition ratio is proportional to the partition coefficient and to the volume ratio of the stationary and mobile phases in the column. Similarly, in GSC k may be expressed from equations 4-16 and 4-20 as

$$k = K_a A_S/V_M \tag{4-22}$$

The ratio of the gas volume to the volume of the stationary phase, β, is a characteristic value of column construction and may be called the *phase ratio* of the column:

$$\beta = V_M/V_L \tag{4-23}$$

Hence,

$$k = K/\beta \tag{4-24}$$

For a given solute, the phase ratio is usually constant along the column except gradient-loaded columns (22), but can be substantially different in various column types. It is not independent of column temperature when the volume of stationary phase changes. The partition ratio is easily calculated from the chromatogram (Fig. 4-2) if the flow rate was maintained constant:

$$k = V_N/V_M = (t_R - t_A)/t_A = t'_R/t_A = (t_R/t_A) - 1 \qquad (4\text{-}25)$$

The value of k defines the position of a peak relative to the starting point as well as to the "air peak" and it is an important parameter both for peak identification and for evaluating the separation efficiency of the column.

The *retardation factor*, R_f, is frequently employed for defining band position in other chromatographic techniques. This quantity is related to the partition ratio by

$$R_f = 1/(1 + k) \quad \text{or} \quad k = (1 - R_f)/R_f \qquad (4\text{-}26)$$

The partition ratio may be also interpreted as the ratio of the solute residence time in the stationary phase to that in the gas phase and the retention as well as the velocity of a solute can be expressed by the following equations:

$$V_R = V_A(1 + k) = V_A/R_f \qquad (4\text{-}27)$$

$$t_R = t_A(1 + k) = t_A/R_f \qquad (4\text{-}28)$$

$$\bar{u}_R = \bar{u}(1 + k) = \bar{u}R_f \qquad (4\text{-}29)$$

where $\bar{u}_R$ and $\bar{u}$ are the average respective linear velocity values of the retained and unretained solutes.

The partition ratio of a solute in a given column varies with the temperature mostly due to change in the value of the equilibrium constant. Thus, in temperature programming, k is a function of the temperature range and of the program. The phase ratio, β, may vary considerably with the column construction. Standard open tubular columns coated with a liquid stationary phase and low-loaded packed columns have high phase ratios ($\beta = 100–1000$) while standard packed columns are characterized by low values ($\beta = 5–20$). Table 4-1 shows some β and k values typical in GLC columns.

The partition ratio of a solute connects the equilibrium constant, which is characteristic for the solute–stationary phase interaction, with the phase ratio, which is related to the column construction. It can be used in correlation plots instead of equilibrium constants or retention values. The partition ratio is the basic parameter to characterize retention. It is also termed in the literature as the *capacity ratio, capacity factor*, or *distribution ratio*.

TABLE 4-1
Some Typical β and k Values

Packed columns			Per cent liquid per weight	β	Ref.	Partition ratio, k, at	
Column	Support	Particle size, mm				$K = 50$	$K = 1000$
Standard	Chromosorb	0.15–0.17	16	7	23	7.1	143
Low loaded	Chromosorb	0.15–0.17	1	205	23	0.24	4.9
Low loaded	Glass beads	0.15–0.17	0.05	417	23	0.12	2.4

Open tubular columns	Tube i.d., mm	Film thickness, μ	β	Ref.	Partition ratio, k, at	
					$K = 50$	$K = 1000$
Standard (liquid coated)	0.25	0.578	123	—[a]	0.41	8.1
Standard (liquid coated)	0.25	0.147	405	—[a]	0.12	2.4
Porous layer (liquid impregnated)	0.50	—	35.5	24	1.4	28

[a] Calculated.

IV. Relative Retention

A. Definition

The previously discussed expressions of the equilibrium constant have found limited applications in practical utilization of gas chromatography. Their calculation requires the knowledge of certain values (e.g., amount, density, or surface area of the stationary phase in the column) generally not known, and the exact measurement and correction of flow rate and correction for extracolumn dead volume, which are difficult and time consuming. However, these factors cancel out when the retention of a solute is measured relative to that of a reference solute on the same column and under the same conditions. For this reason the most widespread method used today for presenting retention data utilizes relative retention data. In most cases, the reference substance is actually part of the sample and the relative retention is obtained directly from the chromatogram. Thus, the determination is simplified to the measurement of the appropriate distances on the recorder chart paper.

The relative retention of solute 2 to solute 1, $\alpha_{2,1}$, is in fact the ratio of the corresponding equilibrium constants of the two solutes:

$$\alpha_{2,1} = K_2/K_1 = V_{g2}/V_{g1} = U_{g2}/U_{g1} = K_{a_2}/K_{a_1} \qquad (4\text{-}30)$$

In the same column, the relative retention is also given by the ratio of the two partition ratios k_1 and k_2

$$\alpha_{2,1} = k_2/k_1 \tag{4-31}$$

and measured as

$$\alpha_{2,1} = V_{N2}/V_{N1} = t'_{R2}/t'_{R1} \tag{4-32}$$

Symbol $\alpha_{2,1}$ is used for the description of the relative retention of any two solutes. By definition, the faster moving solute 1 is used as reference so that the value of $\alpha_{2,1}$ is always greater than one. Retention values related to a given standard are expressed by the symbol r. For example, the relative retention of diethyl ether using n-pentane as standard is denoted as: diethyl ether r_{nC_5} or $r_{\text{diethyl ether}/nC_5}$.

Relative retention measured as t'_{R2}/t'_{R1}, is in agreement with the definition given by equation 4-30 only under isotherm, constant flow conditions. Relative retention may also be meaningful in programmed gas chromatography as an expression of the relative retention times or distances of two peaks on the chromatogram and is subject of correlation studies. However, in practice, in such cases, it is very much dependent on instrumental constants and therefore data obtained in a given system cannot be transferred to other systems without corrections.

The term *relative volatility* is sometimes used for relative retention although its original meaning is the ratio of the vapor pressures of two components in the distillation theory. While the relative retention is equal to the relative volatility of the sorbed components, it may be different from the relative vapor pressures of the pure solutes as a consequence of their interaction with the stationary phase. Since this interaction is often predominant, the relative retention should rather be attributed to the stationary phase and consider as its *selectivity* for the solute pair in question.

If the relative retention of two solutes and the equilibrium constant of one are known, the equilibrium constant of the other may be calculated according to equation 4-30. For example, the specific retention volume of solute 2, V_{g2}, if V_{g1} is known is given by

$$V_{g2} = \alpha_{2,1}V_{g1} \tag{4-33}$$

B. Effect of Temperature

The temperature dependence of the relative retention can be expressed as

$$\log \alpha = (a/T) + b \tag{4-34}$$

where T is the absolute column temperature and a and b are constants. Very often $a > 0$ and thus the relative retention increases with decreasing temperature. For a large number of similar substances Scott (25) found $a \simeq 0$, in which case the relative retention remains practically constant while the temperature is changed. Infrequently a/T becomes smaller than b when the temperature changes, and thus the order of peaks is reversed.

This variation of the relative retention with temperature, molecular structure of the solutes, etc., is similar to that of the equilibrium constant or of the retention volumes. Therefore, linear plots of log relative retention versus carbon number or reciprocal absolute temperature can be obtained

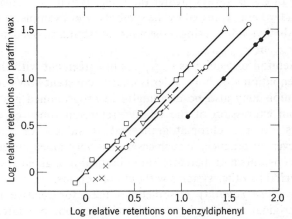

Fig. 4-7. Two solvents plot of log relative retention data for various hydrocarbons at 78.6°C (26). □, Branched aliphatics; ×, olefins; ○, naphthenes; ●, aromatics; △, naphthenes with side chains; ▵, straight-chain aliphatics.

in many cases and used in much the same way as the various graphs shown previously. Figure 4-7 shows that the plots of logarithms of relative retentions measured in two different stationary phases also result in straight lines for members of a given homologous series.

C. Measurement

According to equation 4-32 relative retention $\alpha_{2,1}$ is obtained as the ratio of the net or adjusted retention volumes, $V_{N2}/V_{N1} = V'_{R2}/V'_{R1}$, but more conveniently as the ratio of the adjusted retention times t'_{R2}/t'_{R1}.

It is important to note that t'_{R1} and t'_{R2} are the distances from the "air peak" to the solute peaks on the recorder chart paper and that no correction is necessary for extra column holdup time as is shown by equation 4-4.

In packed columns having a low phase ratio, for slowly moving components, $t_A \ll t'_R$. Consequently, $t_R \simeq t'_R$, and the error in measuring $\alpha_{2,1}$ by using the ratio t_{R2}/t_{R1} may be negligible.

When relative retention is measured in order to report retention data or to study interaction between solutes and stationary phase, the reproducibility of the measurement is paramount. Some of the possible error sources which should be taken into consideration are discussed below:

1. Adsorption by the support or tube wall influences retention values particularly if polar samples are analyzed on a column with nonpolar liquid stationary phase, but the effect can also be observed with other solute–stationary phase systems. The absence of this effect can be verified when the relative retention values, measured on two or more columns containing different amounts of the liquid phase, are identical.

2. If the *sample size* is increased to such an extent that the column is overloaded, relative retention values will alter because of deviation from the linear distribution isotherm, mutual interaction between solutes or flow rate effect, etc. Therefore, the smallest conveniently measurable sample must be used in retention measurements or the retention times should be extrapolated to zero sample size.

3. The purity of the stationary phase also influences the results. Source and grade must be specified unambiguously. Changes in the chemical composition of the phase may occur in the column by oxidation, thermal decomposition, polymerization, etc. Even small amounts of contaminants can cause significant changes in retention values. In order to prevent altering of the stationary phase, overheating of the column should be avoided and the removal of even traces of oxygen from the carrier gas is strongly recommended. In GSC, the history of the column material can influence retention values considerably.

4. Uniform column temperature is necessary for obtaining correct data. Unfortunately, in some instruments the column temperature is not uniform and the measured relative retention is different from that which corresponds to the temperature indicated by the meter of the instrument.

5. If a solute peak contains an *unresolved impurity*, the measured retention time may be different from that of the pure substance because of a possible shift of the peak maximum. This fact stresses the importance of using pure substances or high-performance columns for the determination of relative retention values.

V. Column Permeability

In order to force the carrier gas through the column, a pressure drop is necessary. The gas velocity is determined by the column length, pressure drop, and gas viscosity, and by the column permeability, which is a characteristic of the construction.

The linear flow velocity of the carrier gas is one of the most important operating parameters in gas chromatography due to its effect on column performance and speed of analysis.

In columns packed with porous column material the carrier gas is considered to be moving only in the interparticle volume, V_i, which is calculated from the interparticle porosity, ϵ, and the empty tube volume, V_c, by

$$V_i = \epsilon V_c \tag{4-35}$$

Thus, the average linear velocity of the carrier gas, $\bar{u}_g$, is given as

$$\bar{u}_g = F_c j L / \epsilon V_c \tag{4-36}$$

The average linear velocity of the unretained solute, $\bar{u}$, is often used in practice. Since the solute explores not only the moving interparticle volume but also the total gas volume of the column, V_M, in columns containing porous packing $\bar{u}_g$ and $\bar{u}$ are different. The total gas volume, V_M, is expressed by the total porosity of the packing, a, as

$$V_M = a V_c \tag{4-37}$$

and

$$\bar{u} = F_c j L / a V_c \tag{4-38}$$

Comparison of equations 4-36 and 4-38 shows that the two flow velocities are related by

$$\bar{u}_g = a \bar{u} / \epsilon \tag{4-39}$$

The measurement of $\bar{u}$ does not require knowledge of porosity because it is obtained very conveniently from the column length and the retention time of the unretained solute (air peak time) by

$$\bar{u} = L / t_A \tag{4-40}$$

In columns packed with glass beads and in standard open tubular columns the total gas volume can be considered to be moving, thus

$$\bar{u}_g = \bar{u} \tag{4-41}$$

Packing with usual column materials yields $\epsilon = 0.38$–0.42, indicating a normal mode of random packing, so that the moving gas occupies approximately 60% of the total volume of any packed column. The total porosity, a, depends on the structure of the column material. Dal Nogare and Juvet (1) found $a \simeq 0.8$ in columns packed with Chromosorb P, which means that about 80% of the total column volume is occupied with gas and one-half of the gas volume is moving.

The permeability of the column is expressed by the *specific permeability coefficient*, B_0, given by the following equation (27):

$$B_0 = 2\eta \epsilon L p_o u_0 / (p_i^2 - p_o^2) \qquad (4\text{-}42)$$

where p_i and p_o are the inlet and outlet pressures, η is the viscosity of the carrier gas, L is the length of the column, and u_0 is equal to $F_c L / V_c$ and can be calculated from F_c and the tube dimensions. It can be shown that $u_0 = \bar{u} a / j$; thus B_0 may also be calculated from the air peak time if a is known.

B_0 is a measure of the openness of the column cross section and has the dimension of square centimeters. In order to obtain the right dimension, the quantities in equation 4-42 must be measured in the proper units: L in centimeters, η in poises (dyn sec cm^{-2}), p_1 and p_o in bars (dyn cm^{-2}).

The inlet pressure is limited in gas chromatographs, and thus the permeability determines the maximum column length which can be operated at a desired linear flow velocity. As shown in Table 4-2 the permeability

TABLE 4-2
Permeability of Various Columns without Liquid Stationary Phase

	Packed Columns		
Column	Particle diameter, mm	B_0, cm$^2 \times 10^7$	Ref.
Alumina	0.10–0.15	1.0	24
Chromosorb R	0.15–0.177	1.96	23
Sterchamol	0.15–0.177	2.7	28
Chromosorb R, silanized	0.35–0.42	9.54	23
Chromosorb R, silanized	0.50–0.59	21.4	23
Glass capillary packed with alumina	0.10–0.15	10.0	24

Open Tubular Columns	
Tube diameter, mm	B_0,[a] cm$^2 \times 10^{-7}$
0.10	31
0.25	195
0.50	780

[a] Calculated by equation 4-44.

varies strongly with the column type, with the particle size and the tube diameter in packed and open tubular columns, respectively.

The permeability of packed columns is a function of the effective particle diameter d_p and the interparticle porosity of the packing, but is independent of the tube diameter, as given by the Kozeny-Carman equation (27):

$$B_0 = d_p^2 \epsilon^3 / 180(1 - \epsilon)^2 \qquad (4\text{-}43)$$

Due to the dependence of the permeability on the square of the effective particle diameter, the pressure drop required to maintain a given flow velocity at a given column length increases rapidly with the decrease of the particle size.

The permeability of open tubular columns can be calculated by the Hagen-Poiseuille equation and obtained as

$$B_0 = d^2/32 \qquad (4\text{-}44)$$

where d is the inner diameter of the tube. This relation is valid only for ideal tubes of entirely uniform and smooth bore and for laminar flow. Although the carrier gas flow in both packed and open tubular columns can be considered as laminar under conditions prevailing in analytical work, open tubular columns are not ideal capillary tubes. As a consequence the actual permeability of standard open tubular columns obtained by flow measurement is about 10–20% less than the permeability calculated by equation 4-44. Porous-layer open tubular columns, of course, have significantly lower permeability than calculated from the inside tube diameter.

Generally, open tubular columns have permeability 10–100 times higher than that of packed columns; thus their operating length can be greater with the same factor.

VI. Column Efficiency

A. Expression of Column Efficiency

Provided there is no instrumental deficiency, the separation of a given sample as it is recorded on the chromatogram is the basic measure of column efficiency. It is the result of the complex chromatographic process where stationary phase–solute interaction, parameters of column construction, and conditions are interrelated. Due to the multiplicity of nonindependent variables, quantitative measures derived from the chromatogram for characterizing column effectiveness are restricted to a given set of conditions.

The interpretation of column efficiency is most convenient when the column is operated at constant temperature and flow rate. Column

efficiency may be defined by considering either a particular pair of components, which is convenient for a specific case, or a single solute only,
which leads to more general information on overall column effectiveness,
since the selectivity of the stationary phase is not involved.

1. Single Peak: Plate Height and Plate Number

The efficiency of the column is related to the relative broadness of
the peaks which appear on the chromatogram.

While it is being eluted from one end of the column to the other, the
solute band broadens. This process is chiefly attributed to the fact that the
equilibration of the solute between the mobile and stationary phases does
not take place instantaneously and diffusion of solute molecules occurs
along the column axis.

The result of the band spreading in ideal cases is a normal distribution of
the solute molecules in the carrier gas, and therefore the concentration
peak appears on the recorder chart paper in the form of a Gaussian curve.

a. Measurement of the Bandwidth. A normal distribution is usually
measured by the standard deviation, σ, which is related to the width of the
Gaussian curve. Figure 4-8 shows the widths of a Gaussian peak measured
at different heights expressed by the standard deviation. For practical
calculations, the peak width at three different heights is of importance.

The *peak width at the inflexion points* (w_i):

$$w_i = 2\sigma \tag{4-45}$$

The *peak width at half-height* (w_h):

$$w_h = 2\sigma(2 \ln 2)^{1/2} = 2.355\sigma \tag{4-46}$$

The so-called *peak width at base* (w) or *band intercept* which is equal to
the length cut out from the base line by the two tangents drawn to the
inflection point of the peak:

$$w = 4\sigma \tag{4-47}$$

Since all three peak widths are multiples of the standard deviation, they
are also related to each other, for example,

$$w = 2w_i \tag{4-48}$$

and

$$w = 1.699w_h \tag{4-49}$$

The measurement of w_h and w is the most convenient method for evaluation of chromatograms. In this chapter, the peak width at the base, w, will
be used exclusively because, although w_h can be measured more accurately,
w can be handled more easily in calculations as a substitute for σ, being
an even multiple of it.

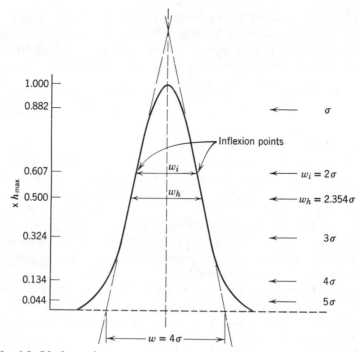

Fig. 4-8. Ideal gas chromatographic peak. h_{max} = peak height at maximum; σ = standard deviation; w_i = peak width at inflexion points; w_h = peak width at half-height; w = peak width at base (band intercept) (29).

Since σ is measured as the standard deviation of the retention time or the retention distance, the peak width is usually expressed in the same dimensions. However, peak width can also be given in volume units as the standard deviation of the retention volume or in length units when it is to be compared to the column length.

b. Plate Height. From the mathematical standpoint, not the standard deviation, but its square σ^2 described as the variance, is the basic measure of the normal distribution. According to the propagation of variance, the total variance of an emerging peak, σ^2, can be considered as the sum of variances contributed by length elements of the column. Assuming that the column is uniform, the variance of the solute distribution at the end of the column is directly proportional to the column length L. The proportionality factor, h, is defined by

$$h = \sigma^2/L \qquad (4\text{-}50)$$

and is described as plate height, or as the *height equivalent to a theoretical plate*, HETP. Although the name originated from the plate theory, plate height is independent of any physical model as a measure of band spreading per unit column length by its definition in equation 4-50. The dimension of h is length, usually expressed in centimeters or millimeters, since in equation 4-50 the variance is given in length units.

The plate height is conveniently obtained from the chromatogram and column length, L. Equation 4-50 may be written as

$$\sigma^2/L = L(\sigma/L)^2 \qquad (4\text{-}51)$$

where σ/L is the relative standard deviation which is dimensionless. This quantity is easily calculated from the peak width, w, and retention time, t_R, measured as distances on the chromatogram by the equation,

$$\sigma/L = w/4t_R \qquad (4\text{-}52)$$

Thus the expression of the plate height becomes

$$h = \frac{L}{(4t_R/w)^2} \qquad (4\text{-}53)$$

where the denominator is called the plate number and will be discussed below.

This definition of plate height is used generally in practice. When variances caused in any length element of the column are different (non-uniform column) the above-mentioned proportionality does not exist over the entire column and therefore h calculated by equation 4-53 varies with the column length. Although practical columns are not uniform in terms of the theory, the dependence of plate height on column length is normally small in the usual range. Thus, plate height provides the most important column characteristic for describing band broadening and connects separation efficiency to the theoretical analysis of the broadening process. The latter constitutes plate height as a sum of the variances of all independent processes which contribute to peak broadening.

The peak width, however, is measured by the standard deviation and is not the sum of the standard deviations caused by the individual broadening processes since

$$\sigma = \sum_i \sigma_i^2 < \sum_i \sigma_i \qquad (4\text{-}54)$$

This fact implies that minor broadening factors are generally negligible since the resulting standard deviation is very much dominated by the largest standard deviation, as shown in the following example.

The variance of an emerging peak, σ^2, is the sum of variances due to the column, σ_c^2, the sampling device, σ_s^2, and the detector and recorder, σ_d^2. Let us suppose that the corresponding standard deviations are

$\sigma_c = 10$ sec, $\sigma_s = 2$ sec, and $\sigma_d = 1$ sec. The standard deviation from the peak width on the chart paper will be $\sigma = \sqrt{105} = 10.25$, so that even when the standard deviation due to extra column broadening is 30% of that caused by the column, it constitutes only about 2.5% of the final peak width.

   c. Plate Number. The first theoretical treatment of the band broadening process (30,31) used an artificial model of the chromatographic column the "plate model." The length of the column was assumed to be divided into separate elements (plates) in which a complete equilibration of the solute takes place between the two phases. This model is similar to that used for characterizing the efficiency of a distillation column by theoretical plates. Thus the efficiency of the column for equilibrating a solute is given by the number of these imaginary plates, n, which is calculated from the chromatogram by the equation

$$n = 16(t_R/w)^2 \qquad (4\text{-}55)$$

The length element of the column occupied by a plate is called the plate height, h, and is given by

$$h = L/n = L/(4t_R/w)^2 \qquad (4\text{-}56)$$

which definition is formally equal to that given by equation 4-53.

   Plate number and plate height can also be expressed by the peak width measured at half height (w_h) as

$$n = 2\ln 2(t_R/w_h)^2 = 5.54(t_R/w_h)^2 \quad \text{and} \quad h = L/5.54(t_R/w_h)^2 \quad (4\text{-}57)$$

   Plate number provides a convenient expression of column performance and it is used widely. Because it is directly proportional to the length of the column, column efficiency is sometimes also expressed as plate number per unit column length, for example, as plate number per foot.

   Plate number is inversely proportional to the variance of the emerging peak

$$n = \left(\frac{t_R}{w/4}\right)^2 = \frac{t_R^2}{\sigma^2} \qquad (4\text{-}58)$$

The variance per unit time, σ^2/t_R, is equal to t_R/n, i.e., to the time necessary for obtaining one theoretical plate. Its reciprocal value, the number of plates generated per unit time,

$$t_R/\sigma^2 = n/t_R \qquad (4\text{-}59)$$

is a practical column efficiency parameter when analysis time is considered to be important.

2. Two Peaks: Resolution

The extent of the separation of two peaks is usually expressed by the resolution, R. By definition, resolution is equal to the ratio of the spacing between the peak maxima, Δt_R, to the mean base width of two neighboring peaks, w_m,

$$R = \Delta t_R / w_m = 2(t_{R2} - t_{R1})/(w_1 + w_2) = \Delta t_R / 4\sigma_m \qquad (4\text{-}60)$$

where t_{R2} and t_{R1} are the retention times, and w_2 and w_1 are the peak widths measured at base as shown in Figure 4-9, and σ_m is the mean standard deviation. The descriptive meaning of the resolution is that $R - 1$

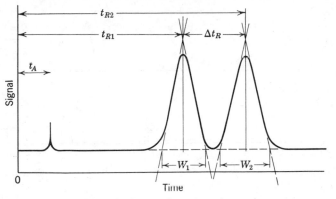

Fig. 4-9. Separation of a solute pair.

peaks can be placed between the two peaks in question, which are considered to be fully resolved when $R = 1.5$, i.e, their separation is 99.7% complete. For practical purposes $R = 1$ (98% separation) is usually adequate. In the literature both values are used to express complete separation. The resolution is a basic measure of column efficiency for separation of two components. The speed of separation may be expressed as resolution per unit time, R/t_{R2}.

For closely spaced peaks the resolution can be written by simplifying assumptions according to Purnell (32) as

$$R = \frac{1}{4} \frac{(\alpha - 1)}{\alpha} \frac{k}{(1 + k)} \sqrt{n} = \frac{1}{4} \frac{(\alpha - 1)}{\alpha} \frac{k}{(1 + k)} \sqrt{\frac{L}{h}} \qquad (4\text{-}61)$$

where k, n, and h refer to the more slowly moving band.

Resolution is proportional to the square root of the plate number, i.e., to the square root of the column length at fixed plate height. This is attributed to the fact that while the space separating two peaks is proportional to the column length, the peak width increases in proportion to the square root of the column length, thus peak separation exceeds peak broadening as the column length increases.

Equation 4-61 shows that the plate number is fundamentally related to the resolution and provides a general definition of overall column efficiency independently of a particular solute when the factor $k/(1 + k)$ is close to

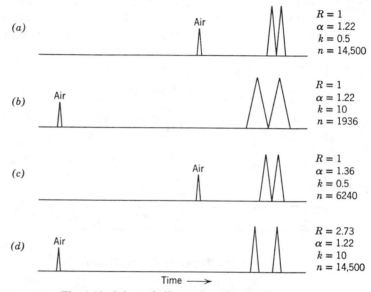

Fig. 4-10. Schematic illustration of resolution.

unity, as in the conventional packed columns. With other column types, however, this factor may be significantly smaller; therefore it is advisable to note the partition ratio for the peak in question when reporting plate number or plate height.

Equation 4-61 shows the effect of various column parameters which can be obtained from the chromatogram on the separation. The three principal factors which determine the resolution of a given solute pair are the following.

1. The relative retention, α, which is defined by the relative position of the peaks and attributed to the selectivity of the stationary phase for the solutes in question.

2. The partition ratio, k, which is connected with the position of the peak relative to the air peak. Since k is determined by the phase ratio, β, and by

the equilibrium constant, K, equation 4-61 can be written

$$R = \frac{1}{4}\frac{(\alpha - 1)}{\alpha}\frac{K}{(\beta + K)}\sqrt{n} \qquad (4\text{-}62)$$

3. The plate number, n, which is related to the band broadening process in the column and depends on almost all variables.

Figure 4-10 illustrates the effect of these parameters on four hypothetical chromatograms calculated by equation 4-61. A comparison of a and b shows that for peaks close to the air peak (a) the plate number must be higher than for peaks of large k values (b) in order to obtain the same resolution. Although the partition ratio is the same in a and c, because of the larger relative retention in c, fewer plates are needed in c than in a in order to obtain the same resolution. Although the relative retention and partition ratio is the same in b and d, the latter shows a significantly better resolution due to the higher plate number. Finally, the better resolution in d than in a, despite the same relative retention and plate number, is due to the higher partition ratio in d. Chromatograms a and d are typical for open tubular columns, while chromatograms b and c are characteristic for packed columns.

Figure 4-11 illustrates the effect of the phase ratio, β, and equilibrium constant, K, on the number of plates necessary to obtain $R = 1.5$ at a fixed relative retention ($\alpha = 1.111$) according to equation 4-61.

3. Effective Plate Number and Effective Plate Height

Open tubular columns are characterized by low k values due to their high phase ratio as shown in Table 4-1. Plate numbers obtained with these columns at low k values do not express the actual separation efficiency of the column since the factor $k/(1 + k)$ in equation 4-59 varies significantly in the low capacity ratio range. Figure 4-11 also illustrates that at low k-values a greater number of plates are necessary to obtain a given resolution than at large partition ratios.

This fact was first studied by Purnell (32), and it induced Desty et al. (8) to introduce the effective plate number, N, defined by

$$N = n[k/(1 + k)]^2 \qquad (4\text{-}63)$$

Substituting N into equation 4-61, the resolution is expressed as

$$R = (1/4)[(\alpha - 1)/\alpha]\sqrt{N} \qquad (4\text{-}64)$$

This equation shows that N is more closely related to the resolution than is the plate number itself. Therefore it is considered to be a better general expression for the overall column efficiency.

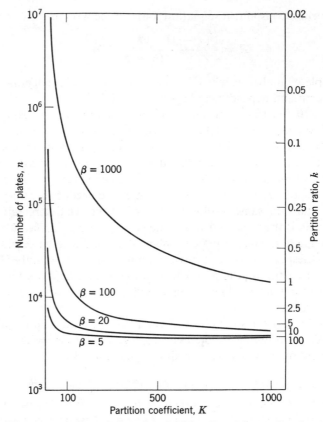

Fig. 4-11. Necessary number of plates for obtaining $R = 1.5$, as a function of partition coefficient k and phase ratio β, at fixed relative retention $\alpha = 1.111$.

Figure 4-12 illustrates schematically the variation of n and N with the partition ratio.

Effective plate height, H, is defined similarly to the plate height as

$$H = L/N = h[(1 + k)/k]^2 \qquad (4\text{-}65)$$

The expressions of effective plate number and plate height take account of the fact that for the disengagement of two peaks, only that time is of importance which the components spent sorbed by the stationary phase, i.e., the adjusted retention time. The gas holdup time, like the time spent by the components in the extracolumn volume, is irrelevant for the disengagement since it is not connected to the equilibration process. Nonetheless, for the separation efficiency the total broadening, which also includes broadening in the gas phase, should be considered. Since the plate theory neglects any broadening not connected with the equilibration, n and h become incorrect performance measures for low-capacity columns of small k values where the contribution of the gas phase broadening is high. Note that the factor $k/(1 + k)$ is equal to the residence probability of the solute in the stationary phase while moving through the column.

With the effective plate number, the total standard deviation is related to the adjusted retention time, i.e., to the time which is effective for the

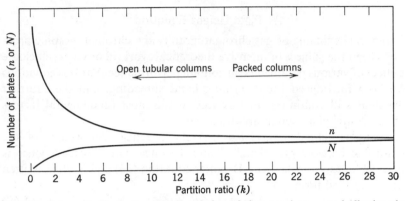

Fig. 4-12. Schematic illustration of the variation of plate numbers, n, and effective plate numbers, N with increasing capacity ratio, k.

separation and N is calculated by

$$N = 16(t'_R/w)^2 = 5.54(t'_R/w_h)^2 \qquad (4\text{-}66)$$

Similarly to equation 4-59, the number of effective plates generated per unit time is given by N/t_R. This expression may be used for measuring the speed of analysis.

4. Required Column Parameters

In practical work it is often desirable to estimate the required plate number or column length for the separation of a given solute pair. Such calculations are based on equation 4-61, which expresses the resolution by quantities obtained from the chromatogram. Since $R = 1$ represents an adequate separation in practice, we obtain the *number of required plates* (n_{req}) by replacing R by the unity in equation 4-61, and on solving for n:

$$n_{req} = 16[\alpha/(\alpha - 1)]^2[(k + 1)/k]^2 \qquad (4\text{-}67)$$

The number of required plates is often used for comparing the difficulty of separation of a particular solute pair on various columns.

The *required length of the column*, L_{req}, can be calculated from equation 4-61 if the plate height h is known, in view of the fact that $L = nh$:

$$L_{req} = 16h[\alpha/(\alpha - 1)]^2[(k + 1)/k]^2 \qquad (4\text{-}68)$$

If a complete separation ($R = 1.5$) is required, the factor 16 should be replaced by 36 in equations 4-67 and 4-68.

VII. Factors Determining Column Efficiency

A. Plate Height Equation

From the beginning of gas chromatography the chromatographic process has been the subject of intensive theoretical work in order to elucidate the effect of various parameters on column performance. Various equations have been introduced for describing band spreading, and their further refinement still continues. In this section the most fundamental factors that determine plate height are discussed.

Keulemans (28) demonstrated first the practical importance of the relationship between plate height h and the linear gas velocity $\bar{u}$ which is expressed by the so-called van Deemter equation (33) and is often written in the simplified form

$$h = A + B/\bar{u} + C\bar{u} \qquad (4\text{-}69)$$

as a sum of the three terms each representing an independent contribution to band broadening.

The constant A is the so-called eddy diffusion term. It describes the band broadening caused by the variation of the gas velocity in the porous structure of packed columns. The second term B/u represents the band broadening as a consequence of longitudinal diffusion of the solute molecules in the gas phase during their residence in the column. Finally, the term $C\bar{u}$ is related to mass transfer resistance in the column which hinders the instantaneous equilibration of the solute molecules between the gas and the stationary phase.

Equation 4-69 is illustrated graphically by a hyperbola, and Figure 4-13 shows a typical plot of h vs. $\bar{u}$ and the effect of the constants of the equation. It is seen that at low gas velocities the longitudinal diffusion, and at high velocities the mass transfer, controls band broadening. There is a minimum value of plate height, h_{min}, at a specific velocity which is called the optimum gas velocity, $\bar{u}_{opt}$.

The plot of h against $\bar{u}$, often called the HETP–$\bar{u}$ curve, is generally accepted as a graphic presentation of various factors on band broadening and as a means for interpreting column efficiency in terms of plate height.

It is a good practice to make such plots for some components of the sample to be analyzed when optimum conditions must be established. Plate height is calculated by equation 4-56 and the linear gas velocity by equation 4-40.

Similar curves can be obtained by plotting the effective plate height H against $\bar{u}$, and can be used in the same way for the interpretation of column efficiency and for the optimization of the conditions.

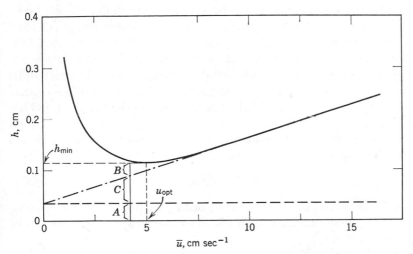

Fig. 4-13. Typical plot of plate height, h, against gas velocity, $\bar{u}$. Optimum gas velocity, $\bar{u}_{opt}$, and minimum plate height, h_{min}, are indicated.

1. Eddy Diffusion

In the original van Deemter equation this term is given by

$$A = 2\lambda d_p \qquad (4\text{-}70)$$

where λ is a constant related to the uniformity of the packing and d_p is the particle diameter. This classical eddy diffusion term is attributed to the flow pattern of the carrier gas in packed columns, and is considered to be independent of the flow velocity and of the nature of the gas when the flow is laminar.

Giddings' coupling theory of eddy diffusion (34) takes into account that eddy diffusion and molecular diffusion cooperate in reducing peak broadening caused by uneven flow patterns in the column. Therefore, their contribution to plate height should be expressed by a velocity-dependent coupled eddy diffusion term. This coupling term is always less than the sum of the classical eddy diffusion and mobile phase mass transfer terms.

The coupling effect is particularly important at high flow velocities resulting in significantly less peak broadening in the mobile phase than predicted
by the classical theory.

In open tubular columns, the flow pattern is uniform when the flow is
laminar and there is neither eddy diffusion nor coupling; consequently,
$A = 0$.

2. Longitudinal Diffusion

During the residence time of the solute in the mobile phase, band
broadening occurs due to diffusion of the solute molecules in the axial
direction. The spreading is directly proportional to the diffusion coefficient
of the solute in the carrier gas and to the time spent by the solute in the
gas phase. For open tubular columns the contribution of the longitudinal
diffusion is given by $2D_g/\bar{u}$, so that the constant B in equation 4-69 is equal
to $2D_g$. D_g is the diffusion coefficient of the solute in the gas phase and has
the dimension of cm²/sec.

In packed columns the tortuosity of the paths must be considered, and
by introducing the labyrinth factor γ, B is given by

$$B = 2\gamma D_g \qquad (4\text{-}71)$$

Since the diffusion rate cannot be increased by the presence of the packing,
γ is smaller than unity. For diatomaceous supports, γ is assumed to be
between 0.5 and 0.7.

The diffusion coefficients in the gas phase vary with the solutes, temperature, pressure, and carrier gas, and are usually in the range of 0.01–1
cm²/sec. The diffusion coefficients in liquids are 10^4–10^5 times smaller
than in gases, therefore the longitudinal diffusion in the liquid stationary
phase is usually negligible. Since D_g is inversely proportional to the square
root of the molecular weight of the carrier gas, the B term is larger in
hydrogen or helium than in nitrogen or argon. As Figure 4-13 shows, the
contribution of the longitudinal diffusion to band spreading is negligible
at high flow velocities.

3. Mass Transfer Terms

The major contribution to band broadening arises from finite rate of
the mass transfer in the mobile and stationary phases. The mass transfer
term C may be expressed as a sum of individual terms which contribute
independently to band broadening:

$$C = C_g + C_l \qquad (4\text{-}72)$$

where C_g and C_l are the gas phase and liquid phase mass transfer terms,
respectively.

For open tubular columns Golay (35) derived the following expressions:

$$C_g = \frac{1 + 6k + 11k^2}{24(1 + k)^2} \frac{r^2}{D_g} \tag{4-73}$$

$$C_l = \frac{k^3}{6(1 + k)^2} \frac{r^2}{K^2 D_l} \tag{4-74}$$

where D_g and D_l are the diffusion coefficients in the gas and liquid phases, respectively, r is the inside column radius, K is the partition coefficient, and k is the partition ratio.

Equation 4-73 shows that the band of an unretained solute will also spread in the column, since when $K = 0$, C_g is equal to $r^2/24D_g$.

Equation 4-74 can be modified by introducing the phase ratio (β) or the film thickness (d_f) as shown in the following equation:

$$C_l = \frac{1}{(k + \beta)^2} \frac{r^2}{6\beta D_l} = \frac{2k}{3(1 + k)^2} \frac{d_f^2}{D_l} \tag{4-75}$$

Packed columns represent a more complex system than the liquid-coated open tubular columns, and a great number of C terms have been calculated (4). The simplest is

$$C_l = \frac{2k}{3(k + 1)^2} \frac{d_f^2}{D_l} \tag{4-76}$$

In the above equation, the liquid film thickness d_f is a hypothetical value for expressing the dispersity of the liquid on the tube's wall or the support's surface. We have to assume that there is no uniform liquid film in any column.

In the original van Deemter equation the resistance to mass transfer in the gas phase was neglected. It has been shown, however, that in the packed columns used today a major contribution to band spreading arises from factors controlling equilibration in the gas phase. According to the classical theory this term can be written for conditions prevailing in gas chromatography as

$$C_g = cd_p^2/D_g \tag{4-77}$$

where d_p^2 is the mean square diameter of the packing granules and c is a dimensionless constant. The value of c is a function of the packing structure and the partition ratio.

In practice, columns are usually operated above the optimum gas velocity in order to reduce analysis time. Thus, the plate height is dominated by $C\bar{u}$, and C becomes the most important parameter. The above equations show that C is directly proportional to the square of the particle, or, in open tubular columns, to the tube diameter as well as to the square of the liquid film thickness, and is inversely proportional to the diffusion coefficients of the solute.

B. Effects of Various Parameters

1. Column Diameter

The size of the sample which can be effectively separated increases, but the performance usually decreases, with the tube diameter. However, the effect of the diameter of packed columns on the performance has not been made clear. It also depends on the way in which the column is packed. The ratio of tube diameter to particle diameter seems to be a very important criterion. For analytical purposes, small-diameter columns (i.d. 2–3 mm) are most adequate.

The performance of open tubular columns is a function of the square of the tube diameter. Therefore, columns having an inside diameter of 0.25 mm (0.010 in.) are preferred if high resolution is required. The minimum plate height at optimum gas velocity, h_{min}, is directly proportional to the diameter of the conventional open tubular columns. In practice, h_{min} varies between $0.5d$ and $3.0d$, depending on the partition ratio and column diameter, d.

2. Column Length

The minimum necessary column length is determined by the number of plates required for obtaining the desired resolution and by the plate height which can be considered to be constant, if conditions and column parameters other than the length are held constant.

The maximum practical length of the column depends on the column type and the instrument. The inlet pressure is usually limited by instrumental factors; thus the maximum length of column which can be operated at a desired gas velocity is determined by the permeability of the column. Owing to their lower permeability, open tubular columns are usually much longer than packed columns. In addition the oven dimensions may also limit the maximum length of column.

Resolution increases with the square root of the column length. This means that the column length has to be increased fourfold if the resolution is to be doubled. Analysis speed, assuming fixed gas velocities, increases linearly with the length. Therefore, the shortest column which performs the separation of all components to be analyzed is the most preferable one.

3. Carrier Gas

The diffusivity of the solutes decreases with the density of the carrier gas. High diffusivity will deteriorate column performance at low flow velocities where the contribution of longitudinal diffusion to the plate height is large. On the other hand, high diffusivity is desirable at high gas velocities where the resistance to mass transfer in the gas phase is a factor determining plate height. The selection of carrier gas, therefore, is mainly dependent on the gas velocities used. Light carrier gas such as hydrogen and helium are preferred for fast analyses, while heavy gases such as nitrogen and argon are of advantage if the column is operated at optimum flow velocity. However, other criteria such as detector response and fire hazard may also influence the selection of carrier gas. In the United States, helium and nitrogen are used most commonly as carrier gases.

In gas–liquid chromatography the effect of the carrier gas on the retention values is usually negligible, in contrast to gas–solid chromatography where significantly different retention values are obtained for low-boiling solutes when different carrier gases are used.

4. Temperature

The effect of temperature on column efficiency is complex. In the first place the equilibrium constants increase with decreasing temperature as was shown in equation 4-19. As a consequence, partition ratio and retention time will also increase.

Usually, the relative retention becomes greater when the temperature is lowered as shown in equation 4-33. Increasing values of k and α will also increase the resolution according to equation 4-61, and this fact suggests the desirability of operating the column at the lowest possible temperature. On the other hand, the plate height increases with decreasing temperature when the flow velocity is fixed at a value higher than $\bar{u}_{opt}$ due to increasing mass transfer terms.

In practice, the optimum column temperature represents a compromise between resolution which decreases and speed of analysis which increases with temperature.

5. Gas Velocity

Figure 4-13 shows the plate height as a function of the gas velocity. Plate height is minimum and resolution is maximum at optimum linear gas velocity which varies between 1 and 25 cm sec^{-1} depending on the column construction, the stationary phase, the carrier gas, the operating conditions, and the solutes. However, the speed of analysis can be increased at higher velocities.

Scott and Hazeldean (36) introduced the concept of the optimum practical gas velocity, OPGV. This is the velocity at which the h vs. $\bar{u}$ curve just becomes linear, and it has about the same value for most peaks on a chromatogram. If a respectively longer column is operated at OPGV, the same overall efficiency can be obtained in a shorter time than at the optimum velocity with a shorter column.

In practice, columns are usually operated at velocities higher than $\bar{u}_{opt}$ in order to save time or to obtain taller peaks when mass-sensitive detectors such as flame ionization detectors are used. Giddings demonstrated, as shown in Figure 4-14, the plate height relative to its minimum value and resolution relative to its maximum value as a function of the ratio of velocity to the optimum velocity. Because at least 80% of maximum

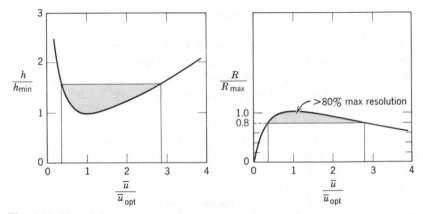

Fig. 4-14. Plate height relative to its minimum value and resolution relative to its maximum value as functions of the ratio of gas velocity to the optimum gas velocity (4).

resolution may be obtained along the horizontal lines, the gas velocity has a rather large practical range unless the maximum efficiency is needed.

6. Particle Size and Shape

In packed columns the size, shape, and pore structure of the column material influence column performance. The pore structure principally determines the distribution of the liquid phase and often the activity of the support in gas–liquid chromatography.

Equation 4-77 shows that the mass transfer term in the gas phase decreases with the square of the particle diameter. In columns which are controlled by the mass transfer in the gas phase, h_{min} is directly proportional to d_p and in practical columns h_{min} varies between $1.5d_p$ and $4.0d_p$. At high gas velocities, h may increase with d_p^2. These rules may suggest that optimum results can be obtained with very small particles. However, the column permeability is inversely proportional to the square particle diameter and thus, by the reduction of the particle size, the necessary inlet pressure may exceed the practical limits. In addition, it is difficult to pack a column uniformly with small particles. Nonuniform packing results in a high eddy diffusion term and low column efficiency.

7. Sample Size

The amount of sample which can be separated effectively by a column varies with the column type. Highly efficient columns are ordinarily less flexible with respect to the effect of sample size on efficiency than columns of low efficiency. The sample capacity of the column is often defined by the sample amount which can be applied without more than 10% loss of the efficiency which is obtained by extrapolation to zero sample size. Generally, the sample capacity is proportional to the amount of stationary phase in the column and thus approximately to the square of the column diameter.

Column overloading will result in poor performance, tailing, and shift in retention times. In addition to the loss of resolution, changing relative retention values and nonlinearity of the peak height–solute amount relationship must be considered in practical work when overloading is suspected.

However, the column is usually overloaded in preparative work and also in trace analysis by the major components. Even so, the evaluation of a trace component peak is often impossible when eluted closely after a major component which appears as a broad and tailing peak due to the overloading. Therefore it is desirable in trace analysis to select a stationary phase on which the trace component is eluted before the interfering major component.

The effect of sample size on efficiency is strongly influenced by the initial width of the sample "plug," which is also determined by the method of sample introduction. As a rule of thumb, sufficient results can be expected when the initial width of the sample band occupies the volume of $\sqrt{n}$ plates where n is the number of theoretical plates in the column.

In quantitative analysis detector overloading has also to be considered. When the sample size is increased, a point is reached where the peak area–solute amount relation becomes nonlinear. Consequently, there is a maximum permissible sample size pertinent to the linear range of the detector under operating conditions.

VIII. The Stationary Phase

A. Solid Stationary Phases

The modern gas chromatographic technique first used was actually gas–solid chromatography for the separation of low-boiling substances. Yet the great success of gas chromatography in general was due to the versatility of gas–liquid chromatography which became about the most versatile tool for the separation of a great variety of samples including high-boiling substances. Although gas–solid chromatography has become an established technique for analyzing very volatile samples (gases), the great majority of analytical work has been done by gas–liquid chromatography. However, recent developments show increasing use of solid phases also for separation of high-boiling and polar samples as a consequence of the availability of highly sensitive detectors and the introduction of new and modified adsorbents as well as novel column types.

The major difficulties in the separation of less volatile solutes by conventional gas–solid chromatography are as follows:

1. Strong tailing and dependence of retention values on sample size.

2. Large equilibrium constants as compared to liquid phases, resulting in excessive retention times.

3. Catalytic effect of the adsorbent.

Tailing and variation of retention by sample size are mainly due to the inhomogeneity of the adsorbent surface and to column overloading. When solid stationary phases having a reasonably homogeneous surface (such as graphited carbon black) and small samples are used, symmetrical peaks and reproducible retention times can be obtained even with very polar samples (37). On the other hand, gas–solid chromatography columns, in which the stationary phase is in the form of a thin porous layer on the tube wall (open tubular columns) or on the surface of a support (packed columns), have a significantly greater phase ratio value, β, than columns packed with a granular adsorbent in the conventional way (24). As a consequence, k values and retention times comparable to that of gas–liquid chromatography can be obtained in spite of relatively large equilibrium constants. Regarding the catalytic effects in gas–solid chromatography one can assume that sample decomposition in an inert carrier gas is less critical in the case of short elution times.

Results obtained on columns packed with granular adsorbent the surface of which have been modified by chemical treatment, also promise a future extension of gas–solid chromatography (38). A major breakthrough in this field has been achieved recently by the introduction of porous cross-linked polystyrene as the stationary phase by Hollis (39).

The author feels that gas–solid chromatography will assume a greater share in solving specific analytical problems, owing to the absence of column bleeding and to the often unusually high selectivity of solid stationary phases. Yet, the present status of gas–solid chromatography does not justify a detailed treatment of the subject.

Carbonaceous Solid Phases. Active carbon has found application in the analysis of permanent gases and low-boiling hydrocarbons (40). Habgood and Hanlan (41) observed that the highest column efficiency was obtained with the most active carbon. On the other hand, several attempts were made for reducing the activity of the absorbent either by pretreatment or by liquid loading. Carbon black was extensively investigated as a stationary phase and the best results were obtained by deactivation with a small amount of liquid phase (42). When carbon black is heated in inert gas atmosphere at high temperatures, it crystallizes to a very finely dispersed graphite. The graphited carbon black* has a high specific surface area and homogeneous unpolar surface. Results obtained by porous layer open tubular columns fabricated with this stationary phase show the unique properties of graphited carbon black in the analysis of relatively high boiling polar materials (37).

Alumina. Alumina is used particularly for the separation of hydrocarbons (43). Alumina becomes dehydrated by heat treatment at 200–1000°C. The retention values and the selectivity of alumina vary very strongly with the extent of hydration, which also influences column efficiency. Highly activated alumina causes tailing and undergoes rapid alteration. Thus, partially deactivated material is used as the stationary phase. A convenient way to maintain the activity of the adsorbent at a constant level is to moisturize the carrier gas. This can be achieved with a cartridge containing wet firebrick and kept at constant temperature or by adding a proportionate amount of steam to the carrier gas.

Several methods have been described for modifying alumina. Scott (44) treated alumina with sodium hydroxide and metal salts. The modified alumina could be used for the separation of C_{15}–C_{23} hydrocarbons at 250°C.

Silica Gel. So far the most widely used solid stationary phase, silica gel is produced with various pore sizes. Most commonly, silica gels have pore sizes in the range of 10–70 Å and a specific surface area of 800–900 m^2/g. The chromatographic performance of silica gel depends on its pore structure and on the extent of hydration. Kiselev and co-workers (16) investigated the effect of pore size on the separation. The modification of the silica gel surface by dehydroxylation and trimethylsilanization was the subject of extensive studies and shows promising approach to extend the use of this material (45).

Adsorbents similar to silica gel have also found application as stationary phases. These are for example, Florisil, a synthetic magnesia–silica gel,

---

* Graphited carbon black is marketed, e.g., under the trade name Spheron by the G. Cabot Co., Boston, Mass.

and Florex, a natural fuller's earth (46). Porous glass was also found effective for the separation of both low- and high-boiling substances (47,48). In most cases best results were obtained by modifying the adsorbent surface.

Molecular Sieves. Molecular sieves are synthetic zeolites (sodium or calcium aluminum silicates) which have a uniform network of cavities and a high specific surface area (700–800 m^2/g). Molecules which are small enough to enter the pore structure become adsorbed in the cavities so that these synthetic zeolites "sieve out" molecules which have diameters smaller than the entrances to the cavities. In addition to this sieving effect, true adsorption of the solutes may also occur.

Linde molecular sieves* 4A, 5A, and 13X are used commonly in gas chromatography (49). The numbers refer to the approximate pore diameters expressed in angstroms. Molecular sieves are highly hygroscopic materials and can also be used very effectively for drying the carrier gas or as a precolumn for removing water from samples. They have to be activated at temperatures of 300–600°C. The activation is preferably carried out in the column itself, in a helium stream.

The major application of molecular sieves as stationary phases is the separation of inert gases, methane, and carbon monoxide. Molecular sieve flour deposited in the pores of a diatomaceous earth support was described by Bombaugh (50) as a column material in gas–solid chromatography.

Organo Clay. The inorganic cations in montmorillonite-type clays can be replaced by amines containing long alkyl chains. Such products are widely used in finely dispersed form as gellants, etc. White (51) introduced dioctadecyldimethylammonium bentonite, deposited on a support, as stationary phase which showed a high selectivity for aromatic hydrocarbons. Unfortunately, however, unsymmetrical peaks and poor column efficiency were observed. Modification of the adsorbent with a liquid phase such as squalane or silicone oil results in a powerful stationary phase for aromatic hydrocarbons (52).

Dimethyloctadecylammonium bentonite is manufactured by National Lead Co. and sold under the trade name Bentone 34.

Porous Polymers. Nonporous crosslinked-polystyrene beads have been used for a long time in the preparation of ion-exchange resins. When the polymerization and crosslinking is carried out in the presence of a diluent which is a good solvent of the monomers but is not soluble in the polymer, porous crosslinked polystyrene beads are obtained.

This material is used as adsorbent as well as for making macroreticular ion exchange resins and in gel permeation chromatography.

* Union Carbide.

Hollis (39) introduced such porous polyaromatic polymer beads as stationary phases. The potential areas of application are still being explored, but excellent results have been obtained in the analyses of water and highly polar volatile substances (53).

The porous polymers used by Hollis were synthetized from styrene, *tert*-butylstyrene, and ethylvinylbenzene with divinylbenzene as the cross-linker. The properties of these polyaromatic beads vary with the chemical nature, pore structure, surface area, and particle size of the material. Very good results were obtained with an ethylvinylbenzene–divinylbenzene copolymer having a specific surface area of 660 m²/g and a relatively fine pore structure. Other porous polymers, with specific surface areas in the range of 100–700 m²/g, were also used successfully.

Solute retention can be attributed to adsorption on the large surface of the solid aromatic polymer, similarly to adsorption observed on the aromatic matrix of some ion exchange resins. On the other hand, the surface of the polymer can also be considered as a highly extended liquid surface and the retention explained by partition. Most probably, at low temperatures adsorption and at high temperatures partition is the dominating mechanism. In any case, pore dimensions and pore structure seem to affect strongly the separation. The excellent symmetry of peaks obtained with highly polar solutes such as water, ammonia, amines, alcohols, and glycols demonstrates that the polymer surface is very homogeneous.

Porous polyaromatic beads are mechanically strong, and metal columns are packed by vibration and tapping in the usual way. The thermal stability of these materials is good so that columns can be operated at temperatures up to at least 250°C with little or no bleeding.

Various porous polymer beads are commercially available under the trade name Porapak (Waters Associates, Inc.), Polypak (F & M Scientific), and Chromosorb 102 (Johns-Manville).

B. Liquid Stationary Phases

1. Advantages and Requirements

For the great majority of analytical problems, gas–liquid partition chromatography has proved to be the most efficient technique. The use of liquid phases has the following advantages:

1. The absorption isotherm is linear under usual operating conditions, so that symmetrical peaks can be obtained.

2. Liquid phases are available in great variety; thus adequate selective phases can be found for a particular separation.

3. The amount of liquid phases in the column can be varied easily;

therefore both preparative and high-efficiency columns can be made with the same liquid phase.

4. Liquid phases are available in great purity and in well-defined quality and thus retention values are reproducible.

5. Both packed or open tubular columns can be fabricated with liquid phases in a simple manner.

The greatest disadvantage of liquid phases is their volatility. Fortunately, many liquid phases have been found which have sufficiently low vapor pressures even at high column temperature. However, when highest detector sensitivity is required, in temperature programming or in tandem operation of gas chromatograph and mass spectrometer, etc., the bleeding of the liquid phase is a major concern.

The general requirements which should be considered in selecting the appropriate stationary phase are the following:

1. Low vapor pressure at the desired operating temperature.
2. Chemical stability at operating temperature.
3. Selectivity for the components to be separated.
4. Sufficient solving power for the sample components.
5. Low viscosity at the desired operating temperature.
6. Adequate wetting of the support surface or the column wall.
7. Reasonable solubility in some common volatile solvent.

The choice of the proper stationary phase is one of the most important judgments in gas–liquid chromatography.

Several hundred liquid phases have been described, and their listing is beyond the scope of this chapter. Several compilations are available from suppliers and may be used as guide when selecting the stationary phase. However, the selection of the stationary phase for a new analytical problem usually has to be made on a trial-and-error basis in spite of the accumulated data on various applications of the phases (54–56). In some cases, a combination of two or more liquid phases might give the desired results. For difficult separations, the use of high-efficiency columns can be more advisable than searching for a very selective stationary phase.

2. Upper and Lower Temperature Limits

The liquid stationary phase in the column always has a vapor pressure, the magnitude of which depends primarily on the nature of the phase and on the operating temperature. It is exposed to the continuously streaming carrier gas which removes a certain amount of the liquid phase per unit gas volume; that is, *bleeding* occurs. This bleeding is undesirable because it can disturb the proper function of the detector; it causes baseline shift in programmed temperature operation; it contaminates the trapped solutes and, due to the loss of the stationary phase, it gradually changes the separation character of the column until an unacceptable deterioration occurs.

There are some rules of thumb for the maximum allowable temperature with respect to the vapor pressure of the stationary phase. For example, one can estimate that the atmospheric boiling point of the liquid phase should be at least 150–200°C greater than the column temperature. Another approximation is that the upper temperature limit should be about 70–100°C below the boiling point of the phase in high vacuum (0.1–0.5 mm Hg). Recommended maximum temperatures of different stationary phases can be found in tables. However, these values should always be considered only as guides and not as absolute values. The sensitivity of the detector, the mode of operation (isothermal or temperature programming), the column construction, etc., always affect the maximum temperature at which the column can be practically operated.

The vapor pressure of the stationary phase in the column might be influenced by the support material and also by the loading. A sharp drop in the vapor pressure was observed when the liquid loading was lowered to 1–2% (57). The maximum operating temperature for a liquid phase in an open tubular column is 25–50°C lower than in a packed column.

Some liquid phases are not homogeneous materials. For example, commercial polyglycols and greases such as Apiezon or silicone greases are composed of homologs and may also contain some chemically different materials. Column conditioning which results in the removal of the volatile constituents can extend the upper temperature limit of these stationary phases.

The thermal stability of the liquid phase is also an important factor. Our knowledge of chemical changes in the column is restricted, but we can assume that they are rather frequent at high temperatures (58). Conformational changes (59), polymerization, crosslinking of silicone oil, condensation of polypropylene sebacate (60) have been observed at high temperatures. A small amount of oxygen in the carrier gas can cause oxidation or may initiate other reactions of the stationary phase. The support material may also catalyze changes of the liquid phases. Acid treatment of the support material has been found to cause bleeding of the silicone polymer SE-30, and to result in decomposition of polyether-type liquids (61).

An interesting approach to investigation of the thermal behavior of the stationary phase is the use of thermogravimetry. The information obtained by this technique is particularly valuable in practice if the effect of temperature on the column material (liquid phase plus support) is studied.

The lower temperature limit for operating a column with a given liquid phase is generally the melting point of the stationary phase. In many cases, however, increasing viscosity of the liquid by decreasing temperature will result in a loss of column efficiency. On the other hand, the solidified stationary phase can also occasionally be effective as an adsorbent (62). Some phases may undergo transition at a given temperature resulting in loss of resolution.

The lower temperature limit is, for example, 75°C for Apiezon L and OS-138 polyphenylether, 100–125°C for SE-30, and 175°C for Versamid 900.

3. Polarity and Selectivity

The retention of a solute is determined by solute–solvent interactions and can be interpreted generally by the solution theory (63). In practice, liquid phases are primarily distinguished by their polarity. The polarity of a stationary phase is related to the polarity of polar or polarizable groups and to their ratio to nonpolar groups in the solvent molecule. From the practical point of view, the greater the polarity of the stationary phase, the greater is the retention of a polar solute relative to that of a nonpolar solute with similar boiling point. The Latin expression *similis similibus solvantur*—like is dissolved by like—expresses the general rule. With respect to their polarity, the stationary phases are divided into three major groups: nonpolar, intermediate (semipolar), and polar phases. Stationary phases with hydrogen bonding and with other specific properties represent further classes of liquid phases.

Phases with hydrogen bonding can be regarded as a special group of the polar phases. Alcohols, amines, etc., are capable of forming hydrogen bonds with these phases, and great selectivity can be observed. Chemical interactions leading to complex formation or other types of weak chemical bonding between solvent and solute cause high selectivity of some specific phases. A classical example is the use of silver nitrate in ethylene glycol, glycerol, triethylene glycol, or benzyl cyanide. Such phases have excellent selectivity for olefins due to variations in the stability of the complexes formed. Paraffins do not form complexes and are eluted rapidly.

The polarity of a liquid phase can be measured in a number of ways. The polarity classification of Rohrschneider (64) allows the graphical presentation of the relative polarity of individual stationary phases as it is depicted in Figure 4-15. The utilization of such polarity charts was also discussed by Maier and Karpathy (65). In this classification, each stationary phase is characterized by a polarity number, which can be obtained

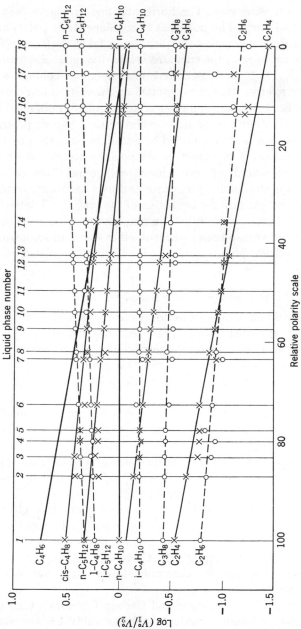

Fig. 4-15. Retention chart of liquid stationary phases (64). Numbers on the top line designate the following liquid phases (relative polarity is given in brackets): *1*. β,β′-Oxydipropionitrile [100]. *2*. N-(Methylacetyl)-β-aminopropionitrile [87]. *3*. Propylene glycol carbonate [83]. *4*. Dimethylformamide [80]. *5*. Polyethylene glycol 600 [87]. *6*. Acetylacetone [73]. *7*. Benzylcyanide [64]. *8*. Diethylformamide [62]. *9*. Epoxypropylmorpholine [57]. *10*. 1,2-Butylene glycol sulfite [54]. *11*. N-β-Hydroxypropylmorpholine [50]. *12*. Dibenzyl ether [44]. *13*. Dibutylformamide [43]. *14*. Ethoxylated lauryl alcohol [36]. *15*. TC (an unsaturated cyclic hydrocarbon) [14]. *16*. 1-Chlorooctadecane [13]. *17*. Silicone oil [7]. *18*. Squalane [0].

graphically in the following way. The horizontal line in Figure 4-15 is divided into 100 equal parts. The polarities of squalane (least polar) and β,β'-oxydipropionitrile (most polar) are arbitrarily taken as 0 and 100, respectively. Using n-butane as the standard solute, the relative retention of butadiene ($r_{\text{butadiene}/n\text{-butane}}$), is measured on a squalane column, and the logarithm of the relative retention is plotted on the vertical line drawn to the polarity number 0. Similarly, the log relative retention obtained on an oxydipropionitrile column is plotted on the vertical line at polarity number 100. The two points are connected by a straight line. The polarity of the other liquid phases is expressed by the polarity number at which $\log r_{\text{butadiene}/n\text{-butane}}$ measured on each individual column fits to the straight line. As shown, straight lines may also be drawn for other paraffins and olefins up to C_5 by plotting the logarithm of the retention relative to that of n-butane. Alkynes give random results, and no linear relation exists. Polarity charts have also been made with other standard solutes and used for evaluation of new phases as well as for calculation of stationary phase combinations.

4. Some Commonly Used Liquid Phases

In Table 4-3 twelve liquid phases are listed which are the most commonly used in present-day analytical work. The great majority of analytical problems, assuming reasonably high column efficiency, can be solved with these phases. As previously mentioned, the best choice is to select a stationary phase having a polarity similar to the polarity of the sample components.

It is advisable first to try some of these phases for the solution of a particular separation problem, and explore only later the potentialities of other stationary phases if necessary.

Many liquid phases are known only by their trade names. Below some of the common groups are described. Similar products made by other manufacturers are also used in gas chromatography.

Carbowaxes. Carbowaxes (Union Carbide) are polyethylene glycols. The numbers refer to the average molecular weights. For example, Carbowax 1540 and Carbowax 20M have average molecular weights of 1300–1600 and 15,000–20,000, respectively. Carbowax 350, 550, and 750 are methoxy polyethylene glycols. Generally, lower molecular weight means a higher polarity.

Ucon Fluids. Ucon Fluids (Carbide and Carbon Chemicals Co.) are polypropyleneglycol-type liquids. Products with the suffix LB are water insoluble and with the suffixes 50-HB and 75-H are water soluble. The number following these series symbols refers to the viscosity in Saybolt

TABLE 4-3
Some Commonly Used Liquid Phases

Stationary phase	Maximum recommended temperature	Solvent	Major application
Squalane (2, 6, 10, 15, 19, 23-hexamethyltetracosane)	150°C	Hexane	Saturated hydrocarbons
Apiezon L grease (high molecular weight aliphatic hydrocarbon)	250–300°C	Methylene chloride	High-boiling substances
DC-200 and DC-500 silicone oils	200°C	Toluene and acetone	Intermediate phase for general purpose
SE-30 silicone gum rubber	300–350°C	Toluene	Steroids, fatty acid esters
Didecyl phthalate	165–170°C	Acetone	Intermediate phase for general purpose
Di-(2-ethylhexyl) sebacate	150°C	Acetone	Intermediate phase for general purpose
LAC 6-R-860; butanediol succinate (BDS)	200–205°C	Chloroform	Fatty acid esters
LAC 3-R-728; diethylene-glycol succinate (DEGS)	205–210°C	Chloroform	Fatty acid esters
OS-138 (6-ring polyphenyl ether)	200–225°C	Toluene	Strongly polar samples, hydrocarbon mixtures
Ucon fluid LB-500-X and 50-HB-2000	200°C	Methanol	Polar samples: alcohols, aldehydes, ketones, etc.
Carbowax 1540	150°C	Methanol	Polar samples: alcohols, aldehydes, ketones, etc.
Versamid 900 (polyamide resin)	350°C	Chloroform and n-butanol	High-boiling amino compounds (on KOH-treated support)

Universal Seconds at 100°F. The letter X or Y following the viscosity number designates certain additives (oxidation inhibitors, etc.) present in the product.

Polyesters. Polyesters are available in great variety. The following products are made by Cambridge Industries Co.: LAC 1-R-296 (polypropylene glycol adipate); LAC 2-R-446 (polydiethylene glycol adipate partly crosslinked with pentaerithritol); LAC 3-R-728 or LAC 4-R-777 (polydiethylene glycol succinate); LAC 6-R-860 (poly-1,4-butanediol succinate); LAC 9-R-769 (polyneopentyl glycol adipate), and LAC 12-R-746 (polydimethylol-cyclohexane succinate).

Silicones. The SE series of silicone gums are products of General Electric. They are polysiloxanes characterized by the substituents which are in SE-30 methyl, in SE-33 methyl and vinyl, in SE-52 methyl and phenyl groups. The DC series of silicone oils is produced by the Dow Corning Corp. DC 200 is a methyl-substituted polyoxysiloxane which is available in three viscosity grades: 350, 12,500, and 2,500,000 stokes at 25°C; DC 550 and DC 710 are phenylmethyl-type silicone oils.

Polymeric stationary phases are not homogeneous materials in the chemical sense. They may contain impurities which affect the polarity and selectivity of the phase. For critical application, purification of the phase might be necessary. Lipsky (66) has found that when commercial Apiezon L was chromatographed on an alumina column using benzene as an eluent, one of the later-eluted fractions was far superior as a stationary phase for the separation of fatty acid esters than the starting material.

5. Combination of Liquid Phases

When one liquid phase fails to effect the resolution of certain sample components, a combination of two or more liquid phases is often adequate. Chromatographic columns with liquid phase combinations are obtained in two ways:

1. Connection of columns in series each containing support material coated with a different liquid phase.

2. Mixed packing in a single column. Either the column is packed with an intimate mixture of column materials, each of which was prepared with a different liquid phase (mixed bed); or the support is coated with a combination of different liquid phases (mixed coating).

All these methods have been used successfully and were the subject of detailed study by Maier and Karpathy (65), Hildebrand and Reilley (67), and others.

In the evaluation of the optimal column for a given separation problem, a major concern is the prediction of retention values and resolution of critical solute pairs for various liquid-phase combinations. In simpler cases, for estimation of the retention behavior of liquid-phase combinations, the equations given by the above-mentioned authors can be used. A method for computer optimization of separation by binary or ternary liquid phases (68) has also been introduced.

The most reliable prediction of retention times can be made when mixed-bed-type columns are used. It has been shown (67) that the retention times can be predicted by a linear combination of the partitioning properties of the individual liquid phases. When three columns having the same load are considered and two of them are coated with a single liquid phase (reference columns) while the third column contains the two liquid phases in a fractional combination, m, the capacity ratio of a solute, k_m, in the mixed phase column with the mixed packing can be expressed by the following equation:

$$k_m = k_{r,0}(1 - m) + k_{r,1}m \tag{4-78}$$

where $k_{r,0}$ is the capacity ratio of the solute on the first reference column (when $m = 0$) and $k_{r,1}$ is the capacity ratio of the solute on the second reference column (when $m = 1$).

When mixed coating is used, the prediction of retention values of a liquid-phase combination is not as simple. Liquid phases usually do not retain their individual partitioning characteristics when blended together. However, blending may produce a new desirable partitioning medium and result in an efficient column, since not only the selectivity but also column performance can be influenced by the relative amounts of the single solvents.

In the column-series method the capacity ratio, k, does not vary linearly with fractional combinations because the pressure drop across the individual columns connected in series is different. Consequently, solute retention times for columns in series will not be constant upon column reversal, and even the elution order of solutes may change.

In practice, good separations can be obtained by all three methods utilizing multiliquid-phase columns. The convenience of preparing mixed-bed columns with several liquid phase combinations and the predictability of retentions values, however, makes the mixed-bed method the most expedient.

6. Tailing Reducer Additives in Gas–Liquid Chromatography

Residual adsorptive sites, either on the support surface in packed columns or on the inner wall of open tubular columns, often can be blocked by adding a small amount of tailing reducer to the liquid stationary phase. Many of these additives are surfactants, and it is assumed that they also facilitate the spreading of the liquid phase by reducing surface tension. They are generally polar and are used most often in conjunction with nonpolar liquid phases.

Averill (69) proposed first the use of surface active additives for open tubular columns. These materials can be divided into three groups: nonionic, anionic, and cationic. The most important nonionic additives are Atpet 80 and Span 80. Both are made by the partial esterification of a polyglycol, e.g., sorbitol, with a long-chain fatty acid, e.g., oleic acid. The anionic tailing reducers are acids, such as terephthalic acid, dinonyl-naphthalene disulfonic acid, etc., while the cationic materials are amines such as Alkaterge T, a corrosion inhibitor.

Nonionic surfactants can generally be used for both polar and nonpolar liquid phases and samples. For acidic samples an anionic and for basic samples a cationic additive has to be chosen.

The amount of tailing reducer which should be applied with the liquid phase depends on the nature of the support or the tube wall. In most cases a weight ratio of liquid phase to additive around 100:1 is adequate. If highly polar samples are analyzed, the ratio can be as small as 8:1.

C. Solid–Liquid Stationary Phases

Coating an adsorbent with a liquid phase was first introduced for the elimination of the strong peak tailing often observed when less volatile substances were chromatographed on conventional adsorbents (70). It is assumed that the active sites on the solid surface are blocked by the liquid phase which may be considered in this application as a tailing reducer. Numerous liquid phases (squalane, silicone oil, etc.) have been employed successfully on various solid phases in quantities of 1–2% (w/w).

The retention properties of the resulting stationary phase are different from that of the original adsorbent due to the coating, and in the simplest cases the total retention time might be expressed as the sum of individual retention times attributable to the uncoated solid and the liquid phase:

$$t_R = t_A + t'_{R \text{ (uncoated solid)}} + t'_{R \text{ (liquid)}} \qquad (4\text{-}79)$$

When an adsorbent is coated with a large amount of liquid phase the solute retention is due to the liquid. However, specific effects caused by the remaining activity of the solid may also be observed.

In most cases the combination of an adsorbent and a liquid results in a stationary phase with new properties, and the separation of the effects of the solid (adsorbent) and liquid phases in terms of retention is impossible. Thus it is justified to consider the combination as a novel stationary phase and gas–solid–liquid chromatography (GSLC) which is also called gas adsorption layer chromatography, as a distinct category of gas chromatography.

Dramatic effects can be observed, for example, when a polar adsorbent such as alumina is coated with a small amount of polar liquid. Figure 4-16 shows the changing polarity of alumina coated with different amounts of squalane, β,β'-oxydipropionitrile and triethylene glycol. When increasing amounts of squalane are applied to the surface of the alumina, the polarity of the phase decreases as a consequence of the blocking of active sites. However, the polarity shows a distinct minimum when the loading of triethylene glycol or β,β'-oxydipropionitrile, both strongly polar liquids, was increased. Similar phenomena have also been observed on other combinations of metal oxides with polar liquid phases. The practical significance of the effect is that the polarity of the stationary phase consisting of a polar adsorbent and a polar liquid can be varied within a

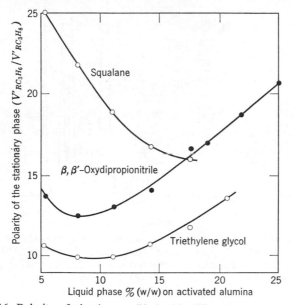

Fig. 4-16. Polarity of alumina modified with different amounts of squalane, β,β'-oxydipropionitrile, and triethylene glycol. Polarity of the stationary phase is measured by the retention time of propene relative to that of propane (71).

reasonably wide range by changing the relative amount of liquid. In Figure 4-17 the chromatogram obtained from glass microbeads coated with a mixture of highly dispersed ferric oxide and triethylene glycol shows that even strongly polar solutes are eluted as symmetrical peaks.

As a consequence of the strong interaction between the adsorbent and the polar liquid, the vapor pressure of the liquid on the adsorbent surface is always smaller than the vapor pressure of the pure liquid in the bulk phase, at the same temperature. Thus, bleeding is reduced. Porous polymer beads can also be used in gas–solid–liquid chromatography when coated with a liquid phase. The properties of such combinations have not yet been investigated in detail, but it was found repeatedly that the chromatographic behavior of such combined stationary phases is different from that of the beads alone or the liquid phase used on an inert support.

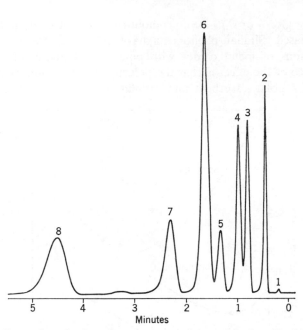

Fig. 4-17. Separation of polar substances on a mixture of ferric oxide (90.91 %) and triethylene glycol (9.09%). Support: glass microbeads. Temperature: 100°C (72). Elution order: *1*, air; *2*, diethyl ether; *3*, ethyl formate; *4*, acetone; *5*, ethyl acetate; *6*, ethylmethyl ketone; *7*, ethyl propionate; *8*, ethyl butyrate.

IX. The Support

The function of the support material is to hold the stationary phase in a finely dispersed form, providing a high interfacial area in the column. An ideal support is characterized as follows:

1. It has a large surface area per unit volume.

2. It possesses chemical inertness and thermal stability and does not adsorb sample components under operating conditions.

3. It is mechanically strong in order to withstand coating and packing procedures without disintegration or agglomeration.

4. It is available as uniform and spherical particles; it permits the preparation of columns with low permeability and a variety of capacity ratios.

5. Its pore structure is favorable for obtaining fast mass transfer in both phases.

Although a material which completely fulfills all these criteria has not yet been found, a wide variety of specially processed supports are commercially available and give satisfactory results. However, since they are far from being ideal, their influence on column performance may be significant. The proper selection of the support is a major concern when high-performance columns are needed and particularly when tailing has to be avoided.

The most commonly used supports consist of porous granules, but nonporous materials such as glass microbeads have also found some application. For further details concerning the chromatographic support, the interested reader is referred to the article written by Ottenstein (73).

A. Porous Supports

Porous supports are able to absorb relatively large quantities of the liquid phase without losing their freely flowing character due to their large internal surface area. A great number of different materials have been proposed as support. The majority of the columns in gas–liquid chromatography have used diatomite-type supports.

1. Diatomite Supports

The starting material for the preparation of these supports is diatomite, also called diatomaceous earth (kieselguhr). It originates from the fossiliz-ation of diatoms, one-celled algae, and it is found in large deposits around the world.

Diatomite consists mainly of amorphous silica with minor impurities and has a specific surface area of approximately 20 m^2/g as a result of the porous structure of the diatom skeletons. The mineral itself, after washing and screening, has been used as a support only to a limited extent. The two basic types of commonly used supports are manufactured from it by heat treatment: the white and pink support materials.

The white material is the filter-aid type which is prepared by heating diatomite with a small amount of flux, sodium carbonate, at temperatures above 900°. During calcination the fine particles aggregate, the amorphous silica is partly converted to crystobalite, and the iron content of the material becomes bound as colorless sodium iron silicate. Celite,* originally used by James and Martin, Chromosorb W,* Embacel,† and Celatom‡ are the best known trade names of this type of support, which is also offered under several other names.

The pink material is the brick type. It is prepared from diatomaceous earth which is pressed into bricks after adding a small amount of clay.

* Johns-Manville, New York, N.Y.
† May & Baker, Dagenham, England.
‡ Eagle-Picher Co.

TABLE 4-4
Typical Properties of Chromosorb Supports

	Chromosorb			
	P	G	W	Ref.
Color	Pink	Oyster white	White	
pH	6–7	8.5	8–10	76
Free fall density, g/cm³	0.38	0.47	0.18	76
Packed density, g/cm³	0.47	0.58	0.24	76
Surface area, m²/g	4.0	0.29	1.0	76
Surface area, m²/cm³	1.88	0.29	0.29	76
True density, g/cm³	2.26	—	2.20	74
Porosity	0.81	0.74	0.91	75
Pore volume, cm³/g	1.1	—	2.78	74

The bricks are fired above 900°C, then crushed and size graded. Ster-chamol,* a German firebrick, and Sil-O-Cel C 22,† brick have been widely used as support materials. The best known pink support is Chromosorb P,† but similar supports are also available under different designations.

Chemical analysis does not reveal significant difference between the various diatomite supports, but the physical data given in Table 4-4 and the microphotographs depicted in Figures 4-18 and 4-19 show that the structure of the pink and white materials is quite dissimilar. The pink support is a dense material of good mechanical strength. The diatomite particles are agglomerated very tightly, retaining the fine pore structure of the mineral. Therefore, the pore volume of the material consists mainly of micropores resulting in a relatively high specific surface area. In the white support the fine structure of the diatomite has been largely destroyed, and the particles consist of loose agglomerates of the diatomite fragments held together by sodium silicate glass. As a consequence of this macroporous structure, the resistance of the white material against breaking down is poor, and its density and specific surface area is significantly smaller than that of the pink material.

These structural differences should be kept in mind when working with diatomaceous supports. The pink material, due to its pore structure and large surface area as well as relatively small internal void space, is a superior support material as far as column performance is concerned. However, it shows undesirable surface effects (tailing), particularly when

* Sterchamol Werke, Dortmund-Wülfrath, Germany.
† Johns-Manville, New York, N.Y.

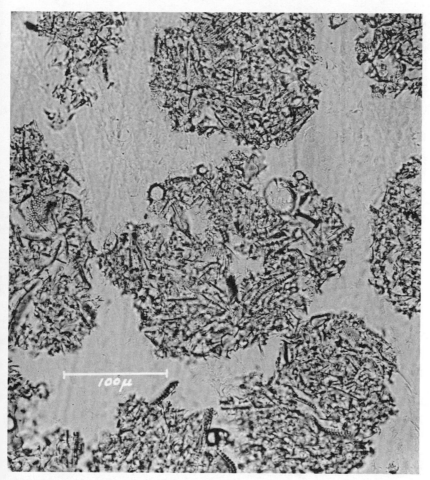

Fig. 4-18. Thin-section of Chromosorb W of Johns-Manville, a white support (73).

a polar sample is analyzed. The white material has a comparatively non-adsorptive surface, but it is not as good with respect to column efficiency and is also very fragile.

A recently introduced diatomaceous support is Chromosorb G,* which—to a substantial degree—combines the high column efficiency and good handling characteristics of the pink material and the less adsorptive surface of the white material, according to the manufacturer.

Due to differences in density, porosity, and specific surface area of various supports, the amount of stationary phase, its dispersion, and the

* Johns-Manville.

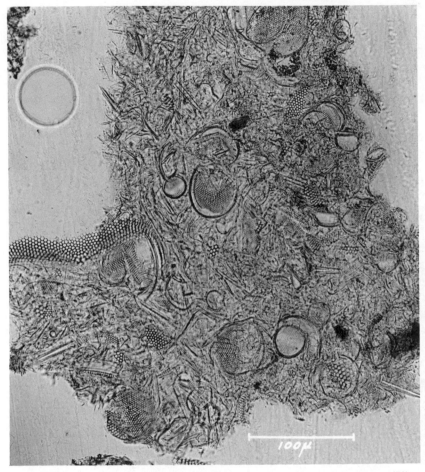

Fig. 4-19. Thin-section of Chromosorb P of Johns-Manville, a pink support (73).

phase ratio in the column are different when different support materials
are used with the same weight per cent coating.

Table 4-5 shows the liquid phase quantities in 100 ml of column
materials prepared from Chromosorb G, W, and P with various loading.
Table 4-6 shows variations in the "film thickness" and phase ratio at
2% (w/w) loading on the above supports. In the calculation of these data
a liquid stationary phase with unit density is assumed. Although there is
no coherent uniform liquid film on the support surface, the calculated film
thickness gives a rough estimation of the dispersion of the liquid phase
deposited in the finest pores, cavities, and at the crossing points of the

TABLE 4-5

Amount of Liquid Phase in 100 ml of Column Material at Various Loadings[a]

Support	Chromosorb G	Chromosorb W	Chromosorb P
Grams support	58.0	24.0	47.0
Grams liquid phase at 1% (w/w)	0.58	0.24	0.47
Grams liquid phase at 2% (w/w)	1.18	0.48	0.95
Grams liquid phase at 3% (w/w)	1.79	0.74	1.45
Grams liquid phase at 4% (w/w)	2.42	1.00	1.95
Grams liquid phase at 5% (w/w)	3.05	1.26	2.47

[a] Data from Johns-Manville.

support granules. The data show that while the amount of stationary phase per unit volume varies only with a factor of 2.4, the phase ratio may vary by a factor of 4 and the "film thickness" by a factor of 8 when various supports are coated with 2% (w/w) stationary phase.

TABLE 4-6

Comparison of Column Materials Made with 2% (w/w) Loading on Various Diatomite Supports (Calculated)

	Dimension	Chromosorb		
		P	G	W
Weight of support per 100 cm^3	g	47	58	24
Weight of liquid phase per 100 cm^2	g	0.95	1.18	0.48
Phase ratio, β	—	86	63	18
"Film thickness"	μ	0.5	4	1.65

As a consequence of the structural differences, the maximum liquid phase loading which can be applied without serious deterioration of column performance is also different.

2. Deactivation of Diatomite Supports

The surface of these supports is not completely inert and therefore can be responsible for tailing, shifting retention, and occasionally even for catalytic effects (77).

Since the support surface is covered with silanol (SiOH) groups, the effects are partly attributed to these hydrogen bonding sites.

The number of silanol groups per unit volume is several times larger on the pink material than on the white supports according to its higher specific surface are and density. This explains the greater activity of the pink support, since no major difference in surface character of the two materials was found. In addition to the silanol groups, acidic adsorption sites may also be responsible for surface effects (78). The acidity of water suspension of the pink material indicates the presence of acidic sites. The basic character of the white material is due to the sodium carbonate flux used for preparation.

Coating the support with the liquid phase results in some deactivation of the adsorption sites, particularly when the liquid phase is of polar character. However, the remaining support activity is still significant in lightly loaded columns or when polar samples are analyzed on nonpolar liquid phases.

In order to suppress support activity several methods have been developed. They may be divided into three groups: chemical treatment of the support (acid washing, silanizing), subcoating, and use of tailing reducer additives in the liquid phase. The latter was discussed in connection with liquid phases.

a. Treatment of the Support. (*1*) *Acid–Alkali Washing.* Acid washing is the most commonly used treatment of diatomaceous supports. It is usually carried out by heating a slurry of the support in concentrated hydrochloric acid for 20–30 min. Then the acid is decanted and the product is washed with water until it becomes neutral. After a methanol rinse the support material is dried.

It is not clear what is the actual effect of acid washing. Zlatkis et al. made microphotographs of the pink support before and after washing with aqua regia (79). The pictures show that the fine dust has been removed from the support by the treatment and the washed particles appear to be regular clear and sharp. The effect of the usual treatment is probably similar and mainly consists of the removal of fines which could be the major carrier of activity. A great disadvantage of acid washing is that the the support becomes friable.

Alkali washing is also used for surface modification. This treatment usually follows the acid washing but may also be applied individually. The support is treated with a 10% solution of sodium hydroxide in methanol under reflux or in the cold, then washed with methanol and water until a neutral effluent is obtained.

In special cases, washing with other acids and bases was found to be effective. For example, Jones (80) used nitric acid for washing firebricks. Bombaugh (81) digested Chromosorb with glacial acetic acid in order to obtain improved separation of methanol and ethanol.

(2) *Surface Treatment with Silicone Compounds.* The most widely used method for deactivation of the support is the treatment with reactive silicone compounds such as dimethyldichlorosilane (DMCS), trimethyl-chlorosilane (TMCS), and hexamethyldisilazane (HMDS).

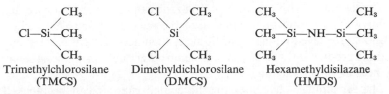

Trimethylchlorosilane (TMCS)	Dimethyldichlorosilane (DMCS)	Hexamethyldisilazane (HMDS)

Both chlorinated silanes derivates are very volatile, toxic and inflammable, therefore, their handling requires special attention. Hexamethyl-disilazane is less toxic and less volatile.

The active silanol groups on the support surface react with DMCS according to the following reactions

$$-\overset{|}{\underset{|}{Si}}-OH + (CH_3)_2SiCl_2 \longrightarrow -\overset{|}{\underset{|}{Si}}-O-\overset{CH_3}{\underset{CH_3}{\overset{|}{\underset{|}{Si}}}}-Cl + HCl$$

and

$$\begin{array}{c} -\overset{|}{Si}-OH \\ | \\ O \\ | \\ -\overset{|}{Si}-OH \\ | \end{array} + (CH_3)_2SiCl_2 \rightarrow \begin{array}{c} -\overset{|}{Si}-O \\ | \qquad\qquad CH_3 \\ O \qquad Si \\ | \qquad\qquad CH_3 \\ -\overset{|}{Si}-O \\ | \end{array} + 2HCl$$

These reactions are assumed to occur simultaneously. The reaction of a single silanol group is predominant; therefore, it is necessary to use methanol washing in order to bring about the etherification of the primary chlorosilyl ether:

$$-\overset{|}{\underset{|}{Si}}-O-\overset{CH_3}{\underset{CH_3}{\overset{|}{\underset{|}{Si}}}}-Cl \xrightarrow{R\text{-}OH} -\overset{|}{\underset{|}{Si}}-O-\overset{CH_3}{\underset{CH_3}{\overset{|}{\underset{|}{Si}}}}-O-R + HCl$$

The reaction with HMDS may be illustrated by the following equation:

$$\begin{array}{c} -\overset{|}{Si}-OH \\ | \\ O \\ | \\ -\overset{|}{Si}-OH \\ | \end{array} + (CH_3)_3Si-NH-Si(CH_3)_3 \rightarrow \begin{array}{c} -\overset{|}{Si}-O-Si(CH_3)_3 \\ | \\ O \\ | \\ -\overset{|}{Si}-O-Si(CH_3)_3 \\ | \end{array} + NH_3$$

The support has to be dried prior to the treatment since the reagents decompose by water. The procedure with DMCS can be carried out in the following way. The support is slurried in a 5% solution of the reagent in toluene. The slurry is gently shaken under reduced pressure to remove entrapped air. After 5 min it is filtered and washed with toluene. Subsequently, the support is suspended in methanol and filtered again. After a final washing with methanol the product is dried.

The treatment with hexamethyldisilazane can be carried out by refluxing a slurry of the support in a solution of the reagent in petroleum ether (bp 60–80°C) for several hours. The liquid is then decanted (it may be reused), and the product is washed with petroleum ether and n-propanol, then dried by heating under vacuum.

The remaining active sites on the coated support can be blocked by in-place silanizing, as suggested by Atkinson and Tuey (82). Hexamethyldisilazane is injected at slow carrier gas flow rate into the column which is already packed with the coated support. The column temperature is preferably around 80°C. Ammonia, produced by the reaction, and the excess reagent are removed by the carrier gas.* Repeated injections are often required for effective deactivation. Of course, this method is not permissible when the liquid phase can react with the silanizing agent.

Dal Nogare and Juvet (1) developed a rapid and effective treatment of the support with an 1% aqueous solution of Siliclad,† a water-soluble silicone which is used widely for rendering the surface of laboratory glassware hydrophobic. One part of the support is heated with approximately three parts of the solution on a steam bath for one hour. Subsequently the slurry is filtered, washed with water and acetone, then dried in vacuo at 110°C for one hour.

The above-described treatments reduces drastically the specific surface area of the starting material, and the support material becomes hydrophobic. The silanized material is superior to the original with respect to reduced surface activity, but no complete suppression of activity can be achieved by these methods. The HMDS-treated pink material shows an activity about comparable to that of the untreated white material. Consequently, a further deactivation of the support may become necessary for very critical applications.

(3) *Subcoating of the Support.*   Effective suppression of support activity has been achieved by coating the surface with solids. Omerod and Scott

---

* During this operation, it is advisable to disconnect the column end from the detector (particularly if flame ionization detector is used) in order to avoid undesirable SiO_2 deposits.

† Clay Adams Inc., New York, N.Y.

(83) deposited silver using the Rochelle salt process on the surface of diatomaceous support. Impregnation of the support with KOH is often used in order to reduce tailing when amines are analyzed.

Recently, polymeric organic materials have been introduced for support subcoating. VandenHeuvel, Gardiner, and Horning (84) found the subcoating of acid-washed diatomite support with 1% polyvinylpyrrolidone solution in methanol prior to coating with the polar liquid phase to be effective. However, the PVP-treated support was not suitable for coating with nonpolar silicone polymers. Onaka and Okamoto (85) treated diatomaceous support with Teflon emulsion and in this way obtained inert support materials.

3. Fluorine-Containing Polymers

Fluorine-containing polymers are relatively inert and have low specific surface area. They were introduced as support material in the analysis of highly polar (aqueous) samples.

The polymers are used in form of porous granules, which consist of aggregates of very fine particles. The various types mentioned in the literature can be divided into two major groups: fluorocarbon and chlorofluorocarbon supports. The most common fluorocarbon support is made of Teflon (du Pont). For example Chromosorb T (Johns-Manville) is prepared of Teflon 6 molding powder. Teflon 6 is chemically inert and insoluble in common solvents. Although it is one of the least adsorptive materials now available, it is still not completely inert as a support. The upper temperature limit for Chromosorb T is about 275°C, but the individual particles begin to sinter at prolonged operation above 225°C. At temperatures over 290°C, Teflon 6 decomposes and releases noxious fumes. Other granular porous fluorocarbon resins for use as support are also available under the trade names Fluoropak-80 and Haloport.

The best known chlorofluorocarbon supports are made of various Kel-F molding powders (Minnesota Mining and Manufacturing Co.). These are less inactive but harder than the fluorocarbon types and can be handled similarly to diatomaceous materials.

Properties of Teflon and Kel-F supports were investigated and compared in a detailed study of Kirkland (86).

4. Other Porous Supports

A great variety of porous materials, such as unglassed tile (87) and microporous polyethylene (88) have been found to be useful supports. The inorganic matrix of the alkylarylsulfonate in the household detergent Tide has also been used as an efficient support (89). A similar material can be made by lyophilization of a mixture of sodium hexametaphosphate, sodium sulfate, and sodium silicate (90). The use of large-pore porous glass as a support, both in acid-washed and silanized form, also received attention recently (91).

B. Nonporous Supports

Glass Microbeads.   Tiny glass spheres used as support material were introduced by Cvetanovic and Kutschke (92) and investigated in detail by Littlewood (93). The properties and use of glass beads are different from those of porous supports. The surface area of the commonly used mesh fractions (particle diameter around 0.1 mm) is 0.1–0.2 m^2/g, much lower than that of other supports. On the other hand, microbeads have a packing density of 1.8–2.0 g/cm^3. Thus the same amount of stationary phase per unit column volume can be obtained at much lower weight per cent of stationary phase with glass microbeads than with diatomaceous supports.

The surface areas per unit volume of glass beads and white diatomaceous support are similar (~ 0.2 m^2/cm^3). Since the porosity of a glass bead column ($a = 0.40$) is about one-half that of a column packed with the diatomaceous support ($a = 0.80$), the phase ratio in a glass bead column is about twice that of a column packed with white diatomaceous support when the "film thickness" is the same.

Microbead columns are used preferably in the analysis of high-boiling compounds and are coated with 0.05–0.5% (w/w) of a liquid phase. The maximum loading is approximately 3% (w/w).

The major disadvantage of glass bead support is that the liquid phase is not uniformly distributed on the surface of the beads but a great part of it is held at the contact points. As a result, the column performance is often poor. However, proper conditioning can improve the distribution and column performance.

Because of the small specific surface area of glass beads, this support is regarded as inert even at very low loading with the liquid phase loading. However, it is not completely inert, and silanization may be needed occasionally. If the glass surface is etched in order to obtain a uniform distribution of the liquid phase, substantial support activity can be expected.

Owing to the spherical shape and uniformity of microbeads, columns can be packed uniformly with this material. Coated beads, however, are rather sticky and difficult to pack so that the regularity of such packing is questionable. Therefore, glass bead columns are preferably made by the in-place coating method.

Glass microbeads, also in siliconized form, are available in various mesh fractions covering the range of 20–325 mesh (Microbeads, Inc., Jackson, Miss.). Naturally, silicone-treated glass beads cannot be coated with polar liquid phases.

The surface area of the support and the uniformity of the liquid phase distribution can be increased by creating a porous layer on the surface of the glass beads. Ohline and Jojola (94) etched microbeads in a stream of air–hydrogen fluoride mixture. They found the treated support to be superior regarding column performance but inferior regarding support activity as compared with untreated beads. Another way of etching glass beads is to heat them with diluted ammonium hydroxide in a closed vessel for several hours at 150°C.

The surfaces of glass beads can be coated with fine particles (72,95) in order to obtain a thin porous layer. When the layer consists of relatively inert material and is impregnated with a liquid phase, efficient GLC columns may be obtained. When the layer is made of adsorbent particles, column materials for GSC are obtained. The combination of an adsorbent with a liquid phase on the surface of microbeads results in column material for GSLC.

C. Selection of the Support

Almost any analytical problem in gas chromatography can be solved with columns made of diatomaceous supports. When more than 5% w/w liquid phase is used, the support usually does not need treatment. Low-loaded columns, however, require treated supports. Subcoating or the use of tailing reducing additive extends the range of diatomaceous supports.

Teflon support or glass microbeads may represent a good choice when highly polar samples are to be analyzed. However, in this area the recently introduced porous polymer beads might have better potentialities.

D. Particle Size

The average particle size of the support is most commonly between 0.6 mm and 0.1 mm. In order to obtain uniform column packing, the variation in particle diameter must be small and the support requires careful size grading. In addition, some porous supports contain a considerable amount of fine dust which has to be removed.

Wet or dry sieving are the most often used size grading and dust removing procedures. As a consequence, the particle size range of commercial support materials is specified in the United States by mesh or screen numbers of the Tyler or the U.S. Standard sieve scales. Table 4-7 shows the specifications of these sieve series.

TABLE 4-7

Sieve Specifications

U.S. Standards screens				Tyler screens			
	Aperture		Tolerance on average aperture, ±%		Aperture		Double Tyler series mesh
No.	in.	mm		Mesh	in.	mm	
3	0.265	6.73	3	3	0.263	6.680	
3½	0.223	5.66	3		0.221	5.613	3½
4	0.187	4.76	3	4	0.185	4.699	
5	0.157	4.00	3		0.156	3.962	5
6	0.132	3.36	3	6	0.131	3.327	
7	0.111	2.83	3		0.110	2.794	7
8	0.0937	2.38	3	8	0.093	2.362	
10	0.0787	2.00	3		0.078	1.981	9
12	0.0661	1.68	3	10	0.065	1.651	
14	0.0555	1.41	3		0.055	1.397	12
16	0.0469	1.19	3	14	0.046	1.168	
18	0.0394	1.00	3		0.039	0.991	16
20	0.0331	0.84	5	20	0.0328	0.833	
25	0.0280	0.74	5		0.0276	0.701	24
30	0.0232	0.59	5	28	0.0232	0.589	
35	0.0197	0.50	5		0.0195	0.495	32
40	0.0165	0.42	5	35	0.0164	0.417	
45	0.0138	0.35	5		0.0138	0.351	42
50	0.0117	0.297	6	48	0.0116	0.295	
60	0.0098	0.250	6		0.0097	0.246	60
70	0.0083	0.210	6	65	0.0082	0.208	
80	0.0070	0.177	6		0.0069	0.175	80
100	0.0059	0.149	6	100	0.0058	0.147	
120	0.0049	0.125	6		0.0049	0.124	115
140	0.0041	0.105	8	150	0.0041	0.104	
170	0.0035	0.088	8		0.0035	0.088	170
200	0.0029	0.074	8	200	0.0029	0.074	
230	0.0024	0.062	8		0.0024	0.061	250
270	0.0021	0.053	8	270	0.0021	0.053	
325	0.0017	0.044	8		0.0017	0.043	325
				400	0.0015	0.037	

Sieves of the Tyler Screen Scale are characterized by the number of meshes per inch. The aperture is determined by the wire diameter which is standardized. The original system is based on the 200 mesh screen and the ratio of apertures of consecutive screens is the square root of 2. For closer sizing, a series of intermediate screens are now available (Double Tyler Series), and the aperture ratio in the complete series is the fourth root of 2.

A sieve fraction is designated by the screen which the particles pass through $(d_{p(max)})$ and by the screen which the particles do not pass through $(d_{p(min)})$. For example, a 115–150 mesh support consist of particles which pass the 115 mesh screen but not the 150 mesh screen, and therefore have a particle size range of 0.104–0.125 mm. The same fraction can also be specified as -150 and $+115$ mesh or 115/150 mesh.

Screens of the U.S. Standard sieves are designated by arbitrary numbers or by sieve openings expressed in microns. The system is based on the 18 mesh screen with 1.00-mm aperture. The aperture ratio of consecutive screens is the fourth root of 2.

Although the screen numbers (U.S. Standard) and the approximate mesh numbers (Tyler) are both occasionally equal, the "mesh fraction" obtained by U.S. Standard sieves should be specified by the sieve numbers, or better, by the particle size range expressed in millimeters or microns. In this way one can avoid reporting a 40–45-mesh fraction since there is neither 40- nor 45-mesh screen in the Tyler system. Nevertheless the screen number of the U.S. Standard sieves is often referred to as "mesh" in the literature.

The British Standard Sieve Series is similar to the Tyler Series with slight variation due to differences in U.S. and British standard wires.

In many European countries, the German DIN standard sieves are used. In this metric system, the sieves are identified by a number and also by the number of meshes per square centimeter.

The particle size range in some commonly used sieve fractions is shown in Table 4-8. It is seen that the range ratio $(d_{p(max)}/d_{p(min)})$ decreases with the aperture. On the other hand, the permissible tolerance of sieve openings increases with the screen number, and thus the actual range ratio of fine grades is significantly greater than indicated by the nominal apertures.

Sedimentation is often employed for removing fines. In the case of friable supports, sieving may be accompanied by some destruction of the particles. It is then advisable to permit the sieved fraction to fall through water in a cylinder and decant the water containing the fines. Continuous elutriation is also an efficient tool for fractionating small particles $(d_p$ less than 60 μ), a method also used occasionally in gas chromatography.

TABLE 4-8

Particle Sizes in Commonly Used Sieve Fractions

| Sieve fraction U.S. Standard screens | Aperture | | Particle diameter | |
	Top screen ($d_{p(max)}$)	Bottom screen ($d_{p(min)}$)	Spread ($d_{p(max)} - d_{p(min)}$)	Ratio ($d_{p(max)}/d_{p(min)}$)
10–30	2000 μ	590 μ	1410 μ	3.39
30–60	590	250	340	2.36
35–80	500	177	323	2.83
45–60	350	250	100	1.40
60–80	250	177	73	1.41
80–100	177	149	28	1.19
100–120	149	125	24	1.19
120–140	125	105	20	1.19
100–140	149	105	44	1.42

X. Preparation of Columns

Although pretested columns and column materials are commercially available, many workers use home-made columns tailored according to their particular analytical problem. Detailed descriptions of column preparation are available in the literature; nonetheless, successful column fabrication requires some experience, and the neglect of small details may jeopardize the desired results.

Different procedures lead to packed and to open tubular columns. The preparation of packed columns is relatively easy, and this fact certainly contributes to their popularity. The somewhat larger technical expenditure necessary to prepare open tubular columns, however, should not suggest that such columns of satisfactory quality cannot be made in any laboratory without special equipment. The preparation of glass capillary tubing or porous layer open tubular columns may represent an exception. Detailed description of the preparation of open tubular columns is given by Ettre (10) and Kaiser (96).

The reproducibility of column preparation is usually an important practical point. When columns having the same permeability, phase ratio, and performance under given operating condition are needed, starting materials of the same origin should be used. On the other hand, reproducibility of results taken from the literature might be influenced by the instruments, and the column should not be blamed for lack of reproducibility without a thorough check of the instrumental aspects.

A. Preparation of Packed Columns

1. Tubing

Packed columns are usually constructed of metal or glass tubing. The most commonly used metal tubings are made of stainless steel, copper, or aluminum. It should be kept in mind that copper and aluminum may catalyze changes in both the liquid phase and sample components above 150°C. Therefore, preference is given to glass columns when the sample components are relatively unstable and high column temperatures are required, although the question of whether the use of glass tubing was really the essential part of successful operation has been the subject of controversy. However, one advantage of the glass tubing is that the packing can be observed.

For convenience, the tubings of packed columns are generally characterized by their outside diameter, which determines the necessary size of fittings. For analytical columns, the most common tube o.d.'s are ⅛, 3/16, and ¼ in. Since the effective column diameter is the inside diameter of the tubing, it should also be specified.

The tube may be shaped in different ways, depending on its length and on the dimensions of the oven of the instrument. Short columns up to 2 m are often made in U-form, but most generally coiled columns are used. The effect of coiling on column performance concerned several investigators who found no deterioration when the ratio of coil diameter to tube diameter exceeded 10. The tubing is usually bent or precoiled before cleaning and filling. Some less commonly used columns, i.e., W-shaped columns and micro packed columns, are bent to the final shape after filling the straight tube. Long columns are made of separate pieces which are packed individually and then connected to each other, preferably without any dead volume at the connections.

The column ends are connected to the corresponding parts of the instrument by tube fittings—for example, Swagelok fittings, which are available in many sizes and are also suitable to connect glass columns. The tubing of a discarded column may be retrieved and reused, after unpacking it by applying vibration and slight pressure from a gas tank.

In order to remove contamination due to the manufacturing process or previous use, the tubing has to be cleaned carefully by washing with hot detergent solution or with solvents. After cleaning, the tube has to be dried in a dry gas stream.

2. Preparation of Column Material

a. Columns for GSC. When a granulated adsorbent, i.e., alumina, silica gel, or molecular sieve, is used as stationary phase, the proper sieve fraction of the material is usually ready for filling into the tube. The activation of solid stationary phase is conveniently carried out in a gas stream, after placing the packed column into the oven of the gas chromatograph.

In special cases, adsorbent powders are used as stationary phases, and the support (e.g., glass microbeads) is "coated" with the finely dispersed solid (50,72). Such a column material may be prepared in the following way. A suspension of the adsorbent is made in an appropriate solvent by using a homogenizer. The support is shaken with the suspension; then the solvent is removed by filtration and evaporation. The small particles form a porous layer on the support surface, and after the fines are removed the material is ready for filling into the column. When polyethylene beads are used as the support, the adsorbent layer can be bonded onto the surface by heat treatment (97). Glass microbeads also were successfully coated with fine dispersed adsorbents from a suspension using the filtration coating method (95).

b. Column Material for GLC. The most frequently used column material consists of a liquid stationary phase on a granular support. The amount of liquid phase on the support (the "liquid loading") is commonly expressed in weight per cent, e.g. 20% (w/w) Carbowax 400 on Chromosorb W. This means that in 100 g column material, there is 20 g Carbowax 400 or that 80 g Chromosorb W is coated with 20 g Carbowax 400. There are three basic methods for the coating of the support: batch coating, in-place coating, and filtration coating.

(*1*) *Batch Coating.* The properly prepared (sieved, washed or silanized) support material is soaked with a solution of the liquid phase, and the solvent is evaporated while moving the slurry. This method is generally used because it is simple to carry it out, the liquid-to-support ratio can be predetermined easily, and the column material can be made up in one batch for a number of columns.

The solvent must be volatile and have high solving power for the liquid phase. Methylene chloride and acetone often fulfill these requirements. Suppliers of stationary phases usually furnish information on the best solvent for a particular liquid phase.

The operation is carried out by adding the solution which contains the required amount of stationary phase to the support in a dish or beaker. The solvent is conveniently evaporated by applying heat from an infrared lamp while the support is gently stirred with a glass rod, in such a manner that a breakup of the solid is avoided. A rotating evaporator, operated at low speed in order to avoid the "ball-mill" effect, may also be used for removing the solvent.

Since Teflon particles tend to agglomerate or to form a paste, the coating of Teflon support should be carried out in a special way (86). Best results are obtained when the support is cooled to 0°C before coating, then mixed with the solution of the stationary phase in a shallow dish, without exerting pressure on the particles. The evaporation of the solvent is facilitated by blowing a stream of nitrogen over the surface of the slurry without applying heat. When the solvent is evaporated, the column material is cooled to 0°C and filled into the column. The coated Teflon support should be stored in a refrigerator. Teflon packing can be handled more easily if plastic dishes and funnels are used instead of glassware.

(2) *In-Place Coating.* With this method the coating is accomplished when the support is already filled in the column. The solution of the liquid phase is forced through the support bed; subsequently the excess solution and the remaining volatile solvent are removed by an inert gas.

This method is more laborious than the previously described one, and its major disadvantage is that the predetermination of the final liquid-to-solid ratio requires an extensive standardization of the procedure. On the other hand, uncoated support can be packed more regularly, and the crushing of the support is diminished so that more uniform packing can be obtained by the in-place coating method. This method is particularly adapted for making liquid-coated microbead columns since the sticky column material obtained from the batch-coating method can hardly be packed uniformly.

Figure 4-20 shows an apparatus used for in-plane coating by Averill (98), who found that for coating silanized Chromosorb W, 80–100 mesh, in a 15-ft-long stainless steel tube (o.d. ⅛ in.), 20 ml of a solution containing 3–4 g liquid phase per 100 ml solvent has given the best results. The pressure drop was 20 psig. When coating 100–200 mesh glass beads in a column of the same dimensions, 10 ml of a solution containing 2 g liquid phase per 100 ml solvent has produced the best results. Variations of this technique are described by Lysyj and Newton (99).

(3) *Filtration Coating.* This technique was introduced by Horning et al. (100) and further developed by Supina (101) and Parcher and Urone (102). The simplest procedure is the following. A known amount of support is placed in a weighed fritted-glass funnel, and the solution of the liquid phase in a volatile solvent is added. After few minutes, the excess solution is sucked off with an aspirator and the funnel is weighed again. Subsequently the remaining solvent is removed with further aspiration. The amount of liquid phase deposited on the support is calculated from the weight and the concentration of the solution held on the support.

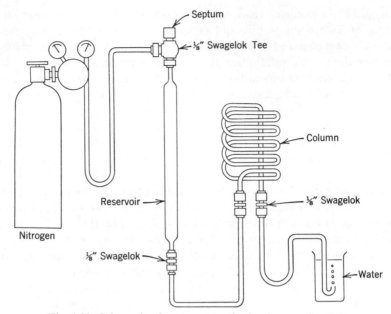

Fig. 4-20. Schematic of an apparatus for in-place coating (98).

Other methods of support coating include a simple mixing of the liquid
phase with the support, originally used by James and Martin, spraying
the stationary liquid onto the support with an atomizer, or using a
fluidized bed and vibrating layer (103). Smith (104) placed the support in
a glass tube and coated it by percolating the solution over the support bed
until a steady state was reached. After the excess solution was removed,
the packing material was extruded and dried.

3. Packing Procedures

This operation should result in a uniform fixed bed of the column
material. Therefore, the solid has to fill up the tube evenly, and any
crushing of the support material should be avoided.

Most commonly, packing is carried out in the following way. One end
of the column is closed and a funnel or container having a conical bottom
is connected to the open end. The column material is poured in and
uniform distribution of the particles is achieved by gently tapping and/or
vibrating the tube. Commercially available vibrators* or an electric hand
drill with a brass rod having an asymmetrical cross section can be used
most conveniently. Holding the tube on the half-flattened shaft of a stirring

* For example, the Burgess Vibro-Graver.

motor can also provide the necessary vibration. The operation is finished when the consolidation of the packing is completed, i.e., when no column material is taken by the tube with further vibrating or tapping. At this point the procedure has to be stopped, since further moving may cause disintegration of the column material which results in an increase of the permeability and decrease of column efficiency.

The packing can also be carried out by pneumatic displacement of the packing material from a reservoir attached to the empty tube by applying moderate gas pressure (40–50 psig). Several devices are commercially available for this method, which has proved to be very expeditious and efficient.

If a support with poor mechanical strength is used, e.g., the acid-washed supports or Chromosorb W, only gentle tapping or vibration should be applied. Similarly, when Teflon support is packed in the column, no vigorous tapping and vibration is allowed, in order to avoid plugging the column with the sticky material. Landault and Guiochon (105) described a procedure for packing Teflon column material which resulted in improved efficiency. The column is laid horizontally, vacuum and vibration are applied, and the column material is fed in very slowly.

When the column material is sticky, as in the case of liquid-coated microbeads or highly loaded supports, very strong vibration is necessary to distribute the particles in the tube. In such cases, the in-place coating might have definite advantages.

After the tube is filled with the column material, porous plugs are inserted into both ends of the column in order to keep the packing tight. The plugs should be thin in order to minimize dead space, and should be placed without applying pressure to the packing directly at the column ends. Glass wool, preferably silanized, is often used for this purpose, but thin disks of sintered stainless steel may represent a better solution for metal columns.

Micro packed columns are made of tubing having an inside diameter of 0.5–1.0 mm. Flaring out one end of the tube may facilitate the flow of column material into the tube, which should preferably be straight. Efficient vibrating of a small-diameter tube can be facilitated by placing it into a larger-diameter tube which transfers the vibration. The in-place method is often preferred for coating the support material in micro packed columns.

While micro packed columns are usually filled with particles having a diameter less than a tenth of the tube diameter, Halász and Heine (6) introduced micro columns, which they called packed capillary columns, with a column diameter to particle diameter ratio of 2:5. These columns are made by drawing out glass tubes which are loosely filled with a granular solid. The procedure is similar to that used for making glass open tubular columns, but it results in a packed column of small (less than 0.5 mm) inside diameter, which has a higher porosity and therefore a higher permeability than conventional packed columns filled with particles of the same size. Due to the high permeability, long columns up to 30 m may be operated at usual inlet pressures. Naturally, in coating the support, the in-place method must be used since the liquid phase would decompose at the temperatures required for melting the glass tube.

B. Preparation of Open Tubular Columns

1. Tubing Material

The tubing material has a great influence on the quality of open tubular columns, since the tube is not only an envelope but also the support for the stationary phase. The requirements for an ideal tubing material may be summarized as follows:

1. It is available in the desired length and with the proper inner diameter which is uniform over the entire length of the tube.

3. The inner wall of the tube can be coated uniformly and permanently with the stationary phase, but does not exhibit adsorptivity to the sample components and under operating conditions does not react with them or with the stationary phase.

3. It has sufficient temperature resistance and mechanical strength, and good thermal conductivity.

4. It can be connected conveniently to other parts of the instrument.

No ideal material has yet been found which could be used universally. In practice, stainless steel tubing is used most frequently, followed by copper and glass tubing.

Several mills supply stainless steel capillary tubing in lengths up to 2000 ft. There are various types of stainless steel which are designated by numbers corresponding to their composition. Types SS 304 and SS 316 are often recommended. For high-temperature operation, types SS 321 and SS 347 are preferred. Type SS 347 has the most uniform and smoothest interior surface and is considered by many workers as the best material for liquid-coated open tubular columns.

The outside diameter of the tubing material used most often in the United States is $\frac{1}{16}$ in. Sometimes, however, it is more convenient to use thin-wall stainless steel tubing (wall thickness 0.006–0.012 in.) which is also available with various inner diameters.

Copper tubing is lower in price than stainless steel tubing, and its inner surface can be coated conveniently with many liquid stationary phases.

However, it is not recommended when the activity of the copper surface might cause undesirable side effects.

Desty, Goldup, and Whyman (106) introduced glass capillary tubing for preparation of open tubular columns. A relatively simple device, depicted in Figure 4-21, is used for drawing the elongated tube of small inside and outside diameter from a thick-walled glass capillary tube.* Adjusting the drawing and heating rate, tubings with different diameters and wall

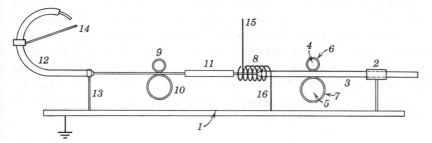

Fig. 4-21. Apparatus for drawing capillary tubes (107). *1*, Brass base plate; *2*, support; *3*, thick-walled glass tube; *4* and *5*, feed rollers; *6* and *7*, rubber tires; *8*, furnace; *9* and *10*, draw rollers; *11*, porcelain tube; *12*, bending tube; *13*, bending tube support and earth connection; *14*, connection to low-voltage transformer 1; *15*, connection to low-voltage transformer 2; *16*, furnace support and earth connection.

thicknesses can be obtained in the form of a compact coil. The composition of the glass is critical for the procedure and for the quality of the column.

Plastic tubings have been used only in special cases because of their poor temperature resistance and coatability. Scott (108) obtained notable results with nylon capillary tubing.

2. Inside Diameter of Capillary Tubes

Open tubular columns most commonly have inside diameters of 0.25–0.50 mm (0.010–0.020 in.). The nominal i.d. given by the manufacturer is often not equal to the actual value, which may also vary along the column. Sometimes it is necessary to determine the actual inside diameter. The average mechanical inside diameter is calculated from the volume and the length of the tube. It is usually larger than the diameter calculated from the measured column permeability (equations 4-42 and 4-44), indicating nonuniformity of the tube interior.

* Such a glass capillary drawing machine is produced and marketed by Dr. Hupe Apparatebau G.m.b.H., Karlsruhe, Germany.

3. Cleaning of the Tubing

The inner wall of the capillary tubing is frequently contaminated in the manufacturing. The adsorbed material can hinder the uniform coating of the inner wall or modify the behavior of the stationary phase. Therefore, cleaning of the tube prior to coating is absolutely necessary. The cleaning procedure is carried out essentially with the same setup used in the dynamic coating method described below.

During cleaning, the tube is flushed with various solvents of different polarity, starting with a nonpolar solvent and ending with the solvent of the stationary phase used for coating. Ordinarily repeated washing with pentane, chloroform, methanol, acetone, and the solvent of the liquid phase provides adequate results. A similar procedure is followed before the recoating of open tubular columns. All solvents and solutions used for washing and evaporating open tubular columns should be filtered in order to avoid plugging the small-bore tube.

4. Coating Procedures

a. Dynamic Method.   This most widely used column coating method was first described by Dijkstra and Goey (109). The solution of the liquid phase, the volume of which is larger than the void volume of the tube, is forced through the tube with the aid of a dry inert gas. Thus, the inside wall of the column is wetted with the solution and the solvent is subsequently removed by blowing dry gas through the column. Figure 4-22 shows a typical system for the dynamic coating procedure.

The basic requirement is that the interior wall of the column be wetted by the solution of the stationary phase, since a fine distribution of the liquid phase, which can be approximated as a thin film, is necessary for obtaining efficient columns. The thickness and uniformity of the liquid film is largely determined by the velocity of the coating solution, the concentration of the solution, and the nature of the solvent.

The coating solution should pass the tubing with a constant flow velocity which is preferably less than 10 cm/sec. It is equivalent to flow rates of 0.29 and 1.18 ml/min for columns having the respective inside diameters of 0.25 and 0.55 mm. Depending on the column length, the gas pressure which is required to force the coating solution through the tube is usually between 10 and 40 psig. The concentration of the liquid stationary phase in the coating solution is generally 10% (w/w).

A variation of the dynamic coating technique is the so-called plug method. Here the volume of the solution is less than the void volume of the tubing, and the solution plug is forced at constant velocity through the

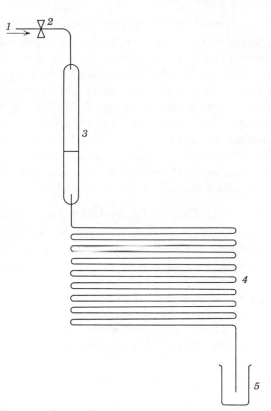

Fig. 4-22. Apparatus for coating open tubular columns by the dynamic method. *1*, Inert gas from tank; *2*, pressure regulator; *3*, reservoir for the coating solution; *4*, column; *5*, small beaker.

column. This method was used by Scott and Hazeldean (36) and studied in detail by Kaiser (96).

b. Static Coating Method. With this method, the tube is completely filled with a solution of the liquid phase, and one end is closed. Then, starting with the open end, the tube is slowly drawn through a heated duct into a heated chamber; the solvent evaporates, and the liquid phase remains on the inner wall of the tube. The film thickness of the liquid phase is predetermined by the concentration of the coating solution. The temperature of the chamber is adjusted so that no condensation of the solvent should occur in the open portion of the tubing. This technique requires elaborated equipment and ordinarily is not used for preparation of liquid-coated columns. However, it has become significant for fabricating open tubular columns which have a porous layer on the inner wall.

5. Treated-Wall Open Tubular Columns

Chemical treatment of the inner walls of several tubing materials may result in open tubular columns with an adsorptive layer for GSC or in an increased interior surface area for coating with a liquid phase (GLC). Glass capillary tubing was etched by Mohnke and Saffert (110) with an ammonia solution, and by Bruner and Cartoni (19) with an NaOH solution. As a result, a porous SiO_2 layer was formed on the inside wall. Such columns were successfully used in GSC and after coating them with a liquid phase, i.e. squalane, in GLC, and in GSLC. The interior of aluminum tubing (111) was oxidized, and the metal oxide layer formed served with or without liquid coating as the stationary phase.

6. Open Tubular Columns Coated with a Porous Layer

A suspension of a finely divided solid can also be used for coating the tube interior in the same way as a solution of the liquid phase. When the suspension contains only an adsorbent the resulting porous-layer open tubular column is used for gas–solid chromatography.

When the solid particles are inert and the suspension also contains a liquid stationary phase, the columns obtained by this technique are for gas–liquid chromatography. The combination of an adsorbent and a liquid phase may provide efficient columns for gas–solid–liquid chromatography.

As an effect of the support layer, such columns usually have a higher loading, i.e., a higher phase ratio, β, and a longer lifetime than the classical open tubular columns. The performance of porous layer columns is equal to or better than that of the classical open tubular column having the same inside diameter, since the porous layer permits a very fine distribution of the liquid stationary phase.

The dynamic coating method was used for preparing open tubular columns lined with an adsorptive layer by Schwartz et al. (112) using colloidal silica; by Kirkland (113), using colloidal boehmite (Baymal, du Pont) and Purcell (114), who used the suspension of silica gel as well as Molecular Sieve 5A.

The static coating method permits a much better control of the composition and thickness of the resulting porous layer than the dynamic method. In addition, it permits the use of practically any kind of solid powders and liquid phases. This technique has been introduced by Halász and Horváth (115) for preparing a great variety of porous layer open tubular columns. Ettre and co-workers (116) have investigated extensively the properties of such columns in GLC, using a diatomaceous support having particle size around $1\ \mu$ for rendering the porous layer. These columns are commercially available with various stationary phases (Perkin-Elmer Corp.).

Porous layer open tubular columns have a greater amount of stationary phase per unit column length than the classical open tubular columns. Therefore, the maximum allowable sample size is also greater, and these columns can be operated often without splitting and with less sensitive detectors. They also show great potentialities in trace analysis. Accordingly, very good results were obtained when these columns were used in the tandem operation of a gas chromatograph with a mass spectrometer (117).

C. Column Conditioning

Every freshly prepared column requires conditioning before starting the analytical work. The conditioning is necessary in order to (*1*) remove the remaining solvent, water, and other volatile contaminants; (*2*) achieve a more uniform distribution of liquid phase on the support or tube wall; or (*3*) activate, or in special cases deactivate, the solid stationary phase.

Most commonly, conditioning is carried out in the oven of the gas chromatograph. The column inlet is connected to the instrument, and the column is heated for several hours in a moderate carrier gas stream. The temperature is slowly raised up to 20–30°C below the maximum recommended temperature for the particular stationary phase. During the initial conditioning period, the column outlet should not be connected to the detector. In a later stage, the column outlet may be connected to the detector and the end of the conditioning can be monitored by the recorder. When the baseline remains steady, the column is ready for operation. Heating overnight at the maximum temperature is usually adequate for conditioning. Another conditioning technique was described by Littlewood (93) for increasing the performance of liquid-coated microbead columns. After removing the volatile contaminants, both ends of the column were sealed and the column was heated to approximately 50°C above the maximum recommended temperature for several hours.

Activation of the solid stationary phase (adsorbent) may be carried out in the oven of the gas chromatograph if no excessively high temperatures are required. The procedure is specific and must necessarily be standardized in order to obtain reproducible results. Occasionally, the solid stationary phase is deactivated with help of a moisturized carrier gas. The moisturization can be achieved by passing the carrier gas through a cartridge containing wet kieselguhr or $Na_2SO_4 \cdot 10H_2O$, etc., as well as by water vapor from a damp generator. When a cartridge is used it must be kept at a constant temperature in order to maintain the partial pressure of water constant in the carrier gas.

D. Column Storage and Handling

When the column is not in the instrument its two ends must be sealed in order to avoid contact with the atmosphere. Open tubular columns are particularly sensitive to oxygen and humidity. All types of columns require careful handling. Shaking, dropping, or bending may cause crushing of the column material in packed columns or breaking of the liquid film as well as plugging in open tubular columns.

E. Column Rejuvenation

The lifetime of a column varies depending on the column material and the operating conditions. Changes in the absolute and relative retention times and deterioration of column efficiency indicate that the column has to be replaced. Loss of stationary phase by bleeding or decomposition is the major factor responsible for column decay in GLC. Contaminants from samples and carrier gas effect column life in both GLC and GSC. The liquid film in open tubular columns may break, causing tailing and poor column performance.

It is often possible and for economic reasons desirable to regenerate the column.

Liquid-coated open tubular columns can be recoated, if the tube is not plugged, after washing off the remaining stationary phase and possible deposits from the inner wall. For removing these residues the consecutive use of methylene chloride, methanol, water, 20% nitric acid, water, methanol, and the solvent of the liquid phase used for recoating is recommended.

Packed columns are less frequently reconditioned than open tubular columns. Sometimes they may be recoated without removing the exhausted column material by the in-place coating method described above. A rejuvenation method using repeated injection of the stationary phase into the heated column while in the gas chromatograph is also described (118). If tailing appears after a period of operation time, the activity of the column material may be reduced by injecting small quantities of hexamethyldisilazane at temperatures of 80–100°C and at reduced carrier gas flow (82). After a few minutes, the agent and its decomposition products are eluted and the column is ready for analytical work.

F. Column Testing

The best way of testing the performance of a newly made column is measuring the resolution of a critical solute pair of the sample which is intended to be separated by the column. In practice, columns are often used for solving different separation problems, and thus a less specific testing procedure is advantageous especially in laboratories where a great number of columns are fabricated periodically.

The following tests, when carried out under standardized conditions, can be used either for testing new columns or for checking column properties.

a. Permeability Test. The air peak time is measured at a standardized inlet pressure and temperature using the same carrier gas. An air peak time longer than that of a standard column indicates breakup of the column material in packed columns or partial plugging of open tubular columns. The measurement of the outlet flow rate of the carrier gas under these conditions provides the same information.

b. Performance Test. The relative peak sharpness, t_R/w, of a peak eluted at a fixed k value, which is preferably larger than 3, is measured and compared to a standard value. In a similar way, plate number or HETP can also be used for comparison.

c. Polarity Test. Relative retention of closely boiling sample components which have different polarity give valuable information on column polarity. For column testing Averill (69) recommends the use of a so-called polarity mixture with the following composition:

Component	Bp (°C)	Composition (vol %)
Ethanol	78.5	40
Methyl ethyl ketone	79.6	20
Cyclohexane	81.4	5
Benzene	80.1	10

XI. Techniques for Analysis of Samples with Wide Boiling Point Range

If the boiling points of the sample components are widely different, the isothermal operation of a column at constant inlet pressure or constant flow usually fails to bring about a complete separation, because the conditions (temperature, flow rate) are favorable for separating only one part of the sample. Frequently, the excessively long retention times of late peaks and the resulting low solute concentration in the effluent make the operation impractical. A somewhat similar situation may exist if the polarity of the sample components varies within a wide range.

Although sometimes highly efficient open tubular columns can also be used successfully under isothermal conditions for solving such difficult separation problems, numerous procedures have been developed which are effective also with less efficient columns and which serve to decrease analysis time and to increase the sensitivity of the technique. These procedures can be divided into two groups: gradient or programmed techniques and grouping techniques.

The techniques of the first group lead to an even spacing of the peaks by methodically changing one of the most important operating parameters—temperature or flow rate (inlet pressure)—while the chromatographic run is made. In gradient techniques, the change occurs along the column axis. Actually, any gas chromatographic operation is characterized by a flow gradient due to the pressure gradient necessary to maintain the carrier gas flow. Temperature gradient gas chromatography (119) has not been investigated in detail, but its result should be comparable to that obtained with gradient-loaded columns (23). A procedure which utilizes a moving temperature gradient along the column is called *chromatothermography*.

The increase of temperature or flow rate with time at any point along the column axis is called *programming*. The two techniques which have been developed are *temperature-programmed gas chromatography* (TPGC) and *flow (or pressure)-programmed gas chromatography* (FPGC).

The procedures of the second group aim first at a rough separation of the sample into groups of which one or more can be separated further into individual components, utilizing backflushing as well as complicated multiple-column systems.

Although the bulk of gas chromatographic work has been done in iso-*thermal* and *isobaric* fashion, some of these techniques are of great importance in trace analysis or if the speed of analysis has to be increased. Due to the simplicity and efficiency of the technique and to the convenience of instruments manufactured for TPGC, temperature programming is used widely in laboratories. On the other hand, grouping techniques find their main application in the domain of process control (see Chapter 10).

A. Chromatothermography

At the beginning of the chromatographic run, the column inlet is heated with a coaxial heater, and thus the temperature gradually decreases along the column. As a result of this, the components of the sample injected into the carrier gas stream will occupy different positions in the column according to their distribution ratios. Solutes with high volatility will be toward the outlet of the column and those with low volatility will be near the column inlet. By moving the heater toward the outlet of the column, the solute bands move with the same speed as the heater in their characteristic temperature zone until they are eluted individually.

This technique, which resembles gradient elution in liquid chromatography, was invented by Turkel'taub (120) and discussed by several authors (121,122). Descriptions of the respective apparatus can also be found in the patent literature.

The advantages of the method are the high speed of separation of multicomponent samples and the self-sharpening of the bands due to the temperature differential between leading and trailing ends. The technique seems to be particularly suited for trace analysis since high solute concentration in the effluent can be achieved by the compression effect of temperature gradient. On the other hand, the column length is limited because of the moving furnace. Therefore the resolution is also limited, which appears to be the greatest handicap of the technique besides the instrumental requirements. Figure 4-23 shows the effect of the gradient operation in chromatothermography in comparison with isothermal operation on two schematic chromatograms constructed from theoretical data.

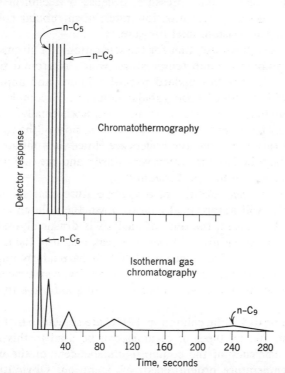

Fig. 4-23. Separation of C_5–C_9 *n*-alkanes by chromatothermography and by isothermal gas chromatography. The schematic chromatograms were constructed from theoretical data for the case of equivalent resolution and of same detector sensitivity (122).

B. Programming Techniques

1. Temperature-Programmed Gas Chromatography (TPGC)

The majority of today's gas chromatographs are built for temperature-programmed gas chromatography. In this technique, the column temperature can be raised with a predetermined heating rate, $r_h°C/min$, and lowered quickly. In most instruments the flow rate rather than the inlet pressure of the carrier gas is regulated, and the detector temperature is controlled separately. The short heating and cooling periods with the elaborate control features also make isothermal operation very convenient with such an instrument.

The rise of temperature is usually linear in time, and r_h varies from 0.5 up to 50°C/min. The regulation of the flow rate is necessary since the viscosity of common carrier gases increases with temperature approximately 25% per 100°C. Consequently, the flow rate would decrease with temperature at constant inlet pressure. Because of technical difficulties involved in a control of very low flow rates, open tubular columns are usually operated at constant inlet pressure.

It was discussed previously that for the separation of a given solute pair there is an optimum column temperature, which is around the boiling points of the solutes with standard packed columns and approximately 50°C lower with standard open tubular columns. If complex mixtures having wide boiling point ranges are analyzed isothermally, any column temperature will be either too high or too low for most of the components. As a result of this, either the low boilers are eluted fast but are not separated, or the high boilers are eluted very slowly and the late peaks often remain undetected due to their broadness.

In TPGC, by proper selection of the temperature interval and heating rate, the solutes will automatically move down the column at optimum temperature. As a result, the time of analysis is drastically reduced and the peaks are spaced evenly, and thus the peak height of the late peaks is significantly increased. This aspect of TPGC is particularly important in trace analysis. Figure 4-24 shows the reduction of analysis time if temperature programming is employed in the analysis of a natural fatty acid ester mixture.

The requirements for the column in TPGC are similar to that in isothermal operation, and all types of columns can be used in this technique. The intrinsic efficiency of the column is independent of the mode (isothermal or temperature programmed) of operation. Obviously column efficiency measured under isothermal conditions also determines the column performance under temperature-programmed conditions. Yet a loss of

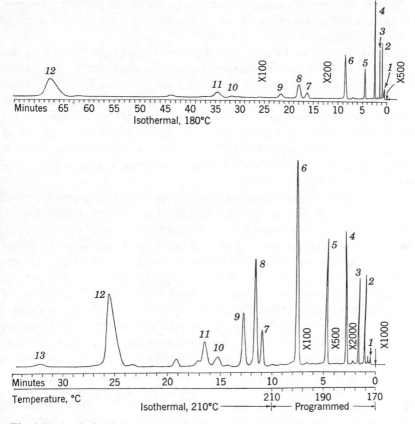

Fig. 4-24. Analysis of a fatty acid methyl ester mixture by isothermal and temperature programmed gas chromatography with the same column. Column: 2 meters, 8% butanediol succinate on silanized Chromosorb W, No. 80–100 sieve fraction. Carrier gas: He, approx 50 ml/min. Elution order: *1*, Caproic; *2*, caprilic; *3*, capric; *4*, lauric; *5*, myristic; *6*, palmitic; *7*, stearic; *8*, oleic; *9*, linoleic; *10*, linolenic; *11*, arachidic (behenic?); *12*, erucic; *13*, (C_{24} saturated?) acid methyl esters (123).

column efficiency will occur due to a nonuniform temperature distribution in the column. Since the deterioration is related to the column diameter (124), small-diameter columns are preferred in TPGC.

The vapor pressure of the liquid phase increases logarithmically with the temperature, thus the bleeding also increases strongly with the temperature and results in a baseline drift which in many cases prohibits the use of sensitive detectors. By introducing differential detector–dual column systems, however, this impediment has been corrected.

Most of the presently available instruments for TPGC provide the degree of reproducibility and reliability which is necessary for successful qualitative and quantitative analytical work.

a. Peak Elution in TPGC.   In TPGC most of the components of the injected sample can be considered as stagnant at the column inlet due to their large distribution ratio at the starting temperature. Raising the temperature of the column, the peaks begin slowly to move so that their velocity is doubled with around 30°C temperature increase. Giddings (125) demonstrated that under this condition each peak arrives at the middle of the column approximately 30° below its retention temperature and as a consequence, the final distribution ratios and peak widths are approximately the same for all solutes.

The theory of temperature programming offers various expressions and graphical methods to link retention in TPGC to isothermal data. A compilation of them can be found in the book of Harris and Habgood (126).

b. Retention Temperature.   The column temperature at which the center of a peak is eluted is called retention temperature T_R, or elution temperature. It is a basic parameter in TPGC, and its importance is comparable to that of the retention volumes or the retention times in isothermal gas chromatography. Also, T_R is characteristic for each solute–stationary phase system. It increases with the logarithm of the heating rate, r_h, and the gas holdup time; therefore small changes in r_h, carrier gas flow rate, column length, or initial temperature do not affect T_R significantly. Drastic changes of the heating rate, however, have a great influence on retention temperatures, so the elution order also may change.

If the temperature program is linear, T_R may replace the logarithm of retention volume or retention time in the previously discussed correlations. Thus, retention temperature increases linearly with the carbon number for some homologous series, e.g., normal alkanes (127). As a result the peaks are equally spaced on the chromatogram, provided the initial temperature is sufficiently low, as compared to the logarithmic spacing on chromatograms obtained under isothermal conditions. In practice, the initial (ambient) temperature is often not low enough and therefore the linearity does not apply to the first members of the series. Nevertheless, the linearity in the case of n-alkanes was found to be adequate to extend the Kováts retention index system (which is discussed in Chapter 7) to data from temperature-programmed operation (128), by using retention temperatures or retention times directly instead of their logarithms.

The correlation of solute boiling point with retention temperature is utilized in *simulated distillation* (129), a technique which originates in the work of Eggertsen et al. (130). It has been developed to replace analytical

distillation by a specially built temperature-programmed gas chromatograph coupled with an electronic integrator. The dual-column system contains SE-30 silicone gum as the stationary phase which separates according
to the boiling points. The instrument, which has to be calibrated frequently
with a mixture of hydrocarbons, supplies boiling point distribution curves

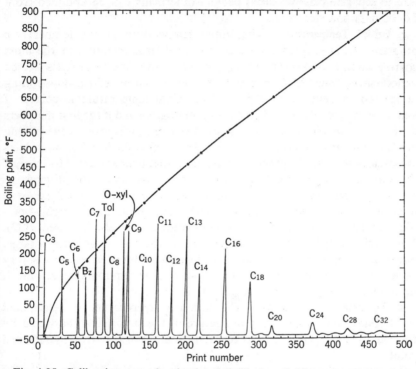

Fig. 4-25. Calibration curve for simulated distillation. Column: 180 cm, 3% SE-30
silicone gum on Chromosorb W, No. 30–60 sieve fraction. Dual-column system.
Temperature program: $r_h = 9°F/min$, $T_0 = -4°F$. Sample: aliphatic hydrocarbons
plus benzene, toluene, and o-xylene. Each print number represents 10 sec (129).

equivalent to that obtained from a 100 theoretical plate analytical distillation, but a hundred times faster. Figure 4-25 shows the calibration curve
of simulated distillation which illustrates correlation of boiling points with
retention parameters in a wide boiling point range. The print numbers of
the readout system represent retention times or retention temperatures.
     Retention temperature is always higher than the temperature at which
the same column performance and the same degree of resolution could be
obtained in an isothermal run. Giddings (125) found that this temperature,

which he called the *significant temperature*, T', is approximately 45°C below the retention temperature:

$$T' \simeq T_R - 45° \tag{4-80}$$

The practical significance of this relationship is that the optimum temperature to separate closely spaced peaks isothermally can be obtained from TPGC data and vice versa.

c. Initial Temperature. The initial temperature of the temperature program, T_0, is selected according to the desired retention of the most volatile sample components. If T_0 is too low, the time of analysis will be unnecessarily long. If T_0 is too high, the resolution of the low-boiling sample components will be poor. The initial temperature is correct if *n*-alkanes are equally spaced on the chromatogram and if the first members of the series are eluted fast. For packed columns, it is around the boiling point of the most volatile component. In practice, the low-boiling solutes are usually separated isothermally at the initial temperature. However, if the sample contains highly volatile components which are difficult to separate, subambient initial temperatures (131) may be required or a multiple column system (discussed later) should be used. For highly volatile samples, TPGC at cryogenic temperatures can also be used (132). Low initial temperatures are chosen also if the sample volume is large. Since the sample is introduced at T_0 into the column where V_R is very large for most of the solutes, the sample volume requirements are much more relaxed in TPGC than at isothermal operation.

d. Terminal Temperature. The terminal temperature is determined by the maximum allowable temperature of the stationary phase and by the retention temperature (and thermal stability) of the strongly retarded solutes.

In practice, the upper temperature limit is determined by the stationary phase and it is often necessary to elute the highest boiling components isothermally at the terminal temperature. Such case is shown in Figure 4-24.

The column is usually kept only for a short period of time at maximum temperature, and the oxygen from the air which is often introduced with the sample and might be responsible for liquid phase decomposition is eluted at low temperature. Therefore, the maximum allowable temperature of the stationary phases is often higher in TPGC than in isothermal operation where the sample is introduced at a much higher temperature.

e. Heating Rate and Flow Rate. The heating rate, r_h, and the carrier gas flow rate, F, are the operational variables most easy to regulate in TPGC. The retention temperature of each component can be related to the ratio r_h/F (133). It was suggested that the optimum value of r_h/F per gram of stationary phase in the column is around $r_h/F = 0.1°C$ g/ml. Hence, the most frequently used heating rates are $r_h = 5$–$10°C/min$ for standard packed columns and $r_h = 0.5$–$1°C/min$ for standard open tubular columns. The effect of the heating rate in TPGC is comparable to that of the temperature in isothermal gas chromatography. Accordingly, the maximum allowable heating rate is inversely proportional to the phase ratio in the column.

The effect of flow rate (flow velocity) on column performance is similar in TPGC to that in isothermal gas chromatography, as it was discussed at the relationship of h and u. However, it should be kept in mind that in TPGC, flow and heating rates should be considered together.

The carrier gas flow rate is adjusted at the initial temperature in accordance with the heating rate. The speed of analysis can be increased by increasing r_h and F by the same factor but, naturally, at loss of column efficiency. Open tubular columns tolerate combinations of high heating and flow rates better than packed columns do.

Since resolution increases as r_h decreases (it would be maximum under isothermal conditions at T_0), low heating rates must be employed for difficult separations. It was already pointed out that the carrier gas flow rate decreases when the inlet pressure is kept constant and the column temperature is increased. This mode is called *isobaric* operation and is used commonly with open tubular columns. If the flow rather than the pressure is controlled (134), the flow rate remains constant and the mode of operation is called *isorheic*. TPGC instruments are most commonly equipped with flow regulators.

f. Column Performance in TPGC. (*1*) *Plate Number.* If plate numbers were calculated in TPGC from the chromatogram in the usual way (equation 4-55), they would not be equivalent to plate numbers obtained isothermally at retention temperature. Hence, the respective plate heights could not be linked to column parameters. In order to measure the proper column performance in TPGC and compare it to performance under isothermal conditions the following equation has been suggested for the calculation of plate number

$$n = 16(t_R^*/w)^2 \qquad (4\text{-}81)$$

where t_R^* is the retention time measured at T_R isothermally and w is the peak width from the TPGC run (133).

Experimental results show a close agreement between isothermal and TPGC plate numbers calculated by equation 4-81.

(2) *Resolution.* The definition of resolution by $\Delta t_R / w_m$ (equation 4-60) should be independent of the mode of operation, and thus it is also used in TPGC. As it was discussed earlier, heating rate and flow rate are the major factors affecting resolution. Since the highest resolution can be obtained at low temperatures and optimum flow velocity, the resolution

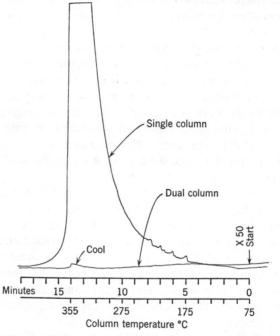

Fig. 4-26. Baseline in TPGC with single- and dual-column systems. Columns: 180 cm, 1.5% SE-30 silicone gum rubber on Chromosorb W, No. 80–100 sieve fraction. Flame ionization detector (137).

decreases with increasing heating and flow rates. Temperature programming always represents a compromise between resolution and speed in order to attain adequate resolution for many solute pairs as fast as possible.

g. Dual-Column Systems. The vapor pressure of liquid phases increases exponentially with the temperature. Consequently the bleeding of the stationary phase strongly increases during a temperature-programmed run. This becomes a major obstacle in TPGC if only a single column is used, because of the heavy baseline drift on the chromatogram which cannot be tolerated. Thus, the number of applicable stationary phases, the terminal temperature, and the useful sensitivity range of the detectors are seriously limited.

These difficulties have been eliminated by a dual-column system which comprises a conventional thermal conductivity cell (135) or a dual or differential flame ionization detector (136,137). Figure 4-26 shows the baseline changes with a single and dual column system during a heating and cooling cycle of a TPGC run.

In the dual-column system, a reference column packed with the same column material is connected parallel to the analytical column into which the sample is injected. Both columns have independent flow regulators and are placed in the same oven. By regulating the flow rate, the bleeding from both columns is matched. In effect, the bleeding of the analytical column is compensated with the bleeding from the reference column and a stable baseline is obtained, as shown in Figure 4-26.

Besides the far-reaching extension of TPGC, the dual-column system also provides the analyst with an instrument which may contain two columns with different stationary phases. Since it is often necessary to separate a sample on more than one stationary phase, the availability of two columns without changing or conditioning them is of obvious advantage.

2. Flow (Inlet Pressure) Programmed Gas Chromatography

Although stepwise increase of the flow rate in order to reduce analysis time was reported by Lipsky et al. as early as 1959 (138), flow programming only recently became established as a technique comparable to TPGC (139–142).

We define flow programmed gas chromatography (FPGC) as a procedure in which the pressure drop across the column, and thus the carrier gas flow rate, is raised during a chromatographic run.

Since the average gas velocity in the column and therefore the band velocity increases linearly with the pressure drop, increasing inlet pressure at constant outlet pressure results in higher band velocities. If the inlet pressure increases exponentially with the time, the retention times of the solutes decrease in a similar manner as in linear TPGC. Fairly simple devices are commercially available for such inlet pressure programming (e.g., from Ionics Research, Inc.).

Chromatograms of the same sample mixture have been made using TPGC and FPGC with the same column and are juxtaposed in Figure 4-27.

The advantage of FPGC in comparison to TPGC is that the flow program provides essentially the same degree of acceleration of peak elution without exposing the stationary phase or high-boiling sample components to excessively high temperature. As a consequence, the number of liquid

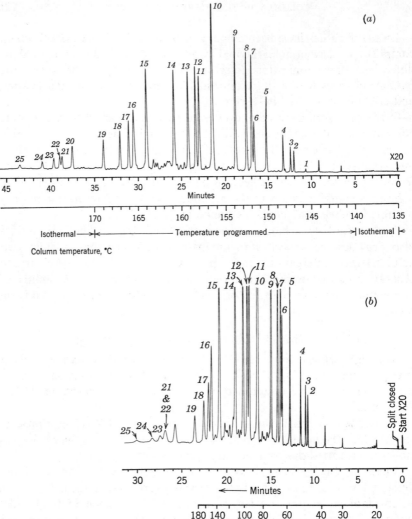

Fig. 4-27. Analysis of a straight-chain alkylbenzene mixture using (a) temperature and (b) flow programming with the same column. Column: 45 meters, 0.25-mm-i.d. open tubular, coated with DC 550 phenyl silicone oil. Sample size: 0.2–0.3 μl, split. Flame ionization detector. (a) Inlet pressure: 20 psig. F_c (140°C): 1.25 ml/min. F_c (170°C): 1.23 ml/min. (b) Temperature: 145°C. F_c (20 psig): 1.25 ml/min. F_c (180 psig): 56.2 ml/min.

Identified peaks: *1*, 2-phenylnonane; *2*, 5-phenyldecane; *3*, 4-phenyldecane; *4*, 3-phenyldecane; *5*, 2-phenyldecane; *6*, 6-phenylundecane; *7*, 5-phenylundecane; *8*, 4-phenylundecane; *9*, 3-phenylundecane; *10*, 2-phenylundecane; *11*, 6-phenyldodecane; *12*, 5-phenyldodecane; *13*, 4-phenyldodecane; *14*, 3-phenyldodecane; *15*, 2-phenyldodecane; *16*, 7- and 6-phenyltridecane; *17*, 5-phenyltridecane; *18*, 4-phenyltridecane; *19*, 3-phenyltridecane; *20*, 2-phenyltridecane; *21*, 7-phenyltetradecane; *22*, 6-phenyltetradecane; *23*, 5-phenyltetradecane; *24*, 4-phenyltetradecane; *25*, 3-phenyltetradecane (142).

phases applicable in FPGC is greater than that in TPGC, and the bleeding at the end of the run is significantly smaller. In addition there is no time-consuming cooling-off period in FPGC.

On the other hand, TPGC can be carried out without significant loss in isothermal column efficiency in contrary to FPGC, which always results in loss of efficiency for the late peaks. This loss is due to the increase of the plate height with the gas velocity at high values of $\bar{u}$ as shown in Figure 4-13. It depends usually on the slope of the linear portion of the plate height versus gas velocity curve and varies from solute to solute, as well as with the column construction.

Thus flow programming is most useful in the analysis of wide-boiling-range samples containing a heavy end which is easy to separate or is sensitive to high temperatures.

Naturally, FPGC requires a detector which is not sensitive to changes in the effluent flow rate. It should be noted that in contrast to the average flow rate in the column $(F_c j)$ which increases linearly with the inlet pressure, the outlet flow rate (F_c) will increase $1/j$ times as fast as the inlet pressure as a result of the gas compression in the column. For FPGC, flame ionization detector is most suitable due to its mass-sensitive character which results in flow rate-independent peak areas.

Generally, FPGC is better suited for working with open tubular columns than with packed columns because the absolute increase of the flow rate due to programming of the inlet pressure is much smaller with open tubular columns. Flow programming can also be combined with temperature programming, thus compensating for the decrease of flow rate which occurs in isobaric TPGC, which is the commonly used technique with open tubular columns. The application of flow programming in preparative work was also found to be promising (140).

C. Grouping Techniques

The programmed gas chromatographic techniques have been developed in order to separate possibly all components of a sample with a wide boiling range by using a single separating column. It occurs, however, quite frequently in routine analytical work that only a portion of the sample is of major interest or the separation cannot be carried out conveniently on a single column at all. In these circumstances some of the grouping techniques may represent a practical solution.

The most significant application of grouping techniques is in the analysis of highly volatile materials where the separation of a wide-boiling mixture would require expensive cryogenic TPGC and would significantly increase the analysis time.

In grouping techniques only a portion of the sample is separated into individual components. The other part is removed from the column as a group, which may be analyzed as a single peak, discarded, or transferred to another column for further separation. Thus the expression "grouping technique" may refer to a single- or multiple-column operation (usually for separation of wide boiling range samples) and not only to the analyses of sample components in groups. The latter is called group analysis (143) and involves a regrouping of the completely or partially separated components. A variation of group analysis, the "flip-flop" technique, is discussed below.

Grouping techniques are particularly preferred in process control gas chromatography dealing with highly volatile samples, owing to their speed and reliability. Since in this field standard packed columns are used exclusively, grouping techniques are most commonly applied to these columns, but promising results were reported with open tubular columns and their combination with packed columns (144).

Although not covered by the above definition, the subtraction of one or more sample components by a column is also discussed here, since it is related to and used with other grouping techniques.

The transfer of solutes forward or backward from one column to another and to the detectors requires a rather complicated system of valves and connecting tubes with a great number of fittings. It is particularly important that the reduction of column efficiency due to the extracolumn dead volume and flow geometry is kept at a minimum and a leak-free operation is secured.

This chapter offers only a brief outline of the basic grouping techniques. Their application in process control is discussed in Chapter 10.

1. Foreflushing and Backflushing

Foreflushing and backflushing are the two fundamental grouping operations in a single column. In both cases a group of sample components is removed practically unseparated from the column and the rest of the sample is separated and analyzed.

If the strongly retarded components (the heavy end) of the sample are of interest, the high-boiling fraction (the light end) can be removed by *foreflushing*. It is similar to the normal operation of the column with respect to the flow direction, but by proper selection of the stationary phase and temperature the light end is practically not retarded by the column but eluted practically as a single group first. The foreflushed material can go through the detector, can be vented or directed into another column.

In *backflushing*, the flow direction of the carrier gas in the column is reversed after the components of interest have been separated, eluted, and analyzed. Thus, the remaining fraction of the sample is swept back and eluted at the column inlet. Figure 4-28 illustrates a very simple system for backflushing through the detector utilizing a four-way valve to reverse the carrier gas flow.

The most common reasons for applying this technique are as follows.

1. Cleaning of the column from high-boiling solutes which are uninteresting from the analytical point of view. Obviously, backflushing represents

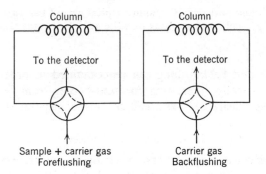

Fig. 4-28. Simple backflushing arrangement with a four-port valve.

a great saving in time, since the time to elute the strongly retarded components backwards (backflushing time) is usually only a fraction of the retention time of these solutes in the normal direction. On the other hand, backflushing also increases the lifetime of the column by removing contaminants from the inlet part of the column.

2. Quantitative determination of the high boilers as a single group. The backflushed solutes are often eluted as a single peak, and their total amount can be determined if the eluent is passed through the detector. The chromatogram in Figure 4-29 shows typical backflush analyses of low-boiling hydrocarbons, where the C_4's and higher homologs are obtained as a single group. The theoretical aspects of backflushing are discussed by Villalobos et al. (145), who also point out the difficulties in exact quantitative determination of the backflushed multicomponent peaks and recommend the use of a regrouping column which reverses the partial separation before entering the detector.

3. Removal of the strongly retarded sample components for separation on another column. In this case, backflushing is part of the operation with a multiple column system which is discussed below.

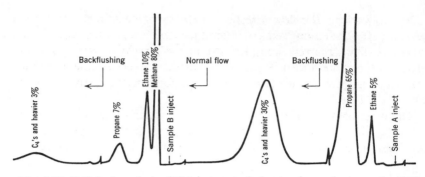

Fig. 4-29. Backflush analysis of C_4^+ in two typical natural gas plant samples (145). Column: 3 m, 20% polyethylene glycol on silica gel. Carrier gas: H_2. Temperature: 87°C.

Foreflushing and backflushing can be combined in order to isolate a group of analytically interesting medium-boiling sample components which is called "heart cut" and can be further separated on a second column.

2. Subtraction of Solutes

We can consider as a special case of grouping the irreversible sorption of one or more sample components by a column called a subtractor, while the other components are being foreflushed into the analytical column.

The reason for this operation is to eliminate before entering the separating column one substance or a specific group of the sample components, which would interfere with the separation of the others or would incapacitate the analytical column. For example, a subtractor column packed with molecular sieve retards normal paraffins irreversibly under usual operating conditions, but permits iso- and cycloparaffins to pass through unretarded (146); also, a column packed with KOH on a porous support material can be used to subtract polar solutes which would deactivate an upstream molecular sieve separating column (147).

3. Multiple-Column Systems

A great variety of systems which use more than one separating column (multiple-column systems) have been developed for grouping and separating multicomponent samples. Indeed, we could conceive a combination of columns or subtractors and operational sequences (backflushing, foreflushing) for almost every analytical problem, which provides fast and reliable results. In the following, a few representative examples of such systems are mentioned.

a. Multistage Systems. These systems consist of gas chromatographs called stages connected in series so that the detector outlet of a preceding unit is linked to the column inlet of the following instrument. Figure 4-30 shows a three-stage system consisting of three column, detector, and recorder units. Stages 2 and 3 are connected via a four-port valve to the preceding units.

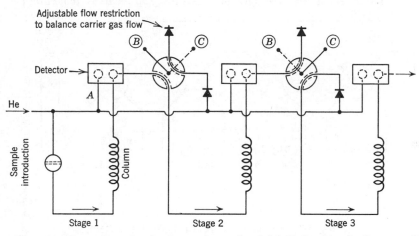

Fig. 4-30. Flow schematic of a three-stage analyzer. (*A*) Outlet side of reference cell is closed after purging. (*B*) Following stage in series with preceding stage. (*C*) Following stage is independent of preceding stage (148).

During introduction of the sample by the sampling device of stage 1, the stages are connected in series. The first column retards the heavy end and the higher-boiling components are foreflushed into stage 2. Now, the first stage is made independent and continues to separate the components of the heavy end, and produces a chromatogram. Meanwhile the process is repeated on the second and third stages so that the three groups of the sample are separated parallel by the three gas chromatographs and three chromatograms are obtained.

Before the advent of programmed techniques in gas chromatography, such two- or three- (or even more) stage instruments were used for separating wide-boiling-range samples, and such an instrument was also available commercially. For example, more than 50 components of automobile exhaust gases were separated by a three-stage instrument (148). At the present, multiple-stage systems have only reduced importance, although similar designs may find application in solving special problems (149).

b. Columns Connected in Series. Multiple-column systems consisting of two or more columns connected in series are frequently used. If the valving permits foreflushing, backflushing, and by-passing of the columns, such a system represents a versatile tool for solving a number of various analytical problems.

Figure 4-31 shows a multipurpose triple-column system which was first proposed for the analysis of light gas mixtures (150). This system equipped

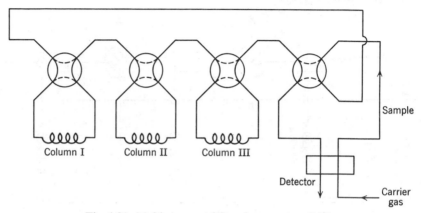

Fig. 4-31. Multipurpose triple-column system (150).

with different columns is also used in natural gas analysis. The following example illustrates one mode of the possible applications. Let us assume that a mixture of H_2, N_2, Ar, and NH_3 have to be separated. The necessary columns are: Carbowax 1500 on Teflon support (column I), alumina (column II), and Molecular Sieve 5A (column III). The columns are used at room temperature, and the carrier gas is a mixture of He and H_2. At the start the columns are connected in series as shown in Figure 4-31. The sample components except NH_3 are foreflushed from column I via column II into column III where they are separated on molecular sieve and analyzed by the detector. Column II is a subtractor for protecting column III from NH_3 which is retarded in column I. Subsequently, the flow direction is reversed and—with or without by-passing columns III and II—NH_3 is backflushed into the detector and analyzed.

A system which employs two columns and two detector cells alternately was also described (151). Figure 4-32 shows the flow schematic and illustrates the separation of the major air components with this system. Column I is packed with silica gel and separates CO_2 from N_2 and O_2 as shown in the first part of the chromatogram. After passing the detector cell, the solutes are directed into column II which is packed with molecular sieve. It separates N_2 from O_2 but adsorbs CO_2 irreversibly. The outlet of this column is connected to the reference cell of the detector, and thus N_2 and O_2 would be detected as negative peaks as indicated. By switching detector polarity, however, a chromatogram in the usual form can be obtained, as shown schematically in Figure 4-32.

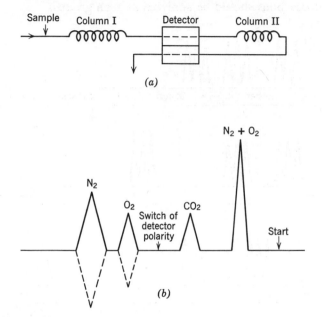

Fig. 4-32. Double-column system (a) for separation of oxygen, nitrogen, and carbon dioxide as shown on the chromatogram (b). Column I: silica gel; column II: Molecular Sieve 5A (151).

This concept was extended for the separation of complex gaseous mixtures (147). The polar gases were separated on a column packed with dibutyl sebacate on Fluoropak support (column I) and the nonpolar gases on a Molecular Sieve 13X column (column II). After leaving the detector, the polar gases were irreversibly adsorbed on a column containing KOH-coated support upstream of the molecular sieve column (between the outlet of the detector and the inlet of column II) in order to avoid the deactivation of the stationary phase. A mixture of CO_2, H_2S, SO_2, CO, CH_4, H_2, O_2, and N_2 was separated rapidly using this technique.

A similar system (column I: squalane on Chromosorb P; column II: molecular sieve) was employed by Terry and Futrell for simultaneous analysis of hydrocarbons and fixed gases (152).

The next example is the "flip-flop" group analysis technique which also employs columns in series. In the following, the operation with a triple column system is described. The "flip-flop" technique can be employed if the amount of some specific groups rather than that of individual sample components is of interest. For example, a mixture of C_1-C_3, C_4-C_6, and C_7-C_9 hydrocarbons should be analyzed as such groups.

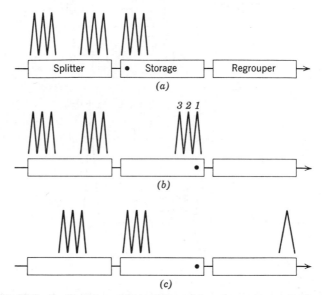

Fig. 4-33. "Flip-flop" group analysis with a triple-column system. Peaks *1*, *2*, and *3* of the three major groups are analyzed together as a single peak. Backflushing of the peaks to be grouped into the regrouper column is indicated by reversal of the storage column (153).

Figure 4-33 shows schematically the columns and the sample components which are used in this operation. The sample is separated in the usual way on the first column (splitter) of the triple-column system, and the components of the first group are eluted into the second column (storage). When all components of the first group are in the storage column, the solutes are backflushed from the storage column into the third column (regrouper). Here the previously separated substances form a group which is eluted as a single band into the detector. Meanwhile the separation and grouping procedure in the first two columns continues, and finally the whole sample is analyzed as three groups. Such regrouping, which is actually the opposite of separation, improves the accuracy of the quantative determination of the backflushed material (145).

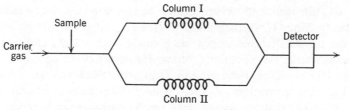

Fig. 4-34. Two columns connected in parallel.

The selection of column material, flow rate, and column length are very critical in these applications and requires some experimentation.

c. Columns Connected in Parallel. Figure 4-34 shows a parallel-column system. Here, the sample is split according to the ratio of the respective flow rates and is swept through both columns. Because the two columns are packed with different column materials, the two sample portions are separated in two different modes. If the flow resistance of the columns and the solute retentions are properly adjusted, the peaks from the two columns emerge consecutively, as illustrated in Figure 4-35.

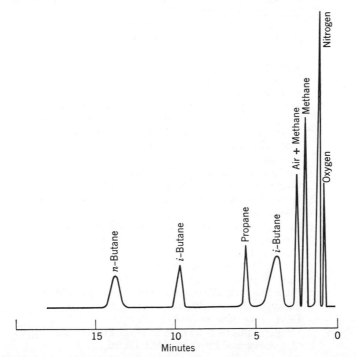

Fig. 4-35. Separation of nitrogen, oxygen, and hydrocarbons with a parallel column system. Column I: 4 meters, sebacate ester. Column II: 1 meter, Molecular Sieve 5A. Temperature 22°C. Flow rate 50 cm/min (154).

Methane, nitrogen, and oxygen cannot be separated on the sebacate ester column (column I) which is used for the separation of the alkanes, and they are foreflushed and appear as a single peak on the chromatogram.

The molecular sieve column (column II) separates the light end but subtracts all the n-alkanes but methane. Thus, with the two columns connected parallel, the separation of such wide-boiling-range mixtures can be achieved. Note that the fourth peak on the chromatogram represents the light end which passes as a group through the sebacate ester column, and the fifth peak is the isobutane which is not subtracted by the molecular sieve.

XII. List of Symbols

a	Total porosity of column packing.
a	Constant in equation 4-34.
A	Eddy diffusion term in van Deemter equation.
A_L	Surface area of liquid stationary phase.
A_S	Surface area of adsorbent.
b	Constant in equation 4-34.
B	Molecular diffusion term in the van Deemter equation.
B_0	Specific permeability coefficient.
c	Constant in equations 4-19 and 4-77.
C	Mass transfer term in the van Deemter equation.
C_g	Mass transfer term for gas phase.
C_l	Mass transfer term for liquid phase.
d	Inside diameter of open tubular column.
d_p	Particle diameter.
$d_{p(\max)}$	Maximum particle diameter in a sieve fraction.
$d_{p(\min)}$	Minimum particle diameter in a sieve fraction.
d_f	"Film thickness" of liquid stationary phase.
D_g	Molecular diffusion coefficient for gas phase.
D_l	Molecular diffusion coefficient for liquid phase.
F	Uncorrected carrier gas flow rate.
F_a	Outlet flow rate at ambient temperature.
F_c	Outlet flow rate at column temperature.
FID	Flame ionization detector.
FPGC	Flow programmed gas chromatography.
GLC	Gas–liquid chromatography.
GSC	Gas–solid chromatography.
GSLC	Gas solid–liquid chromatography.
h	Plate height.
$h_{\min}$	Plate height at the minimum of the HETP curve.
H	Effective plate height.
ΔH	Heat of solution or heat of adsorption.
HETP	Height Equivalent to a Theoretical Plate (Plate height).
	Gas compressibility correction factor,

$$j = \frac{3}{2}\frac{(p_i/p_o)^2 - 1}{(p_i/p_o)^3 - 1}$$

k	Partition ratio.
K	Partition coefficient (equilibrium constant).
K_a	Equilibrium constant in GSC.
k_m	Partition ratio in mixed-phase column.
$k_{r,0}$ and $k_{r,1}$	Partition ratios on reference columns.
L	Column length.
L_{req}	Column length required for a separation.
m	Fractional combination of two liquid phases.
n	Plate number.
n_{req}	Number of plates required for a separation.
N	Effective plate number.
OPGV	Optimum practical gas velocity.
p_i	Carrier gas pressure at column inlet.
p_o	Carrier gas pressure at column outlet.
r	Relative retention (referred to a standard).
r	Tube inside radius.
r_h	Heating rate.
R	Resolution.
R_f	Retardation factor.
T	Absolute temperature.
T_0	Initial temperature in TPGC.
T'	Significant temperature.
T_R	Retention temperature.
t_A	Gas holdup time.
t_D	Extra column holdup time.
t_R	Retention time.
t_R	Adjusted retention time (liquid holdup time).
t_R^*	Isothermal retention time measured at retention temperature.
Δt_R	Distance between two consecutive peak maxima.
TPGC	Temperature programmed gas chromatography.
t_R/w	Relative peak sharpness.
$\bar{u}$	Average linear velocity of unretained solute.
$\bar{u}_g$	Average linear carrier gas velocity.
$\bar{u}_R$	Average linear velocity of a solute band.
u_o	Outlet velocity, $u_o = F_c L/V_c$.
u_{opt}	Optimum gas velocity to give minimum plate height.
U_g	Equilibrium constant in GSC.
V_A	Retention volume of unretained solute (gas holdup of the column).
V_c	Volume of empty column.
V_g	Specific retention volume.
V_i	Interparticle volume in column.
V_D	Extracolumn dead volume.
V_M	Corrected retention volume of unretained solute (column void volume).
V_L	Volume of stationary phase in column.
V_N	Net retention volume.
V_R	Retention volume.
V_R'	Adjusted retention volume.

$V_R{}^o$	Corrected retention volume.
w	Peak width at base (band intercept).
w_h	Peak width at the half height.
w_i	Peak width at the inflexion points.
w_m	Mean peak width.
W_S	Weight of stationary phase in column.
x, y	Distances on chromatogram.
z	Number of carbon atoms.
α	Relative retention.
β	Phase ratio.
γ	Labyrinth factor.
δ	Specific surface area.
ϵ	Interparticle porosity.
η	Viscosity.
λ	Factor for packing irregularity.
ρ_S	Density of stationary phase.
σ	Standard deviation.
σ_c	Standard deviation due to column effects.
σ_d	Standard deviation due to detector and recorder.
σ_m	Mean standard deviation.
σ_s	Standard deviation due to sampling.

References

1. S. Dal Nogare and R. S. Juvet, Jr., *Gas–Liquid Chromatography*, Interscience, New York, 1962.
2. A. B. Littlewood, *Gas Chromatography*, Academic Press, New York, 1962.
3. J. H. Purnell, *Gas Chromatography*, Wiley, New York, 1962.
4. J. C. Giddings, *Dynamics of Chromatography, Part I, Principles and Theory*, Marcel Dekker, New York, 1965.
5. W. F. Wilhite, *J. Gas Chromatog.*, **4**, 47 (1966).
6. I. Halász and E. Heine, *Anal. Chem.*, **37**, 495 (1965).
7. M. J. E. Golay, in *Gas Chromatography 1960*, R. P. W. Scott, Ed., Butterworths, Washington, 1960, pp. 139–143.
8. D. H. Desty, A. Goldup, and W. T. Swanton, in *Gas Chromatography*, N. Brenner, J. E. Callen, and M. D. Weiss, Eds., Academic Press, New York, 1962, pp. 105–138.
9. L. S. Ettre, E. W. Cieplinski, and W. Averill, *J. Gas Chromatog.*, **1**(2), 7 (1963).
10. L. S. Ettre, *Open Tubular Columns in Gas Chromatography*, Plenum Press, New York, 1965.
11. W. Schneider, H. Bruderreck, and I. Halász, *Anal. Chem.*, **36**, 1533 (1964).
12. M. L. Peterson and U. Hirsch, *J. Lipid Res.*, **1**, 132 (1959).
13. H. J. Gold, *Anal. Chem.*, **34**, 174 (1962).
14. J. Janák, *Collection Czech. Chem. Commun.*, **18**, 798 (1953).
15. F. T. Eggertsen and F. M. Nelsen, *Anal. Chem.*, **32**, 302 (1960).
16. A. V. Kiselev, Yu. S. Nikitin, R. S. Petrova, K. D. Shcherbakeva, and Ya. I. Yashin, *Anal. Chem.*, **36**, 1562 (1964).
17. R. L. Martin, *Anal. Chem.*, **35**, 116 (1963).

18. A. B. Littlewood, C. S. G. Phillips, and D. T. Price, *J. Chem. Soc.*, **1955**, 1480.
19. F. A. Bruner and G. P. Cartoni, *Anal. Chem.*, **36**, 1522 (1964).
20. L. D. Belyakova, A. V. Kiselev, and N. V. Kovaleva, *Anal. Chem.*, **36**, 1517 (1964).
21. D. M. Oaks, H. Hartmann, and K. P. Dimick, *Anal. Chem.*, **36**, 1561 (1964).
22. D. C. Locke and C. E. Meloan, *Anal. Chem.*, **36**, 2234 (1964).
23. S. Dal Nogare and J. Chiu, *Anal. Chem.*, **34**, 890 (1962).
24. C. Horváth, *Trennsäulen mit dünnen porösen Schichten für die Gaschromatographie*. Inaugural Dissertation, University of Frankfurt (M), 1963.
25. R. P. W. Scott, *J. Inst. Petrol.*, **47**, 284 (1961).
26. A. T. James and A. J. P. Martin, *J. Appl. Chem.*, **6**, 105 (1956).
27. P. C. Carman, *The Flow of Gases through Porous Media*, Academic Press, New York, 1956.
28. A. I. M. Keulemans, *Gas Chromatography*, Reinhold, New York, 1957.
29. L. S. Ettre, *J. Gas Chromatog.*, **1**(2), 36 (1963).
30. A. J. P. Martin and R. L. M. Synge, *Biochem. J.*, **35**, 1358 (1941).
31. A. T. James and A. J. P. Martin, *Biochem. J.*, **50**, 679 (1952).
32. J. H. Purnell, *J. Chem. Soc.*, **1960**, 1268.
33. J. J. van Deemter, F. J. Zuiderweg, and A. Klinkenberg, *Chem. Eng. Sci.*, **5**, 271 (1956).
34. J. C. Giddings, *Nature*, **184**, 357 (1959).
35. M. J. E. Golay, in *Gas Chromatography*, V. J. Coates, H. J. Noebels, and I. S. Fagerson, Eds., Academic Press, New York, 1958, pp. 1–13.
36. R. P. W. Scott and G. S. F. Hazeldean, in *Gas Chromatography 1960*, R. P. W. Scott, Ed., Butterworths, Washington, D.C., 1960, pp. 144–161.
37. I. Halász and C. Horváth, *Nature*, **197**, 71 (1963).
38. C. G. Scott, in *Gas Chromatography 1962*, M. van Swaay, Ed., Butterworths, Washington D.C., 1962, pp. 36–48.
39. O. L. Hollis, *Anal. Chem.*, **38**, 309 (1966).
40. H. Hrapia and H. G. Konnecke, *J. Prakt. Chem.*, **3**, 106 (1956); *Chem. Abstracts*, **53** (21), 19663 (1959).
41. H. W. Habgood and J. F. Hanlan, *Can. J. Chem.*, **37**, 843 (1959).
42. F. T. Eggertsen, H. S. Knight, and S. Groennings, *Anal. Chem.*, **28**, 303 (1956).
43. G. R. List, R. L. Hoffman, and C. D. Evans, *J. Am. Oil Chemists' Soc.*, **42**, 1058 (1965).
44. C. G. Scott, *J. Inst. Petrol.*, **45**, 118 (1959).
45. K. D. Stscherbakowa and W. K. Tschnikina, in *Gas Chromatographie 1965*, H.G. Struppe, Ed., East German Acad. Sci., Berlin, 1965, Suppl. Vol., pp. 77–88.
46. A. Zlatkis and H. R. Kaufman, in *Gas Chromatography*, H. J. Noebels, R. F. Wall, and N. Brenner, Eds., Academic Press, New York, 1961, p. 339.
47. Ya. I. Yashin, S. P. Zshdanov, and A. V. Kiselev, in *Gas Chromatography 1963*, H. P. Angelé and H. G. Struppe, Eds., Akademie-Verlag, Berlin (Ost), 1963, pp. 402–421.
48. H. L. MacDonell, J. M. Noonan, and J. P. Williams, *Anal. Chem.*, **35**, 1253 (1963).
49. R. M. Barber, *Ber. Bunsenges. Physik. Chem.*, **69**, 786 (1965).
50. K. J. Bombaugh, *Nature*, **197**, 1102 (1963).
51. D. White, *Nature*, **179**, 1075 (1957).
52. J. V. Mortimer and P. L. Gent, *Nature*, **197**, 789 (1963).
53. O. L. Hollis and W. V. Hayes, *J. Gas Chromatog.*, **4**, 235 (1966).

54. *Gas Chromatography Abstract Service*, Preston Technical Abstract Co., 902 Pitner Avenue, Evanston, Ill.
55. C. E. H. Knapman, Ed., *Gas Chromatography Abstracts*, published yearly; Butterworths, Washington, D. C., 1958–1962; Institute of Petroleum, London, 1963–1966.
56. J. S. Lewis, *Compilation of Gas Chromatographic Data*, Am. Soc. Testing Mater., Spec. Tech. Publ. **343**, 1963. American Society for Testing and Materials, Philadelphia, Pa.
57. S. J. Hawkes and J. C. Giddings, *Anal. Chem.*, **36**, 2229 (1964).
58. G Hesse, *Z. Anal. Chem.*, **211**, 5 (1965).
59. C. Chen and D. Gacke, *Anal. Chem.*, **36**, 72 (1964).
60. W. Gerrard, S. J. Hawkes, and E. F. Mooney, in *Gas Chromatography 1960*, R. P. W. Scott, Ed., Butterworths, Washington, 1960, pp. 199–210.
61. J. Vessman, *Acta Pharm. Suesica*, **2**, 73 (1965).
62. A. G. Altenau, R. E. Kramer, D. J. McAdoo, and C. Merritt, Jr., *J. Gas Chromatog.*, **4**, 96 (1966).
63. D. E. Martire and L. Z. Pollara, in *Advances in Chromatography*, Vol. I, J. C. Giddings and R. A. Keller, Eds., Marcel Dekker, New York, 1966, pp. 335–362.
64. L. Rohrschneider, *Z. Anal. Chem.*, **170**, 256 (1959).
65. H. J. Maier and O. C. Karpathy, *J. Chromatog.*, **8**, 308 (1962).
66. S. R. Lipsky, Yale University, private communication.
67. G. P. Hildebrand and C. N. Reilley, *Anal. Chem.*, **36**, 47 (1964).
68. R. S. Porter, R. L. Hinkins, L. Tornheim, and J. F. Johnson, *Anal. Chem.*, **36**, 260 (1964).
69. W. Averill, in *Gas Chromatography*, N. Brenner, J. E. Callen, and M. D. Weiss, Eds., Academic Press, New York, 1962, pp. 1–6.
70. E. Cremer, in *Gas Chromatographie*, A. I. M. Keulemans, Ed., Verlag Chemie, Weinheim/Bergstrasse, 1959, p. 144 (in German).
71. I. Halász and E. E. Wegner, *Nature*, **189**, 570 (1961).
72. I. Halász and C. Horváth, *Anal. Chem.*, **36**, 226 (1964).
73. D. M. Ottenstein, in *Advances in Chromatography*, Vol. 3, J. C. Giddings and R. A. Keller, Eds., Marcel Dekker, New York, 1966.
74. W. J. Baker, E. H. Lee, and R. F. Wall, in *Gas Chromatography*, H. Nobels, R. F. Wall, and N. Brenner, Eds., Academic Press, New York, 1961, pp. 21–32.
75. N. C. Saha and J. C. Giddings, *Anal. Chem.*, **37**, 830 (1965).
76. D. M. Ottenstein, *J. Gas Chromatog.*, **1**(4), 11 (1963).
77. R. G. Scholz and W. W. Brandt, in *Gas Chromatography*, N. Brenner, J. E. Callen, and M. D. Weiss, Eds., Academic Press, New York, 1962, pp. 7–26.
78. D. T. Sawyer and J. K. Barr, *Anal. Chem.*, **34**, 1213 (1962).
79. A. Zlatkis, S. Ling, and H. R. Kaufman, *Anal. Chem.*, **31**, 845 (1959).
80. W. C. Jones, Jr., U.S. Pat. 3,047,992 (1962).
81. K. J. Bombaugh, *J. Chromatog.*, **11**, 27 (1963).
82. E. P. Atkinson and G. A. P. Tuey, *Nature*, **199**, 482 (1963).
83. E. C. Omerod and R. P. W. Scott, *J. Chromatog.*, **2**, 65 (1959).
84. W. J. A. VandenHeuvel, W. L. Gardiner, and E. C. Horning, *Anal. Chem.*, **35**, 1745 (1963).
85. T. Onaka and T. Okamoto, *Chem. Pharm. Bull. Tokyo*, **10**, 757 (1962).
86. J. J. Kirkland, *Anal. Chem.*, **35**, 2003 (1963).
87. V. Lukes, R. Komers, and V. Herout, *J. Chromatog.*, **3**, 303 (1960).

88. E. H. Baum, *J. Gas Chromatog.*, **1**(11), 13 (1963).
89. A. W. Decora and G. U. Dinneen, *Anal. Chem.*, **32**, 164 (1960).
90. J. M. Harper and E. G. Hammond, *J. Dairy Sci.*, **7**, 678 (1964).
91. S. E. Bresler, D. P. Debyehin, and A. G. Popov, *J. Appl. Chem. USSR, English Transl.*, **36**, 67 (1963).
92. R. J. Cvetanovic and K. O. Kutschke, in *Vapour Phase Chromatography*, D. H. Desty, Ed., Butterworths, London, 1957, pp. 87–97.
93. A. B. Littlewood, in *Gas Chromatography 1958*, D. H. Desty, Ed., Academic Press, New York, 1958, pp. 23–35.
94. R. W. Ohline and R. Jojola, *Anal. Chem.*, **36**, 1681 (1964).
95. J. J. Kirkland, *Anal. Chem.*, **37**, 1458 (1965).
96. R. Kaiser, *Chromatographie in der Gasphase, Part II, Kapillar-Chromatographie*, 2nd ed., Bibliographisches Institut, Mannheim, 1966.
97. C. G. Pope, *Anal. Chem.*, **35**, 654 (1963).
98. W. Averill, *J. Gas Chromatog.*, **1**(1), 34 (1963).
99. I. Lysyj and P. R. Newton, *Anal. Chem.*, **36**, 949 (1964).
100. E. C. Horning, E. A. Moscatelli, and C. C. Sweeley, *Chem. Ind. (London)*, **9**, 751 (1959).
101. W. R. Supina, in *Lectures in Gas Chromatography 1962*, H. A. Szymanski, Ed., Plenum Press, New York, 1963, p. 33.
102. J. I. Parcher and P. Urone, *J. Gas Chromatog.*, **2**, 184 (1964).
103. H. Fürst, H. Köhler, H. Seidenschnur, and D. Birke, *Chem. Tech.*, **16**, 669 (1964).
104. E. D. Smith, *Anal. Chem.*, **32**, 1049 (1960).
105. C. Landault and G. Guiochon, *J. Chromatog.*, **9**, 133 (1962).
106. D. H. Desty, A. Goldup, and B. H. F. Whyman, *J. Inst. Petrol.*, **45**, 287 (1958).
107. D. H. Desty, J. N. Haresnape, and B. H. F. Whyman, *Anal. Chem.*, **32**, 302 (1960).
108. R. P. W. Scott, *Nature*, **183**, 1753 (1959).
109. G. Dijkstra and J. De Goey, in *Gas Chromatography 1958*, D. H. Desty, Ed., Academic Press, New York, 1958, pp. 56–68.
110. M. Mohnke and W. Saffert, in *Gas Chromatography 1962*, M. Van Swaay, Ed., Butterworths, Washington, D.C., 1962, pp. 216–224.
111. D. L. Petitjean and C. J. Leftault, *J. Gas Chromatog.*, **1**(3), 18 (1963).
112. R. D. Schwartz, D. J. Brasseaux, and G. R. Shoemake, *Anal. Chem.*, **35**, 496 (1963).
113. J. J. Kirkland, *Anal. Chem.*, **35**, 1295 (1963).
114. J. E. Purcell, *Nature*, **201**, 1331 (1964).
115. I. Halász and C. Horváth, *Anal. Chem.*, **35**, 499 (1963).
116. L. S. Ettre, J. E. Purcell, and K. Billeb, *Separation Science*, **1**, 777 (1966).
117. S. R. Lipsky, C. Horváth, and W. J. McMurray, in *Gas Chromatography 1966*, A. B. Littlewood, Ed., The Institute of Petroleum, London, 1967, pp. 299–317.
118. D. S. Payn, W. D. Rearden, and L. J. Harvey, *Nature*, **200**, 467 (1963).
119. K. Marcali, *Pittsburgh Conf. Anal. Chem. Appl. Spectry.*, *14th*, Pittsburgh, Pa., March, 1963.
120. N. M. Turkel'taub, *Tr. Komisspo Analit. Khim. Akad. Nauk SSSR, Inst. Geokhim. i Analit. Khim.*, **6**, 146 (1955); *Chem. Abstr.*, **50**, 7663f.
121. A. P. Tudge, *Can. J. Phys.*, **40**, 557 (1962).
122. R. W. Ohline and D. D. Deford, *Anal. Chem.*, **35**, 227 (1963).
123. L. S. Ettre, *Sci. Rept. Ist. Super. Sanità*, **2**, 252 (1962).
124. K. P. Hupe and E. Bayer, in *Gas Chromatography 1964*, A. Goldup, Ed., The Institute of Petroleum, London, 1965, pp. 62–76.

125. J. C. Giddings, *J. Chem. Educ.*, **39**, 569 (1962).
126. W. E. Harris and H. W. Habgood, *Programmed Temperature Gas Chromatography*, Wiley, New York, 1966.
127. S. Dal Nogare and W. E. Langlois, *Anal. Chem.*, **32**, 767 (1960).
128. G. Guiochon, *Anal. Chem.*, **36**, 661 (1964).
129. L. E. Green, L. J. Schmanch, and J. C. Worman, *Anal. Chem.*, **36**, 1513 (1964).
130. F. T. Eggertsen, S. Groennings, and J. J. Holst, *Anal. Chem.*, **32**, 904 (1960).
131. C. M. Drew and J. R. McNesby, in *Vapour Phase Chromatography*, D. H. Desty, Ed., Butterworths, London, 1957, pp. 213–221.
132. C. Merritt, Jr., J. T. Walsh, D. A. Forss, P. Angelini, and S. M. Swift, *Anal. Chem.*, **36**, 1502 (1964).
133. H. W. Habgood and W. E. Harris, *Anal. Chem.*, **32**, 450 (1960).
134. S. Dal Nogare and C. E. Bennett, *Anal. Chem.*, **30**, 1157 (1958).
135. E. M. Emery and W. E. Koerner, *Anal. Chem.*, **34**, 1196 (1962).
136. R. Teranishi, G. R. Buttery, and R. E. Lundin, *Anal. Chem.*, **34**, 1033 (1962).
137. L. S. Ettre, R. D. Condon, F. J. Kabot, and E. W. Cieplinski, *J. Chromatog.*, **13**, 305 (1964).
138. S. R. Lipsky, R. A. Landowne, and J. E. Lovelock, *Anal. Chem.*, **31**, 853 (1959).
139. C. Costa Neto, J. T. Koffer, and J. W. de Alencar, *J. Chromatog.*, **15**, 301 (1964).
140. R. P. W. Scott, in *Gas Chromatography 1964*, A. Goldup, Ed., The Institute of Petroleum, London, 1965, pp. 25–37.
141. L. Mázor and J. Takács, *J. Gas Chromatog.*, **4**, 322 (1966).
142. A. Zlatkis, D. C. Fenimore, L. S. Ettre, and J. E. Purcell, *J. Gas Chromatog.*, **3**, 75 (1965).
143. R. Villalobos and G. S. Turner, *ISA J.*, **10**(5), 67 (1963).
144. D. J. McEwen, *Anal. Chem.*, **36**, 279 (1964).
145. R. Villalobos, R. O. Brace, and T. Johns, in *Gas Chromatography*, H. J. Noebels, R. F. Wall, and N. Brenner, Eds., Academic Press, New York, 1961, pp. 39–54.
146. N. Brenner and V. J. Coates, *Nature*, **181**, 1401 (1958).
147. L. A. Robbins, R. M. Bethea, and T. D. Wheelock, *J. Chromatog.*, **13**, 361 (1964).
148. R. W. Hurn, J. O. Chase, and K. J. Hughes, *Ann. N.Y. Acad. Sci.*, **72**, 675 (1959).
149. J. M. Trowell, *Anal. Chem.*, **37**, 1152 (1965).
150. E. W. Cieplinski, W. Averill, and L. S. Ettre, *J. Chromatog.*, **8**, 550 (1962).
151. B. W. Taylor, *Pittsburgh Conf. Anal. Chem. Appl. Spectry.*, *7th*, Pittsburgh, Pa., March 1959.
152. J. O. Terry and J. H. Futrell, *Anal. Chem.*, **37**, 1165 (1965).
153. A. B. Littlewood, *J. Gas Chromatog.*, **2**, 188 (1964).
154. N. Brenner and E. Cieplinski, *Ann. N.Y. Acad. Sci.*, **72**, 705 (1959).

CHAPTER 5

Detectors

Benjamin J. Gudzinowicz,* *Jarrell-Ash Company,*
Waltham, Massachusetts

* Present address: Polaroid Corporation, Cambridge, Massachusetts.

I. Introduction

Since James and Martin (1) first reported their investigations on the gas chromatographic separation of fatty acids, the applications of gas chromatography to complex analytical problems have increased exponentially each year as attested by numerous publications. This can be directly correlated with and attributed to the development of more sensitive methods of detection as well as recent advances in gas chromatographic column, stationary phase, carrier gas, and temperature- and pressure-controlling technology.

From the early days when eluted acidic components were manually titrated to the present time, great progress in vapor sensing devices has occurred with the introduction of highly specific, rapid, sensitive detection systems based on ionization by beta-emitter, electron affinity, and flame.

By comparing such parameters as sensitivity, stability, linearity, response time, and simplicity in design, the relative merits of detectors have been discussed at numerous international symposia by recognized leaders in the field of gas chromatography.

To classify detectors, many terms have been introduced; these are based either on (1) the manner in which their output signals are recorded (yielding either integral or differential chromatograms), (2) their modes of operation, (3) monitoring some selective or specific physical property of a compound, or (4) their reactivity with the eluted molecule (destructive or nondestructive).

The importance of high sensitivity in a detector is well recognized. For this reason, various methods have been proposed to obtain a quantitative comparison of the different types of detector.

Dimbat, Porter, and Stross (2) defined sensitivity as:

$$S = AC_1C_2C_3/W \qquad (5\text{-}1)$$

where S = sensitivity, ml mV/mg
  A = peak area, cm^2
  C_1 = recorder sensitivity, mV/cm of chart
  C_2 = chart speed, min/cm
  C_3 = flow rate at exit of column, ml/min
  W = weight of sample injected, mg

Kaiser (3) proposed a so-called corrected sensitivity, E, which is defined as the ratio of the voltage (relative to drift and noise) to the component's concentration in the carrier gas passing through the detector:

$$E = \frac{16.66hb_{1/2}F_c}{W(R + D)} \qquad (5\text{-}2)$$

where h = peak height, mV
  $b_{1/2}$ = peak width at half peak height, min
  F_c = carrier gas flow rate at detector temperature in liters/hr
  W = amount of substance injected, mg
  R = noise level, mV
  D = baseline drift, mV/hr

By comparing these two methods, one notes that they differ only by the factor $1/(R + D)$.

To estimate the noise level or output of a detector, Ongkiehong (4) expressed it in the following terms:

$$n = dSF \qquad (5\text{-}3)$$

where n = noise
  d = flow fluctuation expressed as a fraction of the total flow
  S = cell current, without sample injection, expressed in microamperes per unit of gas flow rate (ml/sec)
  F = total flow, ml/sec

It has also been proposed that the lower limit of detection L or lower sensitivity limit, based on a recorder deflection two times the noise level, be estimated by using the equation below:

$$L = 2CFR/I \qquad (5\text{-}4)$$

where L = lower limit of detection, g/sec
C = concentration in carrier gas, g/ml
F = carrier gas flow rate, ml/sec
I = detector voltage in mV produced by CF g/sec of substance

For ionization devices, Lovelock (5) introduced an apparent ionization efficiency term A.I.E., defined as the ratio of the charge of ions, in coulombs, collected as one mole of a substance passes through the detector, to that of the charge expected from complete ionization of the substance (9.65×10^4 coulombs):

$$\text{A.I.E.} = (\text{ampere} \times \text{sec per mole})/(9.65 \times 10^4) \qquad (5\text{-}5)$$

Regardless of the method used to compare detector performance, difficulties will be encountered since many of the functions expressed above are not applicable to all types of detectors.

This also might be said about detectors, in general, since most are not "universal" in their applications. Some are capable of performing only one specific analytical function, as you will discover by reading the subsequent sections of this chapter devoted to gas chromatographic detectors.

However, the purpose of this chapter is twofold: (*1*) to describe in basic terms the operating principles of many detection systems and (*2*) to bring to the reader's attention the many types of and recent advances in gas chromatographic detectors based on the most recent data reported in the literature.

II. Thermal Detectors

A. Thermal Conductivity Detector

For many years, the thermal conductivity cell or *katharometer* has been used to detect changes in gas composition with a high degree of accuracy.

In theory, thermal conductivity detection systems are based on two established principles: (*1*) Each gas has its own individual thermal energy transfer characteristic or transmission factor, and (*2*) metal filaments and thermistors (semiconductors of fused metal oxides) have fixed resistance–temperature relationships.

The cell usually consists of a metallic wire or thermistor mounted coaxially within a metal or glass cylinder through which a gas flows. Due to the flowing gas, the rate of heat loss from the sensing element, heated by the application of a constant electric current, is determined by measuring the sensor's resistance which can be then converted to a specific temperature value. When a foreign substance is introduced into the gas stream, the resistance of the sensor and consequently the temperature change. If the detection device is incorporated into some form of a Wheatstone bridge circuit, an "out-of-balance" of the bridge is noted, this signal being a measure of the rate of heat loss.

In the determination of thermal conductivity values, such subsidiary effects as radiation, convection, etc., contribute to the rate of heat loss. However, since they are negligible, they can be ignored.

Based on the kinetic theory of gases, the thermal conductivity of a pure gas is defined by the relation:

$$k = \tfrac{1}{3}(mn\bar{c}lC_v) \qquad (5\text{-}6)$$

where k = thermal conductivity of the gas (quantity of heat in ergs flowing per second through 1 cm^2 under a temperature gradient of 1°C/cm)

$\quad m$ = mass of each molecule

$\quad n$ = number of molecules in 1 ml of gas

$\quad \bar{c}$ = average or mean molecular velocity

$\quad l$ = average or mean free path

$\quad C_v$ = specific heat of the gas at constant volume

In turn, k bears a relationship to the coefficient of viscosity, η, which is equal to $\tfrac{1}{3}(mn\bar{c}l)$ or $\tfrac{1}{3}(\rho\bar{c}l)$, where ρ is the density or mass of unit volume, mn.

Therefore, thermal conductivity may be defined as:

$$k = \tfrac{1}{3}(\rho\bar{c}lC_v) = \eta C_v \qquad (5\text{-}7)$$

From the following expression, the rate of heat loss can be calculated:

$$(i^2R)/J = 2\pi kL(t_f - t_c)/[\ln (r_c/r_f)] \qquad (5\text{-}8)$$

where i = current in the filament

$\quad R$ = resistance of the filament

$\quad J$ = mechanical equivalent of heat

$\quad t_f, t_c$ = temperature of the filament and cylinder wall, respectively

$\quad r_f, r_c$ = radius of the filament and cylinder, respectively

$\quad L$ = length of the filament.

At constant current, the resistance changes as the thermal conductivity varies. The temperature dependence of the thermal conductivity of the gas and of resistance are given by:

$$k_t = k_0(1 + \beta t) \qquad (5\text{-}9)$$

and

$$R_t = R_0(1 + at) \qquad (5\text{-}10)$$

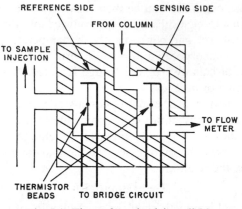

Fig. 5-1. Thermal conductivity cell (6).

where the zero subscript refers to some standard temperature; t, average temperature of the gas in °C; a and β, constants.

Since absolute measurements of thermal conductivity are too tedious and difficult, a differential technique is employed as shown in Figure 5-1 where either filament or thermistor sensing elements can be incorporated into the cell.

A Wheatstone bridge (Fig. 5-2) in which one arm is used as a "sample" sensing element with a second arm as a "standard" or reference sensing element measures the "out-of-balance" signal which is fed to a recorder. With a preselected current flowing through the bridge, equal resistances result when pure carrier gas is in contact with each sensing element. However, if a binary mixture emerging from the column (carrier gas plus separated component) passes over the sample sensing element, this element will be heated or cooled to a new temperature with a consequent change in the resistance ("out-of-balance" signal) of this arm.

Keulemans (7) has investigated in detail factors determining kathar-ometer sensitivity, these being (1) cell geometry, (2) the effect of changing

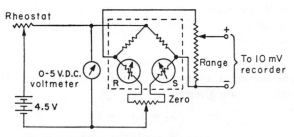

Fig. 5-2. Wheatstone bridge circuit (6).

the current (and temperature) of the filaments, (3) the effect of the thermal conductivity of the carrier gas, (4) influence of the block temperature, etc.

The following conclusions were drawn:

1. Sensitivity increases as the current is increased across the filament. However, a correspondingly lower baseline stability is noted, and this then becomes the predominant limiting factor as to the maximum permissible current one can employ.

2. A higher sensitivity can be obtained with the use of hydrogen and helium than nitrogen as carrier gases; however, catalytic reactions of hydrogen with organic compounds can be initiated by the hot filament wire.

3. At a constant filament current, a reduction in wall temperature increases sensitivity.

Schmauch and Dinerstein (8) performed theoretical and experimental studies to better understand the response of thermal conductivity cells to changes in gas composition and operating temperatures. They concluded that response or sensitivity could be considered as the product of two factors:

1. A cell factor depending upon operating conditions including electrical parameters of the cell and bridge.

2. A thermal conductivity factor depending upon conductivity differences between the carrier gas and the gas mixture passing through the cell when a component is eluted from the column.

(1) Hot-wire cell factor

$$C_w = \left\{ \left[\frac{2\pi L}{\ln(r_c/r_f)} \right] \left[\frac{J}{R_m} \right] \right\}^{1/2} \alpha \, [t_f - t_c]^{3/2} \left[\frac{R_0 R_1}{R_1 + R_m} \right] \qquad (5\text{-}11)$$

(2) Thermistor cell factor

$$C_t = \left\{ \left[\frac{2\pi L}{\ln(r_c/r_f)} \right] \left[\frac{J}{R_m} \right] \right\}^{1/2} \left[\frac{-BR_m}{R_0 T^2} \right] [t_f - t_c]^{3/2} \left[\frac{R_0 R_1}{R_1 + R_m} \right] \qquad (5\text{-}12)$$

where C_w, C_t = wire and thermistor cell factors, respectively

$\quad L$ = length of measuring element, cm

$\quad r_c, r_f$ = radius of cell wall and sensing element, cm

$\quad J$ = Joule's mechanical equivalent of heat

$\quad R_m, R_0, R_1$ = resistance of measuring elements at $T°C$, $0°C$, and the comparison resistance of the bridge, respectively, ohms

$\quad \alpha$ = temperature resistance coefficient

$\quad t_f, t_c$ = temperature of sensing element and cell wall, respectively, °C

$\quad B$ = constant for thermistor material

$\quad T$ = absolute temperature, °K

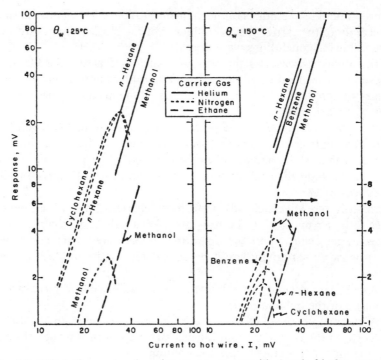

Fig. 5-3. Effect of current and carrier gas on response (8). 4 mole % of component in carrier gas.

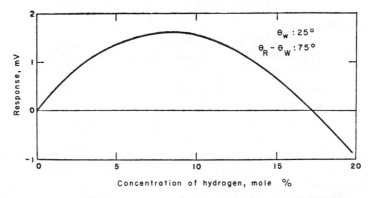

Fig. 5-4. Response vs. composition for hydrogen in helium (8).

The relationship between thermal conductivities and voltage for each cell type are as follows:

(1) Hot-wire cell

$$E_0 \approx C_w\{\sqrt{K_2}[(K_2 - K_m)/K_m]\} \qquad (5\text{-}13)$$

(2) Thermistor cell

$$E_0 = C_t\{\sqrt{K_2}[(K_2 - K_m)/K_m]\} \qquad (5\text{-}14)$$

where K_2 = thermal conductivity of carrier gas, cal (cm sec deg)$^{-1}$
K_m = thermal conductivity of the component/carrier gas mixture, cal (cm sec deg)$^{-1}$:

$$K_m = \frac{K_1}{1 + A_{1,2}[(1 - x)/x]} + \frac{K_2}{1 + A_{2,1}[x/(1 - x)]} \qquad (5\text{-}15)$$

where K_1 = thermal conductivity of the component, cal (cm sec deg)$^{-1}$
x = mole fraction of the component
$A_{1,2}, A_{2,1}$ = Wassiljewa constants.

Their experimental data showed that response, as well as being a function of the current, is nearly linear for quantitative analysis at a specific operating temperature (only one calibration factor needed) when a large conductivity difference exists between the components and the carrier gas, as in the case for organics in helium (Fig. 5-3).

When the difference is small, response is less linear, making calibrations necessary over the concentration ranges being investigated. For example, this is true for organics in nitrogen or hydrogen in helium (Fig. 5-4).

Smith and Bowden (9) developed equations to predict response factors for thermal conductivity detectors; the response to a given component is defined as the derivative dE/dy_2, where y_2 refers to the mole fraction of the component in the detector and the predicted response from the product of the following derivatives:

$$\frac{dE}{dy_2} = \frac{dE}{dT}\frac{dT}{dh}\frac{dh}{dy_2} \qquad (5\text{-}16)$$

where E = the "out-of-balance" voltage
y_2 = mole fraction of the component in the detector
T = temperature of the sensing thermistor
h = heat transfer coefficient of the thermistor surface.

For sulfur dioxide, pentane, and benzene samples, predicted response factors were within 10% of the experimental values.

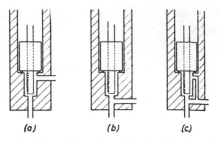

Fig. 5-5. Thermal conductivity cell designs (2). *A*, flow-through; *B*, convection–diffusion; *C*, self-purging.

Since cell geometries can be divided into three main categories (i.e., flow-through, convection-diffusion, and self-purging as shown in Fig. 5-5), investigators (2,10) have shown that a direct relationship exists between the location of the sensing element with respect to the gas flow stream and the response time and flow sensitivity of detectors. Dimbat et al. (2) chose the self-purging cell design as the best compromise between the three cell geometries, having a low flow sensitivity and a satisfactory time constant.

Whereas flow sensitivity of a detector is evaluated by the variation in output with carrier gas flow rate (as determined by noticeable baseline or peak height fluctuations), Schmauch (11) performed experiments and derived mathematical expressions showing the effect of response time in peak height, retention time, band width, and band separation, and calculated theoretical plates for five detectors at 25° and various flow rates.

From experimental data, he confirmed the conclusions of Dimbat et al. (2) and Keulemans (7) that, at any given flow rate, the diffusion-type cell had the longest response time and the direct flow-through the shortest response which, in turn, was directly related to cell volume. Response times for all cells decreased with increasing flow rates. Furthermore, for a given cell, flow noise is enhanced with increased flow rate and temperature of the measuring element.

To circumvent flow rate problems, Scott and Han (12) modified a diffusion-type, 4-filament, thermal conductivity cell which permits the use of any reasonable sample flow rate above a certain minimum value, making the signal independent both of the absolute value of the flow and of flow rate fluctuations. Kieselbach (13) studied the various sources of noise in thermistor detectors and showed that the principal contributors were external to the thermistor, these being flow variations, ambient temperature variations, bridge-current variations, and shock and vibration. Techniques for eliminating these noise sources were described.

As for the relative merits of thermistor and metal filament elements, sensitivities in general of good hot-wire filament and thermistor cells are comparable. Whereas the baseline stability of the hot-wire detector has a decided edge over the thermistor at higher temperatures, the thermistor type, in the opinion of some, had two advantages: (*a*) low dead-volume and (*b*) short response time. However, Ogilvie, Simmons, and Hinds (14) as well as others have pointed out their inherent thermal instability and lower sensitivity at high temperatures, and Naumann and Oster (15) concluded that the thermistor cell's favorable smaller volume does not produce the desired lower response time because of the thermal inertia of the thermistor cells. However, the so-called advantages of the thermistor's small cell volume in recent years have been negated by the advent of micro hot-wire conductivity detectors suitable even for open tubular column studies (16,17) and high temperature operations. In contrast to ionization detectors, these microcells permit trapping of the column effluent, exhibit a response for hydrogen, fixed gases and other compounds that escape ionization detection and do not require complex, expensive electronic circuitry.

The problem of severe baseline drift associated with column bleed at higher temperatures during temperature programming operations was satisfactorily eliminated by Emery and Koerner (18), who developed a dual-column, programmed-temperature chromatograph (Fig. 5-6), extending

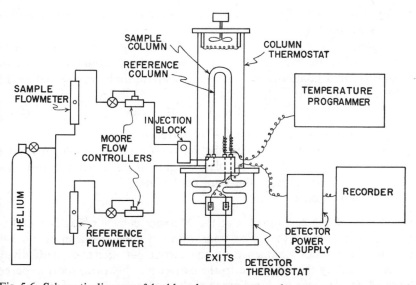

Fig. 5-6. Schematic diagram of double-column programmed temperature apparatus (18).

the upper usable temperature limits for column packings. This was accomplished by programming the temperature of two symmetrical columns, the effluent of the "dummy" column passing through the reference side of a four-filament, hot-wire thermal conductivity cell compensating for the "bleed" of analytical column. Furthermore, to correct for lack of identical column performance, they designed two independent gas flow control systems as well as automatic hold, cool, and reset control features. Comparison of single- and double-column baseline performance is shown in Figure 5-7. Their work has been capitalized upon

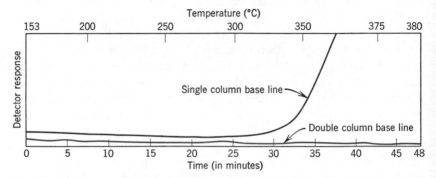

Fig. 5-7. Comparison of single- and double-column baseline performance of a well-conditioned Apiezon-L column (18).

by the introduction of commercial double-column programmed-temperature gas chromatographs.

In 1959, Messner, Rosie, and Argabright (19) reported the existence of a relationship between the molar response relative to benzene and molecular weight within a homologous series; this relationship is represented by the following expression:

$$R = A + BM \tag{5-17}$$

where R = molar response relative to benzene

A, B = constants experimentally derived for each homologous series (response vs. molecular weight where A is the response intercept and B the slope of the line)

M = molecular weight

Hoffmann (20,21) concluded that the Messner et al. finding is a consequence of the kinetic theory of transportation phenomena in binary gas mixtures; the vapor's influence on the carrier gas' thermal conductivity is determined by the resistance to the carrier gas' heat transport imposed by the different cross-sectional areas of the molecules. This conclusion has also been confirmed by Littlewood (22) using the Chapman–Enskog theory of transport properties.

Similar relative response investigations have been performed by Jamieson (23,24) for aliphatic and cyclic ethers and acetals, halogenoalkanes, aliphatic aldehydes, and pyridines. Several correlations between relative detector response and molecular structure were made. In some cases, response differences resulted from chain-branching and isomeric compounds.

B. Heat of Adsorption Detector

In 1952, Griffiths et al. (25) determined the breakthrough times of gases leaving an adsorption column by mounting a sensitive thermocouple either at the end of or in the last portion of the solid adsorbent in the column. A rise in temperature was indicated with the emergence of each compound from the column. Dudenbostel and Priestley (26) described an automatic process gas analyzer for propane in propylene using a simple detector in which thermocouple pairs were placed in a twin-chamber cell, each chamber having 0.40 ml of activated charcoal. On alternating time cycles of 5 sec duration, the effluent hydrocarbon stream was passed through each charcoal-filled chamber followed by carrier gas (in this case, dry air) on each alternate cycle to desorb the charcoal. The heat liberated on adsorption of the vapors eluting from the chromatographic column was recorded by the thermocouples as an oscillating temperature change, the summation of the oscillations being a measure of the component's concentration.

C. Flame Detectors

For the determination of combustible components of organic origin in gas chromatographic effluents, various principles of detection based on flame reactions have been utilized, namely, the hydrogen flame temperature, flame emissivity, and flame ionization detectors. In all reported systems, specific flame properties were monitored. Whereas Scott (27) measured the flame temperature of the exit gas at a small jet and Grant (28) the flame's emissivity by optical means, McWilliam and Dewar (29) and Harley et al. (30) advanced new detection concepts based on the electrical or ionization properties of hydrogen/oxygen flames.

1. Hydrogen Flame Temperature Detector

The hydrogen flame temperature detector, developed and first reported by Scott (27,31) in 1955, is based on the measurement of the flame temperature when column effluents containing combustible organic materials are

burned at a small jet. When an organic vapor in the hydrogen (75%)/
nitrogen (25%) carrier gas enters the flame, the flame temperature change
is determined by a thermocouple of either platinum/platinum and 14%
rhodium, palladium–gold/platinum–iridium, or iron/constantan placed
about 2 mm above the normal hydrogen flame. As the flame lengthens and
engulfs the thermocouple, the thermocouple output is fed through a
circuit either to a spot galvanometer or a potentiometric recorder, the
temperature change being directly related to (1) the amount of substance
burned with the hydrogen and (2) its molar heat of combustion (32).
Scott showed that a linear relationship existed between chromatographic
peak height and a substance's weight and, for benzene, n-pentane, and
n-heptane, a common calibration curve was obtained by plotting peak
areas vs. sample weight. In addition to being able to operate at 300°C, its
sensitivity was good, giving a measurable peak height for 0.05 μg of
benzene per milliliter of carrier gas.

To improve baseline stability and sensitivity, Wirth (33) used nitrogen
as the carrier gas rather than hydrogen because of its high diffusivity, the
column effluent being injected into a constant hydrogen stream and burned
at the tip of a stainless steel capillary.

For hydrogen flow rates of 100–120 ml/min, the nitrogen flow could be
varied from 20 to 60 ml/min. Wirth found that the relative response for
different organic species was closely related to their relative calorific values,
as did Henderson and Knox (32), who showed excellent agreement between
calculated response values from relative heats of combustion and measured
relative values. Furthermore, a linear relationship was reported for molar
heats of combustion and peak area per mole of 24 organic substances.

In 1958, Primavesi et al. (34) made a detailed investigation into the shape
or thermal profile of the hydrogen/nitrogen flame as well as the response
and noise of the detector at various heights above the jet. In the normal
hydrogen flame, the 800°C temperature measured above the burner tip
decreased progressively to 200°C at a position 8 cm above the tip, and the
introduction of 8.93 mg/min of toluene using a saturator at 27°C led to a
temperature increase of about 100°C at all points in the flame. The noise
of the detector was attributed to several factors: (1) air flow variations,
(2) nitrogen flow variations, and (3) fluctuations in atmospheric pressure.
For all heights greater than 0.5 cm above the jet, response was reasonably
linear, and a plot of the temperature recorded at various heights above the
jet versus that recorded at 1.5 cm showed that the relative characteristics
of the response and sensitivities are very similar at all heights, except when
the thermocouple is engulfed at higher sample concentrations and located
at shorter distances above the jet.

2. Flame Emissivity Detector

Another detector based on monitoring a specific property of a flame, its emissivity, was developed by Grant (28), who mixed coal gas in constant proportions with the effluent from a chromatographic column; this coal gas/effluent mixture burned at a wide stainless steel jet. The emissivity of the flame, changing as the flame's carbon content is varied, is measured with the aid of a metal reflector L, glass condensing lens F, and selenium photocell E; these are held in place from each other at their proper optical distances as shown in Figure 5-8. For low background emissivity values, response is nonlinear. However, by controlling the coal gas flow rate to

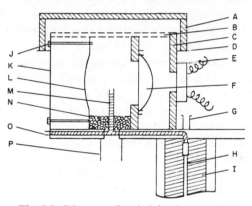

Fig. 5-8. Diagram of emissivity detector (28).

maintain emissivity between 0.60 and 0.80 mV, detector response is linear over a wide temperature range.

For various classes of compounds, the response by emissivity for n-paraffins and cycloparaffins is considerably less than for aromatic compounds, which increases with increasing number of aromatic rings in the molecule. For example, the average emissivity response relative to benzene for n-paraffins is about 0.14 in contrast to a 1.4 value for a series of alkyl-benzenes. On this basis, one could discriminate between components in an alkane/aromatic mixture. Further characterization of organic classes is possible by calculation of response factors, i.e., peak area per unit weight of compound relative to benzene with the emissivity detector divided by the peak area per unit weight of compound relative to benzene with the katharometer.

In 1960, Franc (35) monitored with a photomultiplier the changes in the hydrogen flame detector's light intensity as organic compounds in gas chromatographic column effluents entered the flame. Ultraviolet radiation was removed by placing a glass filter between the flame and photomultiplier. With this arrangement, this detector was said to be 10^3–10^4 times more sensitive than the apparatus used by Grant (28) and its response was nearly linear with sample concentration.

3. Flame Ionization Detector

The ionization properties of flames (36,37) in early studies of combustion processes were measured as early as 1954. In 1958, McWilliam and Dewar (29,38) and Harley, Nel, and Pretorius (30) designed detectors based on the fact that the ion concentration in flames when carbon compounds are introduced for combustion is several orders of magnitude greater than the few ions produced in an uncontaminated oxygen/hydrogen flame.

Several theories have been suggested to explain why the actual degree of ionization in a flame containing an organic molecule is greater than that expected from normal ionization potentials of organic materials. Stern (39) proposed that this discrepancy was due to the formation of carbon aggregates with an ionization potential (4.6 eV) approaching the work function of solid carbon; this view was supported by experimental data indicating that response for a simple paraffin hydrocarbon is proportional to the number of carbon atoms in the molecule.

On the other hand, Calcote (40–42) presented evidence that the mechanism of ion formation in flames results from chemiionization rather than thermal ionization; chemiionization differs from thermal ionization in that product molecules retain the energy released by strong exothermic reactions which lead to ionization. Based on their evidence derived from flame ionization detector studies, Sternberg et al. (43) strongly support the hypothesis of chemiionization as the source of flame ionization. However, the elucidation of the actual processes may result from direct mass spectrographic analysis of flame gases as conducted by Knewstubb and Sugden (44) and De Jaegere et al. (45).

Desty, Geach, and Goldup (46) designed a detector shown in Figure 5-9 to study the effect of various constructional and operating parameters on the detector's sensitivity; the design was not greatly different from those first described in 1958. The hydrogen supplied to the flame mixed with chromatographic column effluent enters vertically into the detector through a small orifice in its base connected to a platinum jet where it is burned to produce a small flame. The air for combustion passes through a porous stainless steel disk which provides a uniform air flow within the chamber and subsequently passes out of the chamber through holes in the detector lid. A brass rod acting as the positive collector electrode is mounted above the jet which acts as the other electrode. By applying a potential across the flame gap, thermally induced ionization of sample molecules in the flame yields a flow of current which is fed into a vibrating reed electrometer, the output of which is sent to a recorder.

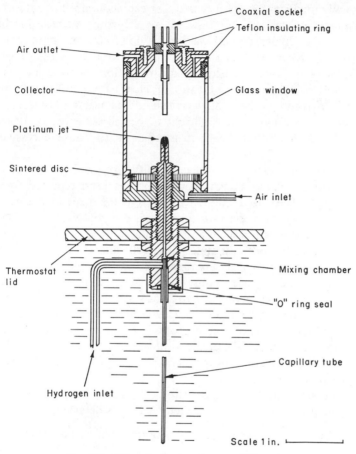

Fig. 5-9. Flame ionization detector (46).

In addition to determining response factors for various types of hydrocarbons, Desty et al. (46) studied the effect of interelectrode distance, electrode shape, polarizing potential, and gas flow rates on the sensitivity of the hydrogen flame ionization detector.

Similar studies have been performed by Ongkiehong (4,47), who noted that below a certain voltage the detector acts as an ohmic resistor for a given electrode spacing and, with higher voltages, sensitivity is independent of applied voltage. As interelectrode distances are increased, higher voltages are required to maintain saturation, 200 V providing in most cases a saturation condition regardless of detector design and operating conditions employed.

Equally important is the fact that, for each column flow rate, there are optimum hydrogen and air flow rates. A further interrelationship also exists between hydrogen and carrier gas flow rates and bore diameter of the jet (48). Whereas a 2:1 ratio of nitrogen to hydrogen is suggested by Ongkiehong for better sensitivity and reduction in noise level, Condon et al. (49) recommend a 1:1 ratio of N_2/H_2 for general use, and it is generally agreed that the air flow rate should be nearly 10 times the hydrogen flow (4,47,49)—a ratio sufficient to permit water vapor to be swept from the detector chamber but insufficient to cause excessive flame instability.

Whereas most detectors show linearity over a 10^4 to 1 range, the linearity of the flame ionization detector has been reported to cover a linear range of 10^7 to 1 and up to 0.5% constituent in the carrier gas stream (4,46,49). Also, detector response is essentially proportional to the carbon content of a molecule and depends upon the amount of material entering the flame per unit time. Ettre (50) and Perkins et al. (51) have confirmed that relative peak area per mole plotted against carbon number showed good linearity of response whereas the relative response from class to class varied considerably. Ettre (50) showed that the response to paraffins, olefins, cycloparaffins, acetylenes, and aromatics is a linear function of the number of carbon atoms in the molecule, but if other atoms or groups (such as Cl, OH, etc.) are substituted for H atoms in the molecule, the relative response now differs from that of the paraffin having the same carbon number.

To eliminate the need for detector calibration, Ongkiehong (47) proposed the use of the so-called C factor which is determined as follows:

$$C = \text{molecular weight}/(12 \times \text{number of carbon atoms}) \quad (5\text{-}18)$$

This converts response per gram of material to response per gram of carbon. This calculation, however, is apparently only valid if the sample consists only of saturated hydrocarbons.

In 1961, Emery and Koerner (18) introduced a new concept to eliminate baseline drift when a column is temperature programmed by using a dual column system. The reference column's effluent entered the reference cell of a hot-wire thermal conductivity detector while the analytical column effluent passes through the normal sensing cell, the output of the detector bridge being a measure of thermal conductivity differences of both cells.

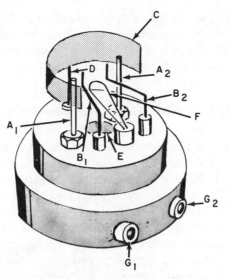

Fig. 5-10. View of the differential flame ionization detector (cover removed). A_1, A_2, jets; B_1, B_2, polarizing electrodes; C, common collecting electrode; D, connection to electrometer input; E, air filter disk; F, igniter; G_1, G_2, column connections (52).

To incorporate flame ionization detection into a dual column system, Ettre et al. (52) developed a differential detector with a single output feeding one amplifier as shown in Figure 5-10 and discussed its application with packed and open tubular columns. A simplified schematic of the electrical circuit of the differential flame detector system is shown in Figure 5-11. The amplifier's output sent to a recorder is the difference

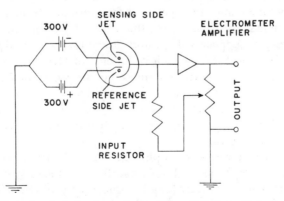

Fig. 5-11. Simplified electrical circuitry of the differential flame ionization detector system (52).

between the signals within the sensing and reference flames. When incorporated into a chromatographic system, it is possible to install two different columns in the instrument and alternately use them for obtaining relative retention times or retention index data.

III. Radioactive Source Ionization Detectors

Detectors based on the measurement of current flowing between two electrodes held at different potentials in a carrier gas ionized by either an internal or external radiation source have been used in gas chromatography for many years. The result observed when an organic or inorganic compound is ionized by high energy radiation bombardment is directly related to the manner in which the detector is operated; the ionization processes occurring within the cell depend to some extent upon the nature of the carrier gas, cell voltage, cell geometry, and radioactive source employed in addition to temperature, pressure, and carrier gas flow rate effects. These techniques, or detection devices, however, have an important and distinct place in gas chromatography since they provide the chemist with some of the most sensitive methods developed for analyzing components of complex mixtures at very low concentration levels.

A. Cross-Section Detector

Although Pompeo and Otvos (53) first suggested the measurement of gas concentration by absorption of ionization radiation, Deisler et al. (54,55) described an apparatus for the analysis of gaseous binary and ternary mixtures using alpha particles for ionization from polonium in an aged radium D source. They noted that a 10^{-8} A current could be obtained by optimizing the applied voltage and electrode spacing in the ion mixture. Graven (56) applied the ionization detector of Deisler et al. (54) for the detection of nitrogen, nitrous oxide, and oxygen in helium carrier gas effluent from a column packed with molecular sieves. He reported that this type of detector was insensitive to temperature and gas flow rate variations and, with the exception of hydrogen, was moderately sensitive to all permanent gases.

In contrast to these weak, alpha-emitting radioactive sources of poor penetrating power, Deal et al. (57) and Boer (58) used strontium-90 as a beta-emitter with a relatively long half-life, nearly 19 years. Whereas Deal et al. (57) constructed a single-cell unit showing a linear response for heptane in nitrogen to 2–3 mole %, Boer (58) developed a differential, dual-cell system; the outlets of both cells, one for the column effluent and one for the carrier gas, were coupled to a common tube to eliminate temperature and pressure fluctuations and their standing currents were balanced electrically.

Regardless of the radioactive source employed, however, the fundamental physical basis of the method as described by Otvos and Stevenson (59) and principles of operation are essentially the same.

Ion pairs formed in an ionization chamber by passing radiation through a gas can be collected by applying a potential across the electrodes. With increasing polarizing voltage, the current increases to a saturation value where all ions formed are collected at the electrodes without significant loss by recombination. Below this saturation "plateau" of applied voltage, the current is limited by ion recombination processes whereas excessive voltages (greater than that required for saturation) produce further ions due to increased acceleration and energy imparted to primary ions.

By operating the detector of known volume, V, at an applied potential within the saturation "plateau," the ionization current, i_c, or concentration of ion pairs is given by:

$$i_c = K(PV/RT) \sum Q_c \qquad (5\text{-}19)$$

where K is a constant determined by radiation intensity and ion chamber geometry, Q_c the ionization cross section of the carrier gas, R the gas constant, and P and T the pressure and absolute temperature of the system, respectively.

Otvos and Stevenson (59) demonstrated that the total molecular ionization cross section is a constitutive property, being the sum of the atomic cross sections.

When a single peak emerges from the chromatographic column, a change in current, Δi, is observed due to the presence of sample vapor and the equation then becomes:

$$\Delta i = K(PV/RT)m_s(Q_s - Q_c) \qquad (5\text{-}20)$$

where m_s is the mole fraction of sample to carrier gas and Q_s the ionization cross section of the sample vapor.

This expression reduces to:

$$i = m_s Q_s + (1 - m_s)Q_c \qquad (5\text{-}21)$$

Provided that the elemental composition of the gas is known, detector response can be predicted from molecular ionization cross section. In Figure 5-12, Clark (60) shows a plot of observed responses for different molecular species versus their calculated molecular cross sections.

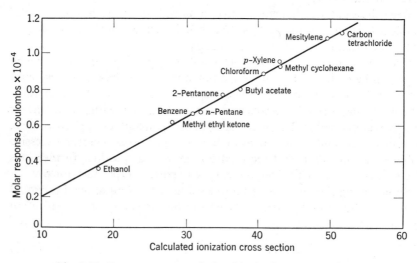

Fig. 5-12. Response versus calculated ionization cross section (60).

For quantitative hydrocarbon analysis, Boer (58) determined a proportionality factor (P.F.) for each hydrocarbon using the expression:

$$\text{P.F.} = (Q_s - Q_c)/\text{Molecular weight of sample vapor} \qquad (5\text{-}22)$$

By dividing the measured peak area of each component by its proportionality factor and then summing these "corrected" peak area quotients, the percentage by weight of each component can be derived by a simple calculation.

Figure 5-13 shows the effect of flow rate and temperature upon the standing current of the detector. The current is essentially insensitive to gas flow rate but inversely proportional to the absolute temperature as predicted by the equation relating current to temperature.

By modifying and reducing the sensing volume of the detector, Lovelock, Shoemake, and Zlatkis (61) increased sensitivity by more than 100-fold using tritium-containing sources of beta radiation. The performance characteristics of their small ionization cross-section detector compared

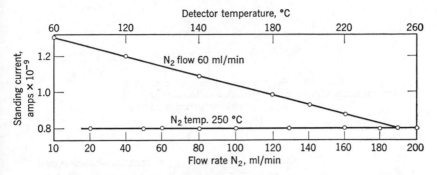

Fig. 5-13. Relationship between standing current and carrier gas flow rate and detector temperature (60).

with those of a typical or normal detector are listed in Table 5-1. With this small-volume ionization cross-section detector, Simonds and Lovelock (62) established conditions for the quantitative analysis of steroids.

More recently, Lovelock et al. (63) developed a micro-cross-section detector with an 8 μl volume capable of providing cross-section responses

TABLE 5-1

Performance Characteristics of Small Ionization Cross-Section Detector Compared with Those of Typical Ionization Cross-Section Detector (61)

(Measurements made with a bandpass of 0–1 cps)

Characteristic	Small detector	Typical detector
Ionization efficiency	10^{-7}	2×10^{-9}
Linear dynamic range	3×10^5	10^4
Noise level (A)	10^{-13}	10^{-13}
Background current in hydrogen (A)	5×10^{-9}	5×10^{-11}
Minimum detectable quantity (g/sec)	10^{-9}	2×10^{-7}
Minimum detectable concentration by volume	2×10^{-6}	2×10^{-5}
Carrier gas	H_2	H_2
Detector volume (ml)	0.08	5
Substances detectable	All	All

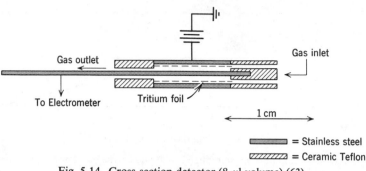

Fig. 5-14. Cross-section detector (8-μl volume) (63).

for components emerging from 0.01-in. diameter open tubular chromatographic columns (Fig. 5-14). The ion chamber, made from 1.6-mm diameter tubing, contains a 200 mCi titanium tritide source deposited as a surface layer on 0.002 in. stainless steel foil and a 0.8-mm diameter collecting electrode mounted axially within the chamber. To provide compensation for large changes in ambient temperature, pressure, and carrier gas composition, an integrated pair of detectors was described (Fig. 5-15); this idea of compensation by two identical cross-section detectors first introduced by Boer (58) and more recently by Abel et al. (64). Experimental arrangement for single-column and parallel-column operation or programmed-temperature operation of the balanced-pair ionization cross-section detector was described with the performance characteristics of the dual detector compared with those of previous ionization cross-section detectors developed by the authors (Table 5-2).

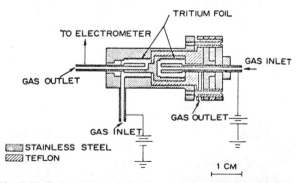

Fig. 5-15. Balanced pair ionization cross-section detector (63).

TABLE 5-2

Performance Characteristics of Dual Ionization Cross-Section Detector
Compared with Those of Previous Ionization
Cross-Section Detectors (63)
(Measurements made with a bandpass of 0–1 cps)

Characteristic	Balanced pair detector[a]	80-μl detector	8-μl detector
Ionization efficiency	10^{-8}	10^{-7}	3.7×10^{-7}
Linear dynamic range	1.5×10^5	3×10^5	3×10^5
Noise level (A) H_2 or He–5%			
$\quad$ CH_4	10^{-13}	10^{-13}	10^{-13}
Background current in hydrogen (A); per single channel			
$\quad$ H_2	2.5×10^{-8}	5×10^{-9}	1.3×10^{-9}
$\quad$ He–CH_4	2.5×10^{-8}		
Minimum detectable quantity (g/sec)[b]	1.6×10^{-9}	3.2×10^{-10}	3.2×10^{-11}
Minimum detectable concentration by volume	3.2×10^{-6}	2×10^{-6}	2×10^{-6}
Carrier gas	H_2 or He 5% CH_4	H_2 or He 5% CH_4	H_2 or He 5% CH_4
Detector volume (ml)	0.250	0.08	0.008
Substances detectable	All	All	All

[a] These parameters determined at 760 mm. Operation at 250 mm will provide an approximate threefold improvement in characteristics.

[b] Assuming an operating time constant of 1 sec.

B. Argon Detector

In 1958, Lovelock (65) was the first to show that a normal beta-ray ionization detector such as the cross-section detector, when used with argon as the carrier gas at a relatively high applied potential, produced greatly magnified signals for most organics at concentration levels as low as 10^{-12} mole. Using the unique ionization properties of argon, the detector's response to molecules with varying functional groups incorporated into their structures was quite similar and somewhat insensitive to pressure, temperature, and carrier gas flow rate variations.

In 1955, Jesse and Sadauskis (66) established the principles behind the argon detector's operation, noting that ionization in irradiated gases increased in the presence of small traces of organic molecules. Under constant irradiation, rare gas atoms are ionized and excited to their metastable state. Upon collision with an organic molecule, these long-lived metastable ions transfer their energy and create ions if the organic molecule's ionization potential is less than the excitation potential of the gas atom. The increase in the level of ionization within the cell results from the ionization processes postulated by Lipsky, Landowne, and Lovelock (67):

$$\text{Argon}^0 + \beta\text{-ray} \longrightarrow \text{Argon}^+ + e^- \text{ (primary)} \tag{5-23}$$

$$\text{Argon}^0 + e^- \xrightarrow{\text{high voltage}} \text{Argon}^* \text{ (11.6 eV)} \tag{5-24}$$

$$\text{Argon}^* \text{ (metastable state)} + \text{organic molecule} \longrightarrow$$

$$\text{Organic molecule}^+ + e^- \text{ (secondary)} + \text{Argon}^0 \tag{5-25}$$

$$e^- \text{ (secondary)} + \text{Argon}^0 \xrightarrow{\text{high voltage}} \text{Argon}^* \tag{5-26}$$

$$\text{or} \quad e^- \text{ (secondary)} \xrightarrow{\text{to anode}} \text{Current in amperes} \tag{5-27}$$

In contrast to the small ionization current resulting from the argon ions and primary electrons formed (these contribute primarily to background current), the secondary electrons, when collected at the anode, yield an increased cell current related to the vapor concentration.

Lovelock noted that above an applied potential of 500 V, the response became linear for wider concentration ranges whereas instability and nonlinearity resulted from voltages in excess of 1200 V.

In addition to the simple argon detector with a 3–8 ml volume designed for use with packed columns, Lovelock (68,69) developed a small detector intended for use with open tubular columns, and a new triode detector having a sensitivity 1000 times greater than his original detector; both are shown in Figure 5-16. The triode detector, a modified form of the small

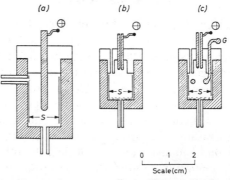

Fig. 5-16. The construction of the three detectors (69): (a) simple, (b) small, (c) triode.

detector, incorporates a ring electrode, in addition to the normal anode and cathode electrodes, which separates the background current (positive ions liberated by vapor/metastable argon reactions or collisions) of the primary electron stream from the signal current.

Basically, both detectors are similar to the simple device in design: (1) their brass or stainless steel chambers function as cathodes; (2) their anodes of the same material are supported coaxially within the chamber by a polytetrafluoroethylene insulator; (3) both contain ports for introduction and escape of the chromatographic column gas effluent from the detectors; and (4) each have a suitable source of alpha or beta radiation.

Furthermore, several added design features were incorporated which are not found in the normal or simple detector. An additional port is included to provide a flow of scavenging gas, and a diffuser of three layers of fine 100-mesh gauze is located at the base to establish a uniform scavenger gas flow. Also, the anode in each is withdrawn 2.5 mm into the cavity in the insulator, thus (1) making the region of metastable atom production small, and (2) weakening and reducing the field near the cathode. This latter effect enhances the development of a positive ion space charge within the chamber, thereby rendering unnecessary the use of a linearizing resistance.

The performance characteristics of the detectors, under controlled but similar operating conditions, are listed in Table 5-3. Experimental data for all detectors were presented on efficiency, response to gas flow rate, linearity, effects of temperature and pressure, influence of anode position in the small and triode cells, effect of the primary electron current, and the effect of contaminant gases in argon.

In Lovelock's original work (65), a strontium-90, 10-mCi source of beta radiation and an 80-μCi radium source of alpha radiation were employed. However, below 250°C, tritium sources have been shown to be the safest and to give the best performance. Condon et al. (49) used a beta-emitting, 10-mCi source of krypton-85, and Prösch et al. (70) evaluated sealed radioactive sources containing 10 mCi ^{90}Sr, 1 mCi ^{90}Sr, 500 mCi tritium and 5 mCi [85]Kr for sensitivity, stability, safety, and convenience in use in conjunction with an argon detector described by Bothe (71), and concluded that [85]Kr sources performed best on an overall basis.

In a series of papers, Gaziev et al. (72,73) described an argon detector using promethium-147 as a source of beta radiation, and Frank and Yanovskii (74) constructed a microionization detector for open tubular gas–liquid chromatography based on [147]Pm without the use of an additional gas stream.

TABLE 5-3

The Performance Characteristics of the Detectors under
Typical Operating Conditions (69)

Conditions of measurement and characteristics	Detector		
	Simple	Small	Triode
Gas flow rate (ml/min)	60	2.2	2.2
Applied potential (V)	1200	1200	1200
Frequency range of the entire apparatus (cps)	0 to 0.3	0 to 1	0 to 1
Radiation source (mCi)	Radium D, 0.07	Tritium, ca. 50	Tritium, ca. 50
Background current (A)	7×10^{-9}	1.2×10^{-8}	3×10^{-10}
Noise level (A)	10^{-11}	10^{-12}	$<10^{-13}$
Ionization efficiency (%)	0.05	0.5	0.5
Minimum detectable quantity (g/sec)	4×10^{-11}	4×10^{-13}	2×10^{-14}
Minimum detectable concentration (g/ml at 20 ml/min)	4×10^{-11}	1.2×10^{-12}	6×10^{-14}
Maximum current consistent with a linear response (A)	7×10^{-8}	3×10^{-7}	4×10^{-7}
Deviation from linearity over a 1000-fold change in vapor concentration (%)	3.1	1.2	1.2

Other alpha radiation sources have been proposed by Takeuchi et al. (75,76) such as Ra E and Ra F, which are isotopes of bismuth and polonium, respectively.

Haahti et al. (77,78) reported in 1960 that Lovelock's detector (65) could be used without a radiation source if it is constructed of glass; this detector possesses the same characteristics as a ^{90}Sr detector. They replaced a ^{90}Sr-covered silver plate as anode with a nonradioactive aluminum plate and suggested that the responses are due to differences in the conductivity of the gases passing the detector. Upham, Lindgren, and Nichols (79), using a stainless steel chamber without a source, failed to obtain results as reported by Haahti et al. but observed limited detector performance when a uranium glass cylindrical sleeve was placed in the sourceless detector. They concluded that a sourceless detector requires a glass surface containing some radioactivity to work.

Since metastable argon atoms do not possess sufficient energy to ionize compounds having ionization potentials above 11.6 eV, the argon detector is not able to analyze the permanent gases. However, using pure helium as the carrier gas, several investigators (80–83) have proposed direct methods for permanent gas analysis in contrast to Willis's indirect procedure (84) using argon containing small amounts of ethylene or acetylene, the permanent gases being detected by their quenching effects upon the standing current of the impure argon.

Lipsky and Shahin (85) noted that with krypton or xenon as carrier gas, the response to various polyatomic gases was 2–3 times greater than that noted with argon.

On the other hand, with a detector of low internal volume with concentric electrodes 1 mm apart and argon as carrier gas, Shahin and Lipsky (86) reported the mechanisms of operation of this new and highly sensitive ionization system for the detection of permanent gases and organic vapors. Operating at 1–2 V, the detection limit of permanent gases approached 10^{-12} mole/sec. When operating at 150–250 V, its sensitivity to organics was equal to or greater than that obtained with the small Lovelock argon detector.

Shahin and Lipsky postulated that at low field strengths permanent gases were ionized by one of two mechanisms, the first involving changes in electron drift velocity caused by the addition of complex molecules to argon; the second resulting from collisions with metastable argon atoms (Ar*) and a fixed gas atom (M) which yield complex ions, (ArM)$^+$, based on the following reaction:

$$Ar^* + M \rightarrow ArM^+ + e^- \qquad (5\text{-}28)$$

C. Electron Mobility Detector

The electron mobility or drift-velocity detector, operated in either a direct or indirect mode, is today best suited for the measurement of permanent gases by gas chromatography.

Both methods are based upon the free electron's mobility or velocity in noble gases in the presence of other gases.

In 1960, Lovelock (87) described a direct technique for permanent gas analysis in an argon carrier gas using a chamber (Fig. 5-17) which is identical to the electron capture detector. The ionization chamber of plane-parallel geometry, filled with flowing argon entering through the cathode inlet (D), is connected directly across a dc amplifier, and short positive pulses of 1–10 μsec duration, rather than a steady potential, are fed through a condenser to the anode (see Fig. 5-18). By applying generated pulses having the form of half-rectified sine waves with a 50–100 V amplitude and a frequency between 0.2 and 0.7 Mc to the chamber

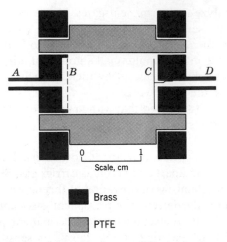

Fig. 5-17. Electron capture ionization detector (88). *A*, inlet for carrier gas and anode; *B*, diffuser made of 100-mesh brass gauze; *C*, source of ionizing radiation; *D*, gas outlet and cathode. This is also the design of the direct electron mobility detector, only the gas flow is reversed.

containing a tritium source of beta radiation sufficient to provide a 1×10^{-8} to 3×10^{-9} A saturation current, the permanent gases may be detected.

In principle, the method is based on the fact that the free electrons with argon gas are accelerated rapidly when a uniform electric field is applied across the chamber; these electrons attain mean energies much greater than those of the argon gas atoms and high mean velocities with little or no energy loss during their elastic collisions with argon atoms. Whereas

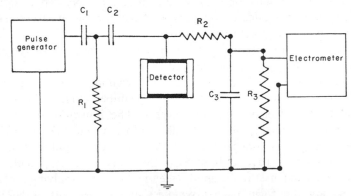

Fig. 5-18. Schematic diagram for connections to a direct electron mobility ionization detector (88).

the application of a uniform electric field to the cell permits these electrons to be collected at the anode, resulting in a flow of current within the detector, little or no current is observed when pulses of short duration are applied, the pulse period selected being insufficient to deflect and collect these fast-moving accelerated electrons. Since a considerable amount of the energy imparted to the electron by the electric field is lost by electrons due to nonelastic collisions with gases other than rare gases, the electrons

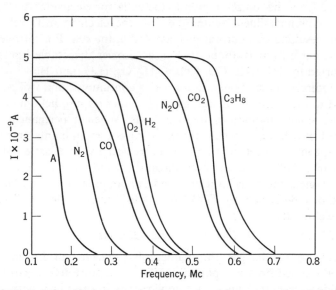

Fig. 5-19. Relationship between signal current and frequency of applied pulses with electron mobility ionization detector (88). Curves are drawn for pure argon and for argon containing 0.1 % by volume of gases indicated.

are sufficiently decelerated by collision to permit their collection at the anode when a pulse is applied. This observed current is proportional to the contaminant gas concentration. In general, as the complexity of the contaminant gas increases (more atoms in the molecule), the greater will be its ability to reduce the electron energy by nonelastic collisions.

Lovelock noted a dependent relationship between response and pulse frequency, higher frequencies at which a current can still be observed being required as the complexity of the molecule increases (Fig. 5-19). By varying the pulse frequency applied to the cell, it is possible to distinguish gases such as N_2, O_2, etc.

The response of the detector was reported to be linear up to 1 % by volume of diatomic contaminant gases in the argon carrier gas stream. At higher frequencies, a nonlinear response was observed with polyatomic gases. Nevertheless, concentration levels of 1 in 10^8 by volume for triatomic and 1 in 10^7 for diatomic gases could be detected.

Recently, Smith and Fidiam (89) investigated the direct electron mobility technique in great detail and developed a detection system with excellent baseline stability and high sensitivity to permanent gases. By applying negative voltage pulses of short duration to the cell (a small-volume, parallel-plate ionization chamber with a tritium source), electrons are accelerated from the ionized region to the collector electrode. As chromatographic column effluents enter the cell, the electron drift velocity is enhanced, resulting in a current increase within the cell. For nitrogen, the lower detectable limit is about 10^{-10} g/sec. Lower detectable limits were also reported for H_2, CH_4, CO, CO_2, C_2H_6, O_2, H_2O, and He.

In the indirect mode of operation where a continuous, uniform potential is applied to the detector, the carrier gas is either impure helium or argon containing small amounts of hydrocarbons. When a permanent gas is introduced into the cell, where the carrier gas contaminants are heavily ionized, the mean electron energy is decreased by nonelastic collisions resulting in a fall in current flow directly related to a decrease in the number of metastable argon atoms and contaminant molecules ionized. The methods described by Willis (84) and Johnson (90) utilized this indirect technique.

D. Electron Capture Detector

In recent years, the gas chromatographic detector of Lovelock and Lipsky (91), based on a compound's ability to capture free electrons, has found wider acceptance and more applications in chemical, agricultural, and medical research.

This detector was originally designed as a qualitative device to differentiate between molecular species (e.g., esters, ethers, halides, ketones, and alcohols) by noting differences in electron absorption due to specific functional groupings or atoms within a molecule (91–93) by varying the applied potential. However, recent advances in technique have shown it to be suitable for quantitative determinations (94–97).

In principle, the operation of the detector is based upon a neutral molecule's (AM) ability to capture or react with free electrons (e^-) to form stable negative ions (AM$^-$) or charged particles (A$^-$, M$^-$) by the following reactions:

$$AM + e^- \rightarrow (AM)^- + \text{energy} \tag{5-29}$$
$$AM + e^- \rightarrow A + M^- \pm \text{energy} \tag{5-30}$$
$$A^- + M \pm \text{energy}$$

In an ionization chamber with parallel plates (see Fig. 5-17) containing tritium as the primary source of ionizing radiation and a carrier gas such as nitrogen which possesses no affinity for electrons, recombination of positive ions and free electrons is unlikely to occur because of the free electron's high mobility. Thus, by applying a small potential across the chamber, all ions formed by ionizing radiation can be collected. When the gas chromatographic effluent containing a compound having an affinity for electrons enters the detector, negative ion formation occurs, which is accompanied by an observed decrease in current flowing in the cell. This loss in current results from the high recombination rate between positive and negative ions, nearly 10^5–10^8 times greater than that for electrons and positive ions.

The probability of electron capture and ion recombination is further decreased with increasing applied potential, until a saturation current is reached at which point these processes are virtually nonexistent.

The fractional loss of ions at a given potential resulting from the presence of a compound with an affinity for electrons can be determined from the following relationship (98):

$$f = (aNd^4)/[(\lambda^+)(\lambda^-)V^2] \qquad (5\text{-}31)$$

where f = fractional loss of ions

N = concentration of ions (related to gas concentration)

a = recombination coefficient (related to the electron affinity of a molecule)

d = distance between electrodes

λ^+, λ^- = mobilities of the positive and negative ions, respectively

V = applied potential

Since there is a relationship established between the recombination coefficient (electron absorptivity of the molecule) and the potential applied to collect a given portion of the ions formed, it is possible to differentiate between compounds having different electron absorptivities.

Lovelock (92) demonstrated that the cell shown in Figure 5-17 can be either used at a fixed potential or by applying a short pulse of potential to the electrodes.

By applying pulses of 50 V amplitude and 1 μsec width at 20–50 μsec intervals, Lovelock and Gregory (94) concluded that detector response follows a Beer's law relationship:

$$I = I_0 e^{-ack} \qquad (5\text{-}32)$$

where I = current in the presence of vapor

I_0 = current with only inert carrier gas (detector saturation current)

a = electron absorptivity of the vapor

c = concentration

k = constant related to detector geometry and operating conditions

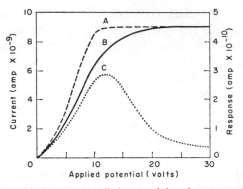

Fig. 5-20. Relationship between applied potential and response (95). *A*, theoretical current–voltage curve; *B*, experimental current–voltage curve; *C*, response curve for 5×10^{-11} g lindane.

Using a detector based on Lovelock's design, Clark (95) investigated its characteristics in detail. He determined the dependence of detector response on applied potential, on nature and flow rate of carrier gas, and on temperature, linear range, and sensitivity. He also compared dc and pulse operating techniques.

The relationship between response and applied potential in a dc polarized cell is shown in Figure 5-20, in which theoretical current–voltage and experimental current–voltage and response curves are compared.

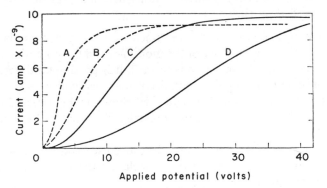

Fig. 5-21. Effect of temperature and nitrogen flow rate upon standing current (95).

	Detector temperature, °C	Flow rate, ml/min
A.	220	160
B.	220	40
C.	120	160
D.	120	40

Although the detector operated in the pulsed mode is (*1*) insensitive to flow rate changes from 40–200 ml/min (short pulse durations permitting electrons to be only collected), and (*2*) not affected by temperature over the 110–225°C range (confirmed by monitoring the standing current), there is a noticeable effect of temperature and flow rate upon the standing current of the detector operated with a fixed dc potential (Fig. 5-21).

Clark noted that under dc conditions, response is linear over 20% of the detector's working range, whereas, using pulsed potentials, response bears

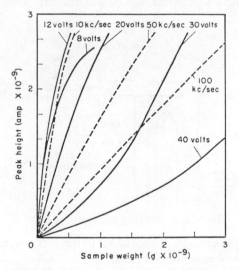

Fig. 5-22. Calibration curves for dc and pulsed operation (95).

a Beer's law relationship over 40% of the current range of the detector as pointed out previously by Lovelock and Gregory (94). Figure 5-22 shows calibration curves for lindane for dc and pulsed operation at various applied potentials and pulse repetition rates, the pulse repetition rate affecting sensitivity rather than linearity. Argon–methane was used as the carrier gas.

IV. Detectors of Nonradioactive Ionization

A. Thermionic or Electron Impact Detector

In 1957, Ryce and Bryce (99) described a sensitive ionization gauge based on the ionization potentials of vapors. It comprised a filament, a grid, and a plate (Fig. 5-23). The potential difference between the filament and grid accelerates electrons which may ionize any gas in their path. If the grid potential is maintained at a level insufficient to ionize the helium carrier gas (below 24.5 eV), no current flows in the plate circuit. If a potential difference of 18 V is maintained between the filament and the grid, compounds of lower ionization potential in the helium will be ionized and the positive ions produced will yield a cathode current, the current noted being a measure of the ion concentration. Into the modified ionizing chamber, operated at reduced pressure, a small fraction of the column effluent gas stream (less than 0.5%) was allowed to flow into the gauge through a controlled leak. Over a 0.02–1.5 mm Hg pressure range, the

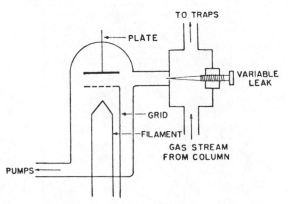

Fig. 5-23. Ionization gauge detector (99).

sensitivity was approximately proportional to the pressure, and sensitivities in the range of 10^{-12} mole were claimed.

Since the emission of primary electrons from the hot filament is inhibited by the deposition on its surface of decomposition products from the organic components in the carrier gas, Hinkle, Tucker, Wall, and Combs (100) and Guild, Lloyd, and Aul (101) corrected this by a system for maintaining the electron emission constant. This was done by monitoring the primary electron current and, by an appropriate feedback system, adjusting the filament temperature to maintain emission constant. Sample size had to be limited to avoid poisoning the heated filament.

Ryce and Bryce (99) claimed the sensitivity of the detector to be 30–100 times that of a thermal conductivity cell, whereas Hinkle et al. (100) and Guild et al. (101) attained sensitivities up to 200 and 1000 times greater, respectively.

Hinkle et al. (100) infer that linearity could be achieved over the 0–95% mole per cent range of vapor in carrier gas with changes in operating conditions. Nevertheless, for the concentration range of 1–10,000 ppm of hydrocarbons, response vs. concentration was shown to be linear.

Guild et al. (101) reported that detector pressure is not critical if held in the region of 0.10–1.0 mm Hg, and that the device is insensitive to changes in temperature as indicated by Ryce and Bryce (99). Baselines were unaffected by changes in carrier gas flow, but should be maintained constant during an analysis since flow does determine the sample/carrier ratio entering the detector.

Varadi and Ettre (102) combined a thermionic ionization gauge and a mass analyzer system in a single detector for gas chromatography; this unit will be discussed in some detail in the section related to the use of mass spectrometers as detectors.

In contrast to low-pressure sensing devices, Hudson et al. (103) constructed a thermionic diode operable at atmospheric pressure in a flowing inert gas stream. When small amounts of hydrocarbons or other organic vapors are introduced, large current increases result. By interaction of the flowing molecules with electrons of the space-charged cloud, the mechanism of detection involves the reduction of the space-charge retarding potential. To study its response characteristics, parameters such as sample size, column flow rate, filament material, and filament temperature were investigated. At a constant sample concentration, anode current exponentially increased with increasing flow rate, whereas at a fixed flow rate the exponential response with rate of solute arrival could be observed by changing the sample size. Filaments tested were made of Pt, Rh, Re and Ir, and filament temperature was measured with an optical pyrometer.

Recently, a special two-stage flame ionization detector developed by Karmen and Giuffrida (198,199) has gained importance. The second stage of this detector acts as a thermionic detector the response of which depends on release of sodium vapor and the consequent increase of the electrical conductivity of the flame. This detector is discussed later, in Section VII of this chapter, under Halogen–Phosphorus Detectors.

B. Photoionization Detector

Ion generation by photoionization has been demonstrated by Lossing and Tanaka (104), and in 1960 Lovelock (88,105) noted that ionization of vapors in an inert gas could be accomplished by irradiating the mixture with photons of appropriate energy. A detector based on this principle is shown in Figure 5-24. It consists of a chamber into which gases suitable for the discharge such as helium, argon, nitrogen, or hydrogen are introduced through tube A which serves as the cathode for the discharge. The ultraviolet radiation or glow discharge in the hollow cathode, maintained by a small current between the cathode A and discharge anode B, is sufficiently energetic to ionize components in the carrier gas effluent entering through tube D, the collecting electrode (anode) for the ions liberated within the chamber enclosed by the second cathode C.

With helium, operation at atmospheric pressure is possible if the discharge is supplied by radio-frequency energy, whereas pressures less than 100 mm Hg are required with either hydrogen, nitrogen, or argon if the discharge is produced by direct current. A linear response to vapor concentration was noted up to a current of 10^{-7} A, but no significant response to water-saturated air was noted. For propane, the ionization efficiency was about 0.01 %.

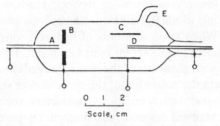

Fig. 5-24. Photoionization detector (88). A, Gas inlet to source of ultraviolet radiation and discharge cathode; B, discharge anode; C, sensing chamber cathode; D, carrier gas inlet and anode of sensing chamber; E, outlet to suction pump.

Yamane (106) modified previous photoionization detectors (107) to study the measurement of small component concentrations in gas chromatographic analysis. With helium as discharge and carrier gas, the detector is very sensitive to permanent gases; the minimum detectable limits for H_2 and O_2 were found to be 4.5 × 10^{-12} and 1.4 × 10^{-11} g/sec, or, in terms of concentration in the carrier gas, 9 × 10^{-12} and 2.8 × 10^{-11} g/ml, respectively.

Roesler (108) evaluated several types of photoionization detectors combined with various power supplies for potential use in air pollution studies. Constructed of Corning 7052 glass and Kovar metal seals, the detector achieved a noise level of about 70 $\mu\mu$A by close regulation of the glow current. With this detector, carrier gas flow (nitrogen and hydrogen) had little effect on sensitivity between 36 and 64 ml/min, but higher flow rates, with argon as the glow discharge gas, caused higher sensitivity and greater noise; argon flow rates of 60–135 ml/min were recommended for best results.

The principal factors found to affect linearity and sensitivity were: (1) carrier gas type, (2) flow rates (carrier and glow discharge gases), (3) polarity with respect to the glow discharge, (4) thermal effects of the glow discharge, and (5) detector shielded from thermal drafts, yet capable of dissipating the discharge heat.

C. Glow-Discharge Detector

In 1956, Harley and Pretorius (109) described a simple discharge detector for gas chromatography based on the electrical properties of a glow discharge, the voltage across the gaseous discharge being a function of the type of gas present. Druyvesteyn and Penning (110) in 1940 reviewed the complex nature of the glow discharge, noting that the discharge is

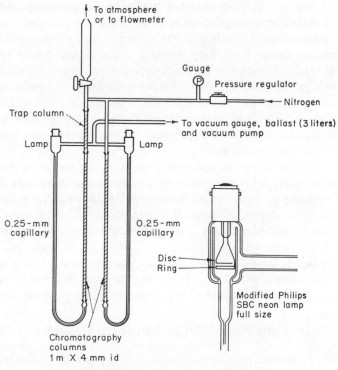

Fig. 5-25. Modified neon lamp detector (111).

maintained by (1) electrons emitted from the cathode which result from processes related to positive ion bombardment, (2) photoelectric emission, and (3) collisions with excited atoms. When trace quantities of a material eluted from a chromatographic column enter the detector (consisting of a small platinum disk cathode and a tungsten wire anode), a voltage change resulted which was recorded. With this diode forming one arm of a Wheatstone bridge and maintained at 900 V, 10^{-12} mole could be detected.

Using modified neon lamps (Fig. 5-25), Pitkethly (111) found from voltage/current/pressure experiments that these detectors were current and pressure independent at 1–1.5 mA and 3–5 mm Hg for the bridge system having paired cells. When operated at 200–300 V, the sensitivity for such a system was high, capable of detecting hydrocarbons in nitrogen at concentrations of 1 in 10^9 with molar responses increasing with molecular weight.

In 1958, Roberts and Hinkle (112) evaluated glow discharge tubes as detectors for compounds in the concentration range of 5–500 ppm and concluded that the detector was not applicable to general-purpose use because it lacked long-range stability as evidenced by gradual fouling of the electrode surfaces by carbonaceous materials, and pronounced hysteresis effects do occur from high vapor concentrations. More recently, Wilhite (113) described glow discharge-type devices which act electrically similar to a gas-filled voltage-regulator tube. Under fixed conditions with helium as the carrier gas, the detector has a breakdown voltage, and the presence of a contaminant in the carrier causes a change in its voltage. After the contaminant has left the detector, the breakdown voltage is returned to its original value.

Riley (114) described the use of an argon purity meter, a glow-type discharge detector, for the determination of small concentrations (0–1500 ppm) of impurity gases in argon. When 6000 V ac at 14 mA is maintained across the electrodes at pressures less than 40 mm Hg, the color of the glow discharge varies with the kind and concentration of the impurity present. Riley suggested the possible application of this principle to gas chromatography. Two detectors would be used, one at the inlet and the other at the column outlet. By comparing the inlet and outlet millivolt output changes, concentrations of impurities in carrier gas could be noted.

D. Radio-Frequency Corona Discharge Detector

In 1958, Pitkethly (111) suggested the possible use of radio-frequency excitation as a method of detecting changes in discharge characteristics. This method would take advantage of the rectifying properties of the discharge to pick off a dc voltage from a pair of probes using a technique described by Lion (115). Although this radio-frequency glow discharge approach was not investigated by Pitkethly (111), Karmen and Bowman (116–118) developed a radio-frequency glow discharge ionization detector by applying an rf voltage between two electrodes in a very small cell through which helium, used as the carrier gas, was passed at atmospheric pressure. With the introduction of any substance in the gas chromatographic column effluent into the cell, the dc current is reduced, resulting from partial quenching of the discharge. This current reduction, without amplification, provides a sufficient voltage signal to be fed to a potentio-metric recorder.

Unlike the glow discharge detector, this cell is not markedly affected by decomposition products deposited upon its surfaces, and at temperatures near 200°C a wide linear sensitivity range is claimed, capable of detecting one molecule of fatty acid methyl ester in 10^9 molecules of helium. Although the detector can be operated with neon or argon as the carrier gas, best detector performance results from the use of helium. Karmen and Bowman noted a direct relationship between dc current and carrier gas pressure and flow; carrier gas pressure/flow was inversely proportional to observed dc current. However, the direct current was only slightly affected by small fluctuations in these operating parameters.

When this method was applied to the analysis of oxygen, nitrogen, methane, and carbon monoxide, Klaasse and Hampton (119) reported a methane detection limit of about 3×10^{-10} moles, and that response to organic materials rose with increased molecular weight.

Andrew, Phillips, and Semlyen (120) used a simple rf coil around a glass tube containing two noninductive electrodes, and argon carrier gas at atmospheric pressure. With 2 kV between the electrodes, they report good linearity and a 5 V output signal across $10^9 \, \Omega$ for $0.20 \, \mu g/ml$ of heptane in argon.

E. Other Gas Discharge Detectors

As a means of exciting noble gases at atmospheric pressures, Lovelock (121) developed a spark device of high sensitivity, capable of detecting as little as 10^{-13} mole of most organic materials. The detector consisted of a spark gap made of platinum wire sealed in a glass tube. The voltage across the 5–10 mm spark gap is measured with an electrostatic voltmeter. With pure argon subjected to an applied voltage of 2000 V to create sparks, the breakdown potential measured was logarithmically related to the concen-tration of vapor added to the argon.

Karmen and Bowman (122) developed a dc discharge detector based on a low-current electric discharge in argon or helium in the presence of a high-intensity electrostatic field. The gas becomes a conductor at a specific value of the electrostatic field; this value is directly related to the tempera-ture, composition, and pressure of the gas. They reported detection limits for organic vapors as being 1 part per billion of carrier gas and, for atmospheric gases, 1 part per million. For organics, the sensitivity of the argon discharge was 10 times greater than that of helium.

Sternberg and Poilson (123) developed a Tesla discharge detector as a result of spectroscopic studies of glow discharges in gases created by a high-frequency Tesla coil. Based on the properties of these discharges, two detectors were designed, one measuring emitted light intensity and the other measuring a direct signal across two electrodes inserted asymmetrically in the discharge. The Tesla coil maintains a visible glow discharge in air, nitrogen, helium, or argon carrier gases, which is visibly altered by the introduction of traces of organic materials. By mounting a cadmium sulfide or selenide photoconducting cell near the capillary discharge area, light intensity measurements can be made. Sternberg and Poilson reported that with dc measurements, response increased with the number of carbon atoms in a homologous series, and the best sensitivity was achieved with argon as carrier gas.

Evrard, Thevelin, and Joossens (124) described a nonradioactive, self-sustained discharge detector for the detection of permanent gases. The dc discharge was induced in argon carrier gas containing 200 ppm ethylene. On the other hand, Karmen and Bowman (125), using the same procedure previously described (126), showed that a self-sustained discharge with argon as carrier gas, without traces of hydrocarbon present, was extremely suited for the detection of atmospheric gases. The decrease in electrical conductivity of the discharge in argon when oxygen, nitrogen, or carbon dioxide was introduced, was determined by measuring the voltage across the discharge through which a constant current was passed.

In 1964, Schaal and Schellhase (127) investigated the spark discharge described by Wulfhekel and Schaal (128) as to its zero-line stability, sensitivity, and reproducibility. With argon as carrier gas, most errors could be attributed to changes in the electronic, current, and pressure parameters and in carrier gas flow rate variations. Sensitivity for oxygen and nitrogen was reportedly twice that obtained with a thermal conductivity cell.

V. Radiation Counters as Detectors

Radioactivity measurements of gas chromatographic column effluents have been performed by various modified sensing devices. However, all of these are based on two primary methods: (1) condensation of the radioactive components out of the gas stream for subsequent radioassay, and (2) direct measurement of radioactivity in the gas phase.

A. Proportional Flow/Ionization Chamber Counters

In 1955, the use of a flow-type Geiger counter in series with a gas chromatographic thermal conductivity cell was first reported by Kokes et al. (129) for monitoring separated reaction products of radioactive ethylene and nonradioactive propylene formed at 400°C over a cracking catalyst in the presence of hydrogen. Using a thin-walled flow-through counter sensitive to hard beta and gamma rays, Evans and Willard (130) measured the radioactivity in more than 20 column effluent fractions derived from neutron-irradiated *n*-propyl bromide.

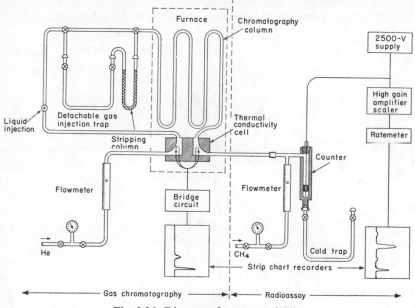

Fig. 5-26. Diagram of apparatus (131).

In both cases, these arrangements were unsatisfactory for carbon-14 and tritium. Tritium radiations are so weak that they cannot penetrate the counter window, whereas carbon-14 radiation does so only with low efficiency.

To permit radioassay by gas chromatography of tritium- and carbon-14-labeled compounds, Wolfgang and Rowland (131) converted the helium carrier gas into a suitable counting gas by continuous injection of methane (Fig. 5-26). The mixed helium/methane gas stream is then passed directly through a specially designed internal proportional counter (Fig. 5-27) which detects the radioactivity of the material separated chromatographically. Simultaneous gas chromatography/radioactivity tracings could be recorded on a strip chart. Operating at temperatures as high as 200°C, the counter's high efficiency could readily detect as little as 10^{-8} to 10^{-9} Ci.

James and Piper (132) described a simple proportional flow counter operated at room temperature for use with gas chromatograms. With argon as the carrier gas, all eluted organic compounds (whether derived from the stationary phase or an eluted zone) are converted to CO_2 over heated copper oxide. Water is removed from the stream by powdered magnesium perchlorate and, after injecting CO_2 to give a final concentration of 5%, the stream is passed into the proportional counter. For tritium counting, magnesium perchlorate could be replaced by calcium carbide to generate acetylene from the water produced by sample combustion.

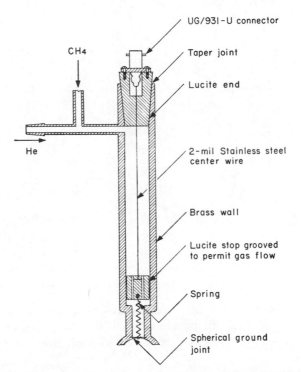

Fig. 5-27. Flow proportional counter for gas chromatograph (131).

Using a modified proportional counter of the type described by Wolf-gang and Rowland (131), Whittemore's system (133) included a printing timer set to print out the number of registered pulses recorded on the scaler each minute, thus giving a quantitative minute-by-minute record of the counting rate of the tube. As the counting gas mixture, pure methane, both as carrier and counting gas, was employed rather than helium as the carrier gas for chromatography and CH_4 as the counter gas to be added to the carrier gas effluent stream (131). At temperatures over 60°C, plating the inside of the tube with gold eliminated instability.

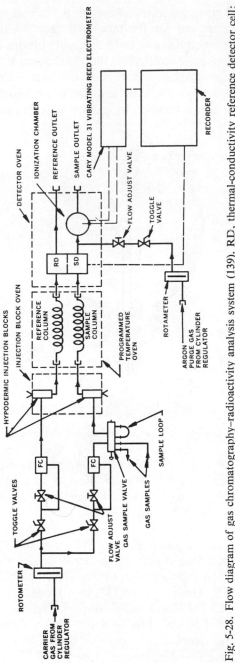

Fig. 5-28. Flow diagram of gas chromatography–radioactivity analysis system (139). RD, thermal-conductivity reference detector cell; SD, thermal-conductivity sample detector cell; FC, flow controller.

Lieser et al. (134) also used methane as both the carrier gas for chromatography and counting gas for the tube, and they could determine at $\pm 10\%$ accuracy an activity as low as 10^{-3} μCi of chlorine-36.

In 1963, Gudzinowicz and Smith (135) showed that some strong oxidants eluted from a gas chromatographic column do react with a krypton-85 quinol clathrate, releasing radioactive krypton atoms which subsequently are detected by a Geiger ratemeter. In series with a thermal conductivity

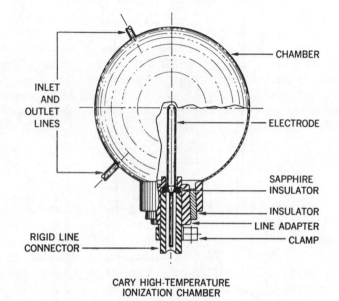

CARY HIGH-TEMPERATURE
IONIZATION CHAMBER

Fig. 5-29. Cutaway of high-temperature ionization chamber construction (139).

chromatograph, comparison of the chromatogram and the ratemeter trace identifies the oxidants in a gas mixture. Results of exploratory studies showed the following gases to possess high reactivity with the ^{85}Kr clathrate: Br_2, NO_2, OF_2, Cl_2, NO_2F, F_2, and NO_2Cl.

In addition to the above, ionization chambers have been used as flow-type counters for measuring radioactivity. Wilzbach and Riesz (136) used an ion chamber employing a ceramic insulator in series with the usual mass-detecting thermal conductivity cell. Its applicability was limited to about 200°C whereas Mason et al. (137) and Hobbs (138) constructed chambers operable to 240°C and 190°C, respectively.

Nelson, Ressler, and Hawes (139) described an ion chamber which was contained in the same temperature-controlled oven as the normal chromatography detector and could be heated to over 300° (Fig. 5-28). Activity was measured in an ion chamber of 275-ml volume as shown in Figure 5-29. They noted that sensitivity of radiation detection in terms of peak height for a given amount of injected activity is a function of many variables: (*1*) chamber volume, (*2*) type of radioactive emitter (^{14}C, ^3H, etc.), (*3*) noise and background level, (*4*) diluent gas, and (*5*) carrier and diluent gas flow rates. To reduce the time constant for better resolution (20 sec or less) the argon purge gas is introduced between the thermal conductivity detector and the ionization detector. Argon is used as the purge gas to enhance sensitivity due to its high density and low specific ionization (electron volts/ion pair). Because of its relatively high ionization energy, helium is a poor gas compared to argon for ion-pair formation.

Winkelman and Karmen (140) used a similar ionization detector, but the organics in the column carrier gas effluent were first combusted over heated copper oxide with the carbon dioxide formed being conducted to the ionization chamber for carbon-14 assay. By reacting the water produced with heated iron, hydrogen was released for tritium assay. With this technique, 202 $\mu\mu Ci$ of carbon-14, or 227 $\mu\mu Ci$ of tritium, in a compound emerging 8 min after injection could be detected.

B. Scintillation Counters

In contrast to Geiger-type proportional flow/ion chamber-type counters, scintillation counting devices of several types have been employed. Lowe and Moore (141) detected eluted carbon-14 compounds by condensing each emerging component in a circulating liquid phosphor (diphenyl oxazole in xylene); the scintillations by ^{14}C in the phosphor were detected with a photomultiplier.

By using an automatic fraction collector, Karmen and Tritch (142) condensed high boilers on successive cartridges containing anthracene crystals coated with silicone oil; each cartridge was subsequently measured by scintillation counting.

Popják and co-workers (143) designed a trap containing a scintillator in toluene held between two photomultiplier tubes. As all of the radioactive effluent materials are accumulated in the trap, an automatic range-changing device continuously monitors and keeps the record of the count rate on the recorder scale. The emergence of a radioactive compound from the column appears as an increment in the counting rate of the scintillator.

Karmen, McCaffrey, and Bowman (144) used a cartridge filled with anthracene crystals as a "flow-through" detector; the effluent leaving the column is passed over heated copper oxide to convert all organics to CO_2 and H_2O. The CO_2 (for carbon-14 assay) is passed through the cartridge where the counting rate is monitored by an efficient, low-background scintillation counter. The anthracene-filled detector cell, consisting of a transparent tube with a gas inlet and outlet, is mounted between opposing faces of two photomultiplier tubes for coincidence counting. If tritium is to be converted, the formed water is reacted with hot iron to release hydrogen and tritium gases.

In addition to all these techniques, Behrendt (145) developed a method in which chromatographically separated nonradioactive compounds are subjected to exchanges, after combustion to CO_2. The CO_2 formed is labeled by exchange with hot $Na_2{}^{14}CO_3$. Other radioactive species used in these investigations were ${}^3H$, ${}^{18}F$, ${}^{31}Si$, ${}^{35}S$, and ${}^{221}Fr$.

VI. Density/Weight/Flow/Volume/Pressure Detectors

A. Gas Density Detector

In 1956, Martin and James (146) designed a detector of high sensitivity whose response was independent of the chemical structure of the substances separated chromatographically. The gas density balance or meter, a miniaturized version of Claesson's original apparatus (147), measures a readily calculable property—a simple function of the densities of the carrier gas and vapors passing through it. Since a response is also directly related to the molecular weight differences of component and carrier gas (148), calibration for every new substance is not required. In addition to converting the Claesson pressure differential to an electric signal, problems associated with the corrosion of the sensing elements by the chromatographic column effluents were avoided by designing a detector which permitted only the carrier gas to come in contact with the thermocouple junctions.

With the advent of commercially available detectors (149,150), renewed interest has arisen in this type of detector.

The Nerheim design (151) marketed by the Gow-Mac Instrument Company operates on similar basic principles; it differs only in configuration and sensing elements. On the basis of equations showing the interrelationship of changes in density, flow, and electrical response, Nerheim developed a simplified gas density detector.

The basic flow pattern is shown in Figure 5-30. With the apparatus in a vertical plane, the reference gas enters A, is split into two streams, and then exits at D. The chromatographic sample effluent enters at C, is also split into two streams, and is exhausted at the exit. If the density of the sample effluent is equal to that of the reference, an equilibrium in the gas streams and measuring bridge will exist.

As integral parts of a Wheatstone bridge, the sensing elements (B_1, B_2)—
either hot wire filaments or thermistors whose resistance varies linearly
with flow rate due to cooling—are located and placed in each stream so
that neither of the two sensing elements will come in contact with column
effluent. When the density of the chromatographic effluent entering C is
increased, the $A/B_2/D$ gas stream is retarded whereas stream $A/B_1/D$ is
accelerated; this flow rate differential causing a net resistance change in the
measuring bridge in one direction. If the effluent density is lower than that

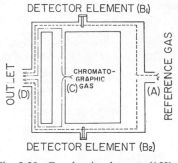

DETECTOR ELEMENT (B_1)

OUT-LET

(D)

CHROMATO-
GRAPHIC
(C) GAS

(A)

REFERENCE GAS

DETECTOR ELEMENT (B_2)

Fig. 5-30. Gas density detector (150).

of the carrier gas, the retardation/acceleration phenomenon is reversed
producing a signal of opposite sign.

Guillemin et al. (152,153*a*), in their study of the influence of various
operating parameters on the Gow-Mac detector, have shown that response
is a function of (*1*) the nature of the carrier gas and (*2*) the ratio of the
flow rates in the reference and measuring circuits; highest sensitivities
obtained with carrier gases decreasing in the following order: CO_2 >
N_2 > Ar. Also, sensitivity is optimized by operating at the highest ratio of
reference/measuring flow rates as determined with a constant reference
flow rate for a given carrier gas.

Furthermore, this detector gives directly concentrations in weight per
cent for each component in a mixture. This is accomplished by multiplying
each peak area by its area factor, summating all corrected areas, and then
dividing each corrected area by the sum of all corrected peak areas.

The area factor can be calculated as follows:

$$\text{Area factor} = M_c/(M_c - M_g) \tag{5-33}$$

where M_c = the molecular weight of the component
M_g = the molecular weight of the carrier gas

More recently, Guillemin and Auricourt (153) showed that, by using sulfur hexafluoride (which has a density 5 times that of air) as the carrier gas, the detector's sensitivity is increased threefold, and the determination of permanent gases is made possible, yielding weight per cent results for such gases as H_2, O_2, CO, CO_2, N_2, CH_4, C_2H_4, C_2H_6, C_2H_2, etc.

Of great significance is its application to the determination of molecular weights of chromatographic effluents; this was demonstrated and adequately verified by Liberti et al. (154), Phillips and Timms (148), and Parsons (155), who used a bracket method for the identification of pyrolysis products of polymers.

B. Gravimetric Detector

In 1963, Bevan and Thoburn (156) introduced a new concept in gas chromatographic detectors—a quantitative integral detector. These

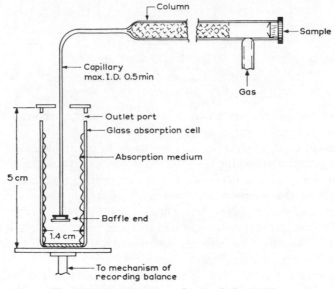

Fig. 5-31. Mass detector—simplex design (156).

investigators made a practical gravimetric detector using an automatic-recording vacuum balance (Fig. 5-31). Since the gravimetric detector integrates, a step-to-step pattern is provided (Fig. 5-32) instead of the usual chromatographic succession of peaks. The weight increase from each step-to-step increment is the amount of component present in that fraction and the total weight increase is the total sample weight. If absorption is complete, calibration with synthetic mixtures is not necessary.

Whereas Piel (157) utilized this integrating technique for the analysis of known mixtures of pure benzene, toluene, and *m*-xylene, with all weighings performed with an ordinary chainomatic analytical balance, Cahn (158) developed a detector using an activated charcoal adsorber in an aluminum bucket. The entire assembly weighed about 650 mg, and, with this load, the Cahn electrobalance in air or vacuum had a precision of slightly better than 1 μg. It had the same precision in a helium stream, so that 0.1 % accuracy could be obtained with a 1-mg sample. With a 10-mg sample, an accuracy of 0.01 % would be possible; this is one or two orders

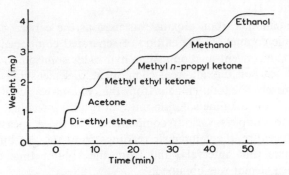

Fig. 5-32. Mass integram from recording balance (156).

of magnitude better than results with previous detectors. For a series of 10 analyses, Piel reported an average relative standard deviation of 0.5% and the relative error range was 1.4% for his technique.

C. Flow-Impedance Detector

Griffiths et al. (25,159), in addition to their work on surface potential, heat of adsorption and dielectric constant detectors, reported the use of a flow-impedance sensing device to determine gas composition. Using either a simple recording or an inclined-tube manometer, they established that gas composition is a function of the pressure drop developed across a capillary at the exit of the column through which a gas flows at a constant rate. In this manner, small changes in carrier gas containing eluted mixture components was indicated by measured pressure variations. For more accurate results, James and Phillips (160) devised a better carrier gas flow controller for the flow rate range of 10–1000 ml/min and planned to incorporate an electronic system to indicate pressure. Two other relationships were noted: (*1*) the pressure drop was a function of gas viscosity when a long true-bore capillary was used, whereas (*2*) it was related to gas density with an orifice restriction. The results with the flow-impedance detector were reported to be as good as those obtained with early thermal conductivity cells with a sensitivity estimated at 1 part in 1000.

D. Volume Detector

The applicability of an integral, gas volume detector in gas chromatography for the quantitative determination of permanent gases and some volatile petroleum gases containing hydrogen and hydrocarbons up to C_4 but excluding acetylenic compounds was first established by Janák and co-workers (161–171).

In Janák's method, carbon dioxide was used as the carrier gas in the chromatographic column for the elution of separated components. After its absorption in a concentrated potassium hydroxide solution, the volume of each eluted (carbon dioxide-free) component was measured in a gas buret or nitrometer. The total effluent from the column was continuously bubbled through the alkaline solution until all resulting residual volumes representing the sample's various components had been measured. In the original procedure, the volumetric readings from the gas buret were taken at suitable time intervals, and from the volume–time data, an integral step height plot was obtained.

Accuracy depended upon several factors: (1) the scale of the buret, (2) amount of component measured, and (3) purity of the carbon dioxide carrier gas. Trace impurities such as carbon monoxide, air, and hydrocarbons, all nonabsorbed by potassium hydroxide, had to be excluded for accurate analysis.

In addition to the simple nitrometer, Janák (162) designed a modified volume detector permitting the effluent component vapors to accumulate in one of a series of measuring burets. This was accomplished by tilting the nitrometer, which allowed the separate fractions to be collected in burets of different sizes.

To circumvent the tedious process of manually plotting volume–time data, Janák (172) developed an automatic photographic-paper recording system which was subsequently replaced by an electronic strip-chart recorder (173) which monitored the movement of a piston coupled to a pen producing the typical volume–time curve.

A similar instrument based on volume increase at constant pressure was built by Leibnitz et al. (174). As a supplement for the analysis of combustible organic vapors, Behrendt (175) designed a combustion detector which registers the volume increase resulting from the formation of new molecules when organics in the nitrogen carrier gas stream are burned at atmospheric pressure over heated copper oxide in a silica combustion chamber to which is attached a microburet. In principle, the gas amplification within the detector increases with molecular weight of the substance.

E. Pressure Detector

In contrast to the automatic recording instruments monitoring volume increases at constant pressure, van de Craats (176) maintained the volume constant and recorded automatically the pressure changes by means of an electromagnetic manometer devised by Kinkel (177). With this apparatus operating at reduced pressures, van de Craats could determine the percentage of C_5 and C_6 hydrocarbons in mixtures. In addition to van de Craats' work with pressure-sensing devices, Novák and Janák (178) constructed a detector which represents the pneumatic analog of a Wheatstone bridge, employing the dynamic effects of pneumatic obstructions such as capillaries and constrictions for determining component fractions emerging from the gas chromatographic column. Requiring no electrical power yet having an accuracy comparable to high precision thermal conductivity cells, it expresses the pressure differential, either differentially or integrally, caused by the eluted component as a diagonal from zero. Furthermore, the substance analyzed is never in contact with the detector.

VII. Titration/Coulometric/Halogen–Phosphorus Detectors

A. Titration Detector

The visual or automatic titration methods of James and Martin (1) provided techniques for the titration of chromatographically separated volatile monocarboxylic acids. In the presence of an indicator, the titration can be followed visually (1,179) or automatically recorded (1,180).

With the automatic titration buret, the separated acidic or basic components in the carrier gas pass directly into the titration cell. A suitable colorimetric indicator (0.001% phenol red for acids, 0.007% methyl red for bases) is used with a photoelectric relay to control the addition of titrant from a syringe-type dispensing buret, the plunger of which is coupled to a recording pen.

Further improvements on the James and Martin automatic titrator were reported by McInnes (181), who included a polyethylene gland incorporating a mercury seal for the recording buret, an automatic switch-off device for the apparatus, and a photoelectric unit which provides stable and full control for dispensing titrant.

The method of dispensing titrant automatically was an improvement over the manual titration methods, which initially utilized a screw buret. The amount which the tight-fitting screw had been turned was a direct measure of the volume of titrant consumed.

Using either the manual or automatic method, an integral plot was obtained, the step height indicating the amount of separated component present. With this type of detecting device, amounts of acetic acid in water as low as 0.02 mg (180), aliphatic amines at levels of 0.002–0.01 mg (182), and aniline as little as 0.10 mg (183) were detected. In the case of aniline and other weakly basic aromatic amines, the titrations were performed in glacial acetic acid with perchloric acid as titrant.

B. Coulometric Detector

Whereas gas chromatographic/coulometric detection systems have normally been associated with the determination of sulfur and halogens in organic compounds, Liberti and co-workers (184–188) published a series of papers on coulometric methods for the analysis of acids, bases, aldehydes, ketones, and mercaptans with various absorbing media and endpoint detection systems (photometric, potentiometric, and amperometric).

In 1962, Thielemann, Behrens, and Leibnitz (189) also described a unique titration/coulometric method for individual components separated by gas chromatography. The acid or base required for titration is produced by electrolysis, and the current measured by a special register is recorded in the form of chromatographic peaks. In their apparatus, the titration electrode is contained within the titration cell whereas the opposite electrode is placed in a separate tube filled with electrolyte solution, and this tube is connected to the cell by a diaphragm. The recorder's sensitivity is adjustable so that the peaks remain on the chart with peak areas proportional to the amount of electrolytically generated acid or base. This scale expansion allows a simultaneous determination of trace components as well as the main constitutents of a mixture. Fatty acids and nitro-bases were reported to be readily analyzed, although the method was not recommended for the determination of substances that have been converted to carbon dioxide by combustion.

These initial investigations made coulometry in principle an attractive method to be used in conjunction with gas chromatography because of its specificity for certain atoms and functional groups in molecules and its accuracy and sensitivity.

With a lower detection limit approaching several nanograms for sulfur or halogen, the microcoulometer is an ideal, accepted, specific detection system for gas chromatography. It finds applications in petroleum chemistry, pesticide residue analysis, and organic chemistry.

In 1960, Coulson and Cavanagh (190) developed an automatic-combustion coulometric titration method for determining chloride in organic materials. The titration cell described (Fig. 5-33) is connected to the exit

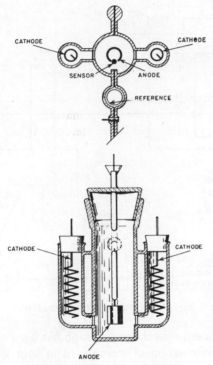

Fig. 5-33. Titration cell (190).

of the combustion unit, and the absorbed chloride effluent is automatically titrated with silver ions generated by a coulometric system (Fig. 5-34), the current of which is varied as needed to maintain a constant silver ion concentration in the electrolyte at all times. The total silver ion generated is proportional to the halide present, and by integrating the generated current as a function of time, the digital output of the integrator in turn indicates the chloride content present. During titration, the ion deficiency is detected by the sensor electrode which instantaneously sends an electrical signal to a sensitive servo amplifier. In turn, the amplifier supplies a balancing voltage to the generator electrodes; the balancing voltage initiates the internal generation of titrant to restore its ionic strength in the electrolyte.

By replacing the silver-plated generator anode with a platinum electrode and the acetic acid electrolyte with a potassium iodide/acetic acid solution, sulfur dioxide can be oxidized iodometrically to sulfur trioxide.

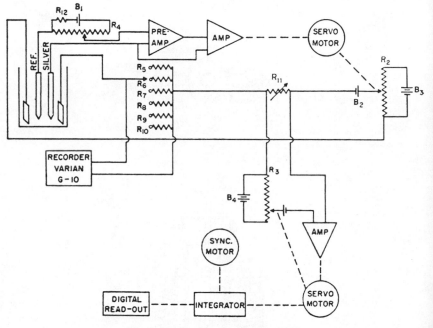

Fig. 5-34. Coulometer system (190).

The microcoulometric gas chromatograph has been successfully applied to the routine determination of mercaptans in sour natural gases (191), chlorinated organic pesticides (192–195), and thiophosphates (192,195).

C. Halogen–Phosphorus Detectors

In addition to microcoulometry for the quantitative analysis of halogens (chlorine, bromine, and iodine), other selective halogen detectors have been proposed.

Based on the classical Beilstein test, Gunther et al. (196) devised a simple copper-screen detector held in the outer cone of a cool Bunsen burner flame (Fig. 5-35) to qualitatively identify organically bound chlorine or bromine emerging from a chromatographic column by the immediate

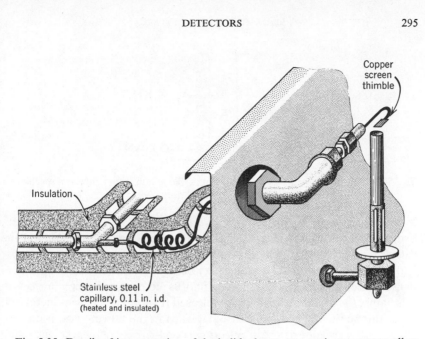

Fig. 5-35. Details of incorporation of the halide detector on an instrument to allow a constant portion of the effluent gas flow from the thermal-conductivity cell to be tested (196).

appearance of an intense green flame at concentration levels less than 5 μg. The "flame" detector responds also to organic compounds containing iodine, thiocyanate, cyanide, and other groups that are converted to cyanide in the flame.

In 1961, Cremer, Kraus, and Bechtold (197) designed a detector consisting of a cell with heated alkali activated electrodes built into a quartz tube with their length axis in the direction of the nitrogen gas stream. The normal positive ion current between the electrodes is greatly increased in the presence of halogen compounds, and for comparison purposes both the halogen detector and thermal conductivity cells were used. With a nitrogen carrier gas flow of 60 ml/min, 0.01 ppm of chlorine could be detected. For CS_2, CO_2, carbonyl compounds, amines, and mercaptans, the sensitivity was reported to be 10–200 ppm.

Karmen (198,199) reported a hydrogen flame ionization detector sensitive only to compounds containing phosphorus, bromine, chlorine, and iodine. He noted that halogens or phosphorus increased the electrical conductivity of the flame in the presence of a wire, ceramic, or glass probe containing a sodium compound. This increase in electrical conductivity resulted from the release of sodium vapor from the probe. Using a two-stage flame detection system, one flame placed above the other but

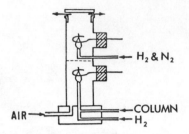

Fig. 5-36. Schematic of a two-stage hydrogen flame ionization detector specific for halogens and phosphorus (198).

separated from it by a sodium hydroxide-treated wire mesh screen, hydrogen gas was added to the effluent of the column (Fig. 5-36), and the carrier gas–air–hydrogen mixture was burned in the lower flame detector with its resulting electrical conductivity being the same as that of the usual flame detector. When halogen–phosphorus compounds were burned in this flame, the rate of sodium vapor released from the screen was increased. Since this sodium vapor was carried upward in the flowing gas, it did not affect the lower flame detector's electrical conductivity. However, the rising sodium vapor was excited or ionized in the second or upper hydrogen flame mounted above the screen; this flame detector's electrical properties are very sensitive to phosphorus or halogens present in the lower flame.

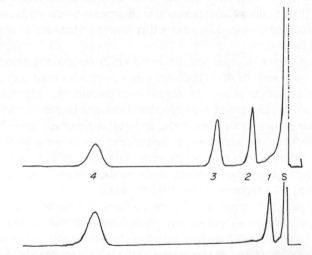

Fig. 5-37. Analysis of a 1-μl sample of diethyl ether solution containing (v/v): (1) 0.1% carbon tetrachloride, (2) 1.0% fluorobenzene, (3) 1.0% toluene, (4) 1.0% chlorobenzene (198). The upper graph is the record of the electrical conductivity of the lower flame, the lower graph that of the upper flame of the detector shown in Fig. 5-36.

Furthermore, since little unburned material reached the upper flame, it did not detect compounds free of halogens and phosphorus. With this arrangement, nanogram quantities of organic halogen or phosphorus could be distinguished from materials free of these elements, as shown in Figure 5-37.

VIII. Electrical/Potential Sensing Devices as Detectors

A. Dielectric Constant Detector

In 1952, Griffiths, James, and Phillips (25) first proposed the dielectric constant principle as a nondestructive detector in displacement chromatography to monitor gas composition. Although used with little success because of its inherent low sensitivity, its operating principle was simple. A small cylindrical condenser having a small amount of charcoal between its plates was attached to the end of the column. Its capacity variation was converted into a frequency-modulated signal in series with a discriminator, from which the output signal was sent to a recorder.

In contrast to the sensing device of Griffiths et al. (25), a twin-cell brass dielectric constant sensor of high resolution and fast response was designed and developed by Turner (200) in 1958 specifically for gas chromatography. In this device, the adsorbent in the small 0.3-ml volume cell was eliminated, thereby enhancing its sensitivity and extending its linear range of detection. Although capable of detecting acetone and diethyl ether in nitrogen at concentration levels of 2 and 8 μg/ml, respectively, it reportedly possessed these other attractive features: insensitivity to changes in (1) flow rates up to 500 ml/min and (2) nitrogen pressures below 10 cm of mercury.

More recently, Winefordner et al. (201) described a special, more sensitive cell based on changes in dielectric constant and constructed to allow gas flow between the plates of a capacitor which is a part of the tank circuit of a 70-Mc/sec Clapp oscillator, the output of which is beat against that of a reference oscillator. With the difference frequency between oscillators adjusted to zero with pure carrier gas flowing through the detector, the presence of a foreign vapor in the cell will produce a difference frequency which is (1) linearly related to the amount of material introduced through an injection port in the carrier gas stream and (2) inversely proportional to the absolute temperature for a given component at a constant density or concentration in the cell and for a particular operating frequency.

Based on the work described above by Winefordner et al. (201), Winefordner and Williams (202) in 1965 developed a modified capacitor detector cell showing very good sensitivity to such gases as O_2, N_2, CO, CO_2,

H_2, CH_4, C_2H_2, Ar, NO_2, NO, N_2O and SO_2 when present in trace amounts, with helium as carrier gas.

A block diagram of this detector is shown in Figure 5-38. C_R and C_S are variable condensers in the reference and sample Clapp oscillators, respectively. The coils (L_R and L_S) were adjusted until both oscillators were oscillating at about 65 Mc with carrier gas only flowing through the cell.

Using this sensitive, nonselective gas detector, the approximate limits of detection for permanent gases were between 8×10^{-8} and 2×10^{-10} g/sec or 5×10^{-3} and 1×10^{-4} μl/sec.

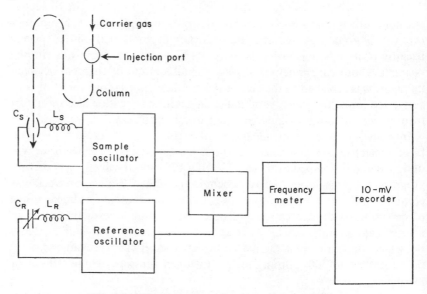

Fig. 5-38. Block diagram of new gas detector (202).

Another sensing device equal to or better than a thermal conductivity detector used microwave circuits for highly accurate measurements of dielectric constants (203). A simple arrangement of two cavities in series showed the feasibility of detecting traces of one gas in another. A klystron was used to generate microwave power which was fed through a wave guide to a transmission-type cavity. Another cavity was mounted in series with and tuned to the same frequency as the first; both cavities were identical except that the second had gas inlet and outlet ports. From this measuring cell, its microwave energy was sent to a crystal detector. By frequency-modulating the klystron with a 50-cps sine wave voltage on the repeller, a burst of energy passes to the detector each time the generator frequency equals that of the cavities. The detector current is amplified and measured with an oscilloscope. At the beginning of the run, the two cavities are filled with the nitrogen carrier gas and, if the composition in one of the cavities is changed, its electrical size will change (same as detuning the cavity), causing a decrease of current from the detector. Johansson stated that the detector could be used to its best advantage at high temperatures, the metal cavities being as capable of withstanding high temperatures as any other part of the chromatographic system.

B. Surface Potential Detector

In 1954, Griffiths and Phillips (204) built a surface potential detector for vapors, in connection with their work on displacement analyses, using sand and small glass beads as weak adsorbents. The instrument incorporated design features of Phillips' original apparatus for the detection of vapors by measurement of surface potential changes (205).

Briefly, the method is based on a known principle that two plates of dissimilar metals held closely together and joined by a conductor exhibit different potentials. By applying a direct current to both plates, the vibration of one produces an oscillating condenser, the alternating emf produced being dependent upon the particular surface potential of the gas between the oscillating and fixed plates. After compensating the potential obtained with pure carrier gas (nitrogen) by a potentiometric circuit, the adsorption of vapors from the gas stream alters the surface potential; this change in alternating potential is a measure of vapor concentration. Although serious problems of irreversibility of adsorption and nonlinearity of response were encountered, good sensitivity was obtained only with polar compounds. However, no signals were observed for benzene, Decalin, and carbon tetrachloride.

Griffiths and Phillips also showed that it was more effective to use two steel plates, one of which was coated with a thin film of stearic acid or octadecanol, than plates of different metals.

Analogous to the surface potential detector above, another device to detect polar vapors has been developed for use with gas chromatographic systems, the detector being capable of discriminating between molecules on the basis of differences in their polarities (206). By recording the change in contact potential caused by the physical adsorption/desorption of a polar vapor on a nickel surface, polarity differences between various molecular species can be determined.

The detector cell consisted of two circular plates. One was a 0.0005-in. nickel foil disk functioning as the sensor plate; the other, a 0.002-in. gold foil disk, is called the vibrating plate. The gold disk is vibrated at 12 cps to produce alternating current readings for the oscilloscope, whereas the nickel sensor is thermally cycled by current surges. A 0.10-in. mica spacer separates the plates so that vapor can be passed between them.

The shift in contact or surface potential of the sensor disk, when polar vapors are adsorbed on its surface with respect to the less sensitive reference surface, is measured by a capacitor. This system of measurement is known as the Kelvin-Zisman method. By alternately heating and cooling the nickel sensor, the polar vapor is desorbed and adsorbed, respectively. Cooling is accomplished by precooled nitrogen flowing behind the plate, whereas a 6-V battery is used for the heating cycle. With a flow rate of about 200 ml/min, the detector's response time and sensitivity are approximately 3 sec and 10^{15} molecules/ml, respectively.

C. Semiconductive Thin Film Detector

Using the known principle that the adsorption and desorption of gases cause a change in electrical conductivity of semiconductors, Seiyama et al. (207) developed a new chromatographic detector for gaseous components.

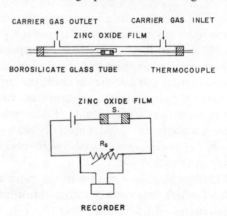

Fig. 5-39. Experimental arrangement (207).

As shown in Figure 5-39, the current, depending upon the resistance of the film, S, is converted to voltage by the variable resistance, R_s, which is fed without amplification to a recorder. Resistance R_s also adjusts the input voltage of the recorder at desired sensitivity. Using zinc oxide as an example of a typical film material, the conductivity of its film maintains a fixed value when the nitrogen carrier gas is passed at a constant flow rate through the borosilicate glass tube. When a small amount of another gas or vapor is added to the carrier gas, its conductivity is changed. Increases due to the adsorption of benzene, carbon dioxide, ethyl alcohol, etc., result from the fact that these molecules act as electron donors to the *n*-type zinc oxide semiconductor, whereas the adsorption of oxygen (behaving as an electron acceptor) decreases the conductivity. As the gases are successively desorbed, the original steady conductivity value of the semiconductor is restored. The authors noted that the peak widths in their method

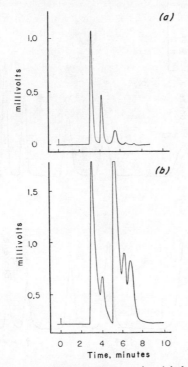

Fig. 5-40. Results of commercial propane gas using (*a*) thermal conductivity cell, and (*b*) zinc oxide film (207).

were generally larger than those obtained using a thermal conductivity cell. The results of a comparison between this method and a thermal conductivity cell are shown in Figure 5-40. The sensitivity of the thin film detector is reported to be approximately a hundred times greater than that of the thermal conductivity method.

D. Piezoelectric Sorption Detector

Piezoelectric quartz crystals, long used as frequency and time standards to one part in 10^8 or better, have been shown by King (208) to be selective

gas detectors when coated with various chromatographic liquid phases.
Used as detectors, such coated crystals have several advantages: (1) sensitivity increases with solute or sample boiling point, (2) detectors selective
to compound type can be made with response times of the order of 0.05 sec,

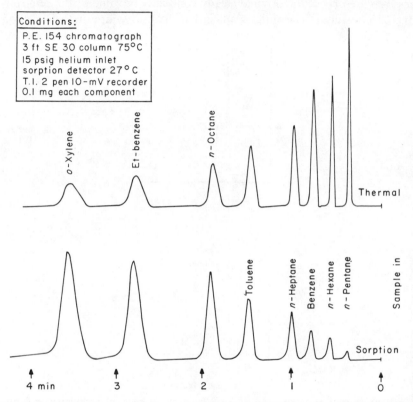

Fig. 5-41. Simultaneous recordings of thermal conductivity and squalane sorption
detectors (208).

and (3) the output signal is a frequency which simplifies integration of peak
areas and digital presentation of data.

In this study, both the amplitude-change method and the frequency-
change method were employed to detect and measure the composition of
gases.

In 1959, Sauerbrey (209) showed that a relationship existed between the
weight of metal films deposited on quartz crystals and the change in frequency. For common crystals, his expression reduces to:

$$\Delta F = 2.3 \times 10^6 \, F^2(\Delta W/A) \tag{5-34}$$

where ΔF = frequency change due to coating, cps
$\quad F$ = frequency of the quartz plate, Mc
$\quad \Delta W$ = weight of deposited film, g
$\quad A$ = area of quartz plate or electrode, cm²

From this, King related the detector signal quantitatively to the coating material's sorption isotherm:

$$\Delta F = \Delta F_0 (\Delta W / \Delta W_0) \qquad (5\text{-}35)$$

where ΔF_0 = frequency change due to application of coating
$\quad \Delta W_0$ = weight of coating
$\quad \Delta F$ = frequency change due to sorption of solute vapor
$\quad \Delta W$ = weight increase due to sorbate

In his study, King showed that quartz crystal plates, $\frac{1}{2}$ in. in diameter, 7.3 mils thick and vibrated at 9 Mc, gave a measurable signal of 1 cps corresponding to a weight increase of 10^{-9} g.

Figure 5-41 shows simultaneous recordings of an eight-component mixture of aromatics and n-paraffins run on an isothermal chromatograph. Connected in series with the thermal conductivity cell's effluent, the squalane sorption detector showed increased sensitivity with increasing time and with higher-molecular-weight components.

E. Electrolytic/Electrical Conductivity Detectors

As a new detection device, Piringer and co-workers (210,211) introduced an electrolytic detector for gas chromatography utilizing the advantages of component combustion to carbon dioxide and the differential electrolytic conductivity of gases. In their system, carbon dioxide-free distilled water flows at a rate of 1–5 ml/min through a comparison cell. The nitrogen carrier gas, containing the carbon dioxide produced by combustion of organics eluted from the chromatographic column and flowing at the same rate as the water, comes into contact with the demineralized distilled water in a 1-mm i.d. capillary tube. The water, from which only the carrier gas is removed in the phase separation chamber (Fig. 5-42) at the end of the capillary, flows subsequently through a measuring cell (0.06 ml in volume) equipped with two platinum electrodes. Changes in resistivity are then accurately determined by means of an ac bridge electronic switch system shown in Figure 5-43.

Principal advantages of the detector given are: (1) the components are registered directly; (2) its operating dependability is good; (3) its small measuring volume and high sensitivity are useful in capillary analyses and trace studies; (4) the detector is usable without limitations for high-temperature chromatography. However, its use is restricted to carbon-containing compounds, and its sensitivity is lower than that of the microflame ionization or argon detector.

Sternberg and Jones (212) designed a simple attachment for the flame ionization detector for halogenated and sulfur-containing compounds,

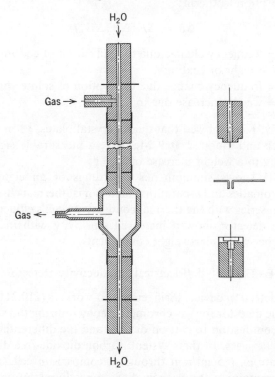

Fig. 5-42. Construction details of the measuring and reference cells, the phase contact and separation areas (211).

which measures the change in electrical conductivity of a thin film of flowing solution containing extracted soluble combustion products from the flame ionization exhaust gases. Its response was reported to be comparable to that of the flame ionization for carbon.

On the other hand, Boer (213) determined lower-molecular-weight acids with electrodes mounted in a titration cell. The conductivity change of the $0.01N$ sodium hydroxide solution as C_1-C_5 acids were absorbed individually was monitored with linear neutralization curves obtained over a 0–30 meq acid range.

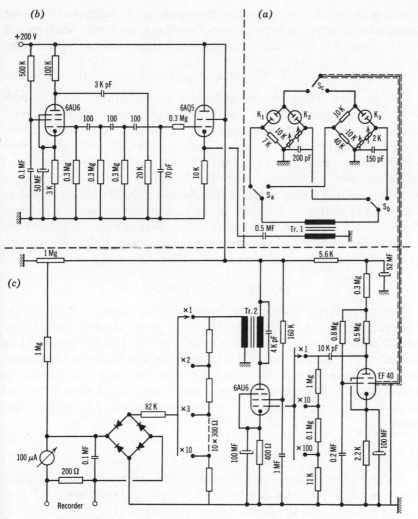

Fig. 5-43. Circuit for the differential electrolytic conductivity measurement (211). K_1 = reference cell; K_2 = measuring cell; K_3 = cell for water purity control.

Dijkstra et al. (214) recently devised a recording conductometer employing a four-electrode conductivity cell and a novel absorption vessel for the determination of small amounts of carbon dioxide. Its applicability in combination with the combustion technique in gas chromatography was discussed with results presented for 12 analyses of a mixture of cyclohexane, cyclohexene, and benzene. The decrease in conductivity of a sodium hydroxide solution after absorbing a component's CO_2 formed by combustion was directly related to its concentration. Suggested areas for application were: (*1*) determination of carbon in elemental analyses, (*2*) carbon content in steel, and (*3*) CO_2 determination in metabolism studies.

F. Galvanic Cell Detector

For gas chromatographic investigations of food aromas (215), vapors and gases in the atmosphere (216), and traces of gaseous, liquid, or solid substances (217), Berton (218) designed special galvanic batteries as extremely sensitive detectors. Consisting of two electrodes made of the same or different material, one of the battery's electrodes (the sensing electrode) is simultaneously in contact with the electrolyte and the vapors to be detected, whereas the other acts as the reference electrode and is completely immersed in electrolyte solution. By an electrochemical reaction between the electrolyte and sample vapor, the sensing electrode becomes polarized, resulting in a change in the galvanic current. The magnitude of the current is directly related to component concentration.

G. Hersch Cell Detector

Phillips et al. (219) applied a simple form of Hersch cell to the gas chromatographic analysis of oxygen. This specific detector gave higher sensitivities for oxygen than were obtained with thermal conductivity detectors. Its sensitivity is reported to approach that of a helium ionization detector. The detector consists of a silver cathode and a lead anode in contact with an electrolyte containing hydroxide ions. Oxygen is reduced at the cathode (Fig. 5-44) and a current is generated, based on the following reactions:

$$\tfrac{1}{2}O_2 + H_2O + 2e^- \to 2OH^- \qquad\qquad (5\text{-}36)$$

$$Pb + 3OH^- - 2e^- \to PbO_2H^- + H_2O \qquad\qquad (5\text{-}37)$$

In the analysis of argon/oxygen mixtures, the oxygen need not be separated from argon since this can be accomplished with the Hersch cell connected in series with the katharometer. Because of this, molecular sieves used for the analysis of permanent gases can be operated at room temperature rather than $-70°C$. For samples or reaction mixtures containing oxygen as the only permanent gas, which make unnecessary the separation of the various constituents of the inert gas peak, the cell may be used without a chromatographic column. Such samples are injected directly in the carrier gas passing through the detector. Response for oxygen was linear up to 1 % in a 0.3 μl sample of nitrogen. The cell's output of 60 mV at this limit corresponded to a cell oxygen concentration of nearly 0.005% (v/v).

The cell has had other application (220), namely the detection of organic

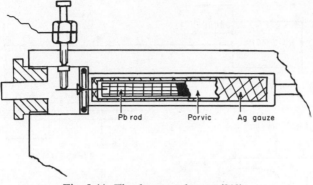

Fig. 5-44. The detector element (219).

compounds in gas chromatographic column effluents. The carrier gas containing a known concentration of oxygen leaves the chromatographic column with the eluted organic component, and this organic–oxygen–carrier gas mixture is passed into a combustion chamber containing a platinum-metal catalyst. The concentration pulse of the combustible organic material is detected with the Hersch cell by a transient deficiency of oxygen in the outgoing gas.

H. Redox Potential Detector

For the determination of volatile aliphatic mercaptans in gas chromatographic effluents, Sunner, Karrman, and Sunden (221) used a potentiometric method based on passing the effluent into a solution prepared from 0.2 ml. of $0.025M$ alcoholic iodine and 0.4 ml. of $0.05M$ aqueous potassium iodide made up to 50 ml. with 70% ethanol. The thio-compounds were quantitatively absorbed and oxidized to disulfides with a resulting change in the $[I^-]^2 : [I_2]$ ratio. The change in redox potential at the platinum electrode was recorded, the recorder deflection being essentially linear below 2.5 μmoles of mercaptan added.

IX. Analytical Instruments as Detectors*

A. Ultraviolet Spectrophotometer Detector

In contrast to absorptivities of organic molecules in the infrared region, nearly all organic compounds at a wavelength of 1700 Å have absorption coefficients which may be 1000 times greater than infrared values. Furthermore, in the far-ultraviolet region, many organic and inorganic gases of

* Such systems are discussed in more detail in Chapter 8.

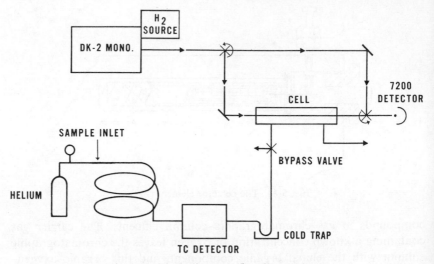

Fig. 5-45. Block diagram of equipment (222).

low molecular weight exhibit characteristic discrete spectra associated with electronic transitions in the molecules.

Kaye (222) adapted a Beckman far-ultraviolet DK-2 spectrophotometer as a gas chromatographic effluent detector to record the spectra of eluted, absorbing materials (Fig. 5-45). Using heated flow-through cells of 1.0-, 5.0- and 10.0-cm optical path length coupled directly to the thermal conductivity cell's outlet, he found that absorptivities of most organic vapors were sufficiently large to permit quantitative analysis, and in some instances identification, where specific absorption patterns could be attributed directly to a functional group in certain molecular species. Furthermore, the sensitivity of the far-ultraviolet detector for many compounds possessing intense absorption bands exceeds that of the normal thermal conductivity detector and, in some cases, the hydrogen flame ionization detector. Kaye also evaluated the effects of cell holdup and wavelength and, to illustrate the method's sensitivity, showed that naphthalene with an absorptivity of 125,000 liters/mole-cm could be readily determined at a concentration level of 10^{-8} g. Whereas resolution with the thermal conductivity cell decreased with increasing carrier gas flow rate, resolution with the optical detector increased with carrier gas flow rate. To obtain additional data that might be useful for characterizing molecular structure, the 1650–2200 Å wavelength region can be repetitively scanned in 20 sec.

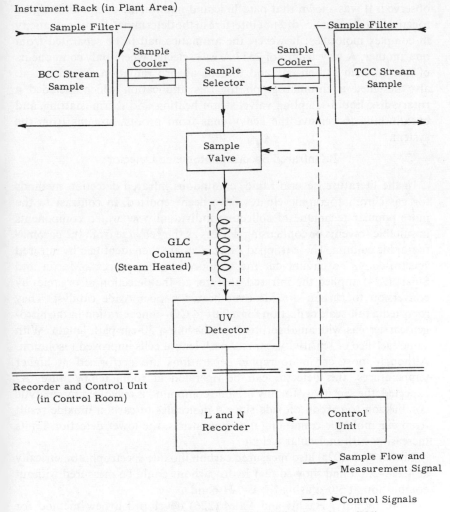

Fig. 5-46. Simplified block diagram of UV-GLC analyzer (223).

For the determination of aromatics in process streams, Merritt et al. (223) developed a special-purpose process chromatograph (Fig. 5-46) showing a simplified block diagram of the UV–GLC analyzer. For this type of process monitoring, the ultraviolet detector proved extremely advantageous, eliminating the need for complete separation of all components and simplifying the analysis by reducing the number of peaks observed. It was shown that paraffinic and naphthenic compounds eluted together with aromatics did not interfere in the determination of aromaticity in complex molecules; however, the aromatics had to be separated from one another. A wavelength of 2357 Å was selected where only components of interest such as benzene and toluene absorb radiation. Merritt et al. also designed a chromatograph for this application which included a rotary-disk liquid-sampling valve, steam heating and thermostatting, and backflushing to remove the heavy ends from process streams from the system.

B. Infrared Spectrophotometer Detector

In the literature, several rapid, continuous infrared detection methods for gas chromatographic eluates have been reported, in contrast to the more popular technique of collecting individually separated components in suitable solvents or condensing devices as they emerge from the chromatographic column. These trapped substances are then identified by infrared spectroscopy. To circumvent the tedious trapping process, Martin and Smart (224) applied the infrared analyzer to the detection of organics by conversion to carbon dioxide over heated copper oxide catalyst. They reported a full-scale deflection for a 0.01 % CO_2 concentration in the nitrogen carrier gas with an absorption cell having a 30-cm path length. With some sacrifice of sensitivity, shorter path length cells improved resolution. Although most chromatographic separations are performed at higher temperatures, this detector can be operated at room temperature. As expected, the sensitivity for any organic compound is enhanced by catalytic combustion to carbon dioxide since n molecules of carbon dioxide result from *one* molecule containing n carbon atoms, the lower detection limits increasing with molecular weight.

Liberti et al. (225) also measured carbon dioxide spectrophotometrically at 4.22–4.28 μ and showed that hydrocarbons could be measured without combustion at 3.0 μ using the C—H band.

More recently, Haahti and Fales (226) developed a new method for continuous infrared scanning of the gas chromatographic effluent. In their method, the hot gas stream effluent was passed into a circulating solution cell designed on the basis of a scintillation-counting apparatus built by Popják et al. (143). By monitoring a desired adsorption frequency and adjusting the spectrophotometer's chart speed to equal that of a thermal conductivity cell placed in the gas stream, the absorption curves represent integrals of the absorbing components since each successive fraction is accumulated in the infrared cell and the front of the mass or chromatographic peak was matched with the initial increase in adsorbance. For

groups absorbing with moderate intensity, a 6-mm cell length was found
to be adequate, and chromatographic peaks separated by 15 sec were easily
resolved. When overlap of functional group absorption occurs, rapid,
repetitive scans can be performed over the desired wavelength regions.

In direct contrast to the operation of the spectrophotometer at a fixed
absorption frequency for effluent analysis as reported by Haahti and Fales

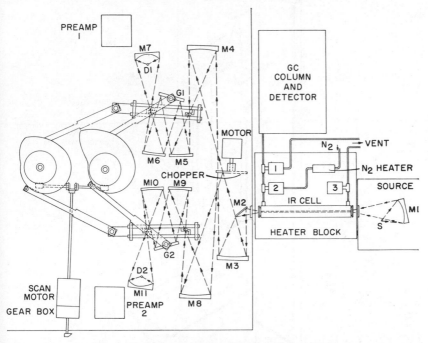

Fig. 5-47. Optical path of infrared radiation (227).

(226), Bartz and Ruhl (227) designed a rapid scanning infrared gas chromatography unit to utilize the chromatograph's ability to separate individual
components in complex mixtures and the infrared's capabilities to identify
the reasonably pure eluted fractions by their specific adsorption spectra.
The helium carrier gas effluent from the chromatograph is passed through
a heated cell with a large optical path length-to-volume ratio as shown in
Figure 5-47. By using two single-beam grating spectrophotometers in
parallel, one covering the 2.5–7.0 μ range and the other scanning from 6.5
to 16.0 μ, the infrared spectrum of a component is obtained. With this
arrangement, with a high chopping rate and fast recorders, 16 sec is
required for a complete spectrum comparable to a normal 12 min scan.

This fast scanning speed permits spectra to be obtained for successive eluted chromatographic peaks.

Using a similar fast-scan infrared spectrophotometric approach, Wilks and Brown (228) modified a commercial infrared spectrophotometer for fast scanning (15 sec from 2.5 to 7.0 μ) and used a long internally reflecting

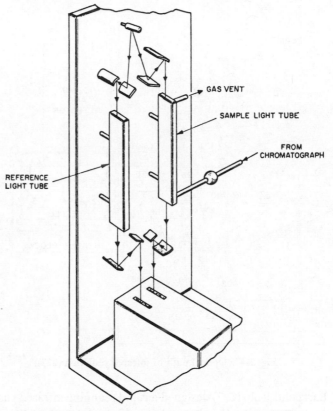

Fig. 5-48. Schematic of rapid scan infrared analyzer (228).

light tube as the spectrophotometric cell (Fig. 5-48). By incorporating automatic control circuits, the instrument can be programmed to scan any selected portion of an infrared spectrum every 30 sec. The authors showed that useful spectra can be obtained for as little as 0.3 μg of a compound having a boiling point above 300°C.

Recently, Behrendt (229) noted that the high resolution afforded by open tubular columns is often of no help in analysis since the samples handled are too small to permit further examination of separated components. To circumvent this disadvantage, he developed an infrared microspectrometer using a molecular beam detector to monitor chromatographic open-tube effluents. The sensitivity achieved was comparable to that of mass spectrometry. The infrared microspectrometer utilizes the recent application of the electrostatic quadruple mass spectrometer to molecular beams as a rotational state selector for molecules with dipole moments. Both rotational state selector and analyzer (preferably parts of a single device) are then turned to the same appropriately selected rotational state, the analyzer rejecting those molecules which briefly experience transitions in the infrared cell. The resulting plot of detected molecular-beam intensity against wavelength of the radiation is the infrared spectrum of the compound.

C. Flame Photometric Detector

For the determination of metal chelates separated by gas chromatography, Juvet and Durbin (230) applied a flame photometer as a sensitive, selective, and quantitative detector for the determination of chromium(III), iron(III), and rhodium(III) hexafluoroacetylacetonates measured at 425.4 mμ, 372.0 mμ, and 369.2 mμ, respectively. They noted that in the determination of volatile inorganic compounds with this method, the wavelength may be adjusted to monitor the concentration of only one element at a time without interference from other elements even though overlapping chromatographic peaks are observed. The amount of excited atomic species present is directly related to the intensity of its characteristic emission line.

The choice of slit width can be optimized, based on several considerations: (1) the efficiency of the chromatographic separation, (2) the degree of spectral resolution required, (3) the relative emission intensity of various components in the mixture, (4) the sensitivity of detection required, and (5) the amount of background radiation at the selected wavelength.

Figure 5-49 shows chromatograms for Cr(HFA)$_3$ and Fe(HFA)$_3$ measured at 425.4 mμ and 372.0 mμ, respectively, each in the absence and presence of the other. Figure 5.50 shows a calibration curve for chromium relating concentration to peak area.

D. Mass Spectrometer Detector

Analytical chemists have long recognized the limitations of gas chromatography for the analysis of nonroutine mixtures since the method does not and cannot absolutely identify separated compounds found in chromatographic effluents. Furthermore, the recognized technique of trapping chromatographic effluents by cold-trap condensation or solvent-extraction

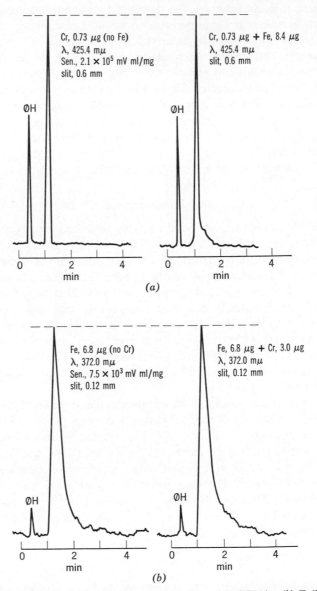

Fig. 5-49. (a) Cr(HFA)₃ in the absence and presence of Fe(HFA)₃. (b) Fe(HFA)₃ in the absence and presence of Cr(HFA)₃ (230).

processes for subsequent analysis by either infrared, ultraviolet, or mass spectrometric means after sample transfer is too time consuming.

Since organic compounds incorporating various functional groups in molecules yield predictable and distinct mass spectra, the combination of both the chromatograph and spectrometer provides more meaningful data than that obtained from each singly. This combination permits partially resolved chromatographic peaks to be identified by the mass spectrometer

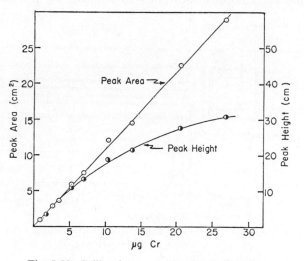

Fig. 5-50. Calibration curves for Cr(HFA)₃ (230).

whereas mass spectra derived from multicomponent mixtures cannot be adequately interpreted without prior gas chromatographic separations.

In 1959, Gohlke (231) first described the combination of a gas chromatograph with a time-of-flight mass spectrometer capable of scanning a m/e range from 1 to 6000 at a rate of 2000 times per second; the schematic of such a combination is shown in Figure 5-51. With this arrangement, mass spectra of components can be scanned and recorded simultaneously with gas chromatographic tracings or observed on an oscilloscope screen.

In addition to scanning the complete mass spectrum, the spectrometer can be adjusted to monitor any portion of the mass spectrum or one characteristic mass; this latter process is repeated for other masses (232–234).

With the time-of-flight spectrometer, Ebert (235) modified the recording system, employing an analog output system capable of monitoring accurately small and large peaks by integration of the multiplier current produced by single ion peaks. By scanning the spectrum on a second or minute time scale, a spectrum can be obtained with a recorder with a 0.01-sec or less time response. To reduce the time necessary to reproduce a tracing, yet preserving resolution and precise intensity measurements, three analog scanners were used for different mass ranges: m/e 10 to 50, 40 to 100, and 90 to 200+.

In contrast to time-of-flight instruments found suitable for the analysis of pyrolytic hydrocarbon products (236), low-molecular-weight ketones (237), fluoro- and chlorohydrocarbons (235), orange oil, pea extract (238),

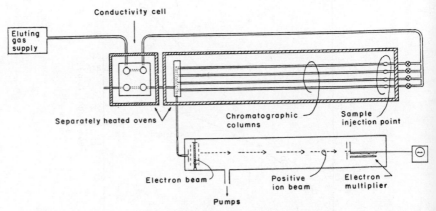

Fig. 5-51. Schematic view of method of attachment of time-of-flight mass spectrometer to gas chromatographic apparatus (231).

fruit volatiles (239), hop oil (240), phenylcyclohexane (241), etc., Lindeman and Annis (232) used a conventional cycloidal path spectrometer coupled to a gas chromatograph. With this instrument, temperature programming was recommended to insure sharp, narrow chromatographic bands over a wide boiling range, thus permitting (*1*) good mass spectra to be obtained with the instrument's relatively slow scan rate and (*2*) the determination of materials by computation from mass spectra without measuring peak areas from spectral change versus time curves, as shown in Figure 5-52.

For the analysis of effluents emerging from high-temperature GLC columns, Ryhage (242) used a modified spectrometer with a mass unit resolution at m/e 600 and a 3-sec scanning rate over the m/e 12–400 mass range (Fig. 5-53). For continuous registration of the effluent, only 10% of the total ion current is used. To obtain good spectra of material in fractional microgram concentrations, two molecular separators built on the principle of Becker (243) are coupled in series between the column and gas-inlet line to the spectrometer. This arrangement permits a 100-fold increase in sample-to-helium ratio.

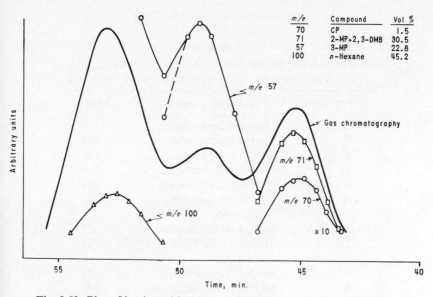

m/e	Compound	Vol %
70	CP	1.5
71	2-MP+2,3-DMB	30.5
57	3-MP	22.8
100	n-Hexane	45.2

Fig. 5-52. Plot of ion intensities characteristic of compounds in peak (232).

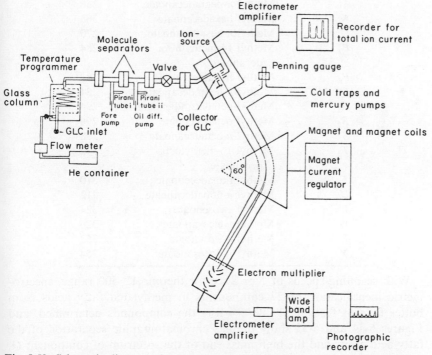

Fig. 5-53. Schematic diagram of gas chromatograph–mass spectrometer combination (242).

TABLE 5-4

Identified Methyl Esters of Fatty Acids from Butterfat (242).
(Identification based on their mass spectra only)

Component	Identified compound	Mol wt
A	Methyl n-hexanoate	130
B	Methyl n-octanoate	158
C	Methyl n-decanoate	186
D	Methyl n-undecanoate	200
E = F	Methyl n-dodecanoate	214
G	Methyl 10-methyldo-decanoate	228
H	Methyl n-tridecanoate	228
I	Methyl 11-methyltri-decanoate	242
J	Methyl tetradecenoate	240
K	Methyl n-tetradecanoate	242
L	Methyl 12-methyltetra-decanoate	256
M	Methyl n-pentadecanoate	256
N	Methyl hexadecenoate	268
O	Methyl n-hexadecanoate	270
P_1	Methyl 14-methylhexa-decanoate	284
P_2	Methyl heptadecenoate	282
Q	Methyl n-heptadecanoate	284
R_1	Methyl octadecandienoate	294
R_2	Methyl octadecenoate	296
S	Methyl n-octadecanoate	298
T_1	Methyl 16-methylocta-decanoate	312
T_2	Methyl nonadecenoate	310
U	Methyl n-nonadecanoate	312
V	Methyl eicosenoate	324
W	Methyl n-eicosanoate	326
X	Methyl docosenoate	352
Y	Methyl n-docosanoate	354

With scanning speeds of 1 or 2 sec for the m/e 12–500 range, spectro-metric identification of 27 components in methylated fatty acids from butter fat was feasible. Table 5-4 lists the compounds determined, and Figures 5-54 and 5-55 show the gas chromatographic separation of the fatty acid esters and the high mass end of the spectrum of component O, respectively.

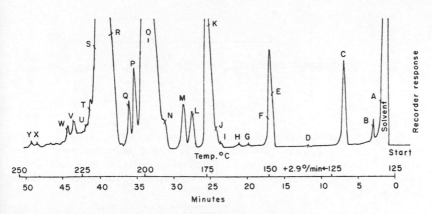

Fig. 5-54. Chromatographic separation of methyl esters of fatty acids from butterfat (242).

In contrast to Ryhage's technique for enhancing the sample-to-carrier gas ratio and its introduction to the spectrometer, Watson and Biemann (244) used an all-glass, valveless pressure reduction system (Fig. 5-56) to feed continuously the effluent from a packed column into a Mattauch-Herzog-type high-resolution spectrometer capable of reliable mass identification and the determination of the elemental composition of the fraction and of the spectrometric fragments formed.

With repetitive scanning speeds of 0.5–300 sec, Banner et al. (245) used the mass spectrometer to identify open tubular column effluents, identification of spectra being possible at concentration levels of 10 ppm when the standard deviation on the height of the base peak is only 5%. Also, Henneberg and Schomburg (246) showed that complete elucidation of molecular structure of open-tubular-column effluents is possible using

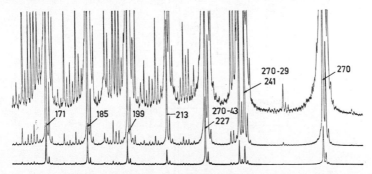

Fig. 5-55. High-mass end of mass spectrum of component O from chromatogram of butterfat (Fig. 5-54) (242).

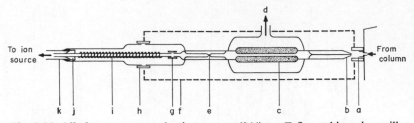

Fig. 5-56. All-glass pressure reduction system (244). *a*, Teflon tubing; *b*, capillary orifice, 0.1-mm i.d.; *c*, fritted-glass tube, 5-μ pore size; *d*, mechanical pump; *e*, constriction, 0.12-mm i.d.; *f*, heating mantle; *g*, Teflon connection; *h*, silicone rubber connection; *i*, silver wire (for heat conduction); *j*, Teflon plug; *k*, heated glass connection to ion source.

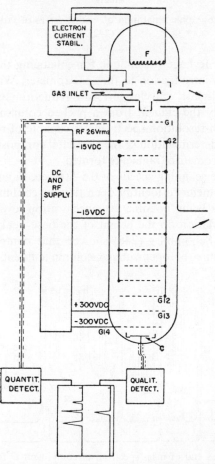

Fig. 5-57. QQ detector tube and typical operating voltages (102).

relative intensities of 5–12 selected masses with the determination of the class of the substance or of the carbon number possible after measurement of 1–3 masses.

The combination of a thermionic ionization gauge and a mass analyzer system in a single quantitative and qualitative (QQ) detector for gas chromatography was developed and applied by Varadi and Ettre (102). This single detector unit is novel and unique, since quantitative measurements and qualitative identifications are performed from the same sample, at the same place and at the same time. The QQ detector has been applied to the identification of unknown peaks in the chromatogram, to retention time calibration (marker), and to analysis of overlapping peaks. Figure 5-57 is a schematic of the QQ detector tube. The gas effluent stream entering the ionization tube is ionized by electron impact with a voltage which, although it is insufficient to ionize the carrier gas, is capable of ionizing the organic vapors in the effluent. The ions produced are divided into two portions: (*1*) One portion is collected immediately by one electrode, which results in an ion current proportional to the concentration of the compound, and (*2*) the other portion is directed to a mass analyzer, making it possible to determine the compound's molecular weight and to obtain its characteristic ion pattern for qualitative identification. By setting the qualitative part of the detector to a preselected mass number, it can be used as a so-called selective detector (Fig. 5-58).

In cases where the gases to be analyzed contain noble gases, inorganic gases, or simple organic compounds, the analysis of these can be performed by direct measurement without using a chromatographic column. The gases which can be so simply analyzed include, for example, H_2, He, CH_4, H_2O, Ne, CO, N_2, C_2H_6, A, CO_2, and Kr.

E. Polarographic Detector

For the further identification of substances in gas–liquid chromatography, Mairanovskii and Yanotovskii (247) described the use of a rapid, sensitive polarographic method and apparatus. They found it feasible to pass column effluent directly into a polarographic cell. As the components are eluted from the column in the vapor state, they first pass through a thermal conductivity detector into the polarographic cell connected in series where the vapors are condensed and dissolved. The continuous flow of inert carrier gas through the cell's solution ensures a rapid equilibrium distribution of the substance in the solvent. The results of the analysis are reproduced in the form of a chromatogram by means of an automatic recording potentiometer, and as a polarogram by means of the secondary polarographic apparatus.

In addition to the above studies, Kemula and Stachurski (248) used polarography to analyze liquid chromatographic column effluents.

In conjunction with gas chromatographic separations of halogens, Janák et al. (249) used a polarographic cell described in detail by Nedorost (250). The effluent was passed into a Ti(III) ion solution, and the halogen

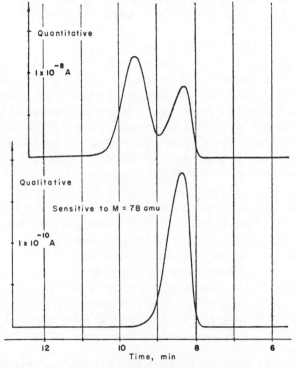

Fig. 5-58. Marking of the benzene peak in a QQ chromatogram of a benzene–methyl cyclohexane mixture (102).

concentration was shown to be proportional to the increase in the Ti(IV) wave height. An integral polarogram is obtained relating halogen-containing components to step-increase in wave height.

F. Ultrasonic Detector

In 1955, Kniazuk and Prediger (251) described a sensitive prototype sonic gas analyzer for studying respiratory gases which later was made commercially by National Instruments Laboratories, Inc., Washington, D.C. Its schematic is shown in Figure 5-59. With the exception of the ultrasonic whistle system of Testerman and McLeod (253) and the phase change measuring system of Noble (254), all previous methods were not applied to the analysis of gas chromatographic effluents. In their method, Testerman and McLeod determined sound velocity by measuring the beat frequency between a sensor whistle operated by the column carrier gas effluent and a reference whistle operated by a flow of pure carrier gas. The beat frequency between the whistles was converted to pulses, and this

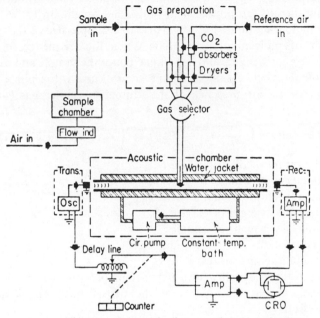

Fig. 5-59. Schematic diagram of analyzer (252).

conversion of frequency to voltage permitted the area of the chromatographic peak to be measured by counting the number of pulses transpiring during the passage of a component through the sensor detector, whereas when only pure carrier gas passes through both whistles, a zero beat is recorded. This provides a digital presentation of the chromatographic peak areas. Robinson (255) used two resonant cavities (one for pure carrier gas and one for column effluent) and measured resonant frequency differences.

In the method of Noble (254) which was an extension of a concept used by Lawley (256) and later by Kniazuk and Prediger (251), the frequency was kept constant. Wavelength changes due to velocity changes were measured differentially by comparing phase changes of the sine wave received by a transducer at one end of a gas-filled tube with those transmitted from a second transducer at the other end of the tube.

More recently, Noble et al. (257) discussed the performance and characteristics of an ultrasonic gas chromatograph effluent detector. In their study, the ultrasonic detector measured the phase-shift change that occurs between transmitting and receiving crystals separated by a pure carrier gas as sample gases pass through the cell. The propagation of sound through binary mixtures (hydrogen or helium carrier gas and sample component) permits one to predict response quantitatively, response (at constant mole fraction) being directly proportional to molecular weight up to 400 and linear from a mole fraction of 1 % to a detectable sample size of the order of 10^{-14} mole of molecular weight 100. When the frequency, crystal separation, molecular weights, and heat capacities of the sample and carrier gases and mole fraction of sample to carrier are known, the phase-shift which occurs due to the presence of the sample in carrier gas can be calculated.

$$\Delta\Phi = 180 \, sfn \left(\frac{M_1}{RT\gamma_1}\right)^{1/2} \left\{\frac{M_2}{M_1}\left[1 + \frac{Cp_2}{Cp_1}\left(\frac{\gamma_1}{\gamma_2} - 1\right)\right] - 1\right\} \quad (5\text{-}38)$$

where s = separation of the transducers

f = frequency of transmitted sound

n = mole fraction of sample to carrier

M_1 = molecular weight of carrier gas

M_2 = molecular weight of sample

R = gas constant

T = absolute temperature

γ_1, γ_2 = the ratio of specific heat at constant pressure to the specific heat at constant volume of the carrier and sample gases, respectively

Cp_1, Cp_2 = specific heat at constant pressure of carrier and sample gases, respectively

When hydrogen is used as a carrier gas in gas chromatography, the specific heats can be disregarded, which then leads to a more simplified expression:

$$\Delta\Phi = [(180 \, sfn)/(RT)^{1/2}](M_1/\gamma_1)^{1/2}[(M_2 - M_1)/M_1] \quad (5\text{-}39)$$

Since

$$V_c = (\gamma_1 RT/M_1)^{1/2} \quad (5\text{-}40)$$

where V_c is the velocity of sound in the carrier, equation 5-39 is further simplified:

$$\Delta\Phi = [(180 \, sfn)/V_c][(M_2 - M_1)/M_1] \quad (5\text{-}41)$$

Using cells with internal volumes of 5–50 μl, they reported that they could be used with either packed or open tubular columns, corrosive samples, and at temperatures up to 270°C.

X. Biological Detectors

To determine the presence of biologically active substances, biological objects placed directly in gas chromatographic column effluents have been successfully employed as detectors.

Based on initial investigations of Butenandt (258), who observed that male silk moths reacted in a characteristic fashion in the presence of the female's sex attractant, Bayer and Anders (259–261) used this technique to study secretions from the female species. In their method, the extracted sex attractant was chromatographed and then carried into a series of chambers, each occupied by a male moth. In this study of sex lures, the characteristic wing movement and whirling dance of the males served as the indicator. By means of serial dilutions, the detectable limit of activity under the most favorable conditions approached 10^{-11} $\mu g/ml$ of carrier gas.

In 1960, Jacobson et al. (262,263) pursued similar studies related to the isolation, identification, and synthesis of the principal sex attractant of the gypsy moth. In their program, the active ingredient from abdominal segments of female moths was extracted and then identified by gas chromatography. Field tests of the purified liquid substance indicated that concentration levels as small as 10^{-7} μg were attractive to males. These tests led to the formulation of a synthetic attractant which rivaled the effectiveness of the female's sex excretion.

Along similar lines, by gas chromatographic and ancillary analytical means, Wharton et al. (264) published their findings on the isolation of the sex attractant of the American cockroach.

References

1. A. T. James and A. J. P. Martin, *Biochem. J.*, **50,** 679 (1952).
2. M. Dimbat, P. E. Porter, and F. H. Stross, *Anal. Chem.*, **28,** 290 (1956).
3. R. Kaiser, *Gas Phase Chromatography*, Vol. I, Butterworths, Washington, D.C., 1963, p. 119.
4. L. Ongkiehong, in *Gas Chromatography 1960*, R. P. W. Scott, Ed., Butterworths, London, 1960, p. 7.
5. J. E. Lovelock, *Anal. Chem.*, **32,** 162 (1961).
6. V. J. Coates and N. Brenner, *Petrol. Refiner*, **35** (11), 197 (1956).
7. A. I. M. Keulemans, *Gas Chromatography*, Reinhold, New York, 1959.
8. L. J. Schmauch and R. A. Dinerstein, *Anal. Chem.*, **32,** 343 (1960).
9. B. D. Smith and W. W. Bowden, *Anal. Chem.*, **36,** 82 (1964).
10. D. H. Desty, *Nature*, **180,** 22 (1957).
11. L. J. Schmauch, *Anal. Chem.*, **31,** 225 (1959).
12. D. S. Scott and A. Han, *Anal. Chem.*, **33,** 160 (1961).
13. R. Kieselbach, *Anal. Chem.*, **32,** 1749 (1960).
14. J. L. Ogilvie, M. C. Simmons, and G. P. Hinds, *Anal. Chem.*, **30,** 25 (1958).

15. A. Naumann and H. Oster, in *Gas Chromatography*, E. Bayer, Ed., Elsevier, New York, 1961; personal communication, to be published.
16. N. Sasaki, K. Tominaga, and M. Aoyagi, *Nature*, **186**, 309 (1960).
17. D. L. Camin, R. W. King, and S. D. Shawhan, *Anal. Chem.*, **36**, 1175 (1964).
18. E. M. Emery and W. E. Koerner, *Anal. Chem.*, **33**, 523 (1961).
19. A. E. Messner, D. M. Rosie, and P. A. Argabright, *Anal. Chem.*, **31**, 230 (1959).
20. E. G. Hoffmann, *Z. Anal. Chem.*, **164**, 182 (1958).
21. E. G. Hoffmann, *Anal. Chem.*, **34**, 1216 (1962).
22. A. B. Littlewood, *Nature*, **184**, 1631 (1959).
23. G. R. Jamieson, *J. Chromatog.*, **8**, 544 (1962).
24. G. R. Jamieson, *J. Chromatog.*, **15**, 260 (1964).
25. J. Griffiths, D. H. James, and C. S. G. Phillips, *Analyst*, **77**, 897 (1952).
26. B. F. Dudenbostel, Jr. and W. Priestley, Jr., *Ind. Eng. Chem.*, **48**, 99A (1956).
27. R. P. W. Scott, *Nature*, **176**, 793 (1955).
28. D. W. Grant, in *Gas Chromatography 1958*, D. H. Desty, Ed., Butterworths, London, 1958, p. 153.
29. I. G. McWilliam and R. A. Dewar, *Nature*, **181**, 760 (1958).
30. J. Harley, W. Nel, and V. Pretorius, *Nature*, **181**, 177 (1958).
31. R. P. W. Scott, in *Vapour Phase Chromatography*, D. H. Desty, Ed., Academic Press, New York, 1957, p. 131.
32. J. I. Henderson and J. H. Knox, *J. Chem. Soc. (London)*, **1956**, 2299.
33. M. M. Wirth, in *Vapour Phase Chromatography*, D. H. Desty, Ed., Academic Press, New York, 1957, p. 154.
34. G. R. Primavesi, G. F. Oldham, and R. J. Thompson, in *Gas Chromatography 1958*, D. H. Desty, Ed., Butterworths, London, 1958, p. 165.
35. J. Franc, *Collection Czech. Chem. Commun.*, **25**, 2225 (1960).
36. K. E. Shuler and J. Weber, *J. Chem. Phys.*, **22**, 491 (1954).
37. D. P. Duclos and W. M. Grounds, *Rev. Sci. Instr.*, **27**, 111 (1956).
38. I. G. McWilliam and R. A. Dewar, in *Gas Chromatography 1958*, D. H. Desty, Ed., Butterworths, London, 1958, p. 142.
39. B. Lewis and G. von Elbe, *Combustion, Flames, and Explosions of Gases*, 1st ed., Academic Press, New York, 1951, p. 206.
40. H. F. Calcote and I. R. King, in *Symp. Combust. 5th, Pittsburgh, 1955*, p. 423.
41. H. F. Calcote, "Ion Production and Removal in Flames," *Symp. Combust., 8th*, Pasadena, Calif., Aug. 29–Sept. 2, 1960.
42. H. F. Calcote, *Combust. Flame*, **1**, 385 (1957).
43. J. C. Sternberg, W. S. Gallaway, and D. T. L. Jones, in *Gas Chromatography*, N. Brenner, J. E. Callen, and M. D. Weiss, Eds., Academic Press, New York, 1962, p. 231.
44. P. F. Knewstubb and T. M. Sugden, *Proc. Roy. Soc. (London)*, **A255**, 520 (1960).
45. S. De Jaegere, J. Decker, and A. Van Tiggelen, "Identity of the Most Abundant Ions in Some Flames," *Symp. Combust. 8th*, Pasadena, Calif., Aug, 29–Sept. 2, 1960.
46. D. H. Desty, C. J. Geach, and A. Goldup, in *Gas Chromatography 1960*, R. P. W. Scott, Ed., Butterworths, London, 1960, p. 46.
47. L. Ongkiehong, Ph.D. Thesis, University of Eindhoven, 1960.
48. W. S. Gallaway and M. R. Burnell, *Pittsburgh Conf. Anal. Chem. Appl. Spectry.*, Feb. 29–March 4, 1960.
49. R. D. Condon, P. R. Scholly, and W. Averill, in *Gas Chromatography 1960*, R. P. W. Scott, Ed., Butterworths, London, 1960, p. 30.

50. L. S. Ettre, in *Gas Chromatography*, N. Brenner, J. E. Callen, and M. D. Weiss, Eds., Academic Press, New York, 1962, p. 307.
51. G. Perkins, Jr., G. M. Rouayheb, L. D. Liveley, and W. C. Hamilton, in *Gas Chromatography*, N. Brenner, J. E. Callen, and M. D. Weiss, Eds., Academic Press, New York, 1962, p. 269.
52. L. S. Ettre, R. D. Condon, F. J. Kabot, and E. W. Cieplinski, *J. Chromatog.*, **13**, 305 (1964).
53. D. J. Pompeo and J. W. Otvos, U. S. Pat. 2,641,710 (1953).
54. P. F. Deisler, Jr., K. W. McHenry, Jr., and R. H. Wilhelm, *Anal. Chem.*, **27**, 1366 (1955).
55. P. F. Deisler, Jr. and R. H. Wilhelm, *Ind. Eng. Chem.*, **45**, 1219 (1953).
56. W. M. Graven, *Anal. Chem.*, **31**, 1197 (1959).
57. C. H. Deal, J. W. Otvos, V. N. Smith, and P. S. Zucco, *Anal. Chem.*, **28**, 1958 (1956).
58. H. Boer, in *Vapour Phase Chromatography*, D. H. Desty, Ed., Butterworths, London, 1957, p. 169.
59. J. W. Otvos and D. P. Stevenson, *J. Am. Chem. Soc.*, **78**, 546 (1956).
60. S. J. Clark, *Gas Pipe*, No. 1, January, 1963, Jarrell-Ash Co., Waltham, Mass.
61. J. E. Lovelock, G. R. Shoemake, and A. Zlatkis, *Anal. Chem.*, **35**, 460 (1963).
62. P. G. Simonds and J. E. Lovelock, *Anal. Chem.*, **35**, 1345 (1963).
63. J. E. Lovelock, G. R. Shoemake, and A. Zlatkis, *Anal. Chem.*, **36**, 1410 (1964).
64. K. Abel and H. De Schmertzing, *Anal. Chem.*, **35**, 1756 (1963).
65. J. E. Lovelock, *J. Chromatog.*, **1**, 35 (1958).
66. W. P. Jesse and J. Sadauskis, *Phys. Rev.*, **100**, 1755 (1955).
67. S. R. Lipsky, R. A. Landowne, and J. E. Lovelock, *Anal. Chem.*, **31**, 852 (1959).
68. J. E. Lovelock, *Nature*, **182**, 1663 (1958).
69. J. E. Lovelock, in *Gas Chromatography 1960*, R. P. W. Scott, Ed., Butterworths, London, 1960, p. 16.
70. V. Prösch, G. Vormum, and H. J. Zöpfl, *Kernenergie*, **7**, No. 1, 26 (1964).
71. H. K. Bothe, *Isotopen Tech.*, **1**, 163 (1960).
72. S. N. Osiranĕv, G. A. Gaziev, and V. S. Janovskij, *Zavodsk. Lab.*, **6**, 760 (1959).
73. G. A. Gaziev, S. N. Osiranĕv, M. I. Yanovskii, and V. S. Kornyakov, *Zh. Fiz. Khim.*, **35**, 1150 (1961).
74. Y. A. Frank and M. I. Yanovskii, *Kinetika i Kataliz*, **2**, 292 (1961).
75. T. Takeuchi, D. Ishii, and S. Tsuge, *Kogyo Kagaku Zasshi*, **66**, 1295 (1963).
76. T. Takeuchi, D. Ishii, and S. Tsuge, *Kogyo Kagaku Zasshi*, **66**, 1299 (1963).
77. E. Haahti and T. Nikkari, *Acta Chem. Scand.*, **13**, 2125 (1959).
78. E. Haahti, T. Nikkari, and E. Kulonen, *J. Chromatog.*, **3**, 372 (1960).
79. F. T. Upham, F. T. Lindgren, and A. V. Nichols, *Anal. Chem.*, **33**, 845 (1961).
80. R. Berry, *Nature*, **188**, 578 (1960).
81. W. A. Wiseman, *Nature*, **190**, 1187 (1961).
82. J. Serpinet, *Anal. Chim. Acta*, **25**, 505 (1961).
83. R. V. Parish and W. H. Parsons, *Chem. Ind.* (*London*), **48**, 1951 (1961).
84. V. Willis, *Nature*, **184**, 894 (1959).
85. S. R. Lipsky and M. M. Shahin, *Nature*, **200**, 566 (1963).
86. M. M. Shahin and S. R. Lipsky, *Anal. Chem.*, **35**, 467 (1963).
87. J. E. Lovelock, *Nature*, **187**, 49 (1960).
88. J. E. Lovelock, *Anal. Chem.*, **33**, 162 (1961).
89. V. N. Smith and J. F. Fidiam, *Anal. Chem.*, **36**, 1739 (1964).
90. R. E. Johnson, *Symp. Instrument Soc. Am.*, Montreal, Quebec, 1960.

91. J. E. Lovelock and S. R. Lipsky, *J. Am. Chem. Soc.*, **82**, 431 (1960).
92. J. E. Lovelock, *Nature*, **189**, 729 (1961).
93. J. E. Lovelock, A. Zlatkis, and R. S. Becker, *Nature*, **193**, 540 (1962).
94. J. E. Lovelock and N. L. Gregory, in *Gas Chromatography*, N. Brenner, J. E. Callen, and M. D. Weiss, Eds., Academic Press, New York, 1962, p. 219.
95. S. J. Clark, in *Residue Reviews*, Vol. V, F. A. Gunther, Ed., Academic Press, New York, 1964, p. 32.
96. R. A. Landowne and S. R. Lipsky, *Anal. Chem.*, **34**, 726 (1962).
97. D. M. Coulson, *Stanford Res. Inst. Pesticide Res. Bull.*, **2**, 1 (1962).
98. J. Sharpe, *Nuclear Radiation Detectors*, Methuens, London, 1955, p. 130.
99. S. A. Ryce and W. A. Bryce, *Nature*, **179**, 541 (1957).
100. E. A. Hinkle, H. C. Tucker, R. F. Wall, and J. F. Combs, in *Gas Chromatography*, H. J. Noebels, N. Brenner, and R. F. Wall, Eds., Academic Press, New York, 1961, p. 55.
101. L. V. Guild, M. I. Lloyd, and F. Aul, in *Gas Chromatography*, H. J. Noebels, N. Brenner, and R. F. Wall, Eds., Academic Press, New York, 1961, p. 52.
102. P. F. Varadi and K. Ettre, *Anal. Chem.*, **34**, 1417 (1962).
103. B. E. Hudson, Jr., W. H. King, Jr., and W. W. Brandt, in *Gas Chromatography*, N. Brenner, E. J. Callen, and M. D. Weiss, Eds., Academic Press, New York, 1962, p. 207.
104. F. P. Lossing and I. Tanaka, *J. Chem. Phys.*, **25**, 1031 (1955).
105. J. E. Lovelock, *Nature*, **188**, 401 (1960).
106. M. Yamane, *J. Chromatog.*, **14**, 355 (1964).
107. M. Yamane, *J. Chromatog.*, **11**, 158 (1963).
108. J. F. Roesler, *Anal. Chem.*, **36**, 1900 (1964).
109. J. Harley and V. Pretorius, *Nature*, **178**, 1244 (1956).
110. M. J. Druyvesteyn and F. M. Penning, *Rev. Mod. Phys.*, **12**, 87 (1940).
111. R. C. Pitkethly, *Anal. Chem.*, **30**, 1309 (1958).
112. G. L. Roberts and E. A. Hinkle, private communication, Monsanto Chemical Co., Texas City, Tex., 1958.
113. W. F. Wilhite, *Tech. Rept.* No. 32-428, Jet Propulsion Lab, California Institute of Technology, Pasadena, Calif., 1963, p. 7.
114. B. Riley, in *Gas Chromatography 1960*, R. P. W. Scott, Ed., Butterworths, London, 1960, p. 81.
115. K. S. Lion, *Rev. Sci. Instr.*, **27**, 222 (1956).
116. R. L. Bowman and A. Karmen, *Nature*, **182**, 1233 (1958).
117. A. Karmen and R. L. Bowman, *Ann. N. Y. Acad. Sci.*, **72**, 714 (1959).
118. A. Karmen and R. L. Bowman, in *Gas Chromatography*, H. J. Noebels, N. Brenner, and R. F. Wall, Eds., Academic Press, New York, 1961, p. 65.
119. J. M. Klaasse and W. Hampton, *Preprints, ISA Instrument-Automation Conference* Houston, Texas, Feb. 1–4, 1960.
120. T. D. Andrew, C. S. G. Phillips, and J. A. Semlyen, *J. Gas Chromatog.*, **1** (1), 27 (1963).
121. J. E. Lovelock, *Nature*, **181**, 1460 (1958).
122. A. Karmen and R. L. Bowman, in *Gas Chromatography*, N. Brenner, J. E. Callen, and M. D. Weiss, Eds., Academic Press, New York, 1962, p. 189.
123. J. C. Sternberg and R. E. Poilson, *J. Chromatog.*, **3**, 406 (1960).
124. E. Evrard, M. Thevelin, and J. V. Joossens, *Nature*, **193**, 59 (1962).
125. A. Karmen and R. L. Bowman, *Nature*, **196**, 62 (1962).
126. A. Karmen, L. Giuffrida, and R. L. Bowman, *Nature*, **191**, 906 (1961).

127. G. Schaal and R. Schellhase, *Medizin Technik*, **6**, 245 (1964).
128. H. Wulfhekel and G. Schaal, *Exptl. Tech. Phys.*, **10**, 231 (1962).
129. R. J. Kokes, H. Tobin, Jr., and P. H. Emmett, *J. Am. Chem. Soc.*, **77**, 5860 (1955).
130. J. B. Evans and J. E. Willard, *J. Am. Chem. Soc.*, **78**, 2908 (1956).
131. R. Wolfgang and F. S. Rowland, *Anal. Chem.*, **30**, 903 (1958).
132. A. T. James and E. A. Piper, *J. Chromatog.*, **5**, 265 (1961).
133. I. M. Whittemore, *Bio-organic Chem. Quart. Rept.*, Lawrence Radiation Lab., Berkeley, Calif., June–August, 1960, p. 49.
134. K. H. Lieser, H. Elias, and F. Sorg, *Z. Anal. Chem.*, **191**, 104 (1962).
135. B. J. Gudzinowicz and W. R. Smith, *Anal. Chem.*, **35**, 465 (1963).
136. K. E. Wilzbach and P. Riesz, *Science*, **126**, 748 (1957).
137. L. H. Mason, H. J. Dutton, and L. R. Bair, *J. Chromatog.*, **2**, 322 (1959).
138. H. E. Hobbs, *J. Chromatog.*, **5**, 32 (1961).
139. D. C. Nelson, P. C. Ressler, Jr., and R. C. Hawes, *Anal. Chem.*, **35**, 1575 (1963).
140. J. Winkelman and A. Karmen, *Anal. Chem.*, **34**, 1067 (1962).
141. A. E. Lowe and D. Moore, *Nature*, **182**, 133 (1958).
142. A. Karmen and H. R. Tritch, *Nature*, **186**, 150 (1960).
143. G. Popják, A. E. Lowe, D. Moore, L. Brown, and F. A. Smith, *J. Lipid Res.*, **1**, 29 (1959).
144. A. Karmen, I. McCaffrey, and R. L. Bowman, *J. Lipid Res.*, **3**, 372 (1962).
145. S. Behrendt, *Z. Physik. Chem. (Frankfurt)*, **20**, 367 (1959).
146. A. J. P. Martin and A. T. James, *Biochem. J.*, **63**, 138 (1956).
147. S. Claesson, *Arkiv. Kemi. Mineral. Geol.*, **23A**, 1 (1946).
148. C. S. G. Phillips and P. L. Timms, *J. Chromatog.*, **5**, 131 (1961).
149. Griffin and George, Ltd., Ealing Road, Alperton, Wembley, Middlesex, England.
150. Gow-Mac Instruments Co., Madison, New Jersey.
151. A. G. Nerheim, *Anal. Chem.*, **35**, 1644 (1963).
152. C. L. Guillemin and F. Auricourt, *J. Gas Chromatog.*, **1** (10), 24 (1963).
153. C. L. Guillemin and F. Auricourt, *J. Gas Chromatog.*, **2**, 156 (1964).
153a. C. L. Guillemin, F. Auricourt, and P. Blaise, *J. Gas Chromatog.*, **4**, 338 (1966).
154. A. Liberti, L. Conti, and V. Crescenzi, *Nature*, **178**, 1067 (1956).
155. J. S. Parsons, *Anal. Chem.*, **36**, 1849 (1964).
156. S. C. Bevan and S. Thoburn, *J. Chromatog.*, **11**, 301 (1963).
157. E. V. Piel, *Anal. Chem.*, **36**, 696 (1964).
158. E. Cahn, *Research/Development*, October, 1964, p. 34.
159. J. Griffiths, Ph.D. Thesis, Oxford University, 1954.
160. D. H. James and C. S. G. Phillips, *J. Sci. Instr.*, **29**, 362 (1952).
161. J. Janák, *Chem. Listy*, **47**, 464 (1953).
162. J. Janák, *Chem. Listy*, **47**, 817 (1953).
163. J. Janák, *Chem. Listy*, **47**, 837 (1953).
164. J. Janák, *Chem. Listy*, **47**, 1184 (1953).
165. J. Janák and M. Rusek, *Chem. Listy*, **47**, 1190 (1953).
166. J. Janák and I. Paralova, *Chem. Listy*, **47**, 1476 (1953).
167. J. Janák and M. Rusek, *Chem. Listy*, **48**, 207 (1954).
168. J. Janák, *Chem. Listy*, **48**, 397 (1954).
169. J. Janák and A. Lazarev, *Chem. Listy*, **49**, 700 (1955).
170. J. Janák, *Collection Czech. Chem. Commun.*, **19**, 684 (1954).
171. J. Janák, *Collection Czech. Chem. Commun.*, **19**, 700 (1954).
172. J. Janák, *Mikrochim. Acta*, **1956**, 1038.

173. J. Janák, in *Vapour Phase Chromatography*, D. H. Desty, Ed., Butterworths, London, 1957, p. 247.
174. E. Leibnitz, H. Hrapia, and H. G. Konneche, *Brennstoff-Chem.*, **38**, 14 (1957).
175. S. Behrendt, *Z. Physik. Chem. (Frankfurt)*, **30**, 357 (1961).
176. F. van de Craats, *Anal. Chim. Acta*, **14**, 136 (1956).
177. J. F. Kinkel, *Proc. Instr. Soc. Am.*, **7**, 188 (1952).
178. J. Novák and J. Janák, in *Gas Chromatographie*, H. P. Angelé and H. G. Struppe, Eds., Akademie-Verlag, Berlin, 1963, p. 100.
179. A. T. James, A. J. P. Martin, and G. H. Smith, *Biochem. J.*, **52**, 238 (1952).
180. A. T. James and A. J. P. Martin, *Analyst*, **77**, 917 (1952).
181. A. G. McInnes, in *Vapour Phase Chromatography*, D. H. Desty, Ed., Academic Press, New York, 1957, p. 304.
182. A. T. James, *Research (London)*, **8**, 8 (1955).
183. A. T. James, *Anal. Chem.*, **28**, 1564 (1956).
184. A Liberti, *Anal. Chim. Acta*, **17**, 247 (1957).
185. A. Liberti and G. Cartoni, *Atti Accad. Nazl. Lincei, Rend. Classe Sci. Fis. Mat. Nat.*, **20**, 623 (1956).
186. A. Liberti, G. Cartoni, and U. Pallota, *Latte*, **30**, 581 (1956).
187. A. Liberti and G. Cartoni, in *Gas Chromatography*, D. H. Desty, Ed., Butterworths, London, 1958, p. 248.
188. A. Liberti and G. Cartoni, *Chim. Ind. (Milan)*, **39**, 821 (1957).
189. H. Thielemann, V. Behrens, and E. Leibnitz, *Chem. Tech. (Berlin)*, **14**, 162 (1962).
190. D. M. Coulson and L. A. Cavanagh, *Anal. Chem.*, **32**, 1245 (1960).
191. E. M. Fredericks and G. A. Harlow, *Anal. Chem.*, **36**, 263 (1964).
192. D. M. Coulson, L. A. Cavanagh, J. E. De Vries, and B. Walther, *J. Agr. Food Chem.*, **8**, 399 (1960).
193. L. C. Erickson and H. Z. Hield, *J. Agr. Food Chem.*, **10**, 204 (1962).
194. J. Burke and L. Johnson, *J. Assoc. Offic. Agr. Chemists*, **45**, 348 (1962).
195. W. A. Bosin, *Anal. Chem.*, **35**, 833 (1963).
196. F. A. Gunther, R. C. Blinn, and D. E. Ott, *Anal. Chem.*, **34**, 302 (1962).
197. E. Cremer, T. Kraus, and E. Bechtold, *Chem. Ing.-Tech.*, **33**, 632 (1961).
198. A. Karmen, *Anal. Chem.*, **36**, 1416 (1964).
199. A. Karmen and L. Giuffrida, *Nature*, **201**, 1204 (1964).
200. D. W. Turner, *Nature*, **181**, 1265 (1958).
201. J. D. Winefordner, D. Steinbrecher, and W. E. Lear, *Anal. Chem.*, **33**, 515 (1961).
202. J. D. Winefordner and H. P. Williams, *Anal. Chem.*, **37**, 161 (1965).
203. G. Johansson, *Anal. Chem.*, **34**, 914 (1962).
204. J. H. Griffiths and C. S. G. Phillips, *J. Chem. Soc.*, **1954**, 3446.
205. C. S. G. Phillips, *J. Sci. Instr.*, **28**, 342 (1951).
206. Anon., *Chem. Eng. News*, **42** (22), 39 (June 1, 1964).
207. T. Seiyama, A. Katu, K. Fujiishi, and M. Nagatani, *Anal. Chem.*, **34**, 1502 (1962).
208. W. H. King, Jr., *Anal. Chem.*, **36**, 1735 (1964).
209. G. Sauerbrey, *Z. Physik*, **155**, 206 (1959).
210. O. Piringer and M. Pascalau, *J. Chromatog.*, **8**, 410 (1962).
211. O. Piringer, E. Tataru, and M. Pascalau, *J. Gas Chromatog.*, **2**, 104 (1964).
212. J. C. Sternberg and D. T. L. Jones, *Pittsburgh Conf. Anal. Chem. Appl. Spectry.*, Pittsburgh, Pa., March 5–9, 1962.
213. H. Boer, *World Petrol. Congr., Proc. 4th, Rome, 1955*, Sect. V, p. 1.
214. A. Dijkstra, C. C. M. Fabrie, G. Kateman, C. J. Lamboo, and J. A. L. Thissen, *J. Gas Chromatog.*, **2**, 180 (1964).

215. A. Berton, *Ind. Aliment. Agr.*, **78**, 521 (1961).
216. A. Berton, *Chim. Anal. (Paris)*, **45**, 585 (1963).
217. A. Berton, *Chim. Anal. (Paris)*, **41**, 351 (1959).
218. A. Berton, *Bull. Soc. Chim. France*, **1959**, Part 3, 536.
219. T. R. Phillips, E. G. Johnson, and H. Woodward, *Anal. Chem.*, **36**, 450 (1964).
220. P. Hersch, Brit. Pat. 880,965 (March, 1962).
221. S. Sunner, K. J. Karrman, and V. Sunden, *Mikrochim. Acta*, **1956**, 1144.
222. W. Kaye, *Anal. Chem.*, **34**, 287 (1962).
223. J. Merritt, F. Comendant, S. T. Abrams, and V. N. Smith, *Anal. Chem.*, **35**, 1461 (1963).
224. A. E. Martin and J. Smart, *Nature*, **175**, 422 (1955).
225. A. Liberti, G. Costa, and E. Pauluzzi, *Chim. Ind. (Milan)*, **38**, 674 (1955).
226. E. A. Haahti and H. M. Fales, *Chem. Ind. (London)*, **1961**, No. 16, 507.
227. A. M. Bartz and H. D. Ruhl, *Anal. Chem.*, **36**, 1892 (1964).
228. P. A. Wilks, Jr. and R. A. Brown, *Anal. Chem.*, **36**, 1896 (1964).
229. S. Behrendt, *Nature*, **201**, 70 (1964).
230. R. S. Juvet and R. P. Durbin, *J. Gas Chromatog.*, **1** (12), 14 (1963).
231. R. S. Gohlke, *Anal. Chem.*, **31**, 535 (1959).
232. L. P. Lindeman and J. L. Annis, *Anal. Chem.*, **32**, 1742 (1960).
233. D. Henneberg, in *Gas Chromatography 1960*, R. P. W. Scott, Ed., Butterworths, London, 1960, p. 124.
234. D. Henneberg, *Z. Anal. Chem.*, **183**, 12 (1961).
235. A. A. Ebert, Jr., *Anal. Chem.*, **33**, 1865 (1961).
236. E. J. Levy, E. D. Miller, and J. W. S. Beggs, *Anal. Chem.*, **35**, 946 (1963).
237. R. S. Gohlke, *Anal. Chem.*, **34**, 1332 (1962).
238. W. H. McFadden, R. Teranishi, D. R. Black, and J. C. Day, *J. Food Sci.*, **28**, 316 (1963).
239. W. H. McFadden and R. Teranishi, *Nature*, **200**, 329 (1963).
240. R. G. Buttery, W. H. McFadden, W. H. Teranishi, M. P. Kealy, and T. R. Mon, *Nature*, **200**, 435 (1963).
241. H. Widmer and T. Gaumann, *Helv. Chim. Acta*, **45**, 2175 (1961).
242. R. Ryhage, *Anal. Chem.*, **36**, 759 (1964).
243. E. W. Becker, *Separation of Isotopes*, Newnes, Ltd., London, 1961, p. 360.
244. J. T. Watson and K. Biemann, *Anal. Chem.*, **36**, 1135 (1964).
245. A. E. Banner, R. M. Elliot, and W. Kelly, in *Gas Chromatography 1964*, A. Goldup, Ed., Institute of Petroleum, London, 1965, p. 180.
246. D. Henneberg and G. Schomburg, in *Gas Chromatography 1962*, M. van Swaay, Ed., Butterworths, London, 1962, p. 191.
247. V. G. Mairanovskii and M. T. Yanotovskii, *Russ. J. Phys. Chem. (English Transl.)*, **37**, 370 (1963).
248. W. Kemula and Z. Stachurski, *Roczniki Chem.*, **30**, 1285 (1956).
249. J. Janák, M. Nedorost, and V. Bubenikova, *Chem. Listy*, **52**, 890 (1957).
250. M. Nedorost, *Chem. Listy*, **50**, 317 (1956).
251. M. Kniazuk and F. R. Prediger, *ISA Proc.*, **10** (1955).
252. National Instruments Laboratories, Washington, D.C.
253. M. K. Testerman and P. C. McLeod, in *Gas Chromatography*, N. Brenner, J. E. Callen, and M. D. Weiss, Eds., Academic Press, New York, 1962, p. 183.
254. F. W. Noble, *Instr. Soc. Am. J.*, **8**, 54 (1961).
255. C. F. Robinson, U.S. Pat. 2,952,153 (Sept. 13, 1960).
256. L. E. Lawley, *Chem. Ind. (London)*, **1954**, 200.

257. F. W. Noble, K. Abel, and P. W. Cook, *Anal. Chem.*, **36**, 1421 (1964).
258. A. Butenandt, *Naturw. Rundschau*, **8**, 457 (1955).
259. E. Bayer, *Angew. Chem.*, **69**, 732 (1959).
260. E. Bayer and F. Anders, *Naturwiss.*, **46**, 380 (1959).
261. F. Anders and E. Bayer, *Biol. Zentr.*, **78**, 584 (1959).
262. M. Jacobson, M. Beroza, and W. A. Jones, *Science*, **132**, 1011 (1960).
263. M. Jacobson, M. Beroza, and W. A. Jones, *J. Am. Chem. Soc.*, **83**, 4819 (1961).
264. D. R. A. Wharton, E. D. Black, C. Merritt, Jr., M. L. Wharton, M. Bazinet, and J. T. Walsh, *Science*, **137**, 1062 (1962).

CHAPTER 6

Applications of Digital Electronic Systems to Gas Chromatography

Hal J. Jones, *Infotronics Corporation, Houston, Texas*

I. Introduction

The unusually rapid rate of acceptance of gas chromatography as a quantitative analysis tool quickly led to a need for improved data processing techniques. The standard presentation method for analysis results has utilized a strip chart recorder, with interpretation accomplished primarily by manual methods. The technician determined which peaks were significant and computed the height or the area of the peaks by various simple methods (1,2,5). A variety of semiautomatic instruments also were applied, including analog electronic integrators and mechanical disc integrators. These methods were time-consuming in application and often unsatisfactory in terms of accuracy and repeatability of results. The heavy work load, plus several other factors, indicated a clear need for a rapid, automatic, instrumental method of data reduction. Wider use of capillary column chromatography, with its consequent sharp, closely spaced peaks, accentuated the requirements. Accurate measurements could not be made

333

on the very sharp peaks either by manual techniques or by the existing semiautomatic instruments. Another influence was the trend away from measurement of peak height toward measurement of peak area. The need, then, was for automatic equipment able to handle the faster analyses: equipment capable of recognizing peaks automatically, computing areas, and presenting the results in simple, easy-to-interpret form.

The first answer to these requirements came in the development of digital, automatic, electronic integrators. These instruments were first introduced in 1961, and in the few years intervening there has been a very sharp increase in application to analytical chemistry in general and to gas chromatography in particular. There is available in the literature a comprehensive summary of the advantages of automatic digital integrators vis-à-vis methods previously used, and this subject will not be treated in detail here (1,2). The advantages of automatic digital integrators have been well demonstrated and need only be itemized: improved accuracy and repeatability of results, substantial savings of cost and time, and more rapid availability of results.

To date several types of digital data collecting and processing systems have been developed. These include:

1. *Real-time digital automatic integrators*, which process the analytical signal as the analyses are being run. These systems automatically detect relative peaks in the analytical signal, compute peak areas and/or measure peak heights, determine the peak elution times, and prepare digital listings of the results either in printed form or in any one of a variety of computer compatible formats. The block diagram of such a system is shown in Figure 6-1. These digital integrators are essentially real-time decision-making machines, in that they are capable of identifying and processing signal peaks as they occur.

2. *Digital computer data collection and processing systems*. Such systems take sample values of the analytical signal as the analyses are run, encode these signals to digital form, convert them to computer-compatible format, and either feed them directly to the digital computer or record them in computer-compatible format on a medium such as punched paper tape, punched cards, or magnetic tape. Systems may collect and process simultaneously the outputs of several analyzers, multiplexing sample values. The block diagram of a computer data collection system is shown in Figure 6-2, for the case in which the data to be processed by the computer are recorded on punched paper tape. The paper tapes thus prepared can be accepted by the computer off-line. The computer program will be designed to accomplish record interpretation, i.e., peak detection, baseline correction etc., as well as area computations. Clearly, the computer can easily

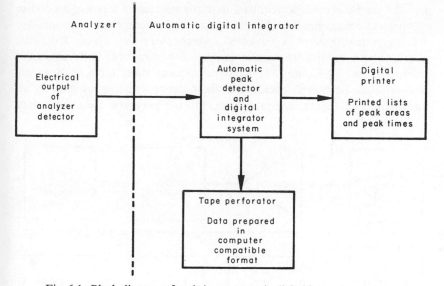

Fig. 6-1. Block diagram of real-time automatic digital integrator system.

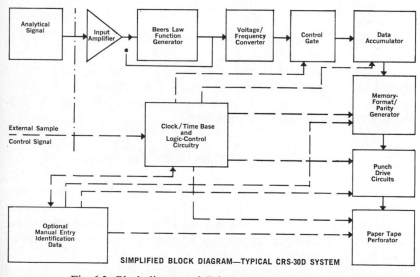

SIMPLIFIED BLOCK DIAGRAM—TYPICAL CRS-30D SYSTEM

Fig. 6-2. Block diagram of digital data collection system.

perform simple arithmetic required to apply correction factors, normalize and present results in tabular form in terms of per cent composition.

3. *Reproducible recording systems*, which store the signals from the analyzers on magnetic tape as the analyses are being run, as shown in the block diagram of Figure 6-3. At a subsequent time, tapes from many analyzers can be played back on a single processing system such as an automatic digital electronic integrator. During playback the signals may

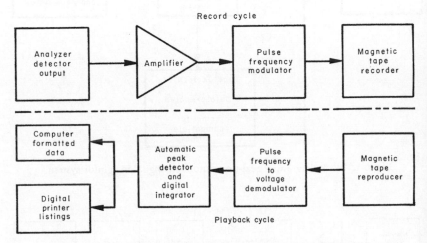

Fig. 6-3. Block diagram of magnetic tape data processing system.

be detected and digitized by the integrator, or alternatively they may be sampled and recorded for computer processing. In other words, the signals which are stored on tape and recovered can be treated just as are the real-time signals from the gas chromatographs.

II. Automatic Real-Time Digital Integrators

The automatic data processing instrument finding the most use to date in gas chromatography has been the digital integrator. The essential features of its use and design will be considered here. The block diagram of the basic automatic digital integrator system for gas chromatography is shown in Figure 6-4.

The input of the digital integrator is connected directly to the electrical output of the gas chromatograph, thus insuring independence from the chart recorder itself. Chart recorders typically are unable to follow properly very sharp peaks and in addition exhibit a dead band near zero, restricting accuracy on small peaks. The input of the digital integrator is an instrumentation amplifier. In electrical terms, the input is isolated and floating, and presents a high impedance to the signal from the chromatograph. This means that the integrator can be connected to a wide range of chromatograph detectors including thermal conductivity bridge detectors (either thermistor or hot wire) and ionization detectors, which typically have an associated electrometer amplifier. The input amplifier of the digital

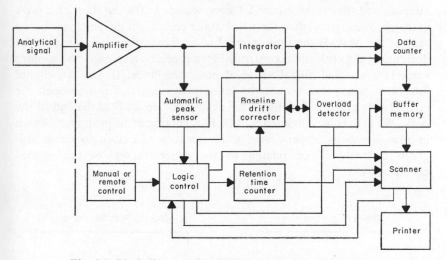

Fig. 6-4. Block diagram of typical electronic digital integrator.

integrator serves, then, two primary functions. First, it feeds the analytical signal directly to the automatic peak detector and integrator, thus providing effective isolation between major components of the system—i.e., the recorder, the integrator, and the chromatograph. Second, the amplifier conditions the analytical signal to the proper level and proper characteristics for optimum use by the digital integrator.

The normal integration computation carried out on gas chromatograph data is linear. However, systems available commercially are capable of providing special-function generators to convert nonlinear signals to linear form prior to integration. Examples are: Beer's law function converters used in integrators optimized for amino acid analysis, and adjustable-function generators which can be tailored to fit a variety of nonlinear responses and are utilized primarily in processing data from spectrophotometers and colorimeters; a possible gas chromatography application is with electron capture detectors.

After conditioning by the input amplifier in the digital integrator, the analytical signal is digitized. The most commonly used method employs a voltage-to-frequency converter which produces a train of electrical pulses whose instantaneous frequency is proportional to the amplitude of the analytical signal. The pulses produced flow into an electronic counter through a control gate. If this control gate is maintained open for a time interval T, the number of counts accumulated in the counter at the end of this interval is proportional to the integral of the detector signal over the interval, and thus if the interval T corresponds to the duration of a peak in the chromatogram, then the value in the counters is proportional to the area of the peak. If the time interval is relatively short compared to the duration of the peak and is controlled by a precision time base, the counter value is a sampled digital value of peak amplitude. If now the digital integrator system can accurately define peak start and end to open the control gate at the beginning of the peak and turn it off at the end of the peak, the counts accumulated will be linearly related to peak area, which in turn—assuming proper design and calibration of a given gas chromatograph system—will be related to the concentrations of the various constituents.

CRS-11 Time and area   CRS-10 Peak No. and area

```
1 7 5       2 5 6 3            1   0 0 2 5 6
2 0 6     1 5 7 8 9            2   0 1 5 7 8
2 4 6   8 5 2 3 6 4            3   8 5 2 3 6
2 7 6   2 1 1 4 9 1            4   2 1 1 4 9
3 1 1       4 5 3 6 0          5   0 4 5 3 6
3 9 1       2 8 9 1 3          6   0 2 8 9 1
4 5 1         1 3 6 6          7   0 0 1 3 6
5 1 8           9 8 7          8   0 0 0 9 8
5 7 3         1 5 8 2          9   0 0 1 5 8
6 8 9       2 1 5 4 5          0   0 2 1 5 4
7 3 7           5 6 1          1   0 0 0 5 6
          1 1 8 2 5 2 1 T    4 7 1. 1 8 2 7 3 T
```

Fig. 6-5. Typical printed format of integrator results.

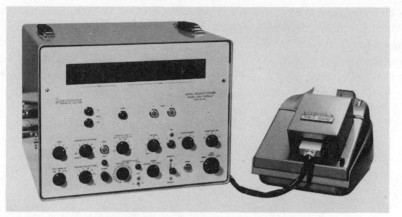

Fig. 6-6. Typical digital integrator system.

The peak area values contained in the electronic counters of the digital integrators may be transferred to a printing mechanism for digital readout. The typical digital readout is a list of sequential peak numbers along with the peak areas or a listing of peak retention times, each associated with a given peak area, as shown in Figure 6-5. The integrator system also determines automatically the peak retention times, measuring them in terms of elapsed time from run start to the crest of each peak.

Of particular significance in an electronic digital integrator is the use of a memory. The peak area values at the end of each peak are transferred immediately by electronic switching to an electronic memory storage unit. The digital printer is in turn fed from this memory storage unit. This means that the peak area counter is immediately free to begin integration of a closely following peak without waiting for the relatively slow operation of the mechanical printer, thus insuring that no counts will be lost in closely spaced peak sequences. Memory is, of course, of less importance in very long-duration analyses with relatively broad peaks that are well separated. But as the analysis time is shortened and the peak elution rate is increased, as peak separation deteriorates, the memory feature becomes more and more important.

Typical digital integrator packages are shown in Figure 6-6. Bench space required is small, usually 17 in. × 17 in. approximately. No care is required in location, other than avoidance of extreme temperature or radiation.

A. Automatic Peak Detection

One of the most important problems in the development of an automatic digital integrator is to provide reliable detection of peaks. Delays in identifying peak start and stop will affect the accuracy of area computation. Automatic peak detection means must be sensitive enough to recognize immediately the start and end of very small peaks, yet must not be overly sensitive to noise signals so that erratic signal variations, which unfortunately will occur in many chromatograph output signals, will not be

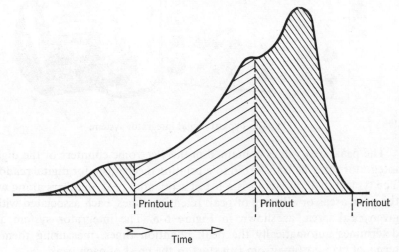

Fig. 6-7. Separation of leading edge shoulder.

improperly identified as peaks. Peak identification circuits in modern integrators are primarily sensitive to the rate of change of the analytical signal, i.e., to slope or first derivative. Peak start is defined as a change from zero to positive slope, exceeding a preset rate. Peak crest is identified by the first derivative going from plus through zero to negative. Peak end is signaled by the slope changing from negative to zero, as occurs, for example, in a valley between peaks or when a peak returns to the baseline.

A cleanly isolated peak is detected and integrated with little difficulty. A properly designed integrator does not begin to integrate until the peak start has been recognized and stops integrating at peak end, and thus it does not accumulate any effects of baseline drift and offset between peaks. An automatic peak detector also can separate unresolved shoulders on both the leading and trailing edges of peaks, even if an interpeak valley does not occur. For example, in Figure 6-7 a shoulder occurs on a leading edge of a peak. The automatic peak detector can recognize the slope sequence zero, plus, zero, plus, and can separate the peak into two separate areas. If the shoulder occurs on the trailing edge of the peak as shown in Figure 6-8, additional criteria are required to effect separation. The automatic peak detector recognizes the slope sequence zero, minus, zero, minus, but also monitors the signal level. If the shoulder occurs above a signal level preset by the operator prior to the run, the automatic peak detector resolves the peak into two areas and provides two separate printouts.

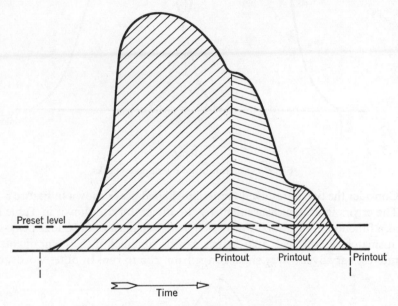

Fig. 6-8. Separation of a trailing edge shoulder.

When overlapping peaks are separated by a valley, the peak detector divides them at the valley and, in effect, drops a perpendicular to the baseline as shown in Figure 6-9. When the peak overlap is significant, this leads, of course, to an area trading effect. The area of the first peak includes part of peak B, but loses part of peak A, and the area of the second peak includes part of peak A, but loses part of peak B. If the peaks are symmetrical and if the mismatch in peak height is not too great, the area trading effect tends to equalize errors so that the absolute accuracy of peak areas as computed by the digital integrator is relatively good. Serious errors can occur, however, if very small peaks occur superimposed on the trailing edges of very large peaks or if peaks are markedly asymmetrical. The actual errors are, however, often less than one would expect intuitively.

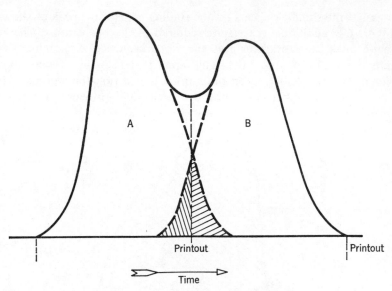

Fig. 6-9. Separation of overlapping peaks.

Consider the two unresolved Gaussian-shaped peaks shown in Figure 6-10. The errors in area measurement by the integrator are shown in Table 6-1 as a function of the ratio of peak heights. Even in cases of serious peak-size mismatch, useful peak area values can be obtained if the components of interest vary over a very small range from run to run. In other words, one

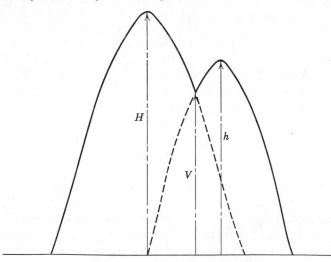

Fig. 6-10. Unresolved peak doublet.

TABLE 6-1

Errors in Peak Areas for Overlapping Peaks
of Figure 6-10[a]

Ratio of peak heights (H/h)	Error in area (%)	
	Peak A	Peak B
1	0.2	0.2
2	0.2	0.5
3	0.2	1.5
5	0.2	5.0
10	0.2	10.0

[a] Gaussian symmetrical peaks, where the ratio of inter-peak valley to smaller peak height (V/h) is less than 0.8.

obtains a reproducible number that can be useful in quantitative analysis even though the absolute accuracy of this value as a true peak area is poor. Furthermore the results are often more accurate than those obtained by other methods.

Relatively sophisticated electronics and filtering techniques are employed in an electronic digital integrator to provide a combination of very sensitive and highly reliable automatic peak detection. As Figure 6-11 illustrates, the problem of automatic peak detection of chromatograph signals may be treated as an energy–frequency filtering problem. If one were to make a Fourier analysis of a chromatogram, resolving it into

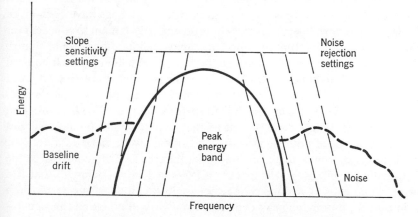

Fig. 6-11. Energy–frequency spectrum of chromatograms.

sinusoidal components, the resultant energy–frequency spectrum would show a concentration of dominant peak energies in a well defined band. Lower frequencies represent baseline wandering or drift. Typically, a variety of high frequency noise occurs, e.g., electrometer spikes. The automatic peak detector must have separate controls to set the rejection of both low- (drift) and higher-frequency noise. If one is to be able to detect very small peaks and also to resolve closely spaced peaks, one must set the band pass of energy as broad as possible. In so doing, of course, the risk of "false alarm" prints, that is of calling a noise signal a peak, is increased. Conversely, if the signal from the analyzer is very noisy electrically, one narrows down the frequency band to minimize printouts due to noise signal, simultaneously taking the chance of ignoring some very small peaks and deteriorating resolution of fast peaks. In typical situations one can arrive at an optimum setting of control positions for routine analyses, insuring automatic detection of all peaks of interest. In some analyses, of course, particularly isothermal analyses, the shape, spacing, and breadth of the peaks change as a function of elution time so that the optimum peak detector settings may be different from run beginning to end.

Usually another control is provided on the automatic peak detector circuits of an integrator in addition to the two noise rejection settings described above. This is a gain control, which in effect changes the level of the driving signal presented to the automatic peak detector. Any increase in gain, of course, is an increase in apparent sensitivity so that one can adjust the sensitivity to match the noise components of the analyzer signal whose frequency composition does not permit rejection by filtering. These three independent controls offer a great amount of flexibility in automatic peak detection and allow the operator to select optimized settings for each particular type of analysis. Once a given suite of settings have been given or determined for a specific analytical problem, they remain fixed whenever that problem is being run, provided that analysis conditions do not change drastically, as for example would be the case if the column were used until it had deteriorated badly, with consequent increasingly poor separation of peaks and possibly with the introduction of electrical noise at the chromatograph output. When the automatic integrator is to be used with a minimum of human attention, it is important to be sure that significant data will not be lost. The use of both signal-slope and signal-level criteria in automatic peak detection tends to insure this desirable result. The controls of the automatic digital integrator include a threshold level setting so that if a noise signal causing a slope change occurs during a peak and results in a printout, the automatic peak detection circuitry will note that the signal is still above the threshold and will immediately reinitiate integration. Since an electronic memory and high-speed switching circuits are employed, the net result may be a splitting of peaks, but no significant data will be lost. Integrators may include other logic to treat special situations. One example is a control for minimum peak size; the integrator will automatically reject (not print) areas below a total count preset by the operator.

With a reasonably noise-free analytical signal and a versatile automatic peak detection system as described above, one may operate the gas chromatograph and integrator as a fully automatic system. For example, after charging the sample the technician can devote his time to other problems with the results being printed out in unattended operation. A moment's reflection will show that the human operator in interpreting a chromatogram introduces a wide range of subjective criteria which are closely interrelated. It is difficult to incorporate these criteria into a machine which can be sold at a reasonable cost. Therefore, the better the analyses—i.e., the more care that is taken in the analyses to produce relatively well separated peaks and to maintain relatively low background noise—the more satisfactory the operation of the automatic digital integrator. Now that automatic integrators have come into wide use, the analytical chemist should treat his over-all analysis on a system basis. He should attempt to optimize the performance of *all* of the instrumentation for a given problem.

B. Baseline Stability

One of the most important points to be made in connection with the accuracy of results that may be expected from an automatic integrator concerns baseline stability. If we consider an isolated peak superimposed on a flat zero baseline, the automatic digital integrator may be expected to provide excellent accuracy in area measurement. The errors which occur in defining peak start and end would, in a properly designed integrator, be very small. Baseline position during integration is, however, quite critical. Any baseline offset under the peak will be added to the machine-determined area values. It is quite important, therefore, to reference the input to the integrator as closely as possible to zero before the start of each peak.

This is accomplished by the use of a continuous-monitoring type of automatic baseline drift corrector (ABDC). The ABDC examines the baseline at all times between peaks, and if the baseline deviates from zero, the input to the quantizing circuits of the integrator is adjusted to provide nominal zero count rate into the peak area counter. Thus, as each peak occurs, it is properly referenced to zero baseline. The ABDC is not operating during the peaks, and it is not allowed to come into operation between unresolved peaks, since it would then be endeavoring to correct a nonbaseline signal and also might not have time to accomplish full correction. Figure 6-12 shows the general procedure by which the automatic baseline drift corrector adjusts the baseline. It must be emphasized that the baseline drift corrector does not operate ahead of the peak sensing circuits, which would, in effect, desensitize them.

The automatic baseline drift corrector limits the possibility of errors in area determination to a rather narrow range by its effective stabilizing of the baseline, and thereby improves accuracy of computation. There are,

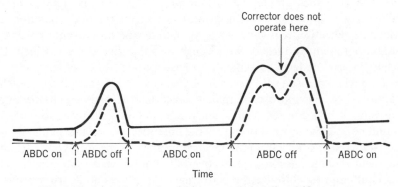

Fig. 6-12. Operation cycle of the automatic baseline drift corrector.

of course, special cases in which the adjustment of the baseline *during* a peak is important. As an example, in certain temperature-programmed analyses the peaks are superimposed on a monotonically increasing baseline, which from run beginning to end varies over a wide range, often in a manner that can be represented by a simple mathematical function. In this case the integrator may include as an option, e.g., a linear or an exponential baseline correction program. By the trial-and-error method the operator determines the baseline correction settings optimum for a given analysis. As the sample is eluted, the baseline is then corrected by a preset program plus the action of an automatic baseline drift corrector. The preset program removes the major variations of the baseline, and the automatic baseline drift corrector insures the smoothing of minor deviations. With this technique, small peaks superimposed on a large and continually changing baseline offset can be integrated accurately.

Another unusual baseline correction problem occurs in connection with peak tailing. In a number of analyses small components are superimposed upon the tail of a very large peak. This situation has proved to be the most difficult problem for automatic digital integrators. A reasonable solution in many problems has been the use of an exponential decay correction program. This option provides controls for adjusting the time constant of an exponential decay correction which compensates for the tail of the large peak. This program can be set into operation manually or can be initiated when the amplitude of a large peak falls to a preset threshold. The automatic baseline drift corrector operates in conjunction with the exponential decay. The tail of the peak is removed by the exponential decay, and the automatic baseline drift corrector insures that minor errors in function fitting will be removed. When exponential decay programs and linear correction programs are used, the corrected chromatogram can be displayed on the strip chart recorder associated with the chromatograph system so the operator can see the corrected baseline that the machine has set.

C. System Dynamic Range

One of the most important considerations in design of a truly automatic digital integrator is the dynamic range. This point is often neglected in choosing the proper instrument. Our definition of dynamic range is the ratio of the smallest and the largest peaks that can be measured on the same chromatograph run with no manual change of integrator controls. This means, in effect, that the automatic digital integrator must be able to recognize the small peak as well as the large peak, that is must have a linear response for both the very small and the very large peak, and further that it must measure these extremes with sufficient resolution.

Modern thermal conductivity bridge detectors and flame ionization detectors usually have a very wide dynamic range. Unfortunately, the electronics associated with them in the gas chromatograph system proper often do not share this range. Particular offenders are the amplifiers associated with ionization detectors. In addition to a simple output attenuation scheme to provide compatibility with the chart recorder, these amplifiers may require a change of gain in the early stages of the amplifier in order to handle the dynamic range of the detector itself. Automatic digital integrators can be connected to the chromatograph amplifier ahead of the output attenuator so that no manual output attenuation changes are necessary. With some amplifiers, however, the full value of the automatic integrator is not obtained because the operator must make manual adjustment of the gain of the chromatograph amplifier. Commercial versions of the digital integrator now in use offer dynamic range in excess of most chromatograph amplifiers, and, in the future, design efforts should be devoted to the entire system so that the chromatograph electronics itself will be compatible with the automatic digital processing equipment.

D. Accuracy Considerations

The primary concerns in the evaluation of the accuracy of a digital integration system are repeatability and linearity of area measurements. Any deviations from linearity can, in principle, in repetitive quantitative analyses be treated as a system calibration factor. In practical systems, however, excellent linearity within a very small variation over the measurement range of interest is also of prime importance. Of most importance, clearly, is the ability of the equipment to repeat results within a very small variation, assuming identical input conditions.

The most significant factors affecting the accuracy of a digital integrator are:

1. Stability or offset of baseline.

2. Deviation from perfect reproduction of the input signal and in the transformation of the signal to a linear form when the input signal is nonlinear, as in the case of electron capture detectors.

3. Errors in defining peak start and end.

4. Stability and drift of the digital integrator itself.

From an instrumentation point of view, the digital integrator may be regarded as accurate if it properly separates peaks and correctly computes areas under the signal curves. Errors in determining "true" peak areas when peaks overlap are treated herein as application rather than instrumental errors, which is another way of saying again: the better the chromatography, the more useful the automatic integrator and the higher the quality of the results.

1. Baseline offset and drift can be a serious source of error if not properly compensated for. This is particularly true because baseline variations are usually not reproducible from run to run and one cannot treat them as calibration factors. It is of prime importance, therefore, to monitor the baseline continuously and to attempt to correct for variations thereof within a very small tolerance. Errors due to baseline variation may be expressed as errors relative to true peak size in the following form:

$$\text{Error } (\%) = \frac{(\text{measured peak area} - \text{true peak area}) \times 100}{\text{true peak area}}$$

$$\propto \frac{\text{baseline offset}}{\text{peak height}}$$

(6-1)

The errors are based on rectangles of baseline offset upon which a peak is superimposed. To stress a perhaps obvious point, a relatively large percentage error in determining the area of a very small peak usually is a small percentage error relative to total sample. It should further be noted that when the integrated data are obtained as percentage composition of total sample by normalization using total area as a divisor, the absolute measurement errors usually are reduced since a small baseline offset change present affects individual and total area in the same direction.

As a final comment on baseline control, reasonable peak separation permits, as stressed above, control of the baseline within specified limits prior to the emergence of the next peak in a series. Between overlapping peaks, however, the corrector does not have time to operate, and thus any drift taking place under the peak is integrated as a quasi-triangular area. However, this effect is insignificant unless baseline drift is extreme. Thus, in most analyses, additional instrumental sophistication in terms of a baseline correction under a peak, based on, for example, a projection of the rate prevailing just prior to the peak, does not prove worthwhile. The exceptions, as previously discussed, are in the cases in which one can determine a program of baseline correction such as linear rise in certain temperature-programmed applications or exponential decays in severe cases of tailing peaks. In these cases, the equipment incorporates an adjustable programmer to compensate for baseline effects during peaks as well as between peaks.

2. *Distortion* in reproduction of the input signal is another source of error. In the typical digital integrator for gas chromatography, these errors concern deviations from linearity. In specific cases such as electronic capture detectors, Beer's law detectors, etc., the error would also include any errors in function conversion in transforming the signal to a linear form prior to integration. If one is sampling a signal to reconstruct it accurately, errors of this type are the primary errors since the system is essentially a digital voltmeter. In area measurement, however, the effect of these errors is reduced. Linearity errors are primarily reproducible errors from run to run and therefore will not significantly affect reproducibility of area measurements. They are a serious problem, nonetheless, when analysis results are interpreted in terms of peak area ratios.

3. *Errors in peak detection* are of minor concern in normal operation. If the peak detection system is marginal in a given application these errors can, of course, be serious; e.g., on some runs the peak may be missed entirely. If baseline control is good, however, the errors which occur due to missing starting and ending tips of a peak are secondary effects.

4. *Stability and long-term drift* of the digital integrator itself are best discussed in terms of repeatability. In other words, if one obtains excellent reproducibility of area measurements from day to day, the stability is acceptable. The instrumental techniques used in the analog circuits of

modern digital integrators are those of transistorized d.c. amplifiers, chopper stabilized. These are the techniques employed in strip chart recorders, and the digital integrator system will certainly exhibit at least the stability associated with the strip chart recorder. Long-term drift and stability characteristics of the integrator generally are far superior to those of the chromatograph itself.

5. *Area count resolution.* One area count in the digital integrator must not be a significant percentage of peak area; otherwise the inherent ± 1-count ambiguity in area values will severely limit accuracy on small, sharp peaks. High count rates for large signals therefore are of considerable importance in automatic digital integrators. Selection of the integrator by the user should be undertaken to assure that the count resolution is consistent with the resolution demanded on the smallest peak of interest.

When all of the major features affecting accuracy are summed up, the typical repeatabilities obtained by the properly designed digital integrator are ± 0.1–0.2% of area value for peaks above $100\ \mu V$ high (10 divisions on a 1-mV chart).

E. Design Characteristics of a Good Integrator

We are now in a position to recapitulate the design characteristics that the user will require in a satisfactory automatic digital integrator. These are:

1. *Compatibility with Other Equipment.* The input circuits of the integrator should be properly isolated and of high impedance so that any type of commercial gas chromatograph output circuit may be connected directly to the integrator. In addition, isolation of the integrator must be proper so that there is no interaction between the integrator, its printer or other output devices, the recorder, and the gas chromatograph.

2. *Wide Dynamic Range.* To be fully automatic, the integrator must be able to recognize a wide range of peak sizes, i.e., pick and compute accurately both very small and very large peaks without the necessity for operator adjustment of controls. Peaks with a height ratio of 10,000 to 1 can be processed by present wide range integrators.

3. *Flexibility of Peak Detection Circuits.* The peak detection circuits should incorporate the following provisions: (*a*) a control to provide various settings for rejection of significant baseline wandering or drift; (*b*) a control to provide adjustable rejection of various types of high frequency noise; (*c*) an adjustable control to set a minimum level below which peaks will not be integrated; (*d*) independent controls to permit separation of shoulders on leading and trailing edges of peaks; and (*e*) a control to reject all peaks below a given count is optional.

4. Adequate Peak Detection Sensitivity. Many integrators simply do not have adequate sensitivity to detect the onset and end of very small, slow peaks. For example, for a 10-μV/sec slope sensitivity, peaks which are 100 μV high in triangular form (in other words, peaks which are actually 10% of a 1-mV full-scale range) and which take over 10 sec of rise time to their crest cannot be integrated at all. Acceptable integrators will have a maximum slope sensitivity to start and stop integration of 0.1–0.2 μV/sec.

5. High Resolution. The integrator should have a high enough count rate at maximum signal so that for the smallest peaks of interest the inherent plus or minus one count ambiguity error in area value will not be a limitation upon accuracy. It is to be noted that high resolution in signal measurement also permits precise automatic baseline control. Commercial automatic integrators now provide for count rates up to 4000 counts/ sec per mV.

6. Precise Automatic Baseline Control. Accurate integration of very small peaks with a high degree of repeatability is not possible without very precise baseline stabilization. Even a small offset will cause a relatively large error in area. The correction should be automatic, i.e., the need for frequent manual adjustments of baseline is not compatible with automatic data reduction.

7. Electronic Memory. The fastest types of outputs from the digital integrator, such as parallel entry printers, have a "dead time" resulting from data hold and/or cycle of operation times. Any loss of counts during these "dead times" is not tolerable on sharp, narrow peaks, particularly overlapping peaks. These conditions, of course, often occur in capillary column chromatography. A built-in one-peak memory is therefore desirable.

8. Flexibility of Output Options. A properly designed integrator will be able to present its digital results to a wide variety of output devices which can be selected according to the particular requirements at hand. These include a digital listing printer, an electrical typewriter, teletype machines, a paper tape punch, a card punch, and digital magnetic recorders.

9. Electronic Design Techniques. The maximum of reliability and ease of maintenance and repairs is facilitated by the use of solid state electronic circuits and of a plug-in modular design. The plug-in concept allows the service engineer to effect repairs in many cases simply by replacement of circuit modules, which can be done *in situ* in the laboratory, thus minimizing down time. The use of these techniques also improves compatibility with other instruments, compatibility being defined as the ability to accept signals from any commercial variety of gas chromatograph and to present signals to any type of digital output device.

F. How to Choose an Integrator

The typical analytical chemist will not be a specialist in modern electronics and often will not have the time, the training, or the inclination to study properly and fully understand the specifications of automatic electronic integrators. He can, however, specify the characteristics that he requires from an instrument with sufficient clarity so that the instrument manufacturer can recommend the proper instrument for the specific problems at hand.

The first step in considering the purchase of automatic digital electronic equipment is to define the problems on which the equipment will be applied. A set of typical records should be collected, and the following steps should be taken:

1. Tabulate range of peak durations, noting particularly the sharpest peak present and the closest peak spacing.

2. Measure the average slope (height over rise time) of the broadest, smallest peak of interest present. This will determine the maximum slope sensitivity of the integrator.

3. Note any unresolved peak situations. Small peaks on tails are of particular concern.

4. Note typical noise background conditions on the chromatograms.

5. Determine the widest range of peak heights that must be processed on a single analysis.

6. Determine the smallest peak area that must be determined and specify the resolution with which it should be measured. This will set the count resolution of the digital integrator.

The more complete the specifications presented to the instrumentation engineer, the greater the likelihood of a selection of the proper data processing device.

The versatility of the digital integrator is, as one might suspect, related to price. If one has a specific problem at hand, it may be feasible to purchase a lower price integrator of more limited specifications; however, it should not be expected that this machine can be applied to a wider range of problems which may arise in the future. The most general approach, then, is to select an integrator with maximum flexibility, with an input dynamic range consistent with the range of peak heights which must be handled automatically in a given analysis. The significant variable here is peak height, not peak area. All digital integrators incorporate analog electronic circuits to interface between the chromatograph output and the digital circuitry. To add additional area count resolution, one has to add only additional electronic counter stages; however, the electronic input circuits must be capable of handling without distortion and without manual adjustment the range of peak amplitudes present in the chromatogram run.

Once again, the analytical chemist should not approach selection of digital equipment with the concept that no change can be made in present analysis conditions and that the digital equipment must be able to perform well despite any defects in the analyses. The problem should be treated as a system problem so that the entire operation from sample injection to listing of answers is studied as a unit operation to be optimized. A final word of caution: the user should evaluate the integrator in his lab on his problems prior to setting final specifications.

III. Magnetic Tape Systems for Analytical Data Processing

The techniques for recording and storing of gas chromatograph signals on satellite magnetic tape recorders for subsequent centralized data processing has now come into relatively wide use. The tape recordings may be brought to a centrally located digital integrator and processed, thus resulting in a lower unit cost of digitizing equipment per chromatograph.

Portable tape recorders are used to record chromatograms as they are run. The electrical output of the chromatograph is connected directly to the magnetic recorder input. Recorder design is illustrated by the block diagram of Figure 6-13. The recorder, just as the digital integrator, incorporates a high impedance transistorized instrumentation amplifier, thus insuring no interaction between the recorder and the chromatograph. Wide dynamic range circuits are included in the recorder electronics. The chromatograph chart recorder can be connected to the output of the amplifier of the tape recorder so that the chart sees the same signals as the magnetic recorder, thus serving as a monitor to insure proper hookup, correct polarity, and proper operation of the critical analog circuits of the magnetic tape recorder. Of course, in routine work an on-the-spot visual chart record may not be essential and the chart recorder may be eliminated. The tape recorder system will incorporate voltage-to-frequency converter circuits such as those used in the digital integrator to convert the analytical signal to a train of pulses of varying frequency. These pulses are fed to the magnetic recording head and recorded on tape in pulse density modulation form. Tape recorders are available in models with one, two, or three simultaneous channels for data recording. Typically, an auxiliary noise cancelling signal is simultaneously recorded. On playback, this noise cancelling signal will be used to minimize baseline instability, thus insuring reliable detection and accurate integration of small peaks. The primary limitation on tape recorder performance when pulse density modulation methods are used is short-term speed variation of the tape transport mechanism, both on record and playback, since after demodulation playback speed variations appear as signal amplitude fluctuations. These are effectively eliminated by the noise cancelling technique.

The feasibility of using magnetic tape recording on gas chromatography depends on the tape recorder selected. If high quality instrumentation tape

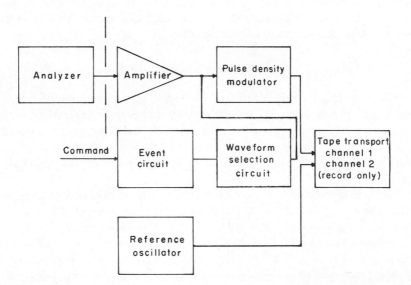

Fig. 6-13. Block diagram of magnetic tape recorder for chromatography.

recorders are used, the cost of the tape recorder may equal or exceed the cost of an individual digital integrator for each chromatograph. With proper techniques such as the noise cancelling described above, inexpensive stereo hi-fi tape transports can be employed. By providing a range of tape recording speeds, recording times up to 24 hr can be obtained with a 7-in. tape reel. For the technician, the operation simply consists of loading the tape reel and engaging a tape drive lever or pushing a tape start button; then the sample is inserted by the technician and an "event" button is actuated. This can be done either manually or from a remote control signal, thus recording start time of a run on the tape as a change of wave form. Recording continues automatically until run end, at which time the tape transport is stopped by manual control or by programmer. At the end of a reel of tape, tape transport stop is automatic, associated with an end-of-reel sensing circuit. Completed tapes are then directly compatible with the central processing facility. Typical tape recorder packages are shown in Figure 6-14.

Usually it is desirable to record identification data on the magnetic tape prior to an analysis. This is done by means of front panel switches so that the operator may introduce a series of numerical digits to indicate, for example, sample number, run number, sample type, time, etc. These digits are recorded serially on the magnetic tape by setting a switch and pressing

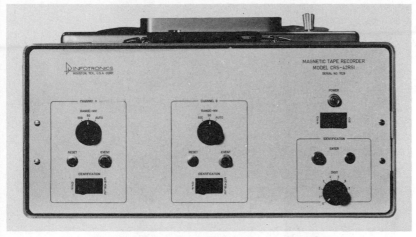

Fig. 6-14. Typical magnetic tape recorder unit.

a button. Any number of digits may be recorded. On playback, this information will be recovered, decoded, and printed serially in a form in which it can be readily distinguished from the analysis results themselves, as shown in Figure 6-15. Recorded identification data eliminate the possibility of confusion of tapes at the playback center.

In the tape recorder the design emphasis is on excellent linearity throughout the system, just as it would be in the digital integrator. However, in special applications, for example, recording of amino acid analyzer data, function generators may be incorporated in the recorder itself so that the detector signals can be linearized prior to tape recording. Tape recorded chromatograms form a convenient memory for large volumes of analytical data. Recorded tapes may be processed in a central playback at any time, i.e., the analyses are always readily available for possible reevaluation at a later date. Also, several playback runs can be made from a single tape, which is often useful in optimization of integrator settings and improvement of results in particularly difficult problems.

The central data processing system will incorporate all instrumentation necessary to reproduce analyzer signals from the magnetic tapes, to detect and integrate the peaks, correct the baselines, and present the results in digital form. The subsystems are: (*1*) the *tape playback unit*, which must be compatible with tapes from all types of recorders to be used at the

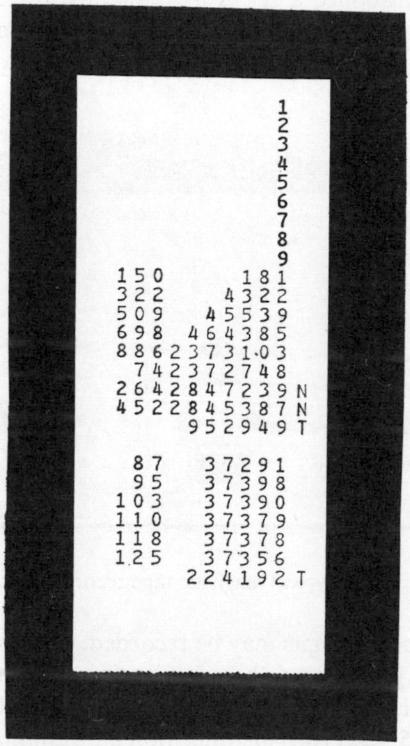

Fig. 6-15. Printed identification data and analysis results from tape playback.

chromatograph; (*2*) an *automatic digital integrator* (incorporating an automatic baseline corrector); and (*3*) a *digital printer* or other output device. The tape playback will be identical to that used in the portable units. The general playback system design is explained in block diagram of Figure 6-16. Magnetic head pickup amplifiers read the tape traces, and both noise cancelling and data signals are demodulated by frequency-to-voltage conversion, thus reproducing the originally recorded signals very accurately. These can be fed to a chart recorder for monitoring as well as to the digital integrator. The noise cancelling signal is, in effect, subtracted from the analytical signal so that the effects of tape speed variation during recording and playback are minimized. The corrected signal goes directly to the digital integrator. Peak recognition and area integration proceed exactly as if the signal were coming directly from the analyzer. The digital integrator, of course, can also be used for on-line operation directly connected to the chromatograph as well as tape playback operation. This means that a system which would include one recorder, one playback, and one integrator could be used as a two-integrator system. The integrator could be connected directly to the chromatograph when tapes are not being processed. Playback speed of recorded tapes is usually at 7.5 in./sec. The tape recording may be at any speed from 7.5 to $1\frac{7}{8}$ in. or down to $\frac{15}{32}$ in./sec. The time to process a chromatogram may be as little as $\frac{1}{16}$ of the

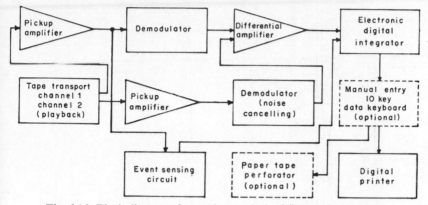

Fig. 6-16. Block diagram of central tape playback/integration system.

recording time; thus a single playback unit can then process tapes from many analyzers in less than the original recording time. The digital integrator can employ expanded wide dynamic range circuitry, and with automatic peak detection will be as sensitive as if the integrator were connected directly to the chromatograph. Timing of the playback operation is controlled by recording a time signal on the magnetic tape and decoding and counting the pulses of the timing signal on playback. One thus obtains an accurate time base just as if the data were originally recorded, and the effects of tape speed variation are eliminated.

Baseline stabilization at the start of the tape playback and proper baseline control during the run are very important. When the event command is decoded during playback, an automatic baseline drift corrector in the integrator is turned on in the fast correction mode. This quickly establishes zero electrical input to the area counter in the integrator. There are a variety of selectable correction rates to optimize for various analyses and to accommodate changes in tape playback speed. Baseline correction

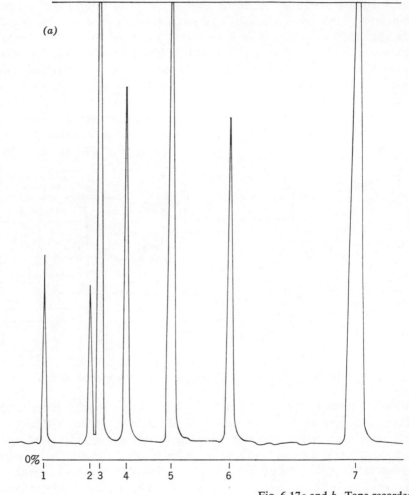

Fig. 6-17*a* and *b*. Tape-recorded

continues on a self monitoring basis through the playback just as in an on-line digital integrator. As in most on-line digital integrator applications, results from the tape playback runs usually are listed in columnar form on adding machine tape. Each peak area is associated with peak retention time on the same line. All of the formats, however, such as electric typewriter, teletype machine, punch paper tape, punch cards, or magnetic tape can also be prepared. Playback systems often are packaged in desk console form to provide a convenient writing space for the operator.

A major design objective in a magnetic tape system, just as in a digital

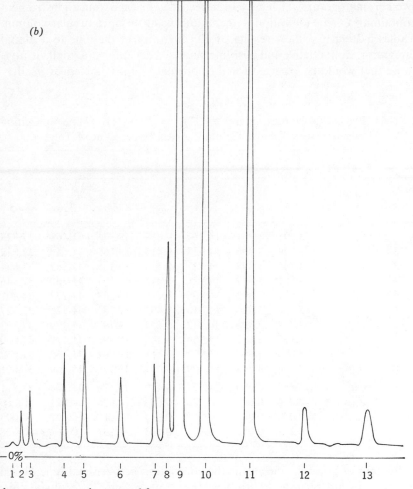

chromatograms—chart record form.

integrator, is a high degree of accuracy and reproducibility of results. Typically, one can record chromatograms, play them back and process peaks just as small as in real-time operation. Repeated playbacks of a recorded tape yield very small area variations. Once a chromatogram has been stored it can be replayed many times with the same integrator settings to yield the same results within a very small deviation. It can, of course, be played back several times with different integrator settings to emphasize particular peak size ranges and to assist in selecting the optimum control settings for a given type of problem. In Figures 6-17a and 6-17b are shown two chromatograms which have been recorded on tape from an instrument containing a flame ionization detector and using an open tubular column. Tables 6-2 and 6-3 show results of 10 playbacks of the tape to a digital integrator. Both relative and absolute standard deviation are small vis-à-vis those that would be expected for the chromatographic system by itself.

TABLE 6-2

CRS-40 Playback, Chromatogram *a* (Fig. 6-17) (4:1). Flame Ionization Detector, Open Tubular Column; Areas as Per Cent of Total

	Peak no.	1	2	3	4	5	6	7
Play-back	Retention time (sec.)	199	238	297	269	308	356	465
1		3.595	3.891	14.910	9.439	19.176	11.168	37.825
2		3.599	3.896	14.929	9.415	19.165	11.159	37.834
3		3.585	3.899	14.932	9.413	19.165	11.162	37.844
4		3.589	3.897	14.928	9.414	19.167	11.162	37.846
5		3.594	3.892	14.906	9.445	19.187	11.177	37.801
6		3.580	3.890	14.910	9.437	19.182	11.171	37.827
7		3.577	3.893	14.912	9.654	19.199	11.179	37.793
8		3.575	3.892	14.908	9.448	19.196	11.178	37.800
9		3.683	3.897	14.927	9.411	19.161	11.160	37.862
10		3.596	3.891	14.909	9.451	19.179	11.169	37.821
	Mean	3.587	3.894	14.917	9.433	19.179	11.169	37.821
	Range	0.024	0.007	0.026	0.043	0.038	0.021	0.080
	σ_{abs} (est.)	0.008	0.002	0.008	0.014	0.012	0.007	0.003
	σ_{rel}	0.223	0.051	0.054	0.143	0.131	0.063	0.008

Perhaps of more significance is the correlation between real time digital integration and recorded/reproduced tape processing. To evaluate this, one computes in real time using a digital integrator and simultaneously records a chromatogram on magnetic tape. The tapes are then replayed several times, thus giving a check on playback repeatability as well as on the difference between real time and tape system results. Figure 6-18 and Table 6-4 present results of such an experiment. Figure 6-18 is a reproduction of the original chromatogram in chart record form; Table 6-4 is a presentation of peak areas integrated from two digital integrators connected in parallel to the chromatograph, operating in real time, one with and one without a baseline drift corrector. Also tabulated are two successive playbacks from a magnetic tape recorded simultaneously. All

TABLE 6-3

CRS-40 Playback, Chromatogram b (Fig. 6-17) (4:1)
Flame Ionization Detector, Open Tubular Column; Areas as Per Cent of Total

Peak no.	1	2	3	4	5	6	7	8	9	10	11	12	13
Retention time (sec)	112	117	123	150	167	198	226	237	247	268	306	352	404
Playback													
1	0.036	0.359	0.591	1.537	1.824	1.701	2.265	6.386	40.988	24.118	16.831	1.407	1.960
2	0.037	0.357	0.589	1.536	1.823	1.739	2.275	6.386	40.962	24.115	16.835	1.378	1.966
3	0.036	0.358	0.592	1.534	1.822	1.734	2.272	6.385	40.960	24.114	16.837	1.406	1.948
4	0.035	0.351	0.589	1.538	1.826	1.744	2.279	6.388	40.965	24.123	16.792	1.417	1.943
5	0.035	0.357	0.590	1.536	1.823	1.735	2.273	6.385	40.955	24.114	16.843	1.402	1.948
6	0.036	0.359	0.590	1.537	1.825	1.744	2.276	6.385	40.938	24.110	16.845	1.405	1.951
7	0.035	0.358	0.590	1.534	1.822	1.736	2.275	6.383	40.936	24.109	16.853	1.409	1.965
8	0.037	0.359	0.593	1.536	1.824	1.746	2.277	6.383	40.918	24.102	16.861	1.415	1.951
9	0.035	0.358	0.589	1.540	1.824	1.745	2.276	6.384	40.937	24.105	16.842	1.403	1.956
10	0.037	0.358	0.592	1.534	1.821	1.745	2.279	6.384	40.928	24.108	16.856	1.413	1.941
Mean	0.036	0.358	0.591	1.536	1.823	1.737	2.275	6.385	40.949	24.112	16.890	1.405	1.953
σ_{abs} (est.)	0.001	0.001	0.001	0.002	0.001	0.015	0.003	0.002	0.023	0.007	0.022	0.017	0.007
σ_{rel}	2.78	0.28	0.17	0.13	0.05	0.86	0.13	0.03	0.06	0.03	0.13	1.21	0.36

values have been reduced to per cent composition. The playback values check almost perfectly, and the differences between on-line digital integration and playback processing are quite small. The particular example chosen is one of relatively sharp, fairly closely spaced peaks from an

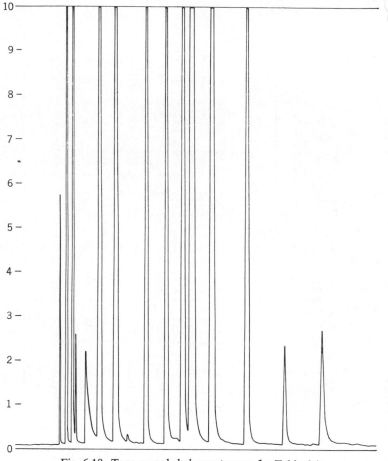

Fig. 6-18. Tape-recorded chromatogram for Table 6-4.

open tubular column, flame ionization detector chromatographic system. Clearly the recoding and playback integration system is just as applicable to broad peaks of long duration. Indeed, the use of the tape recorder in playback with playback recoding at high speed will enhance the performance of an automatic integrator for very small, gently sloping peaks.

Conventional specification tables for this type of magnetic tape data processing system are not very meaningful when stated in the usual terms of signal dynamic range, linearity, etc., since several design parameters must be optimized for the analytical peak integration application. Without this optimization, a much more expensive tape recorder could be expected to produce poor results. Specifications can be stated most meaningfully by

TABLE 6-4

Comparison of On-Line Integrator and Magnetic Tape System Results[a]

Peak no.	Peak crest retention time (sec)	On line CRS-11HS	On line CRS-11HSB	CRS-40T Playback 1 ×4 speed	CRS-40T Playback 2 ×4 speed
1	333	0.35	0.34	0.34	0.34
2	350	3.18	3.18	3.18	3.18
3	365	6.42	6.45	6.45	6.45
4	374	0.19	0.17	0.17	0.17
5	399	0.62	0.60	0.59	0.58
6	432	19.92	20.00	19.95	19.96
7	472	20.90	20.97	20.97	20.96
8	504	0.03	0.01	0.01	0.01
9	548	3.81	3.80	3.80	3.80
10	599	3.41	3.39	3.39	3.40
11	642	6.00	6.00	6.00	6.00
12	667	21.41	21.45	21.46	21.47
13	716	9.24	9.24	9.26	9.26
14	802	3.27	3.23	3.24	3.25
15	898	0.44	0.41	0.42	0.41
16	991	0.76	0.71	0.71	0.72
17	126	0.05	0.05	0.06	0.04

[a] Results obtained from integration of chromatogram of Figure 6-18. All values expressed as per cent of total sample.

presenting actual examples of analyses. In other words, to evaluate the tape system, tests must be carried out on specific problems. Since the analytical chemist is interested in repeatability and accuracy as evidenced in *his* laboratory on *his* problem, this approach is probably the only practical one. Selection of the optimum digital integration system will depend upon specific operating requirements. A maximum flexibility on-line digital integrator for each analyzer represents the ultimate capability. All results are available on the spot, and maximum flexibility performance for each analysis is insured. In practice, of course, each on-line integrator can usually be shared between two or more chromatographs which do not operate simultaneously. Several analyzers can be connected to a single integrator and the chromatographs to be processed at a given time can be selected by means of a front panel switch. The unit cost, of course, is significantly reduced if one uses a central tape playback with a single integrator and several satellite tape recorders. Since the concept of sharing an integrator between two or more chromatographs applies as well to tape recorders, the actual unit cost of digital integrator equipment per analyzer can be quite low. This is particularly true if multichannel tape recorders are employed. This provides a cost saving which, however, is achieved at some loss in operating flexibility. Each data channel on the tape can be recorded independently, and playback also can be completely inde-pendent. However, during the recording, attention must be given to total tape time if one is recording a series of analyses starting at different times and of different durations on the same magnetic tape. Of course, physical location of the chromatographs must also be taken into consideration. In routine operations one can come reasonably close to realizing the improve-ments in time predicted from playback speedup. In other words, the times to handle tapes will be small compared to the playback time. The number of chromatographs that can be processed by a single playback center clearly is a function of chromatograph loading factors. Since some down time is typical, on a single shift operation, tapes from up to seven or eight capillary column chromatographs can be processed. When the analyses incorporate slower, broader peaks, as in most thermal conductivity appli-cations, and a lower tape recording speed and a greater ratio of speedup in tape playback can be employed, records from up to 20 or 30 chromato-graphs can be processed in a single shift in a data processing center. Clearly, if the work load is sufficient, the central equipment can be employed on a multishift operation. The playback center usually should incorporate an inexpensive chart recorder. One can then initially play back and get a monitor record, which will enable the operator to optimize the settings of the digital processing equipment. Playback system performance can be monitored adequately by replaying each day a test tape provided by the manufacturer. To check out the complete system of the recorder plus the playback, one records a standard sample chromatogram and processes this tape through the playback center at regular intervals. Competent technicians are, of course, required to operate the playback center and this labor cost should be added to the basic equipment cost in any economic evaluation. The cost of the magnetic tapes normally are not of great significance since in most cases only a limited amount of tapes will be retained for future review. Most tapes will be erased and used many times. At the chromatographs themselves, the technicians who inject samples, purge the system, etc., can handle the magnetic tapes easily and no additional labor will be required. With a tape data collection system and a playback center in routine operation, some reduction in total labor requirements may be anticipated.

Some advantages of the magnetic tape systems vis-à-vis on-line digital integration include the following:

1. A lower net cost of digital equipment per chromatograph.

2. An ability to add relatively sophisticated computing and data analysis equipment in the playback center at a lower unit cost. For example, the ability to apply correction factors and normalize data may be added to the playback system. The cost per chromatogram will be reasonable, whereas otherwise it might not be economical to add this extra capability to several on-line digital integrators.

3. Records are available for multiple playback so that data processing and presentation of these results can be optimized.

4. Even though the integration operation is off-line (i.e., done independently of and after the running of the actual analyses), physical size of the equipment, the staff required, and the total investment are relatively small vis-à-vis the digital computer installation. Thus such a system can be situated in, or close to, an analytical laboratory with a consequent minimum delay in processing of results. Operating results suggest that in any analytical laboratory operation with a reasonable volume there is a place for a magnetic tape system. It is particularly useful, of course, in routine analyses with a considerable record volume. The multiple replay possibility adds considerable editing capability for difficult analyses. Data reduction programs can be revised on the spot and optimized with another tape playback. Addition of a modest amount of arithmetic capability plus paper tape handling equipment permits execution of a full-scale analytical data reduction operation as typically done; that is, peak detection, area integration and peak timing, application of peak correction factors, normalization to obtain percentage composition, and printing of answers in numerical and tabular form. This capability can be added in the lab at a relatively low cost and forms an attractive alternative in terms of logistics and economics to processing by a digital computing system.

The equipment in Figure 6-19 is a typical complete magnetic tape playback center. The correction factors to be applied to given peaks can be set on panel switches and changed by the operator from run to run. The application of the correction factors to peaks and groups of peaks is controlled by retention time. A suite of retention-time programs is prepared on punched paper tape. As the analysis runs, the tape programmer controls the change of correction factor at preset retention times. As peak areas are being accumulated digitally, correction factors are applied by scaling techniques, so that the area computed by the digital integrator is a corrected area. To normalize one requires accumulation of a corrected total area, as in the following equation:

$$\%A'_j = \frac{a_j A_j}{\sum\limits_n a_i A_i} \tag{6-2}$$

where A'_j = weighted, normalized area of the jth peak
A_j = raw area of the jth peak
a_j = correction factor for the jth peak
A_i = raw area of individual peaks, $i = 1 - n$
a_i = correction factor for the ith peak, $i = 1 - n$
n = number of peaks in a run

In practical operation this means that magnetic recorded tapes are played back two times: once to accumulate the weighted total area which is the denominator in the above equation and the second time to normalize the results and present them in printed tabular form. This dual playback

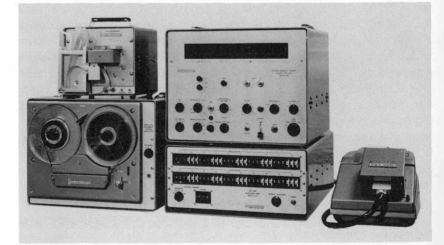

Fig. 6-19. Complete magnetic tape playback and data processing system.

operation is accomplished entirely automatically by automatic logic control of the tape playback deck. The operating techniques, then, may be reviewed:

1. At the chromatograph. The operator loads the tape, presses an event button and the chromatogram is recorded. Before or after recording the chromatogram the operator may insert any type of identification data required directly on the tape recorder. The tapes must be physically carried to the central location for processing. As an alternative, tapes at the chromatogram can be controlled remotely in the central system so that upon command from the central system a recorded chromatogram can be played back directly to the central system for processing.

2. At the central system. Here the tape recorded chromatograms from various locations are loaded onto the tape playback system, a start button is pressed, and the tape playback proceeds automatically. In the simplest system this consists of automatic detection and integration of peaks, baseline correction, and printing of results. In the more complicated systems, such as were shown in Figure 6-19, correction factor programming and normalization are added, and with automatic control the tape is played back to obtain printed answers in the form of tables with the unknown constitutents being expressed as percent of total sample.

IV. Use of Digital Computer Systems in Gas Chromatography

Within the past year there has been increasing emphasis on the use of digital computer systems to process the gas chromatograph data. As mentioned at the outset of this chapter, this can be accomplished by sampling the chromatographs and converting the data to computer form, and then processing them in the computer on an off-line basis. As an alternative, a computer system may be connected directly to a multiplicity of chromatographs, carrying out the processing in real time. The feasibility of real time analyses will depend on the number of chromatographs to be processed, the number of total peaks to be identified and computed, and the complexity of the various analyses to be handled. The computer in such a system is associated with an input scanning, multiplexing, and analog/digital conversion system. A high speed scanning system goes from chromatograph to chromatograph taking a quick sample of the amplitude of the analytical signal. It must be able to scan all chromatographs connected to it and return to the original chromatograph in an interval (ΔT) short enough so that the next sample taken is closely spaced enough to permit accurate reconstruction of the analytical signal. The sampled signals will then be run into a high speed analog to digital converter, and each individual sample will be converted from a voltage or current measurement to a digital form in a language understandable to the computer. The data now are in multiplexed form. Each sample word typically will consist of a number identifying the particular chromatograph followed by the data value. A data frame will be made up of samples from all the chromatographs to be scanned. That is, one encounters first the sample at time t_i on chromatograph 1, then the sample at $t_{(i+\Delta t)}$ on chromatograph 2 and so on, up to the sample $t_{(i+n\Delta t)}$ on chromatograph n, and then returning to the sample at $t_{(i+\Delta T)}$ on chromatograph 1 and so on. These data are fed directly to the computer memory or to an off-line memory such as punched paper tape or digital magnetic tape. A computer program may be devised to pick the beginnings of peaks, detect the crest of peaks, identify the end of peaks, and compute the peak areas. Mathematical operators take the place of the automatic peak detector settings in an on-line digital integrator. In the computer programs used to date, simple linear mathematical operators are used. It should be noted that the mathematical operator can be shown to have a $1:1$ theoretical correspondence with the electrical circuit operator used in the on-line digital integrator. This, of course, means that mathematical operators must be changed for analyses of different speeds and different noise characteristics. This must be accomplished by a change in the computer program rather than by the setting of a front panel control as is the case with a real time digital integrator. Sampled signals of baseline between peaks are, in addition, collected by the computer and a correction program can be devised based on trends of baseline reading and baseline values before and after peaks, so that a computational program can remove the baseline contributions to peak signals. If one encounters a series of peaks and does not have an opportunity to observe the baseline, as is the case in unresolved peaks, the computer is faced with the same limitations as an on-line digital integrator. It must make some assumptions about the form of the baseline, and these assumptions will be similar to those discussed above in connection with linear and exponential decay correction programs. The computer is well suited for the simple arithmetic that is necessary in multiplication of correction factors and normalization of results. Problems arise in determining the correction factor program. In very simple analyses, counting the number of peaks provides sufficient criteria needed to change the correction factor. In most practical problems, however, noise present may cause erratic variations in the signal so that the use of peak number alone as a correction factor program is insufficient. Usually, therefore, peak correction factors are programmed as a function of retention time. The computer stores a program of retention time zones in which correction factors are to be applied. Clearly this program is dependent on the stability of retention times from run to run.

The computer, as noted above, is ideally suited for the routine arithmetic operations and has this advantage over on-line digital integration equipment. To incorporate arithmetic capability in the latter may result in an untenable increase in the cost of each individual unit of equipment. It should be emphasized, however, that the computer data interpretation is not accomplished by black magic. The programs for peak recognition and baseline correction will be based on the use of well-known mathematical operator techniques. The more complex the operator, the more memory will be required for the program and for storage of intermediate computational results, thus limiting the number of chromatographs which can be connected on-line to a given computer. Furthermore, if analysis conditions change, that is, if peak separation deteriorates or signal/noise ratio deteriorates, the mathematical operators chosen for a given analysis will no longer apply, just as the control of settings for a real time digital integrator will not apply. One therefore will start to receive erroneous data printouts from the computer. With an on-line machine the solution is simply to change the control knob settings, or with magnetic playback recording data one can make multiple playbacks of the tape to optimize the digitizer settings. In the computer, the program must of course be changed as the analysis conditions change. In substance this means that many analyses will require considerable human operator editing of data. The optimum application for the on-line digital computer system then would appear to be in process chromatography where analysis conditions have been optimized as far as possible. In these applications one more often finds clearly resolved peaks and stable baselines. Application would also be fruitful in routine analytical labs where again the analytical procedures have been refined. In research chromatography, where in a single laboratory one encounters a wide range of analyses and analyses in which conditions have not been improved sufficiently to apply in process chromatography or routine quantitative analyses, an on-line system will have much less applicability. A wide variety and changes of an analysis conditions will perhaps require too much editing of the computer programming and too many reruns. In this instance, if one is to employ the digital computer system, it is more reasonable to sample, code the data and prepare a hard copy on punched paper tape, magnetic tape, or punched cards, then doing the computer processing off-line. A further comment on computer systems is that computers presently being used are capable of many more operations and contain much greater computational flexibility than is required in the usual chromatograph analysis operation which involves simply programmed application of correction factors, normalization, and occasionally some scaling or very simple additional arithmetic. In other fields—for example, in the collection and processing of seismic data in geophysical exploration—it has been found that a specially designed digital computer system yields better results and lower unit cost of operation than a general purpose computer applied to the problem. This probably will turn out to be the case in the automatic correction and processing of data from analytical instruments.

V. Future Developments

It can certainly be said that the application of modern electronics and automatic signal detection and processing in gas chromatography is but in its infancy; only a small fraction of the gas chromatographs in use are equipped with digital readout. The trend toward use of convenient digital presentation and of automatic digital data processing may then be expected to increase. The specific developments that one might anticipate would include the following:

1. Advanced circuit techniques, such as integrated circuitry, will be applied in digital integrators, and there will be development of lower cost, smaller size digital modules to be used with gas chromatographs. It seems clear that noncentralized, small laboratories will not be able in the foreseeable future to utilize the services of large computer data collection systems. The need for a lower cost digital integrator or peak height digitizer of limited flexibility is then clear. Along with this, one may expect increasing development of small special-purpose computers and programmers intended to accomplish relatively simple data reduction of conventional gas chromatographic analysis, i.e., peak correction and normalization The typical in-lab data processing problem is as follows:

a. To provide automatic peak detection at reasonable cost connected to many chromatographs.

b. To carry out the full computations, usually

$$\% = (a_i A_i)/(\sum_n a_i A_i) \tag{6-3}$$

$$i = 1 - n \tag{6-4}$$

where a_i = peak correction factors

A_i = raw peak areas

n = number of peaks

$\sum_n a_i A_i$ = the weighted total sample value

c. To present results in tabular form as shown in Figure 6-24. One may anticipate development of digital integrators and small computers packaged as a unit at a price attractive to the analytical chemist operating in a small laboratory with a few gas chromatographs.

2. Parallel with this trend will be the increasing use of complex digital computer systems, both on-line and off-line, with gas chromatographs and the necessary interface equipment. We are, after all, in the "computer age" and the glamor of general purpose computers for analytical data reduction will prove impossible to resist. Application is, of course, in its infancy and the next few years will see a true evaluation of this approach. The end result will be that the computer will find its rightful place which would seem to be, e.g., in routine work for process gas chromatography.

One may expect then that on-line digital computer systems, off-line digital computer systems, simple digital integrators, magnetic tape correction and processing systems could all exist side by side in the future. It should be emphasized that many problems will remain indigestible by the automatic digital equipment. A poor resolution of peaks, the presence of high levels of noise at the chromatograph output, etc., will require that certain messy analyses be processed by hand since they will require many subjective decisions on the part of the analyst. The important things to be summarized are that in a wide range of problems the data equipment will be a great boon to the analytical chemist—it will relieve him of a considerable amount of data reduction tedium and it will free the technician from continual monitoring of the analysis. It is not, however, a panacea solution to all analysis data reduction problems. Furthermore, the concept of the design of the entire system as a unit should receive increasing consideration. A decade from now, or perhaps a few years from now, it will probably be regarded as ridiculous to design an automatic digital integrator and a gas chromatograph as unrelated units and expect them to perform in optimum fashion together. The same applies to a general purpose computer connected directly to a variety of gas chromatographs. Considerable attention will have to be devoted there to the design of proper interface circuits. It makes little sense to couple gas chromatographs with output amplifiers of great distortion and limited dynamic range to a digital computer costing $150,000 or more. The beauty of automatic data handling will be lost if the original data to be processed are of poor quality and fidelity. The chemist, then, should not expect results superior to those that he himself is able to achieve in his analysis. A period of several years of evaluation and gradual evolution of advanced systems is to be expected. The usual problem of communications between instrument manufacturers speaking one language and the user, in this case the analytical chemist, speaking another language certainly will occur. If this is accompanied by overzealous sales efforts, the historical sequence of events in a new instrumentation development may be expected to apply here. That is, one first passes through the romance phase (or the glamour phase) in which one user obtains a new system and the others follow, each desirous of not being left behind. To this extent instrumentation fads exist just as clothing fads, although, happily, the cycle of duration of each fad is longer. This phase is followed by the disenchantment phase when the oversold user, often oversold partially by himself, finds that the automatic digital integrator or the on-line digital computer system will not solve all of his problems and that considerable care and planning is required to use it properly—that considerable monitoring and editing of results is essential. One then arrives at the stable operating phase in which the equipment is applied to the problems in which it is useful, with a full realization of both its limitations and its capabilities. This sequence of phases occurred a number of years ago in the application of on-line computer systems to process control in the petroleum and petrochemical industries particularly. And since human beings seem to learn poorly from experience, the same three-act drama will probably be played again with essentially the same cast of characters in the application of digital electronics to analytical chemistry.

References

1. J. M. Gill and H. M. McNair, *Varian Aerograph Research Notes*, Fall, 1965.
2. R. Kaiser, *Quantitative Auswertung* (*Chromatographie in der Gasphase*, Vol. 4), Bibliographisches Institut, Mannheim, 1965, pp. 156–177.
3. H. J. Jones, *Infotronics Corp. Application Notes*, No. 2, November, 1965.
4. H. J. Jones and D. W. Spence, "Automatic real time digital integration of amino acid peaks," 12th annual ANACHEM conference, Detroit, Michigan, October 3, 1964, *Infotronics Corp. Application Notes* No. 1.
5. Techmation, "L'integration automatique en chromatographie en phase gazeuse," *Application Paper* T-8, April, 1966.

CHAPTER 7

The Interpretation of Analytical Results; Qualitative and Quantitative Analysis

Leslie S. Ettre, *The Perkin-Elmer Corporation, Norwalk, Connecticut*

I. Introduction

When investigating samples with a gas chromatograph, the purpose of the task is to *analyze* the sample for its components, i.e., to determine "one or more ingredients of a substance either as to kind (*qualitative analysis*) or amount (*quantitative analysis*)."* This definition expresses the task of

* *Webster's New Collegiate Dictionary*, G. & C. Merriam Co., Springfield, Mass., 1959, p. 32.

the gas chromatographer and the problems in which he is continually involved: he has to interpret his analytical result, the chromatogram, and either determine what is the composition of his sample or calculate the concentration (amount) of the individual components in the sample.

This chapter deals with these two problems: how to identify the components to which the individual peaks correspond, and how to calculate from the chromatogram the concentration (amount) of the sample components.

II. Qualitative Analysis

Gas chromatography is primarily a separation process. If the column used for the separation is sufficiently specific, then theoretically each sample component can be separated from the others and indicated as an individual peak on the chromatogram. However, the chromatogram does not always indicate whether this is the case or not, and two or more components may emerge from the column at the same time resulting in one peak. Furthermore, even if all sample components are separated there is no absolute method of establishing exactly and without any doubt the particular substance to which each peak corresponds.

It is sometimes very difficult to establish whether the chromatographic peak corresponds to only one substance. The investigation of retention data tables or graphs can help in answering this question, because each type of column has a limited separation power, and one cannot expect, e.g., a short packed column to separate two substances which have a relative retention less than 1.1. The collection of retention data on two columns with different polarity further helps in finding components overlapped on one column, because it is less likely that the same peaks will overlap on different columns. However, the only real proof that peak overlapping has actually occurred is the investigation of the corresponding fraction with ancillary techniques (infrared, mass spectrometry, chemical reactions, etc.). These methods are discussed in Chapter 8.

Here, we will discuss briefly only those techniques which utilize retention data collected from known samples, and certain general rules concerning the retention of certain component groups.

A. Comparison of Retention Data

The comparison of retention data would appear to be the easiest method since the retention time of a given column is specific for any particular substance. In practice, however, there are many limitations in using absolute values for comparison.

These limitations concern mainly the fact that the reproducibility of (absolute) retention data depends on both the reproducibility of the column proper (e.g., its partition ratio) and the analytical conditions. Therefore, the *retention time* (t_R), or the *adjusted retention time* (t'_R), is very rarely used for identification purposes. The *retention volume* (V_R), the *adjusted retention volume* (V'_R), the *net retention volume* (V_N), and particularly the *specific retention volume* (V_g) (1) are less dependent than the retention times on the analytical conditions, and the specific retention volume is actually independent of column parameters. For convenience, the meaning of these values is repeated here:

$$t'_R = t_R - t_M \tag{7-1}$$

$$V_R = t_R F_c \tag{7-2}$$

$$V'_R = (t_R - t_M)F_c \tag{7-3}$$

$$j = \frac{3}{2} \frac{(p_i/p_o)^2 - 1}{(p_i/p_o)^3 - 1} \tag{7-4}$$

$$V_N = jV'_R \tag{7-5}$$

$$V_g = (V_N/w_L)(273.16/T) \tag{7-6}$$

where F_c = the volumetric flow rate at column outlet corrected to column temperature

t_M = the retention time of an unretarded substance ("air peak time" gas holdup time)

j = gas compressibility connection factor

p_i = carrier gas inlet pressure (absolute)

p_o = carrier gas outlet pressure (absolute)

w_L = the weight of liquid phase in the column

T = column temperature (°K)

Despite the fact that these values are less dependent on column and operating characteristics, their use was not generally accepted. The most widely used form of retention data expression is that *relative* to a certain standard. The relative retention (r),* proposed by James and Martin in their first paper (2), is given by:

$$r_{i,s} = \frac{t'_{R(i)}}{t'_{R(s)}} = \frac{V'_{R(i)}}{V'_{R(s)}} = \frac{V_{N(i)}}{V_{N(s)}} = \frac{V_{g(i)}}{V_{g(s)}} \tag{7-7}$$

where subscripts i and s refer to the respective values for the individual peak and the peak of the standard.

* Usually, the symbol r is used if the retention is expressed relative to a standard while the symbol α is used to express the relative retention of two adjacent peaks.

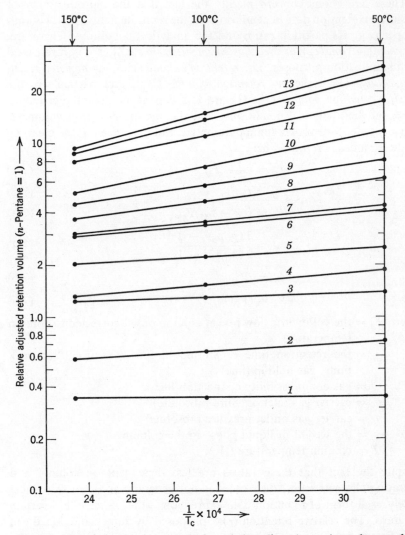

Fig. 7-1. The relationship between the log relative adjusted retention volume and the reciprocal of the absolute column temperature. Liquid phase: DC-200 silicone oil. After the data of Raupp (3). *1*, Methanol; *2*, ethanol; *3*, *tert*-butanol; *4*, *n*-propanol; *5*, *n*-hexane; *6*, benzene; *7*, cyclohexane; *8*, *n*-heptane; *9*, methylcyclohexane; *10*, toluene; *11*, *n*-octane; *12*, ethylbenzene; *13*, *p*-xylene.

If the standard is not an original component of the sample, it is conveniently mixed to it prior to the gas chromatographic analysis so that the respective values can be calculated directly from the chromatogram.

All retention data are *temperature dependent*, and therefore all data should be given at least at two (but more conveniently at three) different temperatures. If values at temperatures other than reported are necessary, a graphical method can help: the plot of the logarithm of the relative retention against the reciprocal of the absolute column temperature is linear. Figure 7-1 shows such plots for some hydrocarbons and alcohols using the relative retention values given by Raupp (3). Using such plots, relative retention values can be inter- and extrapolated for other temperatures.

In general, three rules should be considered in the choice of the standard for the determination of relative retentions: the standard should be easily available, its retention time should not be too small, and it should fall near the middle of the series of substances whose relative retentions are to be determined.

Tables on relative retention values of a series of compounds for different columns and at different temperatures can be found in the literature. The publications of Raupp (3), Tenney (4), Scholly and Brenner (5), Hively (6), and others are important in this respect. Kaiser in his book (7) collected a large number of literature data. The recent book by McReynolds (8) is the most comprehensive collection yet published. The *Journal of Gas Chromatography* publishes in each issue retention data submitted by practical gas chromatographers.

The application of retention data for peak identification is limited in that these data are characteristic but not specific. Therefore, in dubious cases, or if further confirmation is desired, relative retention data on *two different columns* (one polar and one nonpolar, or having different polarities) should be collected and examined. In this way, the identification can be more certain.

Figure 7-2 plots relative retention data for ethanol, ethyl acetate, and diethyl ether on two columns prepared with DC-200 silicone oil and Carbowax 1500 liquid phase respectively. It can be seen that the relative retention values on the only slightly polar silicone oil column are very close to each other; on the other hand, on the polar Carbowax 1500 column they are spread much more and even their order of elution has changed.

B. Special Plots of Retention Data

The retention values of substances belonging to certain homologous series can usually be related to various physical characteristics of the substances or to their structure. In a large number of cases, these plots actually

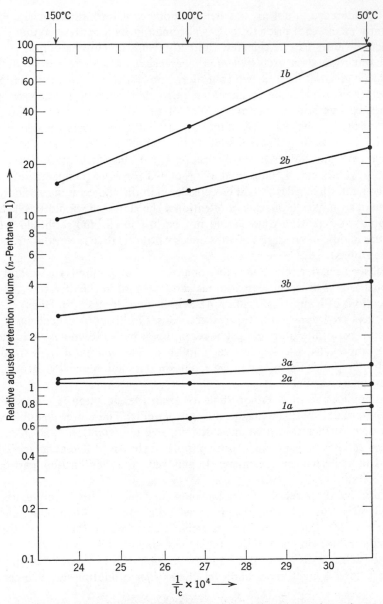

Fig. 7-2. The relationship between the log relative adjusted retention volume and the reciprocal of the absolute column temperature on two different columns. After the data of Raupp (3). Liquid phase: *a*, DC-200 silicone oil; *b*, Carbowax 1500 poly(ethylene glycol). Samples: *1*, ethanol; *2*, ethyl acetate; *3*, diethyl ether.

show a linear relationship while early members of the homologous series might deviate somewhat from the linear relationship (curvature of the plot). The existence of such plots means that if we know the identity of certain peaks in a multicomponent mixture, other peaks belonging to the same homologous series can frequently be related to the respective components.

Although plots for homologous series can be prepared for many physical values, two types of plots in particular are used widely for component identification: plots relating retention to carbon number and plots relating retention to boiling point.

It was observed first by James and Martin (2) that the plot of the logarithm of the adjusted retention time, volume, net retention volume, specific retention volume, or the relative retention against the number of carbon atoms in the molecule is linear for a given homologous series. Figure 7-3 gives some plots for a number of homologous series, utilizing the data of Scholly and Brenner (5).

Naturally, such a plot is only valid at a given temperature, and separate plots are necessary at each column temperature. This is illustrated in Figure 7-4, which gives the plots for normal paraffins at two temperatures.

The second most widely used plot relates the logarithm of the retention values to the boiling point of the individual substances belonging to one homologous series. Such plots also demonstrate one of the most important rules of gas chromatography: the order of elution on a nonpolar or slightly polar column is mainly a function of the boiling point of the sample components, and the chemical structure of the molecules is of little importance; while on a polar column, the chemical structure is critical. This fact is illustrated well in Figures 7-5 and 7-6. On the diisodecyl phthalate column, the plots corresponding to the different homologous series are close to each other; i.e., the separation between substances with similar boiling points but different molecular structure is poor. On the other hand, on the polar poly(ethylene glycol) column, the individual plots are fairly well separated from each other, and substances with similar boiling points but different molecular structures can be separated from each other.

C. Retention Plots on Two Columns

The measurement of retention data on two different columns of different polarity is very valuable for qualitative component identification. This was first described by James (9), who observed that when the retention volumes of aliphatic amines were plotted on two different columns, the respective points of each homologous series (primary, secondary, and tertiary amines) always gave a straight line. James and Martin (10), Pierotti et al. (11), and Lewis et al. (12) later demonstrated that it is more useful to plot

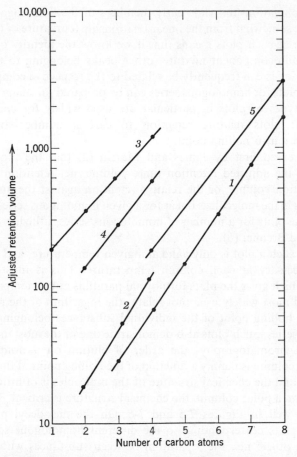

Fig. 7-3. The relationship between the log adjusted retention volumes and the number of carbon atoms for homologous series. Liquid phase: diisodecyl phthalate. Temperature: 100°C. After the data of Scholly and Brenner (5). *1*, Normal paraffins; *2*, acetylenes; *3*, normal primary alcohols, *4*, aldehydes; *5*, ethers.

the logarithm of the retention values than the direct numerical values, because in the latter case the graph became crowded in the region close to the origin.

Figures 7-7 and 7-8 show such plots. As seen on the proportional plot, the *slopes* of the straight lines are characteristic of the chemical nature of the individual homologous series. Using a log/log scale, the resulting plots are almost parallel to each other, and now the *intercepts* are characteristic of the individual homologous series.

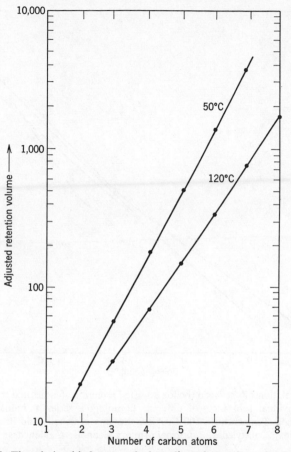

Fig. 7-4. The relationship between the log adjusted retention volumes and the number of carbon atoms for normal paraffins at different temperatures. Liquid phase: diisodecyl phthalate. After the data of Scholly and Brenner (5).

D. Retention Index

As already mentioned, the various retention data discussed until now have many basic shortcomings:

1. The absolute retention values are too much dependent on experimental conditions.

2. The calculation of the specific retention volume requires the knowledge of values (e.g. the amount of liquid phase in the column) which are generally not known and may even change in use; furthermore, since the specific retention volume is always reduced to 0°C, there is no way to describe the temperature dependency of retention.

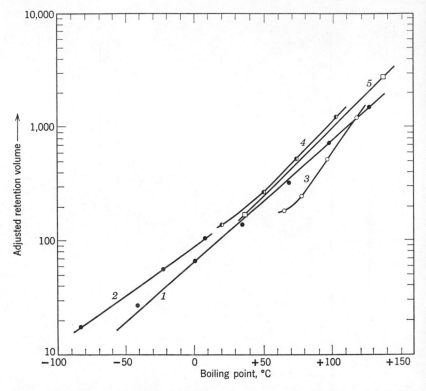

Fig. 7-5. The relationship between the log adjusted retention volumes and the boiling point of the individual substances of different homologous series, I. Liquid phase: diisodecyl phthalate. Temperature: 100°C. After the data of Scholly and Brenner (5). *1*, Normal paraffins; *2*, acetylenes; *3*, normal primary alcohols; *4*, aldehydes; *5*, ethers.

3. When giving relative retention data, one must use more than one standard.

In order to overcome the latter difficulty, Evans and Smith (13) introduced the so-called *theoretical nonane values*: the retention is first determined relative to the closest *n*-paraffin, and consequently, this value is transferred to a system in which *n*-nonane is the standard. However, the shortcoming of this system is that, due to the two-step calculation, there is an obvious increase in the possible error.

The so-called retention index system first proposed in 1958 by E. Kováts (14) is far the most valuable expression of column retention. The basic difference between this system and all previously mentioned expressions is that now the retention behavior of the substance of interest is expressed in a uniform scale determined by a series of closely related standards. In this

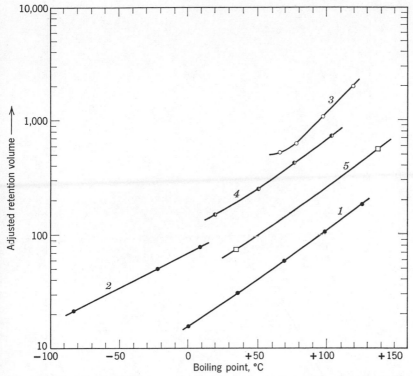

Fig. 7-6. The relationship between the log adjusted retention volumes and the boiling point of the individual substances of different homologous series, II. Liquid phase: Carbowax 1500 poly(ethylene glycol). Temperature: 100°C. After the data of Scholly and Brenner (5). *1*, Normal paraffins, *2*, acetylenes, *3*, normal primary alcohols; *4*, aldehydes; *5*, ethers.

respect, it could be compared well to our common temperature scale where arbitrary numbers are assigned to the temperatures of two specific transitions and the other temperatures are characterized with help of inter- or extrapolation using an arbitrary scale (e.g., 100 equal divisions between two fixed points).

The fixed points used in the retention index system are the normal paraffins, and the retention index (I) of a particular substance can be calculated according to the following equation:

$$I = 100 \frac{\log X_{(\text{substance})} - \log X_{(n\text{-}C_z)}}{\log X_{(n\text{-}C_{z+1})} - \log X_{(n\text{-}C_z)}} + 100z \qquad (7\text{-}8)$$

where X = the adjusted retention time, the net retention volume or the corresponding distance on the recorder chart; $n\text{-}C_z$ = n-paraffin with z

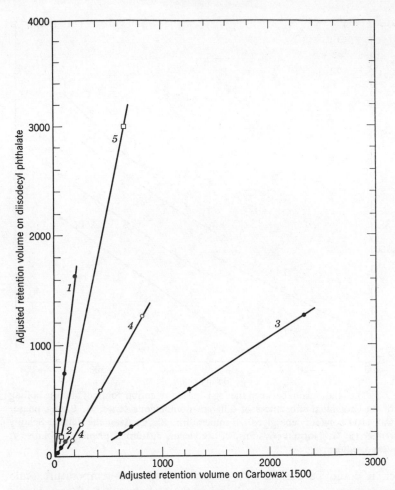

Fig. 7-7. The relationship between the adjusted retention volumes on two different columns. Liquid phases: *ordinate:* diisodecyl phthalate; *abscissa:* Carbowax 1500 poly(ethylene glycol). Temperature: 100°C. After the data of Scholly and Brenner (5). *1,* Normal paraffins; *2,* acetylenes; *3,* normal primary alcohols; *4,* aldehydes; *5,* ethers.

carbon atoms, and $n\text{-}C_{(z+1)}$ = n-paraffin with $z + 1$ carbon atoms; by definition:

$$X_{(n\text{-}C_z)} \leqslant X_{(\text{substance})} \leqslant X_{(n\text{-}C_{z+1})} \tag{7-9}$$

According to equation 7-8, the retention index of the normal paraffins will be 100 times the carbon number—i.e., 200, 300, 400 for ethane, propane, n-butane, etc.

In the calculation of the retention index, a logarithmic scale is used because it is known (as discussed earlier) that the logarithms of the retention values give a linear plot with the chain length of a homologous series. As a conclusion of this, the retention index scale is linear.

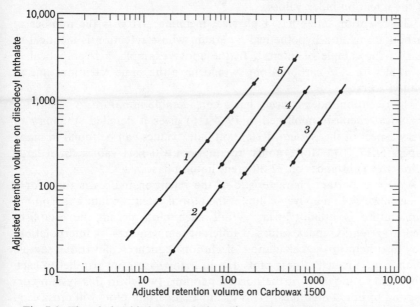

Fig. 7-8. The relationship between the log adjusted retention volumes on two different columns. Liquid phases: *ordinate:* diisodecyl phthalate, *abscissa:* Carbowax 1500 poly(ethylene glycol). Temperature: 100°C. After the data of Scholly and Brenner (5). *1*, Normal paraffins; *2*, acetylenes; *3*, normal primary alcohols; *4*, aldehydes; *5*, ethers.

The retention data for the two adjacent *n*-paraffins can be determined either by a consecutive analysis carried out under identical conditions or, more conveniently, by mixing them with the actual sample.

The following example illustrates the calculation of the retention index of *n*-butyl acetate on an Apiezon L grease column, at 100°C. The two adjacent *n*-paraffins are *n*-heptane and *n*-octane, and the distances on the chart paper corresponding to the adjusted retention times are:

$$n\text{-butyl acetate: } 310.0 \text{ mm; } \log 310.0 = 2.49136$$

$$n\text{-heptane: } 174.0 \text{ mm; } \log 174.0 = 2.24055$$

$$n\text{-octane: } 373.4 \text{ mm; } \log 373.4 = 2.57217$$

The value of z is now 7. Thus:

$$I = 100 \frac{2.49136 - 2.24055}{2.57217 - 2.24055} + 700 = 75.6 + 700 = 775.6$$

Hupe (15) also described a nomographic method for the establishment of the retention index values.

The retention index has a physical meaning: $I/100$ is the number of carbon atoms in a hypothetical n-paraffin whose retention is identical to that of the sample of interest. In the above example, a hypothetical n-paraffin with 7.76 carbon atoms would have the same retention time as n-butyl acetate.

The retention index concept has a considerable literature. A report for analytical chemists published in 1964 (16) gives a detailed summary of every aspect of this system. Retention index values can be found in many papers (7,17–20); McReynolds' recent book (8) lists values for a large number of substances on 77 different liquid phases.

A very important characteristic of the retention indices is that, for a given substance on a given column, the plot of retention index vs. column temperature is usually linear. While such plots permit the establishment of retention index values at different temperatures by interpolation, they also help in the calculation of elution sequences of various sample components; namely, these plots are, in many cases, not parallel to each other and to the plots of the normal paraffins (which in this system correspond to horizontal lines). This means that certain plots will cross each other, and therefore, at different temperatures, the order of elution might change. This fact is of significant help in the further confirmation of peak identification: by analyzing the sample at different temperatures, the peak shifting predicted from the plots can be checked.

Retention index values determined on a polar and a nonpolar liquid phase can be of help in postulating the structure of the substance because the difference in the retention indices (ΔI) is characteristic of the structure of the substance and can be predicted by adding up the individual increments pertaining to various adhering zones in the molecule. With the help of such a calculation, unknown substances can be identified by comparing the experimentally determined ΔI value with values calculated for the possible structure. This technique is discussed in detail in the literature (14,17–20).

It should be emphasized that in certain cases systems similar to the retention index scale but having reference standards other than the homologous series of normal paraffins might be advantageous. In fact, five similar systems have already been described in the literature:

1 and *2*. The scale of Woodford and van Gent (21) and of Miwa et al. (22) for fatty acid analysis.

3. The "effective molecular weight" systems of Evans and Smith (23).

4. The "steroid number" system of VandenHeuvel and Horning (24) where two hydrocarbons with steroidal structure are used as the standards.

5. The "methylene unit" system of VandenHeuvel et al. (25) which is physically identical to $I/100$.

E. Retention Values in Programmed-Temperature Analysis

Principally, qualitative identification of individual peaks in a programmed-temperature run by using retention data may be accomplished in a way similar to any of the previous ones. The basic problem, however, is that the program rate (r_t, °C/min) adds one more operation parameter which has to be taken into consideration, and that in practically all commercial gas chromatographic systems, the *actual* column temperature is lagging behind the temperature which is calculated from the nominal program rate. This fact makes the utilization of published data very difficult.

The essential difference between isothermal and (linearly) programmed-temperature analysis is that while in the former, one is relating the logarithm of the retention values to the carbon numbers, in programmed-temperature analysis one can plot directly the retention values. For example, Figure 7-9 shows—according to Dal Nogare and Juvet (26)—such plots for *n*-paraffins for three different program rates. It was also shown (26,27) that if the carrier gas mass flow rate (F) is kept constant during analysis, the adjusted retention times or the relative retention values of a given substance are linearly proportional to the F/r_t values. This observation may also be used for peak identification.

Retention index values can also be calculated from a programmed-temperature run by replacing the logarithms of the retention data by the corresponding numerical values (28):

$$I \simeq 100 \frac{X_{(\text{substance})} - X_{(n\text{-}C_z)}}{X_{(n\text{-}C_{z+1})} - X_{(n\text{-}C_z)}} + 100z \qquad (7\text{-}10)$$

where X is the adjusted retention time, the net retention volume, or the retention temperature of the given components. Naturally in this calculation one is assuming that linear programming started immediately at sample injection and was not stopped until the last peak emerged.

The reason the approximate equality sign was used in equation 7-10 is that for substances having a retention index vs. column temperature plot (isothermal operation) nonparallel to the corresponding plot of the *n*-paraffins, data calculated from equation 7-10 will differ from data obtained under isothermal conditions.

Further considerations on the determination of retention indices in programmed-temperature operation can be found, e.g., in the papers of

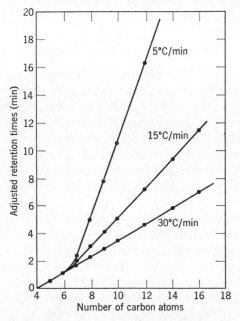

Fig. 7-9. The relationship between the adjusted retention times and the number of carbon atoms for normal paraffins, in programmed-temperature analysis. After Dal Nogare and Juvet (26).

Guiochon (29,30) and Habgood and Harris (31). The recent book of the latter authors (32) provides a detailed discussion on how programmed-temperature operation influences the retention data in general.

F. Error Sources in the Determination of Retention Data

In all cases in which one intends to use tabulated or separately determined retention data for identification purposes, the most important questions are how accurately the values were determined and whether the retention data measured were influenced by any effect other than partitioning itself.

Below, the error sources of retention measurements are summarized according to Keulemans (16).

The error sources can be divided into five main groups.

1. The first group consists of errors resulting from deviation from the linear distribution isotherm and changes in the temperature and flow during partition. In order to avoid any change in the retention value, very small samples have to be used, in which case the possible fluctuations are negligible.

2. The second group of error sources is related to the instrumentation itself. It is evident that inaccuracies in the measurement and regulation of column temperature and carrier gas flow, incorrect registration of the starting point, or unevenness in the chart speed will affect the results obtained.

3. It is very important that the stationary phase used be unambiguously defined and that its characteristics should not change during use. Even slight changes in the chemical composition of the phase can significantly alter its retention characteristics; thus, retention values measured at different times might differ.

4. If the peak of the substance of interest is not completely resolved from another peak, this will result in a small shift of the position of the peak maximum. This fact has to be taken into account if retention values from a complex chromatogram with incompletely resolved peaks are compared with values determined by analyzing pure standards.

5. As a last but perhaps the most important source of error, adsorption by the support must be mentioned. This is particularly harmful if polar samples are analyzed on a nonpolar column, but it can also be observed with polar samples on polar substrates. For example, according to Kováts (18), the retention index of furfural on Emulphor-O at 190°C was found to be 1287 and 1246, respectively, depending on whether only acid-washed or acid- and base-washed and calcinated Celite was used as support.

G. Addition of the Supposed Component to the Sample

Finally, a very convenient method for the identification of peaks should be briefly mentioned. This is to mix the sample successively with the pure substances which are supposed to be its components and to analyze the new mixture. If the substance which was added to the sample was already present in it, one of the peaks will be relatively larger than in the chromatogram obtained by analyzing the original sample, thus indicating that the added substance has the same retention time as the component corresponding to the particular peak.

The identification of peaks with this method presents one familiar difficulty: even if the peak of the standard coincides with a peak of the original chromatogram, it is still possible that the original sample component is some other substance having the same retention time as the added standard only on that particular column and under the given conditions. Repetition of the analysis on other columns prepared with liquid phases of different polarity is always recommended: if the two substances are not identical, it is unlikely that they will overlap on both columns.

This technique can be conveniently used if the composition of the sample is known, only one is not sure in the assignment of the individual peaks to the respective components. Also, this technique is recommended for the *exclusion of the possibility of the presence of a particular substance*. In this case, the chromatogram of the mixture of the original sample and the added standard will show one more peak than the original chromatogram obtained under identical conditions. This fact proves that none of the sample components is identical to the added standard.

It is very important that the purity of the standard to be added to the sample be first checked by a gas chromatographic analysis (under identical conditions) in order to avoid any misinterpretation due to the peaks of impurities.

III. Quantitative Analysis

It is well known that the area under a chromatographic peak (A_i) is proportional to the amount of substance present (C_i) in the carrier gas:

$$A_i = f_i(C_i) \tag{7-11}$$

This means that in order to be able to use gas chromatography for quantitative analysis, one has to know, first, the area of the chromatographic peak, and second the proper proportionality factor to convert this peak area to amount or concentration.

In this treatment, we will discuss first how the peak area values are determined; then the methods for the quantitative interpretation of the chromatogram will be outlined.

A. Peak Area Calculation

Peak areas (or area values relative to them) can be determined using any of the following techniques:

1. Automatic integrators.

2. Planimeters.

3. Cutting out the recorded peaks and weighing the paper on an analytical balance.

4. Multiplying the peak height at maximum by the peak width at half height.

5. Multiplying peak height by the retention time.

6. Calculating the area of the triangle formed by drawing two tangents through the inflection points of the peak, the baseline being the base of the triangle.

Of all these techniques, only methods *1*, *2*, and *4* are used in general practice.

Automatic integrators are more and more used in practice. They are discussed separately in Chapter 6.

Planimeters also are often used for peak area measurements. Their use requires careful curve tracing by the analyst, is time consuming, and needs a lot of attention. For routine analysis, where the measurement of hundreds of peaks per day is often necessary, the use of planimeters is impractical.

Besides using automatic integrators, the best method for establishing peak area values is multiplying peak height at maximum by the peak width at half height. This method was first recommended by Cremer and Müller (33).

The peak height at maximum (h_m) of a Gaussian peak is related to the total peak area (A) and the standard deviation (σ) of the peak:

$$h_m = A/(\sigma\sqrt{2\pi}) \tag{7-12}$$

On the other hand, the width at half height (w_h) of a Gaussian peak is 2.354 times the standard deviation of the peak:

$$w_h = 2.354\sigma \tag{7-13}$$

Substituting this value into equation 7-12, one gets:

$$h_m w_h = (2.354/\sqrt{2\pi})A = 0.94A \tag{7-14}$$

This means that the multiple $h_m w_h$ gives 94% of the total area of the Gaussian peak which would be found by integration (integrator or planimeter). However, since the 0.94 proportionality factor would apply to every peak in the chromatogram and also to the peak of the standard used in the establishment of proportionality of peak area with actual amount present, this fact *per se* does not reduce the accuracy of the calculation. This method has only two basic limitations: (*a*) In the case of unsymmetrical (i.e., non-Gaussian) peaks, the area calculated in this way will be less representative of the true peak area and cannot be compared with sufficient accuracy with other area values calculated for more symmetrical peaks. (*b*) In the case of very sharp or very small peaks, the half width cannot be measured conveniently with the desired accuracy.

The area of a peak can be expressed in counts (using integrator or planimeter) or in area units (square inches or square centimeters). Because the abscissa of a chromatogram is in time units and the height of a peak can also be measured in millivolts or milliamperes, the peak area may also be expressed in min × mV or min × mA units.

B. Partially Overlapping Peaks

In calculating the peak area values, difficulties arise if the individual peaks are not completely separated but they overlap more or less. In such case, the exact form of the individual peaks cannot be determined easily and approximations must be made. Such approximations can be made using either of two techniques (Fig. 7-10).

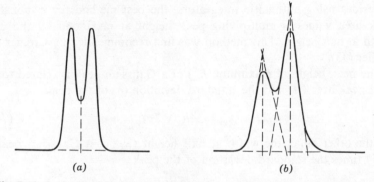

(a)   (b)

Fig. 7-10. Interpretation of peak areas in the case of partially overlapping peaks.

In the first technique, the two peaks are divided by a straight line drawn as a perpendicular to the baseline at the minimum point between the two peaks (Fig. 7-10a). Automatic integrators always operate on this principle, and therefore this is the most commonly used method. In the second technique (Fig. 7-10b), the areas of the two peaks are approximated by computing the areas of the triangles bordered by the tangents to the two peaks at the inflection points and the baseline. This method is recommended if the resolution between two peaks is very poor.

If the minimum point between the two peaks is lower than the half height of both peaks, the calculation of the peak area values by multiplying the peak height by the peak width at half height can be used successfully.

All these methods assume that if present alone, neither peak would show appreciable asymmetry or tailing. In the latter case, the error of peak-area approximation will be relatively high.

In case of overlapping peaks, care must be taken to use the same method for calculating the peak areas in the analysis of the sample with unknown concentration as that used in the calibration run.

An extreme case of peak overlapping is shown in Figure 7-11. This is the case of a trace impurity emerging shortly after the peak of the main component: the peak of the trace will appear on the flank of the large peak. The only convenient method in such a case is to measure the peak area above the interpolated flank of the main peak. The area of this peak should be compared to those found under the same conditions for binary synthetic mixtures containing the component of interest at the same concentration level.

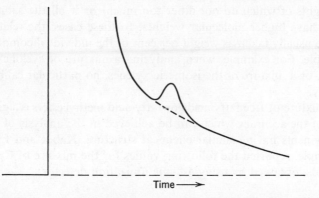

Time⟶

Fig. 7-11. Peak corresponding to a trace impurity on the tail of the main peak.

Two fairly complicated mathematical approaches were also reported for determination of the true areas of overlapping peaks. Both methods are based on the statistical calculation of Gaussian-type distribution curves; they were reported by Bartlet and Smith (34) and Grant and Vaughan (35).

C. Methods for the Quantitative Interpretation of a Chromatogram

1. Internal Normalization Method (Total Peak Area Method)

In this method, the concentration of each component in the sample is calculated.

In the first step, the area of each peak is established by either surface measurements (integrator, planimeter) or calculation by multiplying peak height by the width at half height. The sum of the individual peak area values is calculated, and from it the so-called *relative peak areas* are established:

$$A_1 + A_2 + \cdots A_i + \cdots A_n = \sum A_i \tag{7-15}$$

$$A_i\% = (A_i/\sum A_i)100 \tag{7-16}$$

where $A_1 \cdots A_n$ are the areas of the individual peaks, and $A_i\%$ is the relative peak area of component i expressed as a per cent of the sum of the individual peak areas.

In certain cases, one can assume that the proportionality factor f_i in equation 7-11 is identical for each component; this would mean that the relative peak area would directly give the concentration of that particular component in the sample. This is generally true for most detectors if a relatively small range of closely related compounds is analyzed, the molecular weights of which do not differ too much, or if all the sample components have higher molecular weights. In these cases, the relative peak areas are usually taken as weight per cent of the individual components in the sample. For example, when analyzing a mixture of cyclohexane and benzene, or a mixture of the isomeric xylenes, no particular calibration is necessary.

The mixture of free fatty acids or fatty acid methyl esters is a good illustration of the accuracy which can be achieved in the analysis of mixtures of components having similar chemical structure. Kabot and Ettre (36), for example, reported the following values for the mixture of C_7–C_{12} free fatty acids, obtained by using a flame ionization detector:

	Conc. (wt %)	Peak area (%)
Enanthic acid	28.4	27.3
Caprylic acid	25.5	25.5
Capric acid	29.0	28.8
Lauric acid	17.1	18.4

Similarly, fairly good agreement was obtained in the analysis of a sample consisting of the methyl esters of C_8–C_{20} fatty acids (37). On the other hand, if a sample of C_2–C_8 free fatty acids was analyzed, differences up to 8% absolute (almost 50% relative) were found (36).

For higher accuracy, or if mixtures containing either components of highly different structure or representing a wide molecular weight starting at the lower end are analyzed, detector response factors have to be utilized.

2. Relative Detector Response Factors and Their Use

As given earlier, the area of each peak recorded is proportional to the amount (concentration) of the respective sample component:

$$A_i = f_i(C_i) \tag{7-17}$$

The proportionality factor f_i depends mainly on the chemical nature of the individual component and is different for each type of detector. Therefore it has to be determined carefully, by analyzing known amounts of pure standards. Usually, the *detector response factors*, as they are called, are not given in absolute amount—e.g., peak area per unit weight—but rather relative to a given standard. These *relative detector response factors* can be given in equal mole, equal volume, or equal weight bases. On the other hand, if these factors are known, the concentration of the individual components in the sample can be calculated from the relative peak areas.

The determination of the relative response factors can be explained by the following treatment. From equation 7-17 the peak area for the first two components can be expressed as

$$A_1 = f_1 C_1 \tag{7-18}$$

$$A_2 = f_2 C_2 \tag{7-19}$$

Reduced to C_1 and C_2:

$$C_1 = A_1/f_1 \tag{7-20}$$

$$C_2 = A_2/f_2 \tag{7-21}$$

If the amount (concentration) of both components is the same:

$$C_1 = C_2 \tag{7-22}$$

then

$$A_1/f_1 = A_2/f_2 \tag{7-23}$$

or

$$f_2 = (A_2/A_1)f_i \tag{7-24}$$

Since we are interested in relative response factors, f_1 could be assigned a value of 1.00 (or 100), and then f_2 could be expressed as

$$f_2 = A_2/A_1 \quad \text{or} \quad f_2 = (A_2/A_1)100 \tag{7-25}$$

The relative response factors of the other components can be expressed similarly.

In practice, one does not usually prepare mixtures where each component is present in equal amounts but, assuming direct proportionality between peak area and concentration, calculates the peak area which would be obtained if equal amounts were present. The following example shows how relative detector response factors are determined on an equal weight basis (detector: flame ionization); the corresponding data are listed in Table 7-1.

The mixture of the four acids with the given concentration was analyzed, and the peak areas were recorded with an integrator. Now we calculate the

TABLE 7-1

Example for the Establishment of Relative Detector Response Factors on an Equal Weight Basis

Component	Sample conc. (wt %)	Peak area (counts)	Peak area for equal weight (counts)	Relative response factor (wt)
Acetic acid	35.6	1709	1200	48
Butyric acid	32.4	2786	2150	86
Enanthic acid	20.0	2000	2500	100
Caprylic acid	12.0	1248	2600	104
	100.0			

peak area which would be obtained for equal weight per cent (i.e., in this case 25 wt %). For example in the case of acetic acid:

$$35.6 : 1709 = 25.0 : x$$

From this, $x = 1200$. Consequently, we assign a relative response factor of 100 to enanthic acid; thus, e.g., the relative response of acetic acid is:

$$f = (1200/2500)100 = 48$$

On the other hand if the relative response factors are known, then the concentration of the individual sample components can be calculated. This calculation consists of two steps:

1. First, the peak area values (A)—given, e.g., as integrator counts—are divided by the response factors (f). The new values are the so-called *reduced peak areas*:

$$(A_1/f_1) + (A_2/f_2) + \cdots + (A_i/f_i) + \cdots + (A_n/f_n) = \sum (A_i/f_i) \quad (7\text{-}26)$$

2. Consequently, the concentration of the individual components (C) is calculated:

$$C_1\% = \frac{A_1/f_1}{\sum (A_i/f_i)} \quad (7\text{-}27)$$

This calculation is illustrated in Table 7-2. For convenience, the reduced peak areas are multiplied by 100.

Two very important general rules exist concerning the relative response factors; their validity was proved repetitively for both thermal conductivity (38–43) and flame ionization detectors (36,44–51). These concern the relative *molar* response and the relative response for *equal weight* for homologous series:

1. The relative molar response (RMR) for a homologous series always gives a straight line if plotted against the carbon number or some other characteristic value (e.g., molecular weight). Some deviation from the linear plot might occur for the homologs with low carbon number.

2. The relative molar response for equal weight (RWR), when plotted against the carbon number for a homologous series, gives an asymptotic plot which levels off at higher carbon numbers.

TABLE 7-2

Example of the Calculation of Sample Concentration by
Use of Relative Response Factors

Component	Peak area (counts)	Relative response (equal weight)	Reduced peak areas ×100 (counts)	Sample concentration (wt%)
Acetic acid	2014	48	4196	18.2
Propionic acid	2738	69	3968	17.1
Butyric acid	3297	86	3834	16.5
Valeric acid	3395	90	3772	16.3
Enanthic acid	3652	100	3652	15.8
Caprylic acid	3782	104	3637	16.1
	18878		23059	100.0

Figure 7-12 shows—after the data of Rosie et al. (38,40)—some plots for thermal conductivity detectors. Figure 7-13 depicts the relative molar response plot of a number of homologous series, on a flame ionization detector (51). Figure 7-14 shows a similar plot for chlorinated methane derivatives (47). Finally, Figure 7-15 illustrates relative response plots on an equal weight basis (51).

The first rule permits the establishment of RMR values by interpolation for substances which might not be available in sufficiently pure form; from these RMR values, the corresponding RWR values can be calculated. The second rule is the theoretical reason for the practical observation discussed earlier, that for substances with higher molecular weight, the relative peak area values can be taken with good approximation for concentration by weight.

There are two detector types where, if the substances corresponding to each peak are known, the actual quantitative composition of the sample can be calculated from physical constants. These are the gas density

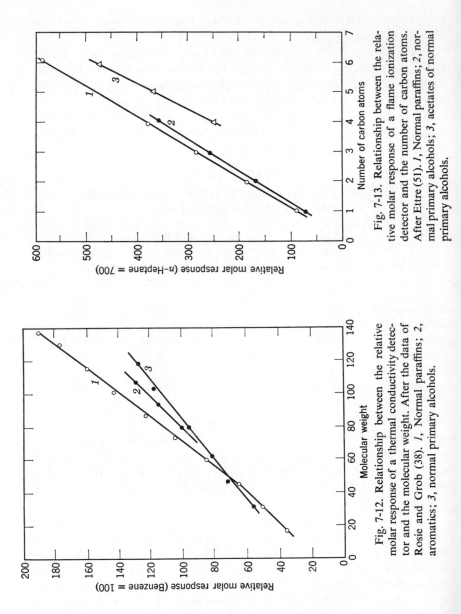

Fig. 7-13. Relationship between the relative molar response of a flame ionization detector and the number of carbon atoms. After Ettre (51). *1*, Normal paraffins; *2*, normal primary alcohols; *3*, acetates of normal primary alcohols.

Fig. 7-12. Relationship between the relative molar response of a thermal conductivity detector and the molecular weight. After the data of Rosie and Grob (38). *1*, Normal paraffins; *2*, aromatics; *3*, normal primary alcohols.

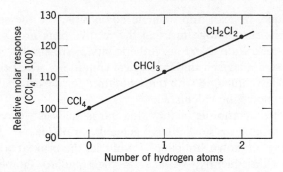

Fig. 7-14. Relationship between the relative molar response of a flame ionization detector and the number of hydrogen atoms for chlorinated methane derivatives. After Condon et al. (47).

balance (52–54) and the micro cross-section detector (55). For more details concerning how the response factors of these detectors can be calculated, readers are referred to the quoted original papers.

3. Bracketing Technique

This is the simplest method of calibration and may be used advantageously for individual analyses where a detailed precalibration procedure or the determination of response factors would extend the analysis time.

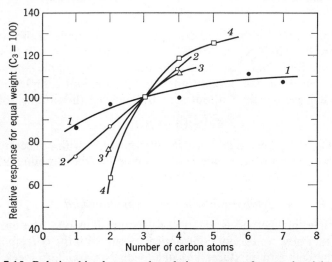

Fig. 7-15. Relationships between the relative response for equal weight of a flame ionization detector and the number of carbon atoms. After Ettre (51). *1*, Normal paraffins; *2*, normal primary alcohols; *3*, acetates of normal primary alcohols; *4*, normal fatty acids.

In this technique, first an approximate composition of the sample is calculated from its chromatogram using the relative peak area values as approximate concentration. Next, a synthetic mixture of similar composition is prepared and analyzed under identical conditions. The peak areas (or peak heights) are compared with those obtained for the original sample and the actual composition calculated.

This method of evaluation is mainly used in gas analysis where devices for metering the sample sizes exactly are generally available.

In analyzing the unknown sample of V volume, the peak area of component i is A_i. Consequently, we analyze the standard sample of V' volume; the relative peak area corresponding to the same component which is present in C_i' concentration by volume, is A_i' %. The actual volume of component i present in the standard sample is

$$V_i' = (V'C_i)/100 \qquad\qquad (7\text{-}28)$$

The unknown volume in the original sample is V_i. Since the amount present is directly proportional to the peak area values, V_i can be calculated:

$$V_i/V_i' = A_i/A_i' \qquad\qquad (7\text{-}29)$$

In this equation, only V_i is unknown.

If V_i is known, the concentration of the component in the sample (C_i) can be calculated:

$$C_i = (V_i/V)100 \qquad\qquad (7\text{-}30)$$

A simplification of this method can be used if the volumes of the original sample and the standard mixture are identical, i.e., $V = V'$. In this case, the concentration of the respective component in the sample can be calculated directly from the concentration in the standard sample and the corresponding peak areas without actually knowing the sample volume:

$$C_i = (A_i/A_i')C_i' \qquad\qquad (7\text{-}31)$$

In this method, one should use synthetic mixtures with concentrations close to those anticipated in the actual sample in order to eliminate the possible influence of detector nonlinearity.

4. Comparison with a Separate Standard

In principle this method is identical to the previous one: the only difference is that now we do not compare each peak with the corresponding peak of the standard mixture, but only with *one* standard peak. This method is used mainly if the amount (concentration) of only a limited number of components in the sample is desired. The calculation is carried out identically to that given in the previous method; however, if necessary,

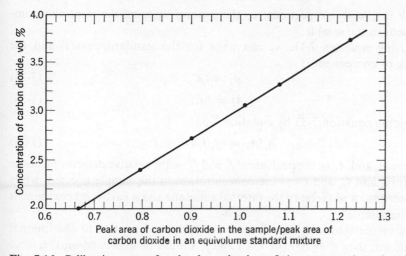

Fig. 7-16. Calibration curve for the determination of the concentration of carbon dioxide in a gas sample by comparison with an equivolume standard gas mixture.

one can also take into account the relative detector response factors, since now we may compare peak areas corresponding to *different* substances.

If the volumes of the unknown sample and the standard mixture are identical, one can actually prepare calibration plots by plotting concentration in the sample against the ratio of peak areas when using a certain standard mixture:

$$C_i = (A_i/A_s)\text{const.} \tag{7-32}$$

Figure 7-16 shows such a plot. Here, the carbon dioxide content of gas mixtures is analyzed by comparing the peak area of carbon dioxide in the sample with the peak area of carbon dioxide obtained when analyzing an equivolume standard gas mixture with fixed composition. For the preparation of such plots, the respective components do not have to be chemically identical; for example, similar plots could also be prepared for the other components in the sample by relating them to the carbon dioxide peak of the standard mixture.

5. Comparison with an Internal Standard

The most generally used method for the quantitative evaluation of a chromatogram is the so-called internal standard method. The principal advantages of this method are that the exact knowledge or the reproducibility of sample volumes is unimportant, and that by fixing the concentration of the internal standard, calibration curves can easily be established because in this case, the ratio of the area of a peak to the area of the standard peak is directly proportional to the concentration of the respective component in the sample.

Using equation 7-11, we can write for the standard peak(s) and the peak of component i:

$$A_s = f_s C_s \qquad (7\text{-}33)$$

$$A_i = f_i C_i \qquad (7\text{-}34)$$

Dividing equation 7-33 by equation 7-34:

$$A_s/A_i = (f_s/f_i)(C_s/C_i) \qquad (7\text{-}35)$$

where A_s and A_i = the peak area, f_s and f_i = the relative detector response factors, and C_s and C_i = the concentration in the sample injected, while subscripts s and i refer to the internal standard and a particular component in the sample.

If the detector response factors are expressed relative to the internal standard, then $f_s = 100$ (or 1.00) and f_i should be expressed on the same basis as the concentration: if the concentration is given in weight per cent, then the response factor should be calculated on equal weight basis, etc. Thus, the concentration of a component in the sample can be calculated as

$$C_i = (A_i/A_s)(C_s/f_i)100 \qquad (7\text{-}36)$$

Since the fraction C_s/f_i is constant for a component,

$$C_i = (A_i/A_s)\text{const.} \qquad (7\text{-}37)$$

Calibration curves plotting A_i/A_s against C_i can easily be established without actually determining the relative response factors but by fixing the

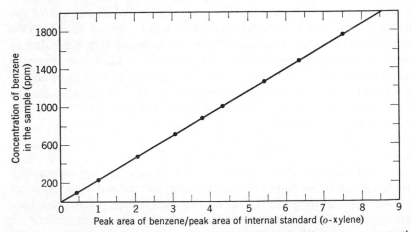

Fig. 7-17. Calibration curve for the determination of small benzene concentrations in a mixture. Internal standard: 250 ppm o-xylene.

concentration of the internal standard. Figure 7-17 shows such a plot established for the determination of trace amounts of benzene in a mixture. In this case, 250 ppm *o*-xylene is added to the sample as the internal standard.

The choice of the substance to be used for internal standard depend. entirely upon the nature of the components to be determined, and also upon the concentration range in which they are present. It is generally recommended that the internal standard peak should be located in close proximity to but without overlapping the particular peaks to be evaluated and that its concentration range be chosen to produce peak heights similar to those of the peaks of interest. In this way, the reproducibility of measurements will be quite satisfactory even if operating conditions vary somewhat from run to run.

In special cases, two or more internal standards may be used.

6. Peak Height Calculations

In some cases, the measurement of peak areas is difficult or tedious. For example, the bands yielded by low boiling components and located at the beginning of the chromatogram are tall and narrow, maximizing errors in band-width measurements. On the other hand, peak heights of such bands are easily and accurately measured on strip chart recorders. Therefore, in many cases, peak heights are used instead of areas for quantitative evaluation.

However, in using peak heights, one has to keep in mind that peak heights are much more dependent on even slight changes of operating conditions than peak areas. Therefore, one should use peak heights only where these effects are eliminated. Such a case is the internal standard method where the influence of changing operation parameters is greatly diminished since the standard is analyzed together with the sample of unknown concentration. As a result of this, one may use the corresponding peak heights instead of the areas in equations 7-36 and 7-37.

Peak height may also be used in the bracketing technique where—if the volume of the sample is fixed—one could actually set up calibration curves where peak heights are directly related to concentration in the fixed volume sample. However, in order to be able to use such calibration curves, the analytical parameters also have to be fixed. Figure 7-18 shows a calibration plot for the determination of the hydrogen content of gas samples by using mixed (He/H_2) carrier gas and 10 ml total sample.

In the internal normalization method, the use of peak heights instead of the areas is generally not recommended.

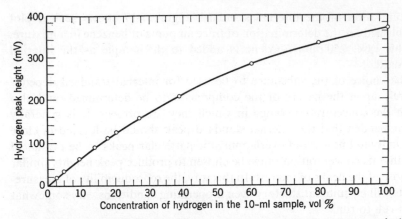

Fig. 7-18. Calibration curve for the determination of the hydrogen content in 10-ml gas samples, by using mixed (H_2/He) carrier gas at 50 ml/min. Column: 1 m × ¼ in. o.d. packed with activated charcoal; temperature: 50°C. After Purcell and Ettre (56).

7. Comparison of the Different Methods Used for the Quantitative Evaluation of a Chromatogram

The following is a brief summary of the considerations which have to be taken into account when selecting the appropriate method for calculation or evaluation.

Internal normalization is advantageous if evaluation of the whole chromatogram is necessary and similar samples are to be analyzed frequently in the laboratory. In such cases, the time-consuming job of determining the response factors is justified.

The *bracketing technique* is to be used if only a few samples of the same type are analyzed. Since here the exact volume of the samples has to be known (or should be reproduced exactly), this method is practically restricted to gas samples where the standard gas sampling valves with fixed volume loops provide a relatively easy way for sample volume reproduction.

Comparison with a separate standard is suitable where only a partial evaluation of the chromatogram is necessary and where the chromatogram does not permit the use of an *internal standard* (e.g., there is "no room" for it in the chromatogram). However, the accuracy of this method depends on the reproducibility of the analytical conditions between the analysis of the sample and the standard.

The *internal standard method* is about the most convenient technique. Its main advantage is that the accuracy is virtually independent of the reproducibility of the analytical conditions. This method is suitable where only partial evaluation of the chromatogram is necessary. It is particularly recommended in the analysis of components present in small concentrations.

Calculations based on *peak height* are preferable for analyses in which the peak width is very small and the concentration of the component is high.

Finally, a general remark is necessary for all calibration methods with regard to obtaining higher analytical accuracy. If the concentration range is too wide, calibration should be made in more concentration ranges (e.g., 0–5%, 5–20%, 20–60%, 60–100%) in order to eliminate the errors which can be introduced by extrapolating calibration data to concentrations too far from the range in which the calibration was made.

References

1. A. B. Littlewood, C. S. G. Phillips, and D. T. Price, *J. Chem. Soc.*, **1955**, 1480.
2. A. T. James and A. J. P. Martin, *Biochem. J.*, **50**, 679 (1952).
3. G. Raupp, *Z. Anal. Chem.*, **164**, 135 (1958).
4. H. M. Tenney, *Anal. Chem.*, **30**, 2 (1958).
5. P. Scholly and N. Brenner, in *Gas Chromatography*, H. J. Noebels, R. F. Wall, and N. Brenner, Eds., Academic Press, New York, 1961, pp. 263–309.
6. R. A. Hively, *J. Chem. Eng. Data*, **5**, 237 (1960).
7. R. Kaiser, *Chromatographie in der Gasphase*, Part 3, Bibliographisches Institut, Mannheim, 1962.
8. W. O. McReynolds, *Gas Chromatographic Retention Data*, Preston Technical Abstracts Co., Evanston, Ill., 1966.
9. A. T. James, *Biochem. J.*, **52**, 242 (1952).
10. A. T. James and A. J. P. Martin, *J. Appl. Chem. (London)*, **6**, 105 (1956).
11. G. J. Pierotti, C. H. Deal, E. L. Derr, and P. E. Porter, *J. Am. Chem. Soc.*, **78**, 2989 (1956).
12. J. S. Lewis, H. W. Patton, and W. I. Kaye, *Anal. Chem.*, **28**, 1370 (1956).
13. M. B. Evans and J. F. Smith, *J. Chromatog.*, **6**, 293 (1961).
14. E. Kováts, *Helv. Chim. Acta*, **41**, 1915 (1958).
15. K. P. Hupe, *J. Gas Chromatog.*, **3**, 12 (1965).
16. L. S. Ettre, *Anal. Chem.*, **36** (8), 31A (1964).
17. A. Wehrli and E. Kováts, *Helv. Chim. Acta*, **42**, 2709 (1959).
18. E. Kováts, *Z. Anal. Chem.*, **181**, 351 (1961).
19. E. Kováts and H. Strickler, *J. Gas Chromatog.*, **3**, 244 (1965).
20. E. Kováts, in *Advances in Chromatography*, Vol. 1, J. C. Giddings and R. A. Keller, Eds., Dekker, New York, 1966, pp. 229–247.
21. F. P. Woodford and C. M. van Gent, *J. Lipid Res.*, **1**, 188 (1960).
22. T. K. Miwa, K. L. Mikolajczak, F. R. Earle, and I. A. Wolff, *Anal. Chem.*, **32**, 1739 (1960).
23. M. B. Evans and J. F. Smith, *J. Chromatog.*, **8**, 303 (1962).
24. W. J. A. VandenHeuvel and E. C. Horning, *Biochem. Biophys. Acta*, **64**, 416 (1962).
25. W. J. A. VandenHeuvel, W. L. Gardiner, and E. C. Horning, *Anal. Chem.*, **36**, 1550 (1964).
26. S. Dal Nogare and R. S. Juvet, Jr., *Gas Chromatography: Theory and Practice*, Interscience, New York, 1962, pp. 337–339.

27. H. W. Habgood and W. E. Harris, *Anal. Chem.*, **32**, 450 (1960).
28. H. Van den Dool and P. D. Kratz, *J. Chromatog.*, **11**, 463 (1963).
29. G. Guiochon, *Anal. Chem.*, **36**, 661 (1964).
30. G. Guiochon, *Anal. Chem.*, **36**, 1672 (1964).
31. H. W. Habgood and W. E. Harris, *Anal. Chem.*, **36**, 663 (1964).
32. W. E. Harris and H. W. Habgood, *Programmed Temperature Gas Chromatography*, Wiley, New York, 1966.
33. E. Cremer and R. Müller, *Z. Elektrochem.*, **55**, 217 (1951).
34. J. C. Bartlet and D. M. Smith, *Can. J. Chem.*, **38**, 2057 (1960).
35. D. W. Grant and G. A. Vaughan, *J. Appl. Chem.* (*London*), **10**, 181 (1960).
36. F. J. Kabot and L. S. Ettre, *J. Gas Chromatog.*, **1** (10), 7 (1963).
37. L. S. Ettre and F. J. Kabot, *J. Chromatog.*, **1** (11), 114 (1963).
38. D. M. Rosie and R. L. Grob, *Anal. Chem.*, **29**, 1263 (1957).
39. G. Schomburg, *Z. Anal. Chem.*, **164**, 147 (1958).
40. A. E. Messner, D. M. Rosie, and P. A. Argabright, *Anal. Chem.*, **31**, 230 (1959).
41. R. L. Grob, D. Mercer, T. Gribben, and J. Wells, *J. Chromatog.*, **3**, 545 (1960).
42. G. R. Jamieson, *J. Chromatog.*, **3**, 464, 494 (1960).
43. G. R. Jamieson, *J. Chromatog.*, **4**, 420 (1960).
44. A. J. Andreatch and R. Feinland, *Anal. Chem.*, **32**, 1021 (1960).
45. L. S. Ettre and H. N. Claudy, *Chem. Can.*, **12** (9), 32 (1960).
46. L. Ongkiehong, in *Gas Chromatography 1960*, R. P. W. Scott, Ed., Butterworths, Washington, D.C., 1960, pp. 7–15.
47. R. D. Condon, P. R. Scholly, and W. Averill, in *Gas Chromatography 1960*, R. P. W. Scott, Ed., Butterworths, Washington, D.C., 1960, pp. 30–45.
48. J. C. Sternberg, W. S. Gallaway, and D. T. L. Jones, in *Gas Chromatography*, N. Brenner, J. E. Callen, and M. D. Weiss, Eds., Academic Press, New York, 1962, pp. 231–267.
49. G. M. Rouayheb, G. Perkins, Jr., L. D. Lively, and W. C. Hamilton, in *Gas Chromatography*, N. Brenner, J. E. Callen, and M. D. Weiss, Eds., Academic Press, New York, 1962, pp. 269–285.
50. L. S. Ettre, in *Gas Chromatography*, N. Brenner, J. E. Callen, and M. D. Weiss, Eds., Academic Press, New York, 1962, pp. 231–267.
51. L. S. Ettre, *J. Chromatog.*, **8**, 525 (1962).
52. A. J. P. Martin and A. T. James, *Biochem. J.*, **63**, 138 (1956).
53. R. L. Martin and J. C. Winters, *Anal. Chem.*, **31**, 1954 (1959).
54. C. L. Guillemin and F. J. Auricourt, *J. Gas Chromatog.*, **1** (10), 24 (1963).
55. J. E. Lovelock, G. R. Shoemake, and A. Zlatkis, *Anal. Chem.*, **35**, 460 (1963).
56. J. E. Purcell and L. S. Ettre, *J. Gas Chromatog.*, **3**, 69 (1965).

CHAPTER 8

Ancillary Systems

Roy Teranishi, Robert E. Lundin, William H. McFadden,*
and James R. Scherer, *Western Regional Research Laboratory,
U.S. Department of Agriculture, Albany, California*

* Present address: International Flavors and Fragrances (U.S.), Union Beach,
New Jersey.

I. Introduction

Each time we separate a mixture by gas chromatography (GC), we observe the recording of the separation and are confronted with the problem of identifying the compound, or compounds, represented by each peak. Although retention times yield some information, and may be sufficient for familiar, known compounds (see Chapter 7, Section II), we must use ancillary methods to obtain chemical and physical properties for a good degree of certainty in chemical structure assignment.

If very closely related compounds are being separated, only small amounts of material will be easily available for analyses, and special techniques must be employed with the ancillary equipment. If large amounts of easily separable material are available with preparative GC, general techniques are applicable, as those in the comprehensive presentation by Bentley (1). Our discussion is limited to the use of ancillary methods for the examination of milligram and submilligram amounts of material purified with high-resolution packed and open tubular columns.

Each investigator must use his own systematic approach in his identification work, based on information as to the source of the material being studied, methods used in sample preparation, equipment readily available, and what degree of certainty is necessary for his conclusions. Overton (2) has presented a general discussion of isolation, purification, and preliminary observations. Some procedures have been briefly reviewed for systematic identifications of peaks in GC analyses (3) and from spectral data (4).

II. Sample Collection

Much of the difficulty encountered with use of ancillary systems for identification involve trapping and manipulation of milligram quantities. Elaborate, time-consuming systems are tolerated only if absolutely necessary, and simple techniques must be developed for frequent, daily analyses.

A. Devices

Various trapping devices and methods have been described: centrifugal, electrostatic, thermal gradient, total eluant, and simple condensation. Each of the methods is useful in a range of amounts for a range of molecular weights.

The centrifugal (5), electrostatic (6–9), and thermal gradient (10,11) traps have been made for relatively large amounts of high boiling compounds which tend to form aerosols. Without the use of such devices, the percentage of material trapped is very low for such compounds. Because these traps were designed for preparative work, they are too large for routine work with milligram quantities.

Two types of total eluant traps have been described. With one type, the carrier gas is condensed with the sample (12,13); with the other, the entire effluent is captured in an evacuated flask (14). These methods are useful when dealing with low boiling compounds. Argon or carbon dioxide can be used as condensable carrier gas, but carbon dioxide is preferred because of ease of condensation with liquid nitrogen and less rapid volatilization upon removal of liquid nitrogen. After the carrier is volatilized, the sample is ready for MS analysis. For IR and proton magnetic resonance (PMR), the trap is rinsed with some carbon tetrachloride and transferred to an appropriate cell with a microsyringe. Nearly quantitative recoveries are claimed for this method in the milligram range. Capturing the total effluent gases in an evacuated flask is a convenient method for MS analyses because the trap can be removed from the chromatograph and then connected directly to the mass spectrometer inlet system without any further manipulations.

The most commonly used method is simple condensation in a glass, Teflon, or polyethylene tube inserted into the GC outlet (10,15–18). It has been shown that nearly quantitative recoveries of high boiling compounds can be made with 50–100-mg quantities in a glass tube if gradient cooling is applied (10). For smaller quantities, glass melting-point capillaries can be inserted into the heated exit of the GC (17,18). Because of the small mass, the glass tubing is quickly heated by the GC outlet system. Thus, because gradient cooling is quickly established down the tube, condensation occurs with a minimum of fog formation. These glass capillaries can be easily sealed at both ends with a torch for storage until it is possible to analyze the condensed material. This method is especially convenient for MS analyses (18).

Figure 8-1 shows how Teflon tubing can be inserted in the stainless steel tubing from the GC detector. If the material is high boiling, the eluant will condense in the Teflon tubing. As with the glass capillaries, very little is lost by fog formation. This type of collector, as well as the glass capillary, is suitable for the large-bore open tubular, 0.03 in. i.d., and high-efficiency packed, 0.1 in. i.d., columns which have about 15 ml/min and 25 ml/min flow rates, respectively. Yields of 70–80% are obtained with oxygenated terpenes and sesquiterpenes with submilligram quantities. For MS analyses,

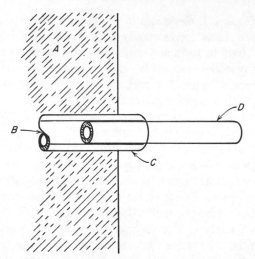

Fig. 8-1. Sample collection in Teflon tubing (16). *A*, Detector housing, ca. 200°C; *B*, detector, nondestructive type; *C*, stainless steel tubing from detector, 0.125 in. o.d., 0.08 in. i.d., ca. 200°C; *D*, Teflon tubing, 0.08 in. o.d., 0.06 in. i.d., 2 in. long.

the Teflon tube is dropped into a container which can be connected to the mass spectrometer inlet system. For IR and PMR analyses, the condensed material can be rinsed out with several small portions of carbon tetrachloride and transferred with a microsyringe.

If the material is too volatile to be condensed in the short Teflon tubing, a piece of Teflon tubing 4–5 in. long can be inserted into the GC outlet, and the effluent gases can be bubbled through some cooled carbon tetrachloride. This method is convenient for PMR and IR analyses.

B. Manipulation

To facilitate manipulation of small quantities, some carrier material can be used. The solution technique, use of carbon tetrachloride for IR and PMR, has been mentioned. For IR analyses, the eluant can also be trapped on KBr crystals and can be pressed into easily handled pellets. Chloroform can be used in place of carbon tetrachloride if its solvent properties are needed. Carbon disulfide can be used if absorptions in the region of 700–850 cm^{-1} are expected, but obviously, special precautions must be taken because of the low boiling point and flammability of this material. For PMR, if solubilities exclude the use of carbon tetrachloride, some deuterated solvents may be used: deuterochloroform, perdeutero-acetone, heavy water, etc. Generally, however, most GC eluants are soluble enough in carbon tetrachloride.

If large preparative GC traps are used with milligram quantities, the trapped material is spread over a large area, and quantitative recovery is difficult. If a solvent is used, the resultant solution is usually too dilute for spectral analyses. Considerable losses of sample can be expected from solvent removal. The material in large GC traps can be vacuum transferred to small containers. In such cases, care must be taken to expose the sample to a minimum amount of stopcock grease. A considerable percentage of material, in the submilligram range, can be lost by the material's dissolving into stopcock grease.

Droplets on the walls of collectors can be centrifuged down to a small-diameter section for transfer. For relatively large amounts, the eluant can be condensed in a centrifuge tube (20). If a simple glass tube is used, one end can be sealed with a torch after collection, and the condensate can be collected at the sealed end by centrifugation (15). The sample can be withdrawn with a microsyringe after the tube is cut just above the condensate. An extension of this method is the use of the Teflon tube and a separate glass collector (see Fig. 8-2). The Teflon tube is less fragile and less adsorptive than glass. The separate glass collector not only permits simple cleaning and reuse, but also permits several collections of a given material to be centrifuged into one collector.

III. Chemical Methods

A. Qualitative Analysis

When a mixture is heterofunctional, the identification of the components cannot be accomplished with any reasonable certainty by retention data alone. Once the functionality is established, the retention data can be analyzed (21) (see Chapter 7).

Walsh and Merritt (22) have developed a simple, rapid, and general method for functional group classification which can be used with any conventional gas chromatograph equipped with thermal conductivity or any other nondestructive detectors. The effluent is divided into equal streams and each of these is allowed to bubble through a vial containing an appropriate classification reagent. Walsh and Merritt studied nine functional groups: alcohols, aldehydes, ketones, esters, unsaturated aliphatic and aromatic hydrocarbons, amines, alkyl halides, sulfur compounds, and nitriles.

B. Thin-Layer Chromatography

Direct coupling of GC with thin-layer chromatography (TLC) offers new possibilities in qualitative analyses (23–26). Kaiser (25) has shown that

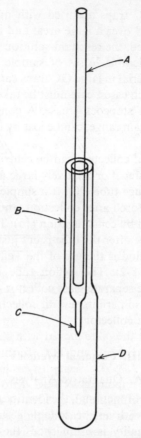

Fig. 8-2. Sample collector (16). *A*, Teflon tubing, 0.08 in. o.d., 0.06 in. i.d., 2 in. long. *B*, Pyrex tubing, 5 mm o.d., 3 mm i.d., 1 in. long. *C*, Pyrex capillary tubing, 1 mm i.d., ¼ in. long. *D*, Pyrex rod, 7 mm o.d., ¾ in. long.

the direct and automatic GC–TLC method is useful in analyzing high boiling polar substances and for further purification for UV, IR, PMR, and MS analyses.

Figure 8-3 shows a diagram of GC–TLC direct coupling. The effluent gases from the GC column impinge on a moving TLC plate. A small percentage of the gases from the GC column is diverted to a flame ionization detector (FID), and the signals from this FID are fed to a recording system to yield the usual GC separation record.

The material deposited on the TLC plate from the GC column can be sprayed with appropriate reagents for qualitative tests for various functional groups, or the TLC plate can be placed in a compartment for usual

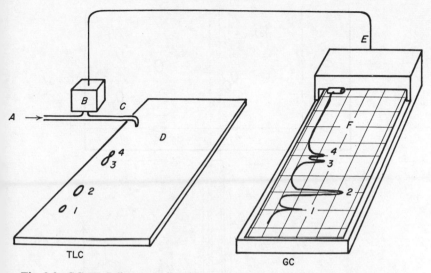

Fig. 8-3. GC–TLC direct coupling (25). *A*, GC column. *B*, Flame ionization detector. *C*, Probe delivering effluent gases to TLC plate. *D*, TLC plate. *E*, GC recorder system. *F*, GC recorder paper.

TLC; i.e., the material on the plate moved with some solvent. Figure 8-4 shows the correlation between GC and TLC. In this example, the material represented by GC peak *1*, which seems to be homogeneous by GC, is shown to be at least two compounds by TLC. Known compounds may be spotted on a side of the TLC plate for a check of R_f values. The material separated by TLC can be recovered by scraping it off and then extracting it from the solid adsorptive material with appropriate solvents for UV, IR, PMR, or MS analyses.

C. Other Methods

Indications of functional groups originally in the mixture can also be obtained by selective removal (27–29) or alteration (30) before injection. Alteration of compounds in a reaction chamber in front of the column will yield useful information (see Chapter 9), as well as the selective removal in the column (31) and the changes in relative retention times with different stationary liquids (see Chapter 4). Also, detectors sensitive only to certain functional groups may be used (see Chapter 5).

Even if the functionality is firmly established, the assignment of chemical structure and retention data can be made with reasonable certainty only with smaller molecular weight compounds, which have only a small number of possible isomers. Great care must be taken as the number of

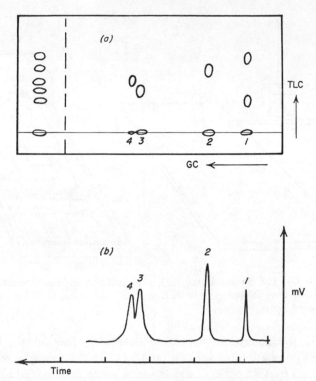

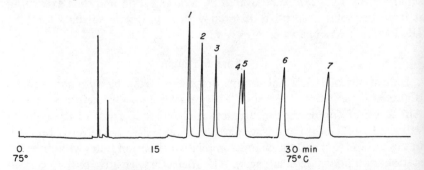

Fig. 8-4. Correlation of GC and TLC (25). (a) TLC plate, developed in one direction. (b) GC separation record. TLC control analysis with known compounds is shown in the left-hand portion of (a).

Fig. 8-5. Analysis of pentyl acetate isomers (32). Column: 500 ft × 0.02-in. i.d. open tubular, coated with SF 96(50) methyl silicone oil. Sample volume: 0.2 μl. Temperature of injection port and column: 200°C and 75°C. Carrier gas (He) inlet pressure 20 psi (gauge), flow 6 ml/min. Peaks (all acetates): (1) 1-butyl, 2,2-dimethyl-1-propyl and 1,1-dimethyl-1-propyl; (2) 3-methyl-2-butyl; (3) 2-pentyl and 3-pentyl; (4) 3-methyl-1-butyl; (5) 2-methyl-1-butyl; (6) 1-pentyl; (7) cyclopentyl.

possible isomers increases. For example, even a column with over 30,000 theoretical plates will not resolve all the pentyl acetate isomers (see Fig. 8-5). However, the investigator who must deal with a mixture of unknown compounds can gain much valuable information from analysis of retention data in combination with qualitative group analyses.

IV. Ultraviolet (UV) Spectroscopy

The use of UV absorption spectroscopy is very well known, and there are many excellent discussions, such as those by Brand and Scott (33), Jaffe and Orchin (34), and Gillam and Stern (35). Automatic recording UV spectrophotometers are commonplace.

In most cases, UV data are used to confirm chemical structures indicated by other spectral data, and molecules with such structures as to be analyzed with UV have such large absorptions that no special techniques are needed. Trapped samples can be weighed and diluted to known volumes with appropriate solvents and transferred to standard cells. For samples too difficult to trap and weigh, the eluants can be bubbled through a solvent, and the extinction coefficient can be calculated from the amount represented by the chromatogram peak area.

Some work has been done with the combination of GC and far-UV spectrophotometers (36,37). This work was for the identification of organic compounds with six carbons or less and has not been used extensively for general identification purposes.

V. Infrared (IR) Spectroscopy

A. Introduction

It was recognized in the early years of infrared spectroscopy (38) that an infrared spectrum could be used as a *fingerprint* for identifying molecules with known spectral features. Fingerprinting has so proceeded that the research worker today has access to about 46,000 catalogued IR spectra in various commercially available files. A few of the larger collections are listed in reference 39, and a convenient index to these files is published by the American Society for Testing and Materials (40).

Sorting through such a collection of spectra to find some similarity to the spectrum of an unknown would be a formidable task were it not for the wealth of information known about the absorption frequencies of molecular functional groups; i.e., *group frequencies*. Infrared spectroscopy provides one of the best ways of determining the functional groups present in a molecule. Recognition of the group frequencies in a sample spectrum often

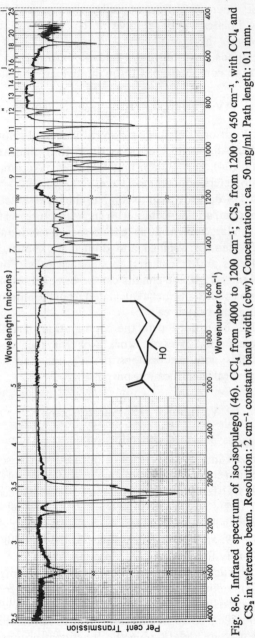

Fig. 8-6. Infrared spectrum of iso-isopulegol (46). CCl₄ from 4000 to 1200 cm⁻¹; CS₂ from 1200 to 450 cm⁻¹, with CCl₄ and CS₂ in reference beam. Resolution: 2 cm⁻¹ constant band width (cbw). Concentration: ca. 50 mg/ml. Path length: 0.1 mm.

narrows the number of possible structures to a few whose reference spectra may be quickly located with an empirical-formula file index. If a compound has never been previously measured, group frequency interpretations can lead, in most cases, to a partial if not complete structural characterization. Several good books have been written which consider group frequency correlations (41–45).

B. Spectrophotometers

The "bench-type" infrared spectrophotometer is suitable for rapid analyses or identification of the more common organic compounds, but it is not adequate for obtaining the quality of spectrum required for careful or thorough characterization of new molecular structures. Since the widths at half height of most absorption bands in liquid or solution phases are of the order of 5–10 cm^{-1}, to obtain reasonably accurate band intensities it is desirable to use instrument band widths of 1–2 cm^{-1}. The requirements of accurate spectroscopic analyses with short scan times and low noise impose constraints which can be removed only with research quality instruments. The following figures in this section were obtained with a research spectrophotometer having a 2 cm^{-1} constant band width (cbw). The spectrum of iso-isopulegol in Figure 8-6 may be compared with the spectrum in Figure 8-26 of the same material run on a bench-type instrument. The absorption at 1465 cm^{-1} (6.8 μ), which is assigned to the higher antisymmetric CH deformation typical of axial methyl groups, is not clearly resolved with the bench-type instrument.

Double-beam instruments are commonly used to obtain spectra free of atmospheric absorption. Two types of double-beam instruments are commercially available: optical-null and ratio-recording. In the former instrument, light is passed alternately through the sample and reference compartments at frequencies of about 13 cps, is dispersed and focused on a detector. The difference signal, which is produced when the light intensity in the two beams is unequal, is used to drive an attenuator comb into the reference beam to reestablish beam balance. In the ratio-recording instrument, the two light beams are chopped at different frequencies, and the signal from the detector is resolved into the two components which are electrically ratioed to give the per cent transmission. The photometric accuracy of the latter system is higher than that attainable with the optical-null because of difficulties in achieving comb linearity, good response of the whole servo system and control of instrument drift under low energy conditions. On the other hand, the ratio-recording instrument wastes at least half of the source energy for optics comparable to the optical-null instrument because of periods of simultaneous blackout of both beams due to chopper coincidence. These losses are usually made up with larger optics. A more complete introduction to instrumentation may be found in reference 42.

C. Optimum Scan Rates

If peak-intensity errors on absorption bands are to be kept less than about 3%, the ratio of instrumental band width to sample half band width (width at half height) must be less than 0.2 (45). For sample band widths of the order of 5–10 cm^{-1}, the required resolution is 1–2 cm^{-1}. The *period*, which is a measure of the response of the instrument, is defined as the time required for the pen to travel 98% of full scale when an opaque object is suddenly thrust into or removed from the sample beam. Most research instruments allow a choice of period settings; however, since the effective period may be changed by varying the amplifier gain, it is wise to determine the effective period under actual scan conditions with a stopwatch. If scan rates equal to the ratio of instrumental band width to period are used for measuring bands having halfwidths of 5 cm^{-1} or more, the dynamic photometric error can be kept within 2%. Slower scan rates must be employed for very accurate work.

Atmospheric water vapor and CO_2 have broad, intense absorption bands in the region of 3800 cm^{-1}, 1600 cm^{-1}, 2350 cm^{-1}, and 660 cm^{-1} which can remove appreciable energy from an unpurged instrument. Within these spectral regions the effective period may be lengthened by factors of 2 to 10, and if the scan rates are not adjusted accordingly, the photometric errors may be 20% or more. A single beam run of the 1600 cm^{-1} water vapor band demonstrates the advantage of purging a double-beam instrument. Pneumatic drying systems are commercially available which produce CO_2-free dry air having greater than 90% transmission in a few meters of path.

Instruments which are not programmed for constant resolution may require either adjustment of scan rate during the course of a run to maintain low dynamic errors or adjustments of slit widths to minimize resolution errors. In practice, the instrumental design will probably not allow complete automation, and some compromise between operational convenience and spectrum quality will be necessary. Some instruments employ *speed suppression* which allows a fast scan rate in absorption-free regions but which slows the scan rate in regions of high pen acceleration (normally on the sides of sharp absorption bands).

D. Sampling

Since most of the samples handled by GC are liquids at room temperature, we will not consider solid-state sampling problems. Furthermore, since most of the compounds are liquids under these conditions, there is no advantage in obtaining their spectra in the gaseous state. In most cases we will find it convenient to obtain the spectrum of the sample in solution to minimize association effects which may be present in the pure liquid. It has been found that if CCl_4 (4000–1310 cm^{-1}) and CS_2 (1310–400 cm^{-1}) are used as solvents, the spectrum is, with two exceptions, relatively free of solvent absorption. The solvent bands are at 1550 cm^{-1} (ca. 50% T in 0.1 mm path length) and 860 cm^{-1} (ca. 90% T in 0.1 mm path length) and, if desired, may be easily removed from the spectrum by reference beam compensation.

The amount of sample required to obtain a moderately intense IR spectrum depends on the absorption characteristics of the individual molecule. But, within one order of magnitude, about 10 μg of sample for each square millimeter of used beam area at the sample space are required. The used beam area is defined by the monochromator entrance slit image in the sampling area; the source image at this point should be large enough to fill completely the entrance slit image at the widest programmed opening of the entrance slits. Because of the falloff in blackbody energy at lower frequencies, most spectrometers have their entrance slits widest at their lowest frequency limit. Any vignetting of the slit image in the sample area by reduced cell dimensions will result in decreased energy relative to the referenced beam. The slit image in the sample area of the instrument used in obtaining the spectra shown in Figures 8-7 and 8-8 is ca. 25 mm high by ca. 5 mm wide at 600 cm^{-1}, and ca. 8 mm wide at 450 cm^{-1} at a constant resolution of 2 cm^{-1}. Figures 8-7 and 8-8 show a slight beam vignetting of the sample cell at 450 cm^{-1}. In order to avoid vignetting of the beam at 2 cm^{-1} resolution, the sample cell should be at least 25 mm high by 8 mm wide. The amount of sample required for an average spectrum is therefore ca. 10 [μg/mm^2] × 25 [mm] × 8 [mm] = 2 mg, and the minimum cell volume for a 0.1-mm path length is 20 μl.

Beam condensers may be used to reduce the slit image in the sample space, and devices are commercially available which provide reduction factors of 4 to 6. They are constructed with either KBr lenses or mirrors, the latter having a higher transmission. However, the longer light path of the mirror system in the sample beam makes efficient purging of the atmosphere water vapor in the sample area mandatory. A fivefold reduction in beam size for the previously mentioned case produces an entrance slit image which is 5 mm high and 1.6 mm wide, or a beam area of 8 mm^2. The amount of sample necessary for a complete spectrum is about 80 μg.

It should be noted that these requirements assume that all the sample is in the light beam. In practice the ease of constructing a cell which has a

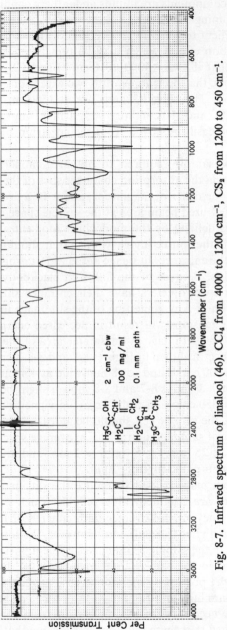

Fig. 8-7. Infrared spectrum of linalool (46). CCl₄ from 4000 to 1200 cm⁻¹, CS₂ from 1200 to 450 cm⁻¹.

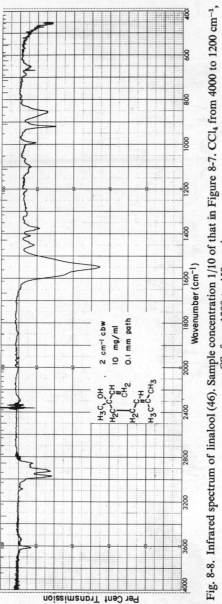

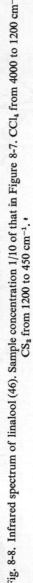

Fig. 8-8. Infrared spectrum of linalool (46). Sample concentration 1/10 of that in Figure 8-7. CCl_4 from 4000 to 1200 cm^{-1}, CS_2 from 1200 to 450 cm^{-1}.

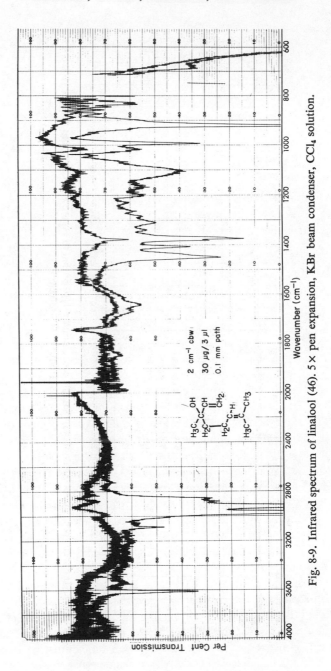

Fig. 8-9. Infrared spectrum of linalool (46). 5 × pen expansion, KBr beam condenser, CCl₄ solution.

minimum of "dead volume" (volume which the beam does not transverse) is directly related to the cell size. Accordingly, our $8 \times 25 \times 0.1$ mm cells have a total sealed volume of 25 μl, and our $6 \times 2 \times 0.1$ mm cells have a total sealed volume of 2.5 μl. In constructing the microcells, prime consideration was given to convenience of sample handling and positive sealing. The latter point is important for containing volatile solvents such as CCl_4 and CS_2 for extended periods of time.

Some spectrometers are equipped with *pen expansion;* i.e., some interval of the %T scale may be expanded to full chart scale. Since a fivefold pen expansion of the 80–100% T range approximately covers the 0–0.1 absorbance range, we may reduce the minimum sample requirement by a factor of about 10 and still produce useful spectra. Figure 8-8 is a spectrum of linalool in CCl_4 (8×25-mm cell with 0.1-mm path) produced with about one-tenth the amount of sample used in Figure 8-7. A compensated spectrum (note the 1550 cm^{-1} region) of the CCl_4 solution in the 3-μl microcell in a KBr beam condenser is shown in Figure 8-9. Superimposed on the sample run is a spectrum of the sample cell containing only CCl_4. The sample cell used in this run had 1-mm wide walls and shows vignetting below 700 cm^{-1}. A number of other spectral features typify the problems inherent in ultramicro sampling. The variable path reference cell contains impurities in the KBr windows which give rise to sharp "transmission bands" in the 1960 cm^{-1} region. The CCl_4 in the reference cell contains an impurity which shows up as a transmission band at 1740 cm^{-1}. The beam condenser absorbs slightly throughout the spectrum but absorbs strongly (viz. ca. 4%) at 1380 cm^{-1} and 1020 cm^{-1}. The general unevenness of the background run is probably caused by the combined absorption characteristics of the sample cell, reference cell, and beam condenser. The spectrophotometer used to obtain the spectrum was a ratio-recording instrument with automatic gain control. Consequently, in the 700–800 cm^{-1} region where CCl_4 absorbs all the energy from both beams, the amplifier gain reaches its upper limit, and the noise level reaches full scale. During this run, the instrument was purged with CO_2-free dry air, and the 2348 cm^{-1} CO_2 absorption region shows none of the excessive noise which is present in Figures 8-7 and 8-8 when the instrument was merely purged with dry air.

As a final comment on this spectrum, it should be noted that the CH stretching bands at 2900 and 3000 cm^{-1} and the vinyl wag at 920 cm^{-1} were all off scale, and therefore ca. 3 μg of this material could have easily been detected. By constructing cells having smaller beam heights (effectively masking the entrance slit image), spectra of 1-μg amounts of material can be obtained. However, in these cases the scan times must be lengthened and the period is increased to compensate the energy losses.

E. On-Line Spectrophotometers

Instruments which are an integral part of the GC unit have been introduced recently, and these obtain the gas-phase spectrum of each fraction as it emerges from the chromatograph. The instrumental band widths presently possible are at least an order of magnitude larger than those of research infrared spectrophotometers. This leads to a loss of spectral detail which might be useful for complete structural characterization. However, the speed of spectral presentation is of the order of seconds rather than minutes, and consequently, the instruments' use for qualitative determination of group functionality is attractive. Final structural characterization should be made on high-resolution instruments which place no premium on scan time. Hopefully, instrumentation will improve so as to remove these objections to fast-scan instruments.

VI. Mass Spectrometry (MS)

A. Introduction

Of the physical methods available to the organic chemist for the study of chemical structure, mass spectrometry has received the least attention, in spite of the fact that excellent instruments have been commercially available for years. This situation is changing rapidly, and now there are a number of excellent discussions of theory and applications in the study of molecules varying from simple aliphatic compounds to amino acids and peptides, alkaloids, steroids, and triterpenes (47–53,55). The list of mass spectra available for reference is growing rapidly (53a).

Reliable mass spectrometers of various types are available from a number of domestic and foreign companies, and the number of research organizations equipped with these instruments is rapidly increasing in spite of the rather high cost. The different types of mass spectrometers have been described by Farmer (54), and commercially available instruments are listed and compared briefly in Table 8-1.

One of the advantages of applying MS in the analyses of GC effluents is that MS analyses can be obtained with less than microgram quantities. This sensitivity and the fact that compounds separated by GC have enough vapor pressure for MS analysis make MS very compatible with GC. Two basic systems of sample introduction, batch and continuous, are being used. In the batch method, the fraction is collected so that the sample can be leisurely analyzed. In the continuous method, the effluent is introduced directly into the mass spectrometer as it emerges from the chromatograph (GC–MS). Both methods have their advantages, and various modifications are used according to the nature of the sample to be analyzed.

TABLE 8-1

Comparison of Different Types of Commercial Mass Spectrometers

Type of MS	Upper mass limit (amu)	Mass resolution ($M/\Delta M$)	Cost ($\times 10^3$ \$)	Uses and advantages
Small deflection	120–150	50–100	10–35	Residual gas analysis (RGA) qualitative analysis of low-molecular weight fractions, low cost and maintenance
Large deflection	1000–2000	400–1500	45–75	Wide range of organic applications, excellent for tandem GC–MS analyses, requires careful operation
Double focus deflection	1000–2000	600–30,000	80–130	Elemental and structure analysis of complex organic molecules, occasional tandem GC–MS, considerable maintenance, careful operation
Time-of-flight	800–1000	150–250	25–50	Organic analysis, particularly tandem GC–MS, careful operation and maintenance but ease of operation when adjusted
Linear radiofrequency	80–100	30–60	—	RGA, limited in organic analysis or tandem GC–MS
Omegatron	80	40	5–15	RGA, limited in organic analysis or tandem GC–MS
Quadrapole	150–500	20–150, 20–500	10–20	RGA, occasional use in organic analysis, and tandem GC–MS will probably increase; but apparent low cost, easy operation, and ease of maintenance will have to be proven in organic analysis
Monopole	300	20–250	10–20	

Below, we summarize briefly the problems connected to these types of sampling methods. A more detailed summary was published recently (54a).

B. Batch Sampling

The batch-sample introduction techniques have been discussed in detail by Biemann (56). Little material is needed, but great care is required to keep all sample containers scrupulously free of any volatile contaminants. If possible, it is preferable to collect the GC fractions for subsequent analyses. There is no doubt that a better quality spectrum can be obtained if ample time is available for an analysis. Furthermore, the GC–MS combination ties up both instruments and personnel, and each GC or MS unit can be used more efficiently if operated independently. Therefore, because usual amounts separated with packed columns are large enough to be collected and transferred, this type of GC column should be connected to the MS only in trace-amount studies, in studies of compounds which decompose very quickly, or of compounds which can be separated only with glass tubing columns.

C. Continuous Sampling

Recently, considerable attention has been given to the direct introduction of effluents from the gas chromatograph into a fast-scan mass spectrometer (57–63) and even into a high-resolution mass spectrometer (64,65). Continuous MS monitoring of column effluents eliminates the manipulation losses, contamination, and decomposition often encountered when submilligram quantities are collected and manually transferred to analytical instruments. Of course, with usual techniques, manipulation of submicrogram quantities is not feasible. Therefore, this GC–MS combination is particularly useful in analyzing small amounts of complicated mixtures that can be fractionated satisfactorily only with the elegant small-bore open tubular columns, such as in the analysis of strawberry oil (66,67) (Fig. 8-10). Furthermore, time and inconvenience of collecting and storing 150 or more samples for batch introduction would be prohibitive even if ample starting material were available.

1. Packed Columns

In addition to problems inherent to both instruments, the combination of the gas chromatograph and mass spectrometer requires consideration of the problem of connecting the two instruments with minimal memory effects, minimal loss of resolution, and minimal catalytic or thermal decomposition after the effluents emerge from the column. The critical

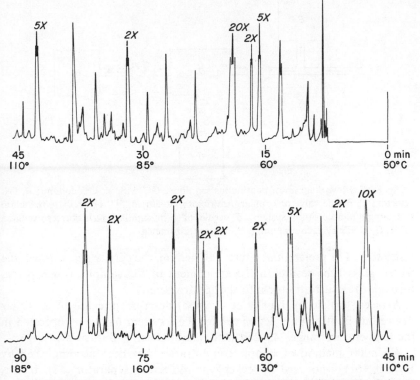

Fig. 8-10. Programmed-temperature analysis of strawberry oil (66,67). Column: 200 ft × 0.01 in. i.d. open tubular, coated with Tween-20. Sample volume: 10 μl split 1/100. Temperature of injection port: 225°C. Carrier gas (He) inlet pressure: 25 psi (gauge), flow 0.5 ml/min.

pressure drop system connecting the two instruments should be as short as possible, heated, and free of metal for unstable compounds.

Figure 8-11 shows a flow diagram of a continuous sampling GC–MS combination. For direct introduction of effluents from a packed column, some form of stream splitting is employed so that only a part of the effluent enters the spectrometer. A simple system can be made with needle valves or short sections of capillary tubing to restrict the amount of effluent into the spectrometer so that most of it continues to a GC detector, as in GC–TLC (Fig. 8-3). Watson and Biemann (65) have modified the pressure reduction system so that it not only provides a pressure drop from 1 atm to about 10^{-5} torr but also concentrates the sample 50-fold or more in the gas stream entering the mass spectrometer. A schematic of this is shown in Figure 8-12. The pressure drop is achieved with the entrance and exit

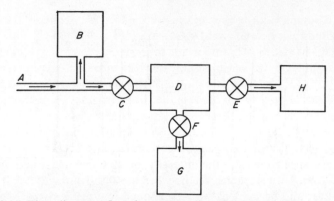

Fig. 8-11. Flow diagram of continuous sampling, GC–MS. *A*, GC column; *B*, GC detector; *C*, needle valve or capillary restrictor; *D*, simple "T" or pressure reduction and sample concentration system; *E*, needle valve or capillary restrictor; *F*, vacuum valve; *G*, auxiliary vacuum pump; *H*, mass spectrometer.

restrictors. The preferential effusion of helium, the carrier gas, through the fritted glass tube results in the enrichment of the sample, which passes through the exit restrictor into the spectrometer.

A recent article by Lipsky et al. (65*a*) describes the use of a similar device but built of thin Teflon tubing. This system has to be operated in the temperature range 240–250°C to obtain effective diffusivity.

A similar method of sample concentration has been accomplished by Ryhage (61), who used a Becker-type molecular separator (68). In this separator, the gas stream of the heavier molecules passes straight through two small-diameter holes which are close together, while the helium gas diffuses to the sides and is pumped away by an auxiliary vacuum pump.

Care must be taken that the connecting system is heated properly, especially in the analyses of high molecular weight compounds. Failure to do so will lead to the loss of separation of components accomplished by

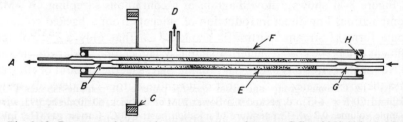

Fig. 8-12. Pressure reducer and connector system between GC and MS (65). *A*, Mass spectrometer; *B*, exit constriction; *C*, flange to bolt system to mass spectrometer; *D*, auxiliary vacuum pump; *E*, porous fritted glass tube; *F*, evacuation chamber; *G*, entrance restriction; *H*, O-ring; *I*, GC column.

the GC column. With proper heating, even such compounds as steroids and alkaloids can be analyzed by GC–MS (65).

In a GC–MS run, it is important to have a record of the chromatographic separation. In the simple case in which most of the column effluent is passed to a GC detector and only a small part is diverted to the MS, no modifications are necessary because the chromatograph is operated in the usual manner. If the fritted glass pressure reduction and sample concentration system is used, some total ion beam monitor must be used because the GC detector cannot be easily incorporated into such a system. With some mass spectrometers, the intensity of a single mass ion may be recorded (69). However, this method has the disadvantage that it is not quantitative; and in some cases, a compound may have virtually no ions at the selected mass.

A continuous oscilloscope display of the mass spectral pattern is useful to note the presence of several compounds in one peak. It is also helpful to see the mass range required for a scan and avoid scanning to an arbitrary point, say 250, when the oscilloscope display shows that 120 is sufficient. However, even with a continuous display on an oscilloscope, it is sometimes difficult to see the presence of impurities if the constituents have very similar mass spectra. Merritt and Angelini (70) have shown that subambient column temperature programming permits separation of pentane isomers which were not separated at room temperature. Figure 8-13 shows the chromatograms and the mass spectral patterns, and it is

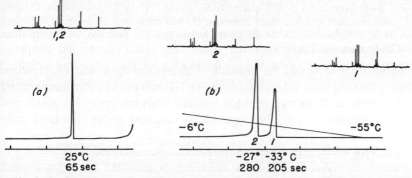

Fig. 8-13. Chromatograms and mass spectral patterns of pentane isomers (70). Column: 10 ft × ⅛-in. o.d. packed: Carbowax 20M on firebrick, 60/80 mesh, 5/95, w/w. Sample volume: 0.2 μl. Temperature of injection port: 150°C. Carrier gas (He) inlet pressure: 20 psi (gauge), flow rate: 10 ml/min. (a) Chromatogram at room temperature; 1,2, isopentane and n-pentane together in one peak. Mass spectral patterns of both pentanes superimposed. (b) Chromatogram with column at subambient temperature program. 1, Isopentane GC peak and MS pattern. 2, n-Pentane GC peak and MS pattern.

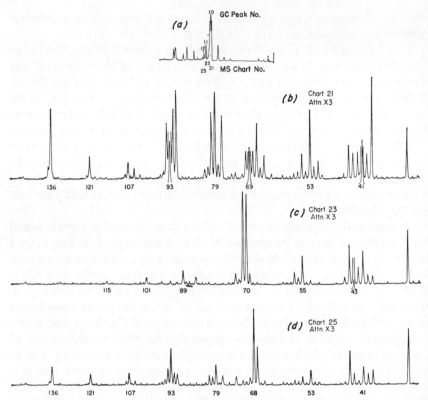

Fig. 8-14. Correlation of MS spectra to GC peaks (71). (*a*) Chromatogram showing GC peak numbers and MS chart numbers. (*b*) MS chart No. 21, myrcene, GC peak No. 10. (*c*) MS chart No. 23, 2-methylbutyl isobutyrate, GC peak No. 11. (*d*) MS chart No. 25, limonene, GC peak No. 12.

apparent that it would be difficult to determine from the oscilloscope display that the material coming from the GC column at room temperature was a mixture of the two pentane isomers. This example also points out the importance of using high-resolution columns under optimum conditions.

When an effluent is observed on the chromatographic trace or on the oscilloscope, its complete mass spectrum is recorded on a high-speed oscillograph, magnetic tape, or photographic plate. The spectra are numbered, and these numbers are written on the GC–MS chromatogram precisely at the time the MS pattern is recorded. In this manner, the mass spectra can be correlated with the material represented by the GC peaks, as shown in Figure 8-14. These mass spectral charts also show how cleanly the material is swept out to give good mass spectra, uncontaminated with previous material even though the preceding material was present in greater quantity.

The manual analysis of MS data from GC–MS analyses of complex mixtures, such as strawberry oil (Fig. 8-10), is very time consuming. Many hundreds of mass spectral pattern charts are obtained in a single run. A computer can handle the arithmetic involved much faster, more reliably, and more exhaustively. Biemann and co-workers (72) have shown that interpretation of MS data, especially with high-resolution instruments (55), is greatly aided by use of computers.

2. Open Tubular Columns

Although some high-plate-value packed columns have been made, no packed column has the resolution possible with the 0.01-in. i.d. open tubular column. Examples of GC–MS analyses of complex mixtures with such high-resolution columns are shown in Figures 8-10 and 8-27. The sensitivity of the mass spectrometer makes it possible to utilize the great separative power of the open tubular columns, even though the 0.01-in. i.d. column can tolerate only up to 5 μg of a single component without endangering the life of the column. The load tolerances of 0.02-in. i.d. and 0.03-in. i.d. columns are 20 and 200 μg, respectively.

Because of the small rate of flow through the 0.01-in. i.d. and the 0.02-in. i.d. columns, about 0.5 and 5 ml/min, respectively, these columns can be connected directly to the vacuum inlet system of the mass spectrometer. Since the 0.03-in. i.d. column has a flow of about 15 ml/min, a pressure-drop system (Fig. 8-11) should be used, and some enrichment may be possible with a molecular separator (65,68).

After conditions as to the stationary liquid and temperature program best suited for a given mixture are determined with the column connected to a flame ionization detector (FID), the column is disconnected from the FID and is connected to the mass spectrometer. If one end of the column is connected directly to the vacuum inlet system, then the inlet pressure to the column must be lowered about 15 psi to maintain the same average linear velocity of the carrier gas obtained with the column attached to the FID. With the same linear velocity, the column operates at the same efficiency as with the exit at atmospheric pressure and the elution times are closely matched (73).

For a pressure drop of about 20 psi across 0.01-, 0.02-, and 0.03-in. i.d. open tubular columns, lengths of 200, 500, and 1000 ft are required. Thus, to maintain the same linear velocities with one end of the column at a pressure reduced by 1 atm, the inlet to these columns must be about 5 psi (gauge). At this pressure, the stream splitting to inject micrograms into the

0.01-in. i.d. column is reduced but still reproducible, but at lower pressures, i.e., with shorter columns, the amount of sample entering the column varies considerably from injection to injection. Because of the greater capacities of the large-bore columns, direct, reproducible injections into the columns are possible at low pressures. Two convenient columns to use for GC–MS analyses are the 200 ft × 0.01 in. i.d. and the 500 ft × 0.02 in. i.d. open tubular columns connected directly to the mass spectrometer inlet vacuum system. Compounds from methane, ethane, etc., on up to sesquiterpenoids have been conveniently separated by these columns (74).

D. MS Background

The GC–MS combination imposes a limitation on the operating temperature range of the stationary liquid phases since column bleeding must not obscure the mass spectral patterns of the material being separated and analyzed. To minimize column bleed, columns should be conditioned for at least several days at temperatures 25–50°C hotter than will normally be used in the analyses (73). With such conditioning, the columns can be used immediately after installation in the instruments without serious bleed

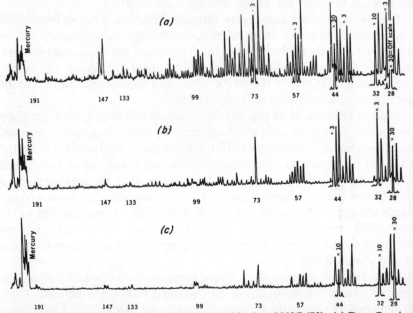

Fig. 8-15. Mass spectral patterns of column bleed at 200°C (73). (a) Dow Corning 710, not properly conditioned. (b) Carbowax 1540 and Tween-20. (c) Versilube F50 and SF 96(50).

problems. Figure 8-15 shows some mass spectral patterns of column bleed at 200°C. It is obvious that a background such as (a), Figure 8-15, would make it difficult to interpret the MS pattern of the material being studied. A column with such bleed at 200°C must be further conditioned or used only at lower temperatures.

High MS background does not necessarily come from stationary liquid phase bleed. High molecular weight compounds from previous injections may slowly elute to give an appreciable background as the column temperature is programmed up, and columns should be cleared of such compounds by keeping them at upper conditioning temperatures at least overnight before connecting to the mass spectrometer. Primary alcohols will "tail" and obscure the following compounds if some polar stationary liquid is not added to a nonpolar stationary liquid phase. Only a very small amount of polar stationary liquid mixed with a nonpolar liquid before coating a column will lessen the "tailing," usually attributed to adsorption on active sites. With proper care, the adsorption can be lessened considerably without changing relative retention times appreciably.

Another source of "tailing" has been briefly mentioned. If compounds emerging from the GC column are of low volatility, they may not pump out of the ion source before the next fraction enters. However, if the connection from the column to the mass spectrometer is kept at the column temperature and if the ionization chamber region is kept no less than 50–80°C lower than the column temperature, no difficulties are encountered with memory effects with compounds as large as oxygenated sesquiterpenes (73), or even as large as alkaloids and steroids (65).

E. MS Recording Techniques and Scanning Rates

1. Recording

The GC–MS combination requires rapid scanning of the mass spectrum which makes special demands on the amplifier–recorder system of the mass spectrometer.

a. Electrometers. The magnitude of the ion currents separated in MS may vary from 10^{-9} A down to a limit determined by the MS detector. Currents as low as 10^{-14}–10^{-15} A can be amplified with a dc electrometer, and 10^{-16} A, with a vibrating reed electrometer. The time constants of electrometers depend upon the input resistance and capacity and thus are proportional to the sensitivity. For most applications, the time constant will be 10^{-2}–10^{-1} sec corresponding to approximate current sensitivities of 10^{-14} and 10^{-15} A. This is fast enough to scan a mass spectrum from a collected sample, but for most GC–MS analyses, a faster amplifying system is preferred.

b. Electron Multipliers.   The present emphasis on qualitative, structural, and elemental analysis has brought the electron multiplier into general use with mass spectrometers. Although this amplifying system does not have the stability of an electrometer circuit, and although it has sensitivity discrimination to different types of ions, low-noise, wide-band amplification is obtained with much higher current sensitivity. For most electron multipliers, the dark current will be 10^{-20}–10^{-21} A, and the sensitivity limit is frequently determined by acceptable statistical errors.

Current gains of 10^6–10^7 are easily attained with electron multipliers. The current from the multiplier is further amplified with a dc electrometer, but the electrometer input resistance is generally reduced by a factor of 10^3–10^5 with a resulting system gain of 10^2–10^4. Further gain is restricted to specific applications in counting techniques. Usually, the mass spectrometer background limits the practical sensitivity. Reduction of the electrometer input resistance results in a corresponding decrease in the time constant, and the combined multiplier–electrometer system can be designed to operate at 10^3–10^4 cps.

c. Strip Chart Recorders.   When a sample is collected from a chromatograph and introduced into the mass spectrometer through a pinhole leak, the mass spectrum is generally scanned in 1–15 min. For this rate of scan, potentiometric pen recorders with full-scale rise times of 0.1–0.5 sec are frequently used and give a clear, precise record. Some inconvenience is encountered if frequent attenuations are desired, but for many of the qualitative aspects of modern mass spectrometry, no more than three or four mass peaks need to be reduced.

Pen recorders are not feasible for most GC–MS applications. In some instances, hot-stylus recorders with frequency response of 200 cps have proven satisfactory, but in order to attain reasonable versatility it is necessary to have a frequency response of at least 600 cps, and for many applications, greater than 1500 cps.

d. Oscillographs.   To obtain a higher-frequency response and to obviate the problem of attenuation, much mass spectral recording is performed with oscillographic recorders. As a rule, four to six galvanometers are used, each receiving the same signal but attenuated by about a factor of three for each successive galvanometer. If accuracy is more important than a fast scan rate, galvanometers with a frequency response of 30 cps are employed. These give a precise record and damp out higher-frequency noise signals. For fast-scan recording a selection of galvanometers with frequency responses up to 5000 cps is available, but most GC–MS work can be performed with 1000–1600-cps galvanometers.

Either light-sensitive or UV-sensitive recording charts are available. The convenience of a direct writing system generally overcomes the modest instability inherent in UV-sensitive papers so that this type tends to be increasingly popular. In the few instances in which frequency response of 5000 cps is used, the faster writing speed of the light-sensitive paper is desirable for clarity of recorded trace.

Current requirements of high-speed galvanometers are such that a power amplifier is necessary to boost the electrometer output and match the output impedance. Many suitable units are available, and this is only of concern for low-cost GC–MS units.

e. Photograph of Oscilloscope Trace. Provision of a cyclic scan and coordinated oscilloscope trigger signal permit visual display of the mass spectral pattern on an oscilloscope. Appropriate circuitry can be provided for most types of mass spectrometer, but for a clear display, scan cycles should be repeated at about 0.1-sec intervals. For many mass spectrometers this is not easily accomplished without interfering with the regular mass spectral scan, and a compromise of 0.5–3-sec cyclic intervals is often used. The Time-of-Flight spectrometer has a scan cycle of 10,000 cps inherent in its operation, and this gives an excellent oscilloscope presentation that does not interfere with other functions.

Photography of oscilloscope displays has been used for recording mass spectra. Such a record has the disadvantage of allowing no attenuation and is severely limited in the mass range that can be clearly displayed. The one advantage is that an instantaneous mass spectrum is obtained. However, with an electron multiplier and properly chosen oscillograph, a mass range of 24–200 can generally be scanned in 0.5–2 sec, and the speed obtained by the photographic system is not needed for most GC–MS applications.

f. Tape Recorders. Mass spectral output can also be stored on magnetic recording tape, and the data can be retrieved later in digital or analog form. Until recently, this has not been used, principally because the much cheaper strip chart recorders, etc. give a suitable analog record when desired and digitizers are available that will operate directly from most mass spectrometers. However, recent interest in fast recording of high resolution mass spectra has stimulated interest in wide band recording systems, and a few mass spectrometers have now been equipped with magnetic tape recorders. The available frequency response of 10–50 kc/sec will permit scanning a high-resolution mass spectrum in a few seconds (76,77).

g. Photoplate Detection. In magnetic deflection mass spectrometers, certain geometries result in focus of the ions of all masses in a plane. Several companies offer a double-focusing mass spectrometer of the Mattauch-Herzog type which provides for insertion of a photoplate at this plane, and the user has the option of electrical detection or photo-detection. The sensitivity of the photoplate to impinging ions is generally about three orders of magnitude lower than that of an electron multiplier, but because it is an integrating system, this disadvantage is overcome in certain applications. The minimal detection limit of a photoplate is generally regarded to be 10^{-15}–10^{-16} coulombs, but to attain this level requires an extremely good vacuum (better than 5×10^{-8} torr) to prevent ion scattering and great care and skill in handling of the photoplates.

2. Scan Rate and Resolution

Scan rate has become an important specification in determining the utility of the mass spectrometer, especially for samples of less than a microgram or for GC–MS analyses. To determine the time constants required for a particular scan rate, it is necessary to specify the resolution of the mass spectrometer. This parameter determines the time-width of the mass spectral peak in scanning a specific mass range in a specified time. For example, a scan from mass 24 to 200 in 3 sec requires a frequency response of about 200 cps at a resolution of 200. The same mass range scanned in 1 sec at a resolution of 400 would require 1200 cps response. In the first case, an electrometer amplifier with slightly reduced sensitivity can be used, but a hot-stylus recorder or oscillograph would be required for the trace. The second case could only be reasonably accomplished with an electron multiplier and an oscillograph with about 1500-cps galvanom-eters. Any attempt to scan faster or with higher resolution would result in peak clipping and distortion. Happily, most GC–MS studies can be accomplished with a resolution of 400 or less, and the necessary compo-nents are conveniently available.

Obviously, fast scanning of chromatographic peaks at high resolution (10,000 or more) requires higher frequency response. Even with a scan period of 10 sec, a response time of 5000 cps is necessary. This can be accomplished with a wide-band-amplifier electron multiplier and high-frequency galvanometers in an oscillograph, but for most purposes the system is not practical for monitoring GC effluents. Chart speeds in excess of 100 in./sec are necessary to obtain a readable analog record, and this introduces the additional problems of coordinating the chart speed (starting from zero) with the scan, handling the charts, and storage. An example of an oscillographic recording of a fast scan at resolution 10,000 is shown in Figure 8-16.

Some of the disadvantages inherent in use of an oscillograph for recording high-resolution fast-scan mass spectra can be obviated by use of a magnetic tape recorder. Continuous recording of repetitive scans has been proposed (76). Such a system would give mass spectral records over the complete chromatographic run, and differences in the front or back of a peak would not go unnoticed. On the other hand, many extra records would be taken, and the researcher would be obliged to scrutinize each before discarding. In actual practice, it is not necessary to obtain high-resolution mass spectra on more than a few of the chromatographic peaks, and a more selective system may be preferred.

Statistical limits are also important in the determination of how rapidly a mass spectrum can be scanned, particularly at high mass resolution. As was indicated, it is often desirable to measure currents of 10^{-15}–10^{-16} A.

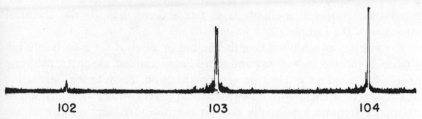

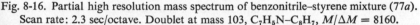

| 102 | 103 | 104 |

Fig. 8-16. Partial high resolution mass spectrum of benzonitrile–styrene mixture (77a). Scan rate: 2.3 sec/octave. Doublet at mass 103, C_7H_5N–C_8H_7, $M/\Delta M = 8160$.

Since 10^{-15} A corresponds to about 10^4 ions/sec, a scan of this peak in 10^{-3} sec would collect only 10 ions, and obviously the practical statistical limit is reached or exceeded. This scan rate corresponds to that generally used in GC–MS runs with resolution of about 400. If the resolution is increased to 10,000, the same scan rate would require 2×10^{-13} A to produce 10 ions. It has been shown that a reasonable precision of mass measurement can be attained with this number of ions, but the current requirements are two or three orders of magnitude higher than is desired (77).

The Mattauch-Herzog mass spectrometer utilizes photoplate detection and gives resolutions in excess of 10,000. A fast high-resolution mass spectrum can be obtained from this instrument because the photoplate integrates all peaks (64,65). If an exposure time of 10–100 sec is conveniently possible, the sensitivity limit occurs at less than 10^{-16} A since the minimal detection limit on a photoplate is about 10^4 ions or 10^{-15} coul.

The sensitivity limits suggested refer in both cases to the minimum current that will give a detectable signal and a reasonably precise mass measurement. (A few parts per million is considered desirable in high-resolution mass spectrometry.) In actual practice, an important mass spectral peak may often be less than 5% of the most abundant peak, and the limiting current required would refer, of course, to the important peak. It is obvious that one should never use a faster scan rate or higher resolution than is necessary.

VII. Proton Magnetic Resonance (PMR)

A. Introduction

During the past few years, high-resolution nuclear magnetic resonance (NMR) has become a most valuable tool for detailed studies of chemical structure. This technique uses magnetic nuclei in the sample as probes for the determination of magnetic properties at the molecular level. Well-established empirical methods then relate these data to the chemical structure of the sample.

The sample, which must be either liquid or gaseous for high-resolution studies, is located in a strong and exceedingly uniform magnetic field and exposed to a source of electromagnetic radiation. Because the interaction of a magnetic nucleus with a magnetic field is very weak, the transition or resonance frequency normally falls in the radio-frequency range of the spectrum. The ratio of this frequency to the magnetic field is a fundamental property of each magnetic nucleus. Thus, unlike other spectroscopic techniques, the NMR spectral behavior of a sample depends on the magnetic field as well as on the frequency of the radiation to which it is exposed.

Most high-resolution spectrometers hold the radiation frequency constant and vary the magnetic field over a narrow interval that is characteristic of a particular isotope in a range of chemical environments. In a magnetic field, each electron creates a local magnetic field which, depending on the molecular geometry and the orbital it occupies, may either reinforce or reduce the applied magnetic field at a particular nuclear position. Thus, the electronic, and consequently the chemical, environment of a nucleus is revealed by the change or "chemical shift" of the external field that is required to compensate for this local field. As the field is slowly varied, a sensitive radio receiver detects and records the resonances arising from nuclei in different chemical environments as they are successively excited.

From the standpoint of organic applications, it is fortunate that of the many stable magnetic nuclei, protons have the highest NMR sensitivity. Among the other nuclei having sensitivities at all comparable to that of hydrogen, only fluorine-19, boron-11, and phosphorus-31 appear significant at this time for GC–NMR applications. Flourine has a sensitivity of 83% relative to that of hydrogen in the same magnetic field; boron-11, 17% with 81% natural abundance; and phosphorus, 7%. Unfortunately, low sensitivity is often combined with low natural abundance. For example, carbon-13, the only magnetic isotope of carbon and hence a nucleus of great potential value, has an abundance of 1 % and a sensitivity of 1.5 %. However, until much higher magnetic fields become available from super-conducting magnets, studies of this isotope in chromatographic effluents appear quite unfeasible. The remainder of this discussion will be concerned with high-resolution proton magnetic resonance (PMR), although the techniques described can be applied directly to fluorine (provided a spectrometer tuned to its resonance frequency is available), and useful information should be obtainable from phosphorus studies in some cases although the 14-fold reduction in sensitivity will be a severe handicap. Although the sensitivity for boron-11 is fair, its resonances are one to two orders of magnitude broader because of nuclear quadropole effects.

A number of excellent books and review articles are available dealing both with the theoretical and experimental aspects of high-resolution NMR and with its applications to organic chemistry. The theory of high-resolution NMR, as well as many early applications, has been thoroughly reviewed (78). For detailed information concerning instrumentation, the papers presented at the Third Annual Varian NMR Workshop are most helpful (79). The application of NMR to organic chemical problems is described in an early book (80) and in two more recent books (81,82). Extensive references to a wide range of applications can be obtained in several review articles (83–85). An excellent introductory article has recently been published (86). As an aid to spectral interpretation, there is a catalog of 700 standard PMR spectra which are indexed by compound, position, and proton environment (87), as well as several other extensive collections of spectra (88,89).

Highly versatile, though complex, research-oriented spectrometers are used for proton studies at frequencies up to 100 Mc. A lower-cost analytical spectrometer for routine studies of hydrogen at 60 Mc is also available. A similar, but more expensive, instrument provides in addition the capability for fluorine studies at 56.4 Mc. The analytical units are more convenient to operate but have a somewhat lower sensitivity. The vast majority of PMR investigations have been carried out on the 60-Mc analytical instrument (Varian A-60). The basic cost of high resolution spectrometers ranges from $27,000 for the analytical instrument to $65,000 for the most elaborate 100 Mc unit. Similar instruments made in England and Japan should be available in the United States in the near future. While the A-60 is not comparable either in price or simplicity and reliability of operation to the bench-top infrared and ultraviolet instruments, it will perform very satisfactorily on a routine basis providing that its thermal and magnetic surroundings are reasonably stable and it is operated carefully.

The principal problem involved in the application of PMR to the analysis of chromatographic effluents is sensitivity. Of the major spectrographic techniques PMR is the least sensitive. Until very recently the minimum practical sample size for the analytical instrument was of the order of 10 mg. Thus, when PMR analyses of GC fractions were desired, only packed columns were practical, and often several passes were necessary. Nevertheless, PMR has been used to analyze GC effluents (89a).

Two recent developments in PMR instrumentation have dramatically improved this situation. A practical microcell and a complex electronic device which essentially averages random noise while summing coherent sample signals over many successive spectral scans have become available. The combination of these two techniques with large-bore open tubular columns has finally made PMR a really significant analytical tool for the gas chromatographer (90).

B. Signal Enhancement

1. Microcells

For maximum sensitivity, it is necessary to confine the sample as completely as possible to the active region of the small receiver pickup coil in the probe, which has a volume of less than 0.05 ml. To do this without distorting the magnetic field, the sample must be spherical. The problem is finding a convenient means of containing liquid samples in spherical volumes of the order of 25–50 μl. Several types of PMR microcells have been described. These give up to a fivefold sensitivity enhancement provided the sample is sufficiently soluble. The usefulness of PMR for chromatographic applications depends to a large extent on the ease of handling and versatility of the microcell that is employed.

The first commercial microcell available in the U.S. was developed and subsequently marketed by Varian Associates. It is shown in Figure 8-17. Two nylon inserts fit snugly into a conventional precision-bore sample tube which is open at the bottom so that inserts can be manipulated from both top and bottom. At one end of each insert, a hemispherical depression is cut out so that when the inserts are pressed tightly together a spherical cavity is created at the center having a volume of roughly 25 μl. A fine hole is drilled along the axis of the upper insert to permit filling. This insert also contains a cavity in the top to hold the sample. A similar depression in the lower end of the bottom insert permits a manipulating rod to engage holes in the side of the lower insert. The top plug is first correctly positioned with respect to the receiver coil, and then the lower plug is pushed up tight against it. After the necessary volume of solvent or solution has been introduced from the top, withdrawing the lower insert causes the solution to be sucked into the spherical chamber. Finally, the bottom insert is pushed up until a small amount of solution is forced out of the hole so that no air remains in the cavity.

In principle, the Varian cell is most ingenious. In practice, it is almost impossible to obtain satisfactory performance with the inserts tight together. Few workers have been able to use them closer than about 7 mm. This spacing provides a cylindrical volume of roughly 150 μl, which gives

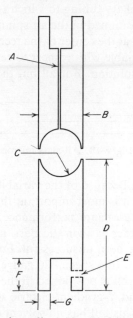

Fig. 8-17. Nylon inserts for microcell. *A*, No. 80 drill hole; *B*, 0.166-in. o.d. (snug fit in tube); *C*, radius of hemisphere: 0.073 in; *D*, 0.5 in.; *E*, 0.040-in. hole; *F*, 0.10 in.; *G*, 0.020 in.

only a little more than an increase of 2 in sensitivity over a standard cell. Nor is this the only difficulty. Air often leaks into the sphere because the inserts are not sufficiently tight. This can be largely avoided by using a syringe with an extremely fine needle to inject the solution directly into the spherical cavity. There is also a severe limitation as to satisfactory solvents because of the difference in bulk magnetic susceptibility between the inserts and the solvent. Only chloroform and carbon tetrachloride can be used successfully, and if these are left in the cell for an extended time, the inserts swell and crack the precision glass tube. To avoid cracking the end of the tube, the rod used to manipulate the lower insert must be handled very carefully. The difference in thermal expansion of glass and nylon prevents the use of the cell at elevated temperatures. For chromato-graphic applications, the temperature and solvent limitations are not too significant, but the virtual impossibility of obtaining an enhancement of more than two together with the fragility of the cell restricts its general usefulness.

A very convenient all-glass microcell is now available (91). As shown in Figure 8-18, it consists of a 25–50 μl sphere blown in the bottom of a length of heavy-wall capillary tubing to which is attached a length of solid rod. When the tube is positioned in the air spinner of the A-60 in the usual way, the cavity is located at the center of the receiver coil. The performance of these cells is quite variable with respect to resolution. The best of them only slightly degrade resolution. For all but the most exacting work, this

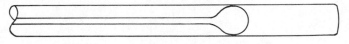

Fig. 8-18. All-glass microcell.

decrease is unimportant. Because of the variability that has been observed with some lots of tubes, it is most important that each cell be checked for resolution. Attempts to correlate performance with visible defects in the cell such as bubbles or other flaws in the glass, nonsphericity of the bubble, or off-axis capillary have been unsuccessful. For loading the cell, a 50- or 100-μl gas-tight syringe with a special 26 gauge, 0.004-in. i.d., 8-in. needle is convenient. After the cell is positioned in the probe, a slight adjustment of both the curvature and Y-gradient electric shim is usually necessary to obtain best resolution. This cell has no solvent or temperature limitations.

As the volume of these microcells is of the order of 50 μl, a sensitivity improvement of about 8 would appear possible. However, because the "active" volume of the receiver coil is not precisely defined, some of the nuclei in the large cell outside the microcell volume are loosely coupled to the coil. For equal concentrations, this microcell gives approximately one-half the signal intensity of the standard cell. An overall enhancement by about 4 is thus possible. While an enhancement of 5 has been estimated for the Varian cell, the strength, simplicity of sample manipulation, and the consistent attainment of fourfold enhancement make the all-glass microcell much more useful.

A technique for trapping directly in a micro glass cell with a larger capillary has been reported (92). This technique should be very helpful in reducing manipulation losses and chances for contamination. However, the larger capillary appears to cause poorer resolution.

Recently, the ingenious microcell shown in Figure 8-19 was described (93). A bulb is blown from fine capillary tubing and supported by its stem at the top of a standard sample tube with a friction-grip Teflon chuck. The bulb can be easily positioned for optimum coupling to the receiver

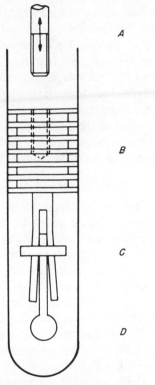

Fig. 8-19. Thin-wall capillary microcell inside standard cell (93). *A*, Metal rod for positioning holder. *B*, Holder (nylon, Teflon). *C*, Slide ring (nylon, Teflon). *D*, Thin-wall glass capillary and sphere.

coil and is prevented from wobbling by a non-proton-containing liquid such as carbon tetrachloride in the cylindrical tube. The advantage of this cell is that it can be made easily in the laboratory.

Sample uncleanliness is much more troublesome with microcells. Solid material of any kind (dust, filter paper fibers, undissolved sample, etc.) degrades resolution severely. In a regular sample tube the probability that this material is located outside the volume sensed by the pickup coil is quite large since the total sample volume is about 10 times the "active" volume. In a microcell, however, the entire volume is "active" and there is no margin of safety. One method for removing solid material from samples is provided by the smallest commercially available filter tube with a medium porous glass disc. The tip is drawn out so that it will fit onto a standard NMR tube. The solution is forced through the filter using clean air or nitrogen and then transferred to the microcell. Dirt is such a common problem with micro samples that time can probably be saved by filtering all samples. Syringe filter holders are also available in which the very inert regenerated cellulose filters can be used, but the smallest of these has a volume considerably larger than that of the microcell.

With the four- to fivefold increase in sensitivity by use of microcells, 2–4 mg of sample in the 150 molecular-weight range yields a good spectrum with the A-60. This sample requirement is reduced by 4 with the high-sensitivity modification on the Varian research-type 60-Mc spectrometer; and with the 100-Mc instrument, by a factor of about 6. Thus, a good spectrum can be obtained at 100 Mc with as little as 0.3–0.6 mg of material.

2. Other Operating Techniques

Higher-field operation offers a possibility for a further improvement in sensitivity, since there is a rough proportionality between NMR resonance frequency and detection limit. High-resolution superconducting magnets have already provided satisfactory proton spectra at 200 Mc (94), and within a few years, 400-Mc proton spectra should be available. Whether or not the full fourfold increase in sensitivity over the current 100-Mc performance can be achieved is more difficult to predict, but some increase seems probable, especially for nuclei other than protons.

A new high-resolution operating technique was recently described (95). In principle it is similar to the interferometric methods used in other branches of spectroscopy. Pulse excitation is employed at a fixed magnetic field to yield the Fourier transform of the usual absorption spectrum which can be very rapidly inverted to the customary spectrum by a small computer. When the equipment becomes available, this technique should provide an increase in sensitivity of at least a factor of 10 over the current operating mode with only moderate deviations from steady-state intensities.

3. Noise Averaging

At the present time, once the sample configuration and operating frequency have been established, some form of data smoothing becomes the only technique for further enhancing sensitivity. Time averaging is certainly the most powerful of all means for improving the signal-to-noise ratio of a PMR spectrum. Essentially by averaging many spectral scans, this method converts operating time into increased sensitivity on a square-root basis.

The technique is based on the principle that noise, being a random process, tends to cancel while signals, if they occur coherently, add directly. That is, if a spectrum is scanned many times in a reproducible fashion, the positive and negative noise components tend to cancel and so only build up in proportion to the square root of the number of scans while coherent components add strictly in a linear manner. Thus, the ratio of signal to RMS-noise intensity increases approximately as the square root of the

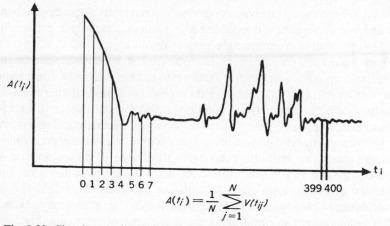

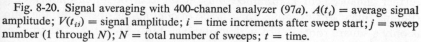

$$A(t_i) = \frac{1}{N} \sum_{j=1}^{N} V(t_{ij})$$

Fig. 8-20. Signal averaging with 400-channel analyzer (97a). $A(t_i)$ = average signal amplitude; $V(t_{ij})$ = signal amplitude; i = time increments after sweep start; j = sweep number (1 through N); N = total number of sweeps; t = time.

number of scans. A detailed theoretical analysis of both this technique and optimum filtering for NMR for a wide range of operating conditions and types of noise has been made (96).

A number of electronic devices are commercially available which perform the summing function for time averaging. While differing in detail, they all consist of a small computer-type memory; timing circuits to serially advance, at a uniform rate, the channel in which the spectral data are stored as the magnetic field is slowly swept; a means for converting the average electrical signal from the spectrometer during the residence time in one channel into a digital signal that is added to, or averaged with, whatever information that is already stored in that memory location; and a means for initiating this cycle at the same field position. Thus, so long as coherence is maintained over successive scans between channel numbers, or address, and magnetic field position, corresponding signals and instantaneous noise components for any number of scans are added in the same memory channel. Figure 8-20 shows diagrammatically the operation of such a device. At the conclusion of the averaging period, the contents of the memory are converted into an analog voltage and played out on the normal spectrometer chart.

Obviously, the resolution of any of these devices is limited by the number of channels in the memory. Thus, with a 1024-channel unit (the size now being marketed by Varian which will directly drive the A-60), the maximum resolution attainable is 1/1024 of the sweep interval. For normal scans at 60 Mc, 1024 channels provide adequate resolution for the standard 500-cps sweep interval. A narrower sweep interval can be scanned, once the overall spectrum is established, to enhance rapidly a portion of the spectrum with correspondingly greater resolution.

Where maximum enhancement is required, the sweep rate can be increased to 5 cps/sec, a somewhat faster rate than is normally considered good practice. However, the small shifts in peak positions and alterations in intensity that occur under these conditions (96) do not appear to be too serious a handicap. In a well-stabilized environment the analytical spectrometer will run unattended for at least a day with a reasonable probability of having acceptable resolution throughout this time. With a scan rate of 5 cps/sec, one can accumulate almost 900 scans during a day for a net improvement of about 30 in signal-to-noise or 550 scans overnight for an enhancement of 23. Beyond a running time of a day, or at most a weekend, further enhancement is obtained only at the cost of unreasonably long running times. For example, for a week of continuous operation, the gain is only a square root of 7 over that obtained for a 24-hr run. The square-root dependence between signal enhancement and operation time emphasizes the importance of the microcell. To obtain the enhancement of 4 provided by the microcell, one would have to increase the scan time 16-fold. Thus, one day's averaging with a microcell is equal to 16 days of continuous scanning with a standard cell!

The use of a 400-channel multiscaler as a device for storing PMR spectra has been described in detail (97). Some early results from a 400-channel "Computer Average Transients" (CAT) (97a) attached to an A-60 have been reported (98), as has later work describing the circuitry needed to use a standard 1024-channel CAT with an A-60 (90). The Varian instrument is a modified form of this latter CAT.

Computer smoothing of spectral data can be used to advantage in conjunction with a CAT since it essentially trades computer operating time, which can be extremely rapid, for spectral scanning time (99). This technique closely approximates an ideal filter and so can provide an enhancement equivalent to as much as a 25-fold increase in scanning time in these cases where the filtering has not been otherwise optimized (100). However, one point needs to be emphasized. All bands that are to be smoothed must be considerably above the noise; otherwise, the smoothing process will not converge. When a small computer is available, the combination of time averaging with curve smoothing undoubtedly forms a powerful tool.

C. Sample Requirements

In summary, Table 8-2 shows the sample requirement for resolving a broad, multiply split, single-proton peak from a 150-molecular weight compound for the three Varian spectrometers with various combinations

TABLE 8-2

Minimum Sample[a] Required for PMR with Various Sensitivity-Enhancing Techniques (in Micrograms)

Instrument	A-60	HR-60	HR-100
With standard sample tube	12,000	3000	2000
With spherical glass microcell	3000	750	500
Plus time averaging			
15 hr (one night)	125	30	20
24 hr	100	25	15
Plus Fourier transform technique	10	2.5	1.5
Plus 25-point computer smoothing	20–40(?)	5–10(?)	3–6(?)

[a] For MW $\cong$ 150, in order to resolve splittings in multiply-coupled single-proton peaks. For a sharp, unsplit signal from a single proton, divide by 7.

of sensitivity-enhancing techniques. For a sharp, unsplit line from one proton, these values can be divided by seven. It is obvious that these techniques provide sufficient additional sensitivity to make PMR extremely valuable for the analysis of fractions from all but the smallest-bore open tubular column gas chromatographs.

Figure 8-21 shows the 60-Mc PMR spectrum of 0.8 mg of isopulegol in carbon tetrachloride in a spherical glass microcell (90). Curve *a* represents the optimum performance from a single scan on the A-60 and was obtained using a 500-sec sweep time, an 0.4 bandwidth filter, and an effective nuclear-sideband rf-field of 60 μG. Curve *b* was obtained by summing 210 scans each requiring 250 sec. Curve *c* is the result of a single scan on the HR-100 under the same conditions as used for *a*.

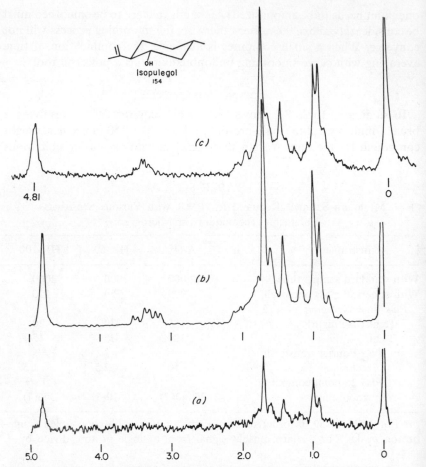

Fig. 8-21. PMR spectra of 0.8 mg isopulegol in all-glass microcell. (*a*) Single scan at 60 Mc. (*b*) 210 scans at 60 Mc. (*c*) Single scan at 100 Mc.

The doublet-split triplet centered at delta = 3.32 in curve *b* of Figure 8-21 arises from the single carbinol hydrogen and so provides a convenient measure of the sensitivity of the various methods. In the single scan, the multiplet cannot be seen while in the 100-Mc scan (curve *c*), it, along with its coarse triplet splitting, is readily apparent, although the magnitude of the fine doublet splitting would be open to some question.

It is obvious from curve *b* that the A-60 with a microcell and with time averaging can yield useful spectra from samples appreciably smaller than 0.8 mg. To establish the minimum sample size for the microcell A-60–CAT combination more definitely, several samples containing from 10 to 100 micrograms of neo-isopulegol (see peak 2, Fig. 8-23) were collected. The samples were transferred to the microcell with carbon tetrachloride and scanned 700 times in order to obtain a 25-fold enhancement. This required about two days at the sweep rate of 2 cps/sec used for curve b of Figure 8-21. A maximum scanning time for one sample of about two days seemed a reasonable choice since the spectrometer is otherwise idle over weekends. From the spectra obtained, it was concluded that a 50-μg sample represents the lower limit on sample size for a fairly usable spectrum, as shown in Figure 8-22. Of course, if the information contained in single-proton peaks such as that from the multiple-coupled carbinol proton can be sacrificed, this amount can be reduced appreciably.

Figure 8-22 provides a comparison of two A-60 spectra of the same 50-μg sample of neoisopulegol: curve a, 853 scans at 5 cps/sec, taken over 24 hr; curve b, 667 scans at 2 cps/sec, taken over 48 hr. Under these optimum operating conditions, it is obvious that 50 μg of this 154 molecular weight

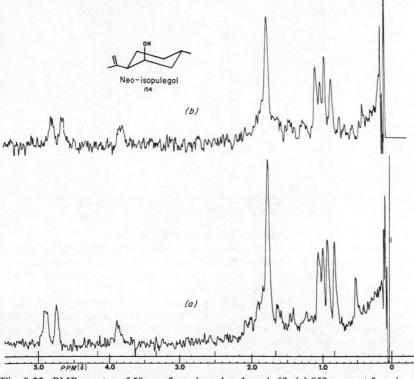

Fig. 8-22. PMR spectra of 50 μg of neo-isopulegol on A-60. (a) 853 scans at 5 cps/sec, 24 hr. (b) 667 scans at 2 cps/sec, 48 hr.

material is more than ample if a scanning time of one day is practical. A weekend of scanning under these conditions might provide a reasonable spectrum from 30 μg. It should, however, be noted that in the neo-isopulegol spectrum, the carbinol peak is sharper than in isopulegol because of the smaller spin coupling (101).

VIII. Identification Examples

The recent developments in instrumentation and sample manipulation discussed here permit routine UV, IR, PMR, and MS analyses with milligram samples or less. With some special effort, it is possible to obtain the analyses with only a few micrograms. Thus, it is now feasible to use ancillary systems with high-resolution GC columns. Following are a few examples of identification of small amounts of material separated by GC.

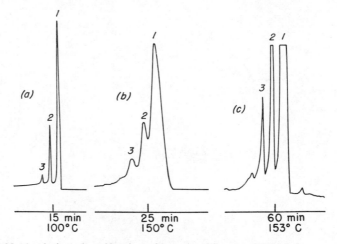

Fig. 8-23. Analysis and purification of isopulegol isomers (103).

(a) Column: 75-ft × 0.01-in. i.d. open tubular, coated with SF 96(50) methyl silicone oil phase. Sample volume: 0.2 μl. split 1/500. Temperature of injection port and column: 235° and 100°C. Carrier gas (He) inlet pressure 7 psi (gauge), flow 0.5 ml/min. Peaks: 1, isopulegol; 2, neo-isopulegol, 3, iso-isopulegol.

(b) Column: 30 ft × 0.5 in. i.d. packed; column material: silicone oil SF 96(50) on acid- and ammonia-washed Chromosorb G, 60/70 mesh (4/96, w/w). Sample volume: 15 μl. Temperature injection port and column 230° and 150°C. Carrier gas (He) inlet pressure and flow rate at outlet: 25 psi (gauge), 500 ml/min. Peaks same as in (a).

(c) Column: 1000 ft × 0.03 in. i.d. open tubular, coated with SF 96(50) methyl silicone oil phase. Sample volume: 0.5 μl. Temperature of injection port and column: 225° and 153°C. Carrier gas (He) inlet pressure 20 psi (gauge), flow 15 ml/min. Peaks same as in (a).

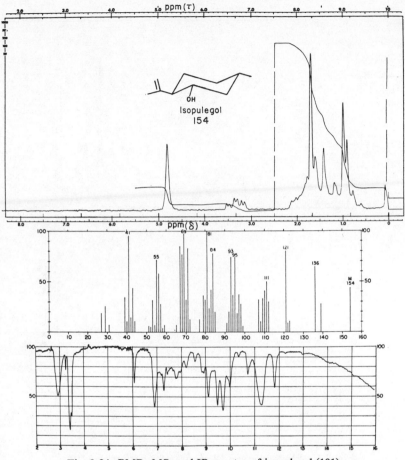

Fig. 8-24. PMR, MS, and IR spectra of isopulegol (101).

A. Isopulegol Isomers

Figure 8-23 shows the separation of commercial isopulegol with three different columns. Chromatogram *a* shows the excellent resolution possible with the 0.01-in. i.d. open tubular columns with microgram quantities. GC–MS analyses showed that these three compounds are very similar; i.e., probably epimers. The presence of three isomers has been reported (102). Chromatogram *b* shows the separation of these compounds with a 0.5-in. i.d. packed column with milligrams per peak. Chromatogram *c* shows the separation of the same commercial isopulegol sample with a 0.03-in. i.d. open tubular column with hundreds of micrograms per peak. With sufficient starting material, a pure sample can be prepared with

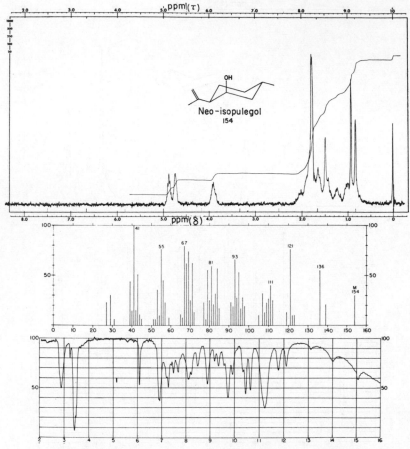

Fig. 8-25. PMR, MS, and IR spectra of neo-isopulegol (101).

multiple passes through the 0.5-in. i.d. packed preparative column. Only one pass is required with the 0.03 in. i.d. open tubular column for spectroscopically pure samples, especially if enriched samples from the packed preparative column are used. Figures 8-24–8-26 show the spectral data, from which detailed chemical structures were determined (101).

B. Pentadeca-6,9-dien-2-one

Figure 8-27 shows a programmed-temperature analysis by Buttery et al. of oxygenated compounds from hops (104). The less important (with respect to flavor) hydrocarbon constituents were removed by liquid chromatography with silica because the hydrocarbon constituents frequently overlap the oxygenated constituents even with the high-resolution open tubular columns. Even with the removal of the hydrocarbons, the complete analysis of the oxygenated compounds is a formidable task because of the number and range of compounds present and because of the small differences between the compounds. However, an open tubular column, 0.01 in. i.d., coated with SF 96(50) silicone oil, with traces of Carbowax 20M and Alkaterge T for tail-reducing, separated most of the constituents.

Of the 75 compounds identified by Buttery et al., most were identified by GC–MS. For those compounds with a small number of isomers possible, such data were considered enough for a good degree of certainty of identification. Figure 8-28 shows programmed-temperature analyses of the

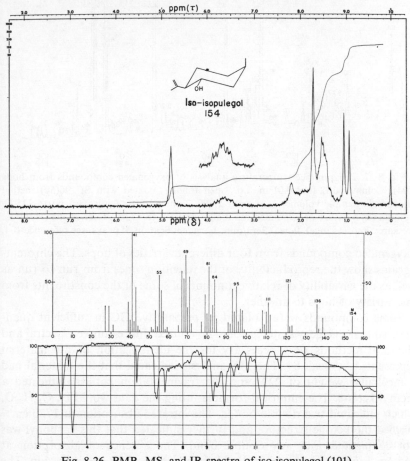

Fig. 8-26. PMR, MS, and IR spectra of iso-isopulegol (101).

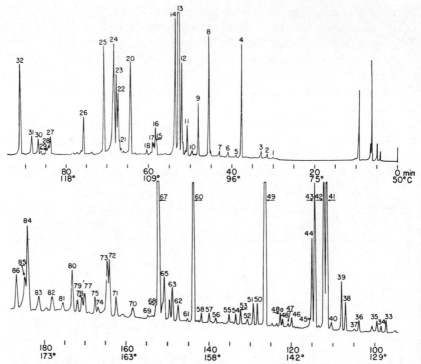

Fig. 8-27. Programmed-temperature analysis of oxygenated compounds from hops (104). Column: 192 ft × 0.01 in. i.d. open tubular, coated with SF 96(50) methyl silicone oil. Sample volume: 1 μl, split 1/300. Temperature of injection port: 225°C. Column temperature programmed manually from 50° to 173°C. Carrier gas (He) inlet pressure: 20 psi (gauge), flow 0.5 ml/min. For identification of peaks, see reference 104.

oxygenated compounds from four different varieties of hops. The chromatograms show the reproducibility of the retention times from run to run as well as the variability of relative amounts of some of the constituents from one variety of hops to another.

Some compounds were isolated by preparative GC in sufficient quantities so that ancillary systems could be utilized. For example, spectral and chemical methods were necessary for the identification of the material represented by peak 84. The MS analysis indicated that the material had a molecular weight of 222, and the fragmentation pattern indicated a methyl ketone. The empirical formula fitting the data would be $C_{15}H_{26}O$, which indicated two double bonds. The infrared absorption at 1720 cm^{-1} verified the ketone structure and further indicated that this carbonyl was not conjugated with any double bond. The absence of absorption at 965 cm^{-1} indicated that both double bonds were of *cis* configuration. The

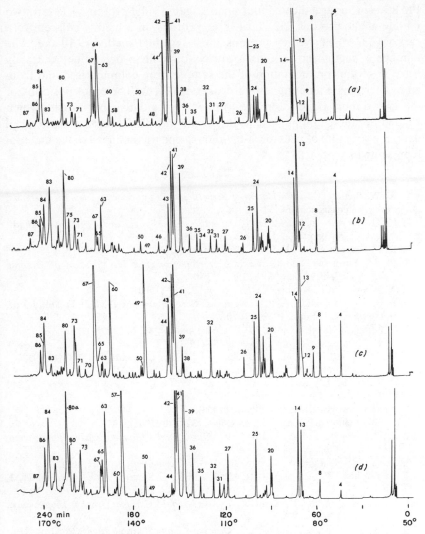

Fig. 8-28. Programmed-temperature analyses of oxygenated compounds from four varieties of hops (105). Column: 150 ft × 0.01 in. i.d. open tubular, coated with SF 96(50) methyl silicone oil. Sample volume: 2 μl split 1/300. Temperature of injection port: 225°C. Column temperature programmed linearly from 50° to 170°C at 0.5 deg/ min. For identification of peaks, see reference 104. Hop varieties: (a) Idaho Cluster. (b) Fuggles. (c) Brewers Gold. (d) Hallertau.

PMR absorptions indicated four unconjugated vinyl protons, 4.73 tau; two double-allylic protons, 7.27 tau; three protons on a methyl adjacent to a carbonyl, 7.96 tau; three protons on a terminal methyl, 9.10 tau. The number of methylene protons is always difficult to determine accurately because of the contamination of the sample from column bleed and from an indeterminate amount of hydrocarbon solvent. The exact positions of the two double bonds were determined by oxidative ozonolysis, which yielded hexanoic and glutaric acids. Thus, with the spectral and chemical data, the structure of pentadeca-6,9-dien-2-one was assigned to the material represented by peak 84.

References

1. K. W. Bentley, Ed., *Elucidation of Structures by Physical and Chemical Methods*, Part I, Interscience, New York, 1963.
2. K. H. Overton, in *Elucidation of Structures by Physical and Chemical Methods*, Part I, K. W. Bentley, Ed., Interscience, New York, 1963, p. 1.
3. R. C. Crippen and C. E. Smith, *J. Gas Chromatog.*, **3**, 37 (1965).
4. R. M. Silverstein and G. C. Bassler, *Spectrometric Identification of Organic Compounds*, Wiley, New York, 1963, p. 104.
5. A. Wehrli and E. Kovats, *J. Chromatog.*, **3**, 313 (1960).
6. E. P. Atkinson and G. A. P. Tuey, in *Gas Chromatography 1958*, D. H. Desty, Ed., Butterworths, London, 1958, p. 270.
7. P. Kratz, M. Jacobs, and B. M. Mitzner, *Analyst*, **84**, 671 (1959).
8. A. E. Thompson, *J. Chromatog.*, **6**, 454 (1961).
9. W. D. Ross, J. F. Moon, and R. L. Evers, *J. Gas Chromatog.*, **2**, 340 (1964).
10. H. Schlenk and D. M. Sand, *Anal. Chem.*, **34**, 1676 (1962).
11. R. Teranishi, J. W. Corse, J. C. Day, and W. G. Jennings, *J. Chromatog.*, **9**, 244 (1962).
12. P. A. T. Swoboda, *Nature*, **199**, 31 (1963).
13. I. Hornstein and P. Crowe, *Anal. Chem.*, **37**, 170 (1965).
14. S. Dal Nogare and R. S. Juvet, Jr., *Gas–Liquid Chromatography*, Interscience, New York, 1962, p. 254.
15. R. L. Hoffmann and A. Silveira, Jr., *J. Gas Chromatog.*, **2**, 107 (1964).
16. R. Teranishi, R. A. Flath, T. R. Mon, and K. L. Stevens, *J. Gas Chromatog.*, **3**, 206 (1965).
17. S. Dal Nogare and R. S. Juvet, Jr., *Gas–Liquid Chromatography*, Interscience, New York, 1962, p. 295.
18. K. Biemann, *Mass Spectrometry, Organic Chemical Applications*, McGraw-Hill, New York, 1962, p. 32.
19. S. Dal Nogare and R. S. Juvet, Jr., *Gas–Liquid Chromatography*, Interscience, New York, 1962, p. 310.
20. W. S. Gallaway, T. Johns, D. G. Tipotsch, and W. F. Ulrich, Pittsburgh Conference of Analytical Chemistry and Applied Spectroscopy, March 1958.
21. L. S. Ettre, *Anal. Chem.*, **36** (8), 31A (1964).
22. J. T. Walsh and C. Merritt, Jr., *Anal. Chem.*, **32**, 1378 (1960).
23. B. Casu and L. Cavalloti, *Anal. Chem.*, **34**, 1514 (1962).
24. J. Janák, *J. Gas Chromatog.*, **1** (10), 20 (1963).
25. R. Kaiser, *Z. Anal. Chem.*, **205**, 284 (1964).

26. G. M. Nano, P. Sancin, and A. Martelli, *J. Gas Chromatog.*, **3**, 85 (1965).
27. R. Bassette and C. H. Whitnah, *Anal. Chem.*, **32**, 1098 (1960).
28. R. Rowan, Jr., *Anal. Chem.*, **33**, 658 (1961).
29. R. Suffis and D. E. Dean, *Anal. Chem.*, **34**, 480 (1962).
30. J. E. Hoff and E. D. Feit, *Anal. Chem.*, **36**, 1002 (1964).
31. R. M. Ikeda, D. E. Simmons, and J. D. Grossman, *Anal. Chem.*, **36**, 2188 (1964).
32. R. Teranishi, unpublished results.
33. J. C. D. Brand and A. I. Scott, in *Elucidation of Structures by Physical and Chemical Methods*, Part I, K. W. Bentley, Ed., Interscience, New York, 1963, p. 61.
34. H. H. Jaffe and M. Orchin, *Theory and Applications of Ultraviolet Spectroscopy*, Wiley, New York, 1962.
35. A. E. Gillam and E. S. Stern, *An Introduction to Electronic Absorption Spectroscopy in Organic Chemistry*, 2nd ed., Edward Arnold, London, 1957.
36. W. Kaye, *Anal. Chem.*, **34**, 287 (1962).
37. W. Kaye and F. Waska, *Anal. Chem.*, **36**, 2380 (1964).
38. W. W. Coblentz, *Investigations of Infrared Spectra*, Publication No. 35, Carnegie Institute of Washington, 1905; republished by the Coblentz Society and the Perkin-Elmer Corporation, 1962.
39. *Sadtler Infrared Spectra* (ca. 26,000 spectra), Sadtler Research Laboratories, Philadelphia, Pa.; *Documentation of Molecular Spectroscopy* (ca. 10,000 spectra), Butterworths, London; *NRC–National Bureau of Standards* (ca. 2500 spectra), National Bureau of Standards, Washington, D.C.; *American Petroleum Institute Research Project 44* (ca. 2600 spectra), Chemistry Department, Agricultural and Mechanical College of Texas, College Station, Texas; *Coblentz Society Spectra* (ca. 4000 spectra), distributed by Sadtler Research Laboratories.
40. *Molecular Formula List of Compounds, Names and References to Published Infrared Spectra*, Special Technical Publication No. 331 and 331A, American Society for Testing and Materials, Philadelphia, Pa.
41. N. B. Colthup, L. H. Daly, and S. E. Wiberly, *Introduction to Infrared and Raman Spectroscopy*, Academic Press, New York, 1964.
42. W. J. Potts, *Chemical Spectroscopy*, Vols. I and II, Wiley, New York, 1963, 1964.
43. K. Nakanishi, *Practical Infrared Absorption Spectroscopy*, Holden-Day, San Francisco, 1962.
44. L. J. Bellamy, *Infrared Spectra of Complex Molecules*, 2nd ed., Wiley, New York, 1958.
45. R. N. Jones and C. Sandorfy, in *Chemical Applications of Spectroscopy*, A. Weissberger, Ed., Interscience, New York, 1956, p. 247.
46. J. R. Scherer, unpublished results.
47. D. W. Stewart, in *Physical Methods of Organic Chemistry* (*Technique of Organic Chemistry*, Vol. I, Part IV), 3rd ed., A. Weissberger, Ed., Interscience, New York, 1960, p. 3449.
48. K. Biemann, *Mass Spectrometry, Organic Chemical Applications*, McGraw-Hill, New York, 1962.
49. K. Biemann, in *Elucidation of Structures by Physical and Chemical Methods*, Part I, K. W. Bentley, Ed., Interscience, New York, 1963, p. 261.
50. H. Budzikiewicz, C. Djerassi, and D. H. Williams, *Interpretation of Mass Spectra of Organic Compounds*, Holden-Day, San Francisco, 1964.
51. H. Budzikiewicz, C. Djerassi, and D. H. Williams, *Structure Elucidation of Natural Products by Mass Spectrometry*, Vols. I and II, Holden-Day, San Francisco, 1964.

52. F. W. McLafferty, *Mass Spectral Correlations*, American Chemical Society, Washington, D.C., 1963.

53. R. M. Elliot, Ed., *Advances in Mass Spectrometry*, Pergamon, London, 1963.

53a. *Am. Petroleum Inst. Catalog of Mass Spectral Data*, Research Project 44, Chemical Thermodynamics Properties Center, Agricultural and Mechanical College of Texas, College Station, Texas, 1948 to data. *Manufacturing Chemists Assoc. Res. Project, Catalog of Mass Spectral Data*, Chemical Thermodynamics Properties Center, Agricultural and Mechanical College of Texas, College Station, Texas, 1959 to date. A. H. Struck, Chairman, ASTM Committee E-14 *File of Uncertified Mass Spectra*, Perkin-Elmer Corporation, Norwalk, Conn., 1958 to date.

54. J. B. Farmer, in *Mass Spectrometry*, C. A. McDowell, Ed., McGraw-Hill, New York, 1963.

54a. W. H. McFadden, *Separation Sci.*, **1**, 723 (1966).

55. K. Biemann, *Pure Appl. Chem.*, **9**, 95 (1964).

56. K. Biemann, *Mass Spectrometry, Organic Chemical Applications*, McGraw-Hill, New York, 1962, p. 20.

57. R. C. Gohlke, *Anal. Chem.*, **31**, 535, (1959).

58. W. H. McFadden and E. A. Day, *Anal. Chem.*, **36**, 2362 (1964).

59. J. A. Dorsey, R. H. Hunt, and M. J. O'Neal, *Anal. Chem.*, **35**, 511 (1963).

60. W. H. McFadden, R. Teranishi, D. R. Black, and J. C. Day, *J. Food Sci.*, **28**, 316 (1963).

61. R. Ryhage, *Anal. Chem.*, **36**, 759 (1964).

62. E. A. Day and L. M. Libbey, *J. Food Sci.*, **29**, 583 (1964).

63. E. A. Day and D. F. Anderson, *J. Agr. Food Chem.*, **13**, 2 (1965).

64. J. T. Watson and K. Biemann, *Anal. Chem.*, **36**, 1135 (1964).

65. J. T. Watson and K. Biemann, *Anal. Chem.*, **37**, 844 (1965).

65a. S. R. Lipsky, C. G. Horvath, and W. J. McMurray, *Anal. Chem.*, **38**, 1585 (1966).

66. R. Teranishi, J. W. Corse, W. H. McFadden, D. R. Black, and A. I. Morgan, Jr., *J. Food Sci.*, **28**, 478 (1963).

67. W. H. McFadden, R. Teranishi, J. Corse, D. R. Black, and T. R. Mon, *J. Chromatog.*, **18**, 10 (1965).

68. E. W. Becker, in *Separation of Isotopes*, H. London, Ed., Newnes, London, 1961, p. 360.

69. E. Selke, C. R. Scholfield, C. D. Evans, and H. J. Dutton, *J. Am. Oil Chemists' Soc.*, **38**, 614 (1961).

70. C. Merritt, Jr., and P. Angelini, *Advan. Chem. Ser.*, **56**, 225 (1966).

71. R. Teranishi, R. G. Buttery, R. E. Lundin, W. H. McFadden, and T. R. Mon, *Am. Soc. Brewing Chemists Proc.*, **1963**, p. 52.

72. K. Biemann and W. McMurray, *Tetrahedron Letters*, **1965**, No. 11, 647.

73. R. Teranishi, R. G. Buttery, W. H. McFadden, T. R. Mon, and J. Wasserman, *Anal. Chem.*, **36**, 1509 (1964).

74. T. H. Schultz, R. Teranishi, W. H. McFadden, P. W. Kilpatrick, and J. Corse, *J. Food Sci.*, **29**, 790 (1964).

75. R. G. Buttery, W. H. McFadden, R. Teranishi, M. P. Kealy, and T. R. Mon, *Nature*, **200**, 435 (1963).

76. P. Issenberg, M. L. Bazinet, and C. Merritt, Jr., *Anal. Chem.*, **37**, 1074 (1965).

77. C. Merritt, Jr., P. Issenberg, M. L. Bazinet, B. N. Green, T. O. Merrons, and J. G. Murray, *Anal. Chem.*, **37**, 1037 (1965).

77a. H. Boettger, private communication.

78. J. A. Pople, W. G. Schneider, and H. J. Bernstein, *High-Resolution Nuclear Magnetic Resonance*, McGraw-Hill, New York, 1959.

79. Varian Associates, NMR–EPR Staff, *NMR and EPR Spectroscopy*, Pergamon, New York, 1960.

80. L. M. Jackman, *Applications of Nuclear Magnetic Resonance Spectroscopy in Organic Chemistry*, Pergamon, New York, 1959.

81. N. S. Bhacca and D. H. Williams, *Applications of NMR Spectroscopy in Organic Chemistry. Illustrations from the Steroid Field*, Holden-Day, San Francisco, 1964.

82. R. H. Bible, Jr., *Interpretation of NMR Spectra: An Empirical Approach*, Plenum Press, New York, 1965.

83. H. Conroy, in *Advances in Organic Chemistry: Methods and Results*, Vol. II, R. A. Raphael, E. C. Taylor, and H. Wynberg, Eds., Interscience, New York, 1960, p. 265.

84. J. B. Strothers, in *Elucidation of Structures by Physical and Chemical Methods*, K. W. Bentley, Ed., Interscience, New York, 1963, p. 174.

85. H. Foster, *Anal. Chem.*, **36**, 266R (1964).

86. F. A. Bovey, *Chem. Eng. News.*, **43**(35), 98 (1965).

87. *Varian HR NMR Spectra Catalog*, Vols. I and II, Varian Associates, Palo Alto, Calif., 1963.

88. *Catalogs of NMR Spectral Data*, sponsored by the Manufacturing Chemists' Association, College Station, Texas, 1960–1965.

89. *Sadtler NMR Spectra* (ca. 2000 spectra), Sadtler Research Laboratories, Philadelphia, Pa.

89a. J. S. Matthews, F. H. Burow, and R. E. Snyder, *Anal. Chem.*, **32**, 691 (1960); J. G. Bendoraitis, B. L. Brown, and L. S. Hepner, *Anal. Chem.*, **34**, 49 (1962); S. A. Francis and E. D. Archer, *Anal. Chem.*, **35**, 1363 (1963); R. Teranishi, T. H. Schultz, W. H. McFadden, R. E. Lundin, and D. R. Black, *J. Food Sci.*, **28**, 541 (1963).

90. R. E. Lundin, R. H. Elsken, R. A. Flath, N. Henderson, T. R. Mon, and R. Teranishi, *Anal. Chem.*, **38**, 291 (1966).

91. NMR Specialties, New Kensington, Pa.

92. E. G. Brame, Jr., *Anal. Chem.*, **37**, 1183 (1965).

93. K. Frei and P. Niklaus, private communication.

94. F. A. Nelson and H. E. Weaver, *Science*, **146**, 223 (1964).

95. R. Ernst and W. A. Anderson, *Rev. Sci. Instr.*, **37**, 93 (1966).

96. R. Ernst, *Rev. Sci. Instr.*, **36**, 1689 (1965); R. Ernst, in *Advances in Magnetic Resonance*, Vol. 2, J. S. Wangh, Ed., Academic Press, New York, 1967.

97. M. P. Klein and G. W. Barton, Jr., *Rev. Sci. Instr.*, **34**, 754 (1963).

97a. Technical Measurements Corp., New Haven, Conn.

98. L. C. Allen and L. F. Johnson, *J. Am. Chem. Soc.*, **85**, 2668 (1963).

99. A. Savitzky and M. J. E. Golay, *Anal. Chem.*, **36**, 1627 (1964).

100. A. Savitzky, 6th Experimental NMR Conference, Pittsburgh, Pa., February 25–27, 1965.

100a. J. M. Read, Jr., and J. H. Goldstein, *Anal. Chem.*, **37**, 1069 (1965).

101. R. Teranishi, R. E. Lundin, W. H. McFadden, T. R. Mon, T. H. Schultz, K. L. Stevens, and J. Wasserman, *J. Agr. Food Chem.*, **14**, 447 (1966).

102. W. H. Houlihan, *Perfumery Essent. Oil Record*, **55**, 261 (1964).

103. R. Teranishi, unpublished results.

104. R. G. Buttery, D. R. Black, and M. P. Kealy, *J. Chromatog.*, **18**, 399 (1965).

105. R. G. Buttery, D. R. Black, D. G. Guadagni, and M. P. Kealy, *Am. Soc. Brewing Chemists' Proc.*, *1965*, p. 103.

CHAPTER 9

Reaction Gas Chromatography

Morton Beroza and Raylene A. Coad,* *Agricultural Research Service,*
U.S. Department of Agriculture, Beltsville, Maryland

* Present address: P.O. Box 1291, Trone, California.

I. Introduction

In reaction gas chromatography, injected chemicals are changed or adsorbed during the gas chromatographic process. Within the closed system —somewhere between the introduction point and the detector—substances react in a specified manner, and the carrier gas moves the products and unaffected substances in a single integrated action through the chromatographic column with the eventual production of a chromatogram.

Reaction gas chromatography does not include reactions completed before injection of the products, but does include reactions whose products are retained within a closed system (usually to allow completion of a reaction) for release as a plug injection.

A. Reaction Sites

As illustrated in Figure 9-1, a reaction may take place at any point in the chromatographic system. If it occurs ahead of the injection port, e.g., within a precolumn (A), the carrier gas enters through the precolumn rather than through the usual injection port. It may occur within the injection port (B), which sometimes happens inadvertently because the injection

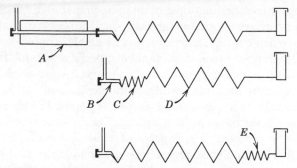

Fig. 9-1. Schematic representation of reaction sites between injection port (at left) and detector (at right).

port is usually held at an elevated temperature to facilitate vaporization of the sample. A reaction may take place just before the chromatographic column (C), in the column (D), or in a short column preceding the detector (E). Independent control of the reaction temperature is frequently required. Additionally, several reactions may advantageously be combined within a single chromatographic run.

B. Historical

Friedrich Drawert and his co-workers (1) in 1960 originated the term "reaction gas chromatography," but the first to report the use of the technique were Kokes, Tobin, and Emmett (2) in 1955, only three years after gas chromatography was first described. By combining a precolumn (called a microreactor) containing a cracking catalyst at an elevated temperature with a gas chromatograph, Kokes et al. were able to study on a micro scale the cracking of compounds up to C_8 in size. With this ingeniously simple device, they could vary catalyst, temperature, carrier gas, or flow rate and identify the products by their retention times. The apparatus is still a valuable tool for evaluating catalyst performance.

C. Scope and Emphasis

There are now almost 500 publications on methodology that may be classified as reaction gas chromatography. In order to condense this information, reviews of past work and types of reactions rather than specific analyses are frequently cited and only recent publications are detailed to illuminate current trends. A more complete survey of the field with detailed bibliography is available (3).

Investigations relating to structure determination or identification are emphasized because this area is of general interest and capable of considerable development. It is reasonable to hope and expect that our usual chemical analyses may be speeded up and integrated into the gas chromatographic process in order that time-consuming preparative gas chromatography, now necessary to get enough compound for macro analyses, may be avoided. When enough material is not available, appropriate reaction gas chromatographic procedures can be especially helpful by making possible analyses on limited amounts of substance. Another consideration is that the handling and transferring of minute amounts of material are difficult, especially if a quantitative answer is required. This difficulty is obviated through the use of a closed system. The detector recording system registers all the products it is capable of sensing. Finally, techniques—presently not in our analytical repertoire—are bound to be devised through the use of reaction gas chromatography. For example, reactions at elevated temperatures hold promise of providing high-speed analytical methodology for use in the laboratory.

In surveying the field, reactions have been divided arbitrarily into six classifications: hydrogen reactions, pyrolysis, elemental analysis, class reactions (including functional group analysis), subtractive reactions, and a final catch-all classification for other reactions. This survey is followed by a discussion of means of setting up or designing a reaction gas chromatographic analysis.

II. Hydrogen Reactions

Reactions involving hydrogen that may be incorporated into reaction gas chromatographic procedures are hydrogenation (hydrogen addition), hydrogenolysis (cleavage with hydrogen addition at points of cleavage), and dehydrogenation (hydrogen abstraction). Hydrogen reactions usually require the use of a catalyst. Hydrogenolysis utilized in elemental analysis is discussed in Section IV.

A. Hydrogenation

Hydrogenation is a much-used technique for determining the structure of unsaturated compounds. Mixtures of hydrocarbons and fatty acids have been chromatographed before and after hydrogenation to determine by difference the amounts of olefins and saturates. The inclusion of a hydrogenation step in a gas chromatographic run is usually accomplished by attaching a catalyst-containing precolumn to the gas chromatograph and employing hydrogen as the carrier gas. The successful use of this procedure with platinum, palladium, and nickel catalysts has been described many times in hydrocarbon analysis and very recently by Mounts and Dutton (4) in the analysis of methyl esters of fatty acids. These authors devised a micro vapor-phase hydrogenator consisting of a 43 × 6.3 mm heated (200°C) precolumn packed with a catalyst made of 1-3 % by weight nickel, platinum, or palladium on a support such as Chromosorb P.* Hydrogen flow rate was usually 60 ml/min. Although the apparatus is similar in many respects to that of carbon-skeleton chromatography described later, the conditions are modified so that hydrogenolytic cleavage of the unsaturated fatty methyl esters is practically eliminated and the reaction is restricted to partial or total hydrogenation. To vary the effective catalyst length from 0 to 43 mm, they placed sleeves of different lengths on the 4-in. needle of a Hamilton microsyringe to control placement of the sample at any depth within the catalyst bed. Samples, from 0.1 to 2 μl, undergo various degrees of hydrogenation depending on length of the catalyst bed passed by the esters. Dutton has also described the use of this unit monitored with tandem chromatography–radioactivity measurements (5).

Recently Beroza and Sarmiento (5a) have described injection port and oven hydrogenation units for almost instant hydrogenation in the gas chromatographic stream of multiple bonds in unsaturated esters, alcohols, ethers, ketones, and other compound types. By-pass techniques were developed that permit the determination of separation factors (ratio of retention times of unhydrogenated and hydrogenated compounds), which are useful for characterizing olefins.

B. Dehydrogenation

Several reports on the coupled use of a dehydrogenation step with gas chromatography have dealt with hydrocarbons. Keulemans and Voge (6) catalytically dehydrogenated C_5–C_8 naphthenes to aromatics in an apparatus comparable to that of Kokes et al. Their platinum–alumina–halogen catalyst was maintained at 350°C, and the carrier gas was hydrogen. Rowan (7) found the aforementioned catalyst best in his dehydrogenation work but used helium as the carrier gas. He suggested dehydrogenation as an analytical procedure for hydrocarbons.

* Mention of a proprietary product or company does not necessarily imply endorsement of the product or company by the U.S. Department of Agriculture.

C. Carbon-Skeleton Analyses and Related Procedures

A few years ago one of the authors (M. B.) advanced a reaction gas chromatographic process, now known as *carbon-skeleton chromatography*, as an aid in determining the chemical structure of microgram amounts of a wide variety of organic compounds. The technique, based in part on the work of Thompson and co-workers (8), includes hydrogenation, hydrogenolysis, and dehydrogenation, and will be discussed only briefly. (A more detailed description of the method is given in references 9–12.)

Carbon-skeleton chromatography has been found useful in the analysis of acids, alcohols, aldehydes, anhydrides, ethers, epoxides, ketones, esters, amines, amides, aliphatic and aromatic hydrocarbons, nitriles, sulfides, halides, olefins, and other types of compounds. Progressive improvements in catalysts and procedure have made the analysis of compounds to at least the C_{30} level possible (13).

1. Apparatus

The procedure utilizes a precolumn as shown schematically in Figure 9-1 (*A*), packed with a catalyst maintained at an elevated temperature. A

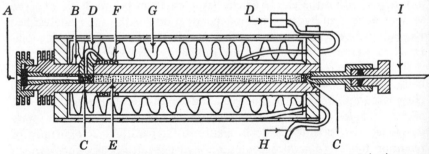

Fig. 9-2. Catalyst assembly for carbon-skeleton chromatography. *A*, Injection port (fins keep septum cool); *B*, aluminum tube; *C*, glass wool; *D*, hydrogen inlet (wrapped around *F*); *E*, catalyst; *F*, heating jacket; *G*, insulation; *H*, heating jacket electric cord; *I*, needle stock attaches assembly to gas chromatographic injection port.

cross-sectional view of the commercially available catalyst assembly (precolumn), which is usually attached to the injection port of a flame ionization gas chromatograph, is shown in Figure 9-2. The carrier gas, hydrogen, conducts the sample over the heated catalyst and in the process saturates multiple bonds and strips functional groups containing oxygen, nitrogen, sulfur, and halogen from the molecule. Products are always hydrocarbons, which pour into the analytical column of the gas chromatograph and separate therein. The resulting chromatogram, the peaks of which are identified by retention time, provides information on the carbon skeleton of injected compounds in addition to other structural features. Details of apparatus construction have been published (10–12). After attaching the catalyst assembly to a chromatograph injection port, the hydrogen source is connected to the inlet tube of the assembly, and either the normal hydrogen inlet port at the flame head is closed, or, for somewhat better response and stability, an inert gas (He or N_2) is led into this port.

2. Preparing the Catalyst

The best catalyst for the analysis of most compounds is a "neutral" one containing 1 % Pd (by wt) on a 60–80 mesh nonadsorptive support, such as GasChrom P (Applied Science Lab., State College, Pa.). Catalysts are easily prepared by evaporating to dryness in a rotating evaporator a palladium chloride solution in 5 % acetic acid in contact with the support. The catalyst is loaded in the tube and activated by passing hydrogen through it (vent into hood) for ½ hr at 125°C, ½ hr at 200°C, and 20 min at the test temperature. Activation reduces palladium chloride to free palladium and HCl. Since acidity causes breakdown of carbon chains longer than C_9, free HCl is avoided by adding enough sodium carbonate to the original palladium chloride solution to neutralize the HCl that forms in activation; the product is the so-called "neutral" catalyst. The use of Chromosorb P as a catalyst support is discussed under the next section.

3. Analytical Results

Table 9-1 summarizes analytical results under conditions found to be most favorable: catalyst temperature 300°C, flow rate 20 ml/min, sample size ca. 20 μg, ³⁄₁₆-in. o.d. analytical column. Results work out rather simply in that *compounds yield the parent hydrocarbon and/or the next lower homolog, and multiple bonds are saturated.* Carbon–sulfide and carbon–halogen bonds (fluorides not tested) are cleaved to give the parent molecule. With carbon–oxygen and carbon–nitrogen bonds, similar cleavage to the parent occurs except for compounds having carbon–oxygen or carbon–nitrogen substituents on the end carbon (primary). Compounds of this type, which are listed under the second heading of Table 9-1, give the next lower homolog. Thus, aldehydes, acids, anhydrides, primary alcohols, and the acid portion of esters and amides give almost exclusively the next lower homolog. Ethers, the alcohol portion of esters, and the amine portion of amides, if primary, give the parent hydrocarbon and the next lower homolog. Amides and esters do not require prior cleavage for analysis.

Since the inorganic products, such as HCl, NH_3, H_2S, H_2O, that form in hydrogenolysis, do not register on a flame ionization detector, only the organic products appear on the chromatograms.

TABLE 9-1

Carbon-Skeleton Chromatography Products from
Different Types of Compounds
Cat. temp. 300°C, flow rate 20 ml/min, 1% Pd catalyst

Compounds giving parent exclusively	Reaction
Paraffin hydrocarbon	None
Unsaturated compound	Multiple bonds saturated
Halogen compound	C—X bond cleaved
Alcohol, *sec* or *tert*	C—O bond cleaved
Ester, alcohol part when *sec* or *tert*	C—O bond cleaved
Ether, *sec* or *tert*	C—O bond cleaved
Ketone	C=O bond cleaved
Amine, *sec* or *tert*	C—N bond cleaved
Amide, amine part on *sec* or *tert* carbon	C—N bond cleaved

Compounds giving parent and/or next lower homolog	Reaction
Aldehyde	RCHO $\longrightarrow$ RH, RCH$_3$[a]
Acid	RCOOH $\longrightarrow$ RH, RCH$_3$[a]
Anhydride	(RCO)$_2$O $\longrightarrow$ RH, RCH$_3$[a]
Alcohol, primary	RCH$_2$OH $\longrightarrow$ RH, RCH$_3$[a]
Ester, alcohol part (OCH$_2$R) when primary, acid part (R'CO)	R'COOCH$_2$R $\longrightarrow$ RH, RCH$_3$ $\longrightarrow$ R'H, R'CH$_3$
Ether, primary	RCH$_2$OCH$_2$R $\longrightarrow$ RH, RCH$_3$
Amide, amine part (NHCH$_2$R) on primary carbon, acid part (R'CO)	R'CONHCH$_2$R $\longrightarrow$ RH, RCH$_3$ $\longrightarrow$ R'H, R'CH$_3$[a]

[a] Little or none of this parent hydrocarbon is obtained.

a. Carboxylic Acids and Derivatives. The palladium on GasChrom P catalyst gives low yields of hydrocarbon from carboxylic acids and their esters. By substituting acid-washed Chromosorb P (Johns-Manville, New York) for GasChrom P as the catalyst support, the yields of hydrocarbon from acids and their esters are greatly increased, and even the parent hydrocarbon, which normally does not appear, is obtained. In general, products from both catalysts are the same and differ only in amount. The Chromosorb P catalyst does, however, cause difficulty in that it is adsorptive, which makes retention times with it less reliable. This difficulty is overcome through the use of temperature programming or by trapping and releasing the products. In a temperature-programmed run, usually with compounds above C_{12}, the products are allowed to exit into and accumulate at the beginning of a chromatographic column at room temperature. On temperature programming the column, peaks emerge sharp and retention times are reliable. With low-molecular-weight acids or esters, a cold trap may be used to retain the products prior to release by rapidly heating the trap (14).

The results of some typical analyses with the Chromosorb P catalyst are given in Table 9-2.

TABLE 9-2

Typical Hydrocarbon Products from Compounds
Subjected to Carbon-Skeleton Chromatography (13)

Type	Compound	Principal product[a]
Acid	12-Hydroxystearic acid	C_{17}, C_{18}
Alcohol	1-Dodecanol	C_{11}, C_{12}
	1-Octadecanol	C_{17}, C_{18}
Aldehyde	Dodecanal	C_{11}, C_{12}
Amide	N,N-Dimethyltetradecanamide	C_{14}, C_{13}
Amine	Hexadecylamine	C_{16}, C_{15}
Ester	Methyl linoleate	C_{17}, C_{18}
Ether	Allyl hexadecyl ether	C_{16}, C_{15}
Halide	Octadecyl bromide	C_{18}
Nitrile	Tridecanenitrile	C_{13}, C_{12}
Sulfide	1-Dodecanethiol	C_{12}

[a] Product listed first is obtained in greater abundance.

b. Long-Chain or High-Molecular-Weight Compounds. Compounds up to C_{30} have been analyzed through the use of shorter catalyst beds. A 4-in. long catalyst bed gives good results with compounds in the C_{12}–C_{30} range. Catalyst beds shorter than the full 9-in. length are prepared by pouring inert material (glass beads or a spacer) into the tube to the desired point and then filling with catalyst.

A common difficulty encountered with long-chain compounds is that they elute from the catalyst bed slowly and appear in subsequent analysis. This difficulty increases with increasing molecular weight and polarity of the molecule and with decreasing catalyst temperatures. Sufficient time

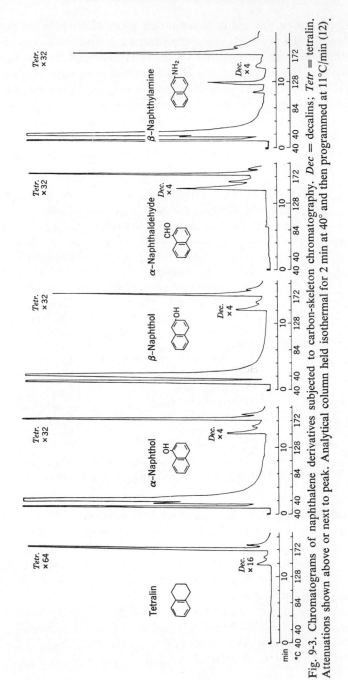

Fig. 9-3. Chromatograms of naphthalene derivatives subjected to carbon-skeleton chromatography. *Dec* = decalins; *Tetr* = tetralin. Attenuations shown above or next to peak. Analytical column held isothermal for 2 min at 40° and then programmed at 11°C/min (12).

should be allowed for elution, or the column temperature should be raised for a short time to clear the apparatus.

Inasmuch as halides generate acid in this analysis, they should not be introduced onto a catalyst to be used subsequently in the analysis of long-chain compounds.

c. Cyclic Compounds. Within a broad range of catalyst temperatures, most types of compounds give the same products. Products from aromatics and 6-membered cycloaliphatics are temperature dependent (15). Thus, toluene, benzyl alcohol, benzaldehyde, and benzonitrile all give only methylcyclohexane at a 200°C catalyst temperature. At 360° these compounds yield only aromatics, i.e., benzene and toluene. Methylcyclohexane is completely dehydrogenated at 360°C. At the intermediate 280° both cycloaliphatics and aromatics appear.

With polycyclic structures, the situation is more complex since one or more rings may be hydrogenated or dehydrogenated and *cis–trans* compounds appear. Naphthalene derivatives produced the chromatograms of Figure 9-3 (12). In each case the product was tetralin with small amounts of *trans*- and *cis*-decalin and naphthalene. The distinctive similarity of the patterns indicates that the compounds have the same parent structure. (Peaks in the first part of three of the chromatograms are due to the solvent used to introduce the solid samples.)

d. Positions of Functional Groups. The discussion thus far has centered around the major products of an analysis. It is frequently possible to determine the position of functional groups (alcohols, amines, ketones) from the smaller fragments. Thus, C_7 ketones give not only the parent heptane, but also fragments resulting from the cleavage of the bonds adjacent to the carbonyl group; e.g., 3-heptanone gives ethane and butane in addition to heptane (11).

e. Larger Apparatus. A larger carbon-skeleton determinator, one with a ⅜-in. bore, has been made for use with thermal conductivity instruments (15). Enough product is usually produced from a single injection to obtain a good ultraviolet or a less well-defined infrared spectrum, which may be useful for verifying an identification based on retention time. Apparatus for these determinations have been described (15).

f. A Practical Example. Carbon-skeleton chromatography has helped identify two degradation fragments from a series of alkaloids (16). A more recent problem illustrates the application of carbon-skeletal determinations. Isoprene was reacted with crotonic acid by one of our colleagues (T. M. Valega, unpublished) and a crystalline product with one of two possible structures was obtained (see equations below). It was injected onto the catalyst at 330°C (deliberately high temperature to aromatize the cyclohexene ring, the compound will also decarboxylate); the product was identified as *meta*-xylene by retention time and ultraviolet spectrum. The crystalline compound is therefore the upper center structure, i.e., 4,6-dimethyl-3-cyclohexene-1-carboxylic acid. Elucidation of the structure by normal oxidative procedures would have been very time consuming.

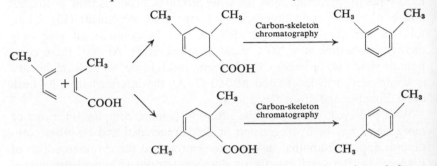

g. Additional Examples. Broderick (17) has used carbon-skeleton chromatography to identify flavor components, such as alcohols and terpene derivatives. Crippen and Smith (18) suggested its use in the analysis of alcohols. Schomburg (19) has mentioned the utility of the technique for qualitative identifications.

4. Related Processes

Okamoto and Onaka (20), using a similar procedure but with a palladium on silica gel catalyst at 360–460°C, distinguished monoterpenes on the basis of their hydrogenation and dehydrogenation products and obtained dealkylation "spectra" from alkylbenzenes.

As an interesting and useful variation of the precolumn hydrogenation apparatus, Franc and Kolouskova (21) included in their catalyst tube a glass capillary which allowed about half of the sample to by-pass the catalyst and the other half to contact it. From the ratio of the elution times of the hydrogenated and nonhydrogenated species, the authors drew conclusions as to the presence of a certain number of double bonds or functional groups.

III. Pyrolysis Reaction Gas Chromatography

Pyrolysis, or thermal degradation of materials, when combined with the sensitivity and separative powers of gas chromatography, is a powerful tool which has become very popular in the past few years. This technique has attained its greatest development and use in the analyses of polymers and copolymers and in the study of polymer degradation mechanisms and polymer structure; but it has also been used for the analyses of natural and bituminous resins and a wide variety of substances, both volatile and nonvolatile.

Several excellent review articles describing pyrolysis gas chromatography have appeared. Pyrolyzers and techniques of pyrolysis have been reviewed by Perry (22), by Voigt and Fischer (23), and by Barbour (23a). McKinney (24) prepared a subject index and complete references in the field of pyrolysis gas chromatography for the period 1960–1963 using Preston Chromatography Abstract Cards (25). Brauer (26) has provided a thorough discussion of pyrolytic techniques with emphasis on polymer identification. Dal Nogare and Juvet (26a) have included a section on pyrolysis in their biennial review of gas chromatography. Accordingly, only some of the recent advances will be mentioned in the following discussion.*

A. Instrumentation

The apparatus for pyrolyzing polymers or other materials is placed just ahead of the injection port or analytical column of the gas chromatograph, and pyrolysis is usually accomplished by one of three different techniques. The first, called flash pyrolysis, utilizes an electrically heated filament on or within which the material is pyrolyzed. The second, called the reaction chamber technique, employs an externally heated reaction tube into which the sample is moved for pyrolysis. The injection port of an ordinary gas chromatograph, when heated sufficiently high, may serve as a pyrolytic reaction chamber; this technique has proved useful, particularly for lower temperature thermal degradations. A third technique, which employs a corona discharge to pyrolyze a sample, has been advanced very recently (27). The sample is placed in a heated port (ambient to 300°C) where it is subjected to a 5000 V corona discharge for a time interval up to 30 sec. The breakdown products are said to give a reproducible pattern, useful for molecular identifications.

1. Flash Pyrolysis

Flash pyrolysis usually gives characteristic reproducible chromatograms inasmuch as the conditions of the thermal breakdown can be maintained constant. Thus, for comparative qualitative measurements of material, or

* In September 1966, an international symposium on pyrolysis–GC was held at the Ecole Polytechnique, Paris where a large number of papers described various applications of this technique. These papers were published in the January–April, 1967 issues of the *Journal of Gas Chromatography*. These papers were not considered when writing this chapter.

when quick information is desired, this technique may be preferred. As basic shortcomings of this method, Perry (22) indicates that the exact temperature of the pyrolysis, although reproducible, cannot be measured and that the amount of sample and residue frequently cannot be determined (depending on the design of the device). Means of introducing the sample include direct coating on the metal filament, placing the sample in a platinum boat to be heated by the filament (28), and wrapping the sample in a special fiberglass paper before placing it on the filament (29).

Flash pyrolysis was used recently by Groten (30) for the qualitative fingerprinting of a large number of polymers and by Esposito (31) in his work on quantitative pyrolytic gas chromatography employing an internal standard. Giacobbo and Simon (32) described a pyrolysis unit in which a sample as small as 0.02–0.8 μg is coated on a small ferromagnetic wire and heated by a high-frequency induction coil in 2×10^{-3} sec.

2. Reaction Chamber Pyrolysis

Ettre and Váradi (33a), who were about the first to describe a simple reaction chamber pyrolysis unit, stated that this technique has three distinct advantages:

1. The amount of sample and residue can be determined.

2. Temperature of pyrolysis can be measured easily and accurately.

3. The pyrolysis chamber, being made of glass or quartz, eliminates the likelihood of metal catalysis influencing degradation.

For many investigative purposes they considered the reaction chamber technique superior to the flash procedure.

Cox and Ellis (34) used a microreactor consisting of a long packed tubular furnace, 9 cm × 7-mm diameter, packed in the lower 7 cm with quartz wool so that only the thermally more stable products would reach the analytical column. The pyrolysis temperature was 700°C, and the sample size 0.1 mg. Use of the furnace technique was also reported recently by Fortina (35), by Garzó and Székely (36), and by Burke and Brandt (37), the latter authors utilizing direct injection of a solution into the microreaction chamber. The pyrolysis of polyolefins with linearly programmed temperature in packed or open tubular columns has been studied in detail by the GC Applications Laboratories of the Perkin-Elmer Corporation (33,200).

B. Types of Pyrolysis

For purposes of discussion and classification of the hundreds of organic compounds and materials that have been subjected to pyrolysis under a multitude of conditions, it has been convenient to group them, whenever possible, according to extent of degradation. In the order of increasing breakdown, four reaction types have been arbitrarily set up: thermal degradation, mild pyrolysis, normal pyrolysis, and vigorous pyrolysis. Extent of breakdown will depend on temperature and time of pyrolysis.

The two extremes are easiest to define. Thermal degradation will be a simple chemical change occurring in an orderly manner to form another compound, the molecular weight of which does not differ greatly from the original. Thermal degradation of a quaternary amine to an olefin or dehydration of an alcohol to an olefin are examples. In this category the rupture of carbon–carbon bonds is minimal, and the temperature usually ranges from 100 to 300°C, but may go as high as 400–500°C for certain compounds or when pyrolysis time is short.

Although little research has been reported in this category, thermal degradation may greatly interest analytical chemists because it is likely to provide straightforward information on chemical structure and thereby become a useful tool of the future.

Vigorous pyrolysis, which is at the other extreme of the pyrolysis scale, takes place at temperatures between 800 and 1100°C. Carbon–carbon bonds break readily and organic molecules cleave into small fragments. Commercial instruments capable of operating at elevated temperatures have facilitated the vigorous pyrolysis of polymers and high-molecular-weight nonvolatile substances. However, breakdown is generally too extensive, and the patterns have not proved to be as useful for identifications as those produced at lower temperatures.

Normal pyrolysis which is in the range of 500–800°C has been most rewarding for identifying and characterizing polymers and copolymers. Although carbon–carbon bonds break, the products are not limited to small fragments like methane, ethane, and carbon dioxide, but include substantial amounts of larger molecules and frequently the monomer or monomers (in copolymers).

Mild pyrolysis, as the name implies, occupies the region between thermal degradation and normal pyrolysis. Carbon–carbon cleavage occurs to some extent and pyrolytic temperatures range between 300 and 500°C, with some overlap on either end of this range, depending on conditions.

It is our hope that the preceding four divisions, although admittedly vague in their demarcations, will help bring order (if only in presentation) to the sprawling mass of pyrolysis data.

1. Thermal Degradation

Whether by accident or intent, many of the mild thermal degradation reactions have been carried out in the hot injection port of a gas chromatograph. Thus, Ainsworth and Easton (38) decomposed aliphatic amine salts at 190°C in an injection port chamber and, by comparing and combining their products with known hydrocarbons, they identified the products of the pyrolysis. Grossi and Vece (39) similarly analyzed quaternary chlorides of methyl amines by decomposing them in a high-temperature injection port to their tertiary amines and methyl chloride.

Using a procedure similar to that of Robb and Westbrook (40), Hetman, Arlt, Paylor, and Feinland (41) pyrolyzed quaternary tetramethyl-ammonium salts of acids of methyl esters in an injection port at 400°C, and in this manner were able to analyze tall oil rosin acids. Hanneman and Porter (42) reported the decomposition of dialkyl phosphates and dithiophosphates (as free acids, zinc salts, and S-bornyl esters) in a helium stream in an injection port at 215°C. The volatile olefin products were structurally related to the alkyl group of the original compound, and skeletal rearrangement of alkyl groups under their conditions of pyrolysis was generally not significant. Pyrolysis of zinc dialkyl dithiophosphates on a platinum dish heated by a filament within the chamber of a gas chromatograph has been described by Perry (43).

Craig, Mary, and Roy (44) have shown that the Cope elimination of tert-amine oxides occurs instantaneously in a gas chromatograph at 260°C. The procedure offers a convenient means of determining the products and the original tertiary amine oxide by gas chromatography. Gudzinowicz, Martin, and Driscoll (45) studied the thermal decomposition products of chloropromazine N-oxide, S-oxide, and the parent compound at injection port temperatures of 340–380°C as well as by static test methods.

In the pyrolysis of pyrazineethanol with a preheater at 370°C by Goldman (46), vinylpyrazine, methylpyrazine, and formaldehyde were produced. Only about 20% of the injected sample emerged unchanged.

A thermal degradation was used by Hyden (47) in studying the decomposition of dialkyl peroxides by direct injection into the injection port heated to about 310°C. The method was termed applicable to quantitative analysis, because a linear correlation was found between peroxide concentration and peak area of product.

2. Mild Pyrolysis

Dhont (48) identified lower aliphatic alcohols by "mild" pyrolysis in a quartz tube, 2 mm i.d. × 20 cm, filled with a 10-cm length of Chromosorb P and heated by a 13-cm long tubular furnace; the assembly was attached to the top of the column with silicone rubber tubing. Principal peaks produced by pyrolysis of a variety of straight- and branched-chain alcohols at 500°C were identified as olefins produced by dehydration of the particular alcohols.

Winter and Albro (29) described the pyrolysis of 30-mg samples of amino acids in a 300°C chamber for 3 min. The amines that formed (C_1-C_5 aliphatics) were stabilized at 110°C prior to chromatographing. Each amino acid gave a unique amine "profile," and proteins gave reproducible amine patterns related to their amino acid content.

Pyrolyses conducted at relatively mild temperatures which border on the classification defined as "normal pyrolysis" have been described. Greenwood, Knox, and Milne (49) studied pyrolysis of starch, cellulose, sucrose, maltose, hemicellulose, and alginic acid at 300°C in nitrogen. The pyrolyzate was condensed in a U-trap and then switched into the nitrogen carrier stream of the chromatographic apparatus. Eight or nine compounds in the C_1-C_6 range were generally identified. Glassner and Pierce (50) degraded cellulose for analysis without intermediate trapping by attaching a small oven to the gas chromatograph and heating at points between 170 and 360°C for varying lengths of time. Of 34 or more volatile degradation products that were produced, 13 were readily identified.

Langenbeck and Dreyer (51) investigated the decomposition of Ni-Mg-formates, oxalates, and carbonates in a stream of hydrogen by the method of reaction gas chromatography at 400–500°C to yield CH_4, CO, and CO_2. The CH_4 probably was formed by hydrogenation of the initial products of decomposition.

3. Normal Pyrolysis

The normal pyrolysis region of 500–800°C was defined as such because this is the region most commonly used by the working polymer chemist in the field of reaction gas chromatography. Since most polymers are noted for absence of functional groups useful for identification (or contain only end groups), low solubility, chemical inertness, and complexity, pyrolysis followed by or integrated with gas chromatographic analysis has offered a fruitful avenue for qualitative and structural identification.

For systematic schemes of polymer identification, it is desirable to employ a single set of pyrolysis conditions, one that will degrade *all* polymers rapidly. If temperatures are too low, some of the material may remain unchanged in the pyrolysis chamber. If temperatures are too high, secondary reactions predominate and lead to increasing amounts of simple molecules that give less characteristic patterns. Pyrolysis temperatures between 500 and 800°C for 10 sec have been most rewarding. Although pyrograms containing from 30 to 50 peaks have been reported (52), and even larger numbers of peaks can be expected from some polymers, the relative retention times and peak height ratios of 3 to 5 major peaks are usually sufficient for identification. Groten (30) and Cox and Ellis (34) have characterized polymers; Nelson, Yee, and Kirk (53) have systematically identified plastics; Voigt (54) and Feuerberg and Weigel (55) have studied elastomers. Additional information and references can be found in the review published by Brauer (26).

Several studies in the normal pyrolysis range that do not involve polymers have been made. Using an unpacked quartz tube at 500°C, Keulemans and Perry (56) performed some qualitative analyses of hydrocarbons of different classes and found it possible to differentiate between isomeric paraffins and paraffins and naphthalenes. Dhont (57) used pyrolysis at 600°C to identify organic compounds from food odors.

Pyrolysis at 600°C of a lipid on the column of a gas chromatograph (not in a precolumn chamber or filament) was utilized by Karmen, Walker, and Bowman (58) for the quantitative but nonselective microdetermination of lipids.

In order to study the mechanisms of the reactions, Burr and co-workers (59,60) pyrolyzed toluene, xylene, and deuterated forms of these compounds at 750°C in the presence of hydrogen or deuterium as carrier gas.

4. Vigorous Pyrolysis

At 800°C, a point which could be considered as the upper limit of normal pyrolysis or the beginning of vigorous pyrolysis, a number of interesting investigations have been made. Janák (61) pyrolyzed oils (olive, coconut) and sodium salts of barbituric acid derivatives; Harkiss (62) characterized plant pigments; and Levy et al. (63) pyrolyzed porphyrins with a filament temperature of 800–900°C.

Haraldson (64) employed pyrolysis at 900–1100°C to determine the products of pyrolysis in the analysis of oxygen in sulfur-containing organic substances. Purines and pyrimidines were pyrolyzed at 1100–1200°C for identification by Jennings and Dimick (65).

5. Studies over a Broad Range of Temperature

A few studies have been conducted at fixed temperatures over a temperature range encompassing several of the arbitrarily defined regions. For example, O'Neill, Putscher, Dynako, and Boquist (66) studied the pyrolysis of furfuryl alcohol resins at fixed temperatures in the range 150–850°C. Ettre and Váradi (33a,67) studied the composition of the breakdown products of three polymers at eight temperatures in the 300–950°C range. Waltz, Wisniewski, and Spencer (68) presented data for use of a pyrolysis unit at various temperatures between 700 and 1200°C.

G. Future of Pyrolysis Reaction Gas Chromatography

In a survey of the literature of pyrolysis combined with gas chromatography in the period 1960–1963, R. W. McKinney (24) reported 205 papers. Some of these were not integrated processes, i.e., the pyrolysis was performed separately from the gas chromatographic analysis, but many could be classified as truly integrated reaction gas chromatographic procedures. The future of the integrated technique appears to be significant and expanding. The ease of a single-stage procedure, the availability of commercial pyrolysis gas chromatographic accessory units, and the accumulation of data needed to interpret pyrograms have all contributed significantly to this field.

Pyrolysis application in the analysis of polymers, the study of polymer degradation mechanisms, characterization of volatile and nonvolatile compounds, and the determination of polymer functional groups can be expected to increase and help clarify some of the difficult problems of polymer chemistry. Reports of polymer pyrolysis greatly outnumber those on the pyrolysis of nonpolymeric materials. The latter area deserves more attention and undoubtedly holds much potential for future development.

IV. Elemental Analysis

Organic compounds exposed to a catalyst and a source of oxygen at high temperatures break down into carbon dioxide, water, and small molecules containing other elements. The exposure of organics to hydrogen under similar drastic conditions gives methane, water, and, again, small molecules with the other elements. These processes (both oxidative and reductive) were exploited initially to improve the detection of organic compounds emerging from a chromatographic column. More recently they have been coupled with gas chromatographic separation in a single sequential operation, a combination that has led to significantly improved methods of elemental analysis. Procedures have been devised for the determination of several elements in a single sample and for ratios of elements present in compounds exiting in a chromatographic effluent. Present detection of products of conventional elemental analyses is almost always by thermal conductivity. However, new detectors, highly sensitive to halogens, phosphorus, and sulfur, have made possible the analysis of compounds containing these elements at extremely low levels, a development of considerable importance in the field of pesticide residue analysis. Reaction gas chromatographic systems have also been adapted to the analysis of

TABLE 9-3

Reaction Gas Chromatographic Processes Used in Elemental Analysis

Elements (or derived compounds)	Agents	Products	Typical references
C	CuO, cobalt oxides, or AgMnO$_4$, 700–1000°	CO$_2$	70, 84, 100
C (or CO, CO$_2$)	H$_2$, Ni, 350–450°	CH$_4$	78, 79, 80, 130
H, deuterium, or tritium	[O] as in C analysis	H$_2$O	85
(H$_2$O)	Fe at 750° or CaH$_2$	H$_2$	83, 84
	CaC$_2$	HC≡CH	82
N	[O]	Nitrogen oxides	86
(Nitrogen oxides)	Cu, 500–800°	N$_2$	87
O	Charcoal, 1120°	CO	92
	1:1 Pt–carbon, 920°	CO	91
S	O$_2$, Pt, 850°	Sulfur oxides	101
	H$_2$, Pt, 800–1000°	H$_2$S	95, 105
Halogen	[O], Pt, 800°	Cl$_2$, Br$_2$	103
	H$_2$, Pt, 750–1000°	HCl, HBr	105, 108
P	H$_2$, 950°	PH$_3$	108

radiolabeled compounds by breaking them down to simple gases, in which form they are readily monitored.

Table 9-3 summarizes the chemical reactions utilized in elemental analysis and the following discussion presents additional information as well as specific applications. In addition to analyses of individual elements, analyses of elements are given under combinations of elements and trace analysis (Sections IV-G, H, I). Some determinations of secondary products, e.g., water and nitrogen oxides, are included.

The general topic of elemental analysis, which includes reaction gas chromatographic processes as well as a multitude of other techniques, has been reviewed biennially by Ma and Gutterson (69). Francis (70) has recently given a detailed description of available and soon-to-be-available instruments for automatic elemental analysis; most of these employ reaction gas chromatography.

A. Carbon Detection and Analysis

The detection of organic materials in a chromatographic effluent was an early problem in gas chromatography. In 1955, Martin and Smart (71) devised a simple detection system (actually a post-column reactor) based on the complete oxidation of the carbon in organic effluents to carbon dioxide by passage through a hot tube of cupric oxide. The carbon dioxide was determined by infrared analysis. Others subsequently used titrimetry (72), coulometry (73), and electrical conductivity (74,75) for this determination. Carbon in a variety of substances, e.g., water (76) and metals (77), has been determined by this basic route.

Zlatkis and Ridgway (78) introduced a reductive procedure which converted selected organic eluates to methane and water by passing them in a hydrogen stream through a tube containing a nickel catalyst at 350–450°C. Water was removed prior to detection of methane by thermal conductivity. The reductive technique was later used for the analysis of carbon monoxide (79) and carbon dioxide (80), which are similarly converted to methane prior to flame ionization detection. In elemental analysis two reactors have been used sequentially, one to oxidize organic substances to carbon dioxide and the other to reduce the carbon dioxide over nickel to methane (81).

Variations of the foregoing oxidative and reductive routes form the basis of carbon analyses in compounds.

B. Hydrogen

Hydrogen, usually determined along with other elements in a compound and seldom by itself, is generally oxidized to water under conditions appropriate for the analysis of the other elements in the compound. Since water is not readily determined in a gas chromatographic system with other elemental products of combustion, it is usually reacted with calcium carbide to give acetylene (82) or with one of two reagents to give hydrogen—iron filings at 750°C (83) or calcium hydride (84). The acetylene or hydrogen, formed in stoichiometric amount, is readily separated and determined gas chromatographically. Mashiko, Konosu, and Morii (85) separated water and carbon dioxide on a column containing 20% polyethylene glycol 6000 and thus were able to determine water directly.

C. Nitrogen

Reitsema and Allphin (86) determined nitrogen and C/N ratios by reaction gas chromatography. Compounds eluted from a chromatographic column with helium are run through a furnace containing CuO at 700° to form CO_2 and NO_2. These gases are separated on a second column and their ratios computed from the peak areas. When CO_2 replaces helium as the carrier gas, the CO_2 product is masked, and only the NO_2 is observable on the chromatogram.

Parsons, Pennington, and Walker (87) subsequently developed a superior procedure for determining nitrogen. The sample is rapidly oxidized by CuO in a helium atmosphere maintained at 800° by means of a high-frequency induction furnace, and the resulting nitrogen oxides are reduced to nitrogen with finely divided copper at 800°. Combustion products other than nitrogen are absorbed in passage through Molecular Sieve 5A so that only the nitrogen reaches the thermal conductivity detector. Analysis time is about 20 min, precision 0.1 %, and sample size 1–10 mg.

Stewart, Porter, and Beard (88) led the nitrogen produced by Dumas combustion into a gas chromatograph for measuring nitrogen content of soil samples in the 1500-ppm range.

Recently, both Coulson (88a) and Martin (88b) have described similar rapid sensitive methods for selective determination of nitrogen compounds. Nitrogen-containing compounds in a gas chromatographic effluent are drastically reduced to form ammonia by passage through a heated reduction chamber in a hydrogen atmosphere with nickel catalyst. The ammonia is determined coulometrically or by electrolytic conductivity.

Nitrogen oxides can be converted to nitrogen as described previously or determined as nitrogen oxide by quantitative gas chromatography. Nitrogen dioxide has been converted to nitrogen oxide by passage through a precolumn of sodium tetraborate on dry support (89) or through a wet molecular sieve column (90).

D. Oxygen

Suchanec (91) and Götz (92) determined oxygen in organic substances by converting it to carbon monoxide. The sample was injected into a quartz tube packed with carbon at 1120°C, or a similar tube packed with 1:1 by weight of platinum–carbon mixture at 920°C. The oxygen in the sample forms carbon monoxide which may be measured gas chromatographically with a molecular sieve or activated charcoal column. Sample size is 2 mg or larger, and analysis time is about 35 min.

Free oxygen may be quantitatively converted to water at room temperature over a palladium catalyst (93), and the water converted to acetylene as already described for gas chromatographic analysis. Abel (94) used this double reaction to determine oxygen in the presence of argon.

E. Sulfur

The procedure of Okuno, Morris, and Haines (95) for determining organic sulfur consists of catalytic hydrogenation at 1000° to produce hydrogen sulfide and methane, trapping of these products, and measurement of them by gas chromatography—all in a continuous system. Analysis time is 30 min, and sample size is 5–10 mg, although estimations of sulfur in samples one-tenth this size are said to be possible. See Sections H-2 and I for other analyses of sulfur by reduction.

Sulfur can also be determined by combustion of the sample in several ways to yield sulfur oxides, which are determined gas chromatographically. Details of these procedures are given in Sections G-3 and I.

F. Halogens

The combustion of organohalogen compounds produces hydrogen halide or free halogen depending upon the conditions. The hydrogen halide is also produced by reaction of compounds with hydrogen at high temperatures, both with and without a catalyst. Specific methods are described under halogen analysis with other elements in Sections G-4, H-2, and I.

Free fluorine is determined (96) by passage through a 10-cm precolumn of anhydrous sodium chloride. The liberated chlorine is determined gas chromatographically.

G. Carbon and Other Elements (CH, CHN, CS, C-Halogen)

1. Carbon, Hydrogen

Two similar methods for C and H analysis were reported simultaneously in 1960, both involving a Pregl-type combustion (CuO at 750°C) with gas chromatographic separation and detection of the products: Duswalt and Brandt (97) combusted their sample in an atmosphere of oxygen using platinum, copper oxide, and silver packing; Sundberg and Maresh (82) burned their sample in a helium atmosphere in the presence of copper oxide and copper (the latter to reduce nitrogen oxides). The combustion gases were passed through calcium carbide to convert water to acetylene. Because the combustion took 10–20 min, a liquid nitrogen trap was required to concentrate the gases for quick release into the gas chromatograph. The acetylene and carbon dioxide were separated on a silica gel column. Sample sizes were the traditional 2–6 mg. The cupric oxide in the Sundberg and Maresh procedure must be periodically reoxidized.

In a more recent method, Miller and Winefordner (84,97a) burned organic samples in pure oxygen over CuO at 1000°C to CO_2 and water in 90 sec. Only the CO_2 passes a filter–desiccant system and is detected gas chromatographically. The water is then rapidly released by heating and reacted with calcium hydride to form hydrogen, which is similarly detected. Halogens, oxides of sulfur, and nitrogen are retained irreversibly. Analysis time is about 10 min, and sample size 0.2–1 mg. By suitable modification of the apparatus and the use of a helium carrier gas, a nitrogen analysis on a separate sample may be run (97a).

2. Carbon, Hydrogen, and Nitrogen

The CHN analyzers presently available are based on the principles of combustion and detection already discussed. Most accommodate samples of 0.2–5 mg, employ combustion zones of about 900°C in the presence of an oxidative catalyst (e.g., cobalt oxides) for rapid combustion, combined with (or followed by) a reduction zone containing heated copper to convert nitrogen oxides to nitrogen. Silver is frequently included in the combustion train to remove halogen and sulfur. Water is measured directly or converted to acetylene prior to measurement. After the sample is weighed, the procedure is largely automatic and requires about 10 min per sample.

Francis (70) described the latest instrumentation available for CHN analyses. There seems to be little doubt that the new instruments have reduced the past minimum sample weight requirement for analysis by a factor of 10, with little or no sacrifice of accuracy.

A discussion comparing the reliability of instrumental and classical means of determining carbon, hydrogen, and nitrogen has been presented recently by Hinsvark and Waltz (98).

Some of the older CHN methods, such as those advanced by Nightingale and Walker (99) and Walisch (100), required from 1 to $1\frac{3}{4}$ hr per analysis; these procedures contributed toward the progress of rapid gas chromatographic CHN analysis.

3. Carbon, Sulfur

Beuerman and Meloan (101) converted organic sulfur and carbon in samples of about 5 mg to SO_2 and CO_2 by combustion at 850°C in a stream of oxygen using a platinum catalyst. The water is removed with calcium sulfate, and the SO_2 and CO_2 are retained in a liquid nitrogen trap for subsequent release and separation on a dinonyl phthalate column. The complete analysis required 20 min, and the error was within 1%. Stuckey and Walker (102) determined carbon and sulfur in ferrous metals using a pressurized stream of oxygen with a high-pressure induction furnace, followed by separation on a temperature-programmed silica gel column. Analysis time was 17 min.

4. Carbon, Halogen

Mamaril and Meloan (103) developed a method for determining carbon, chlorine, and bromine in organic compounds. The compounds were combusted at 800° in a stream of oxygen with platinum catalyst present to CO_2, water, and halogen. Hydrogen chloride and hydrogen bromide, which formed when the oxygen flow rate was too slow, were avoided. After water removal, the gases were held up in a liquid nitrogen trap for subsequent release into a chromatograph with helium as the carrier gas.

H. Other Elemental Analyses

1. Nitrogen, Oxygen

By pyrolysis of organic compounds in the presence of nickel and carbon black, Terent'ev, Turkel'taub, Bondarevskaya, and Domochkina (104) determined nitrogen and oxygen quantitatively as nitrogen and carbon monoxide by separation on Molecular Sieve 5A.

2. Sulfur, Halogen

Huyten and Rijnders (105) used continuous hydrogenation of the effluent over platinum gauze at 1000°C to obtain H_2S, HBr, HI, and water. The carrier gas with these products is divided into two streams, one of which contains soda lime at 250°C to remove the acidic products and water. After appropriate adjustments of flow rate and sensitivity, a difference signal between the two streams corresponds to the amount of H_2S, HBr, or HI generated from the sample. These authors also described means of determining C/H and C/N ratios of an effluent component.

I. Trace Analysis

Classical methods of elementary analysis usually depend on an initial sample weight (generally 3–5 mg), slow combustion, and on a tedious gravimetric or other measure of the products. The latest automated instrumentation for elemental analyses not only speeds up the process through rapid combustion and gas chromatographic measurement, but through the sensitivity of the latter measurement, the size of sample required has been cut at least tenfold. The smallest recommended sample size is now ca. 0.2 mg. The bar to further decrease in sample size appears to be the inability to introduce samples of lesser weight with the required accuracy. Weighing difficulties are intensified as volatility increases; liquids are more difficult to weigh accurately than solids because they spread and present a large surface for evaporation. Thermal conductivity detectors, which are used in elementary analysis, are sufficiently sensitive for accurately measuring products from a 0.2-mg sample. Means of detecting lesser amounts of product are available when problems associated with the initial weighing steps are solved. Thus, the ratio of elements in a compound emerging from a gas chromatograph may be determined on samples too small to be weighed.

The aforementioned ability to detect small quantities has achieved its greatest development in the analysis of pesticide residues. A large number of pesticides contain halogen, phosphorus, and sulfur; the determinations of these elements in a pesticide residue are among the most sensitive chemical analyses routinely used today. A typical process involves passing the column effluent through a combustion furnace and then into a micro-coulometric cell. The furnace can be operated in the usual oxidative mode (Cl and S being determined as HCl and SO_2) or in the reductive mode (hydrogen converts products to HCl, H_2S, and PH_3). An instrument that can operate in both modes has been announced recently (106).

Coulson, Cavanagh, De Vries, and Walther (107) advanced a rapid screening method for pesticide residues based on the analysis of chlorine and sulfur. The pesticide, after separation on a chromatographic column, is burned in a combustion furnace at 800–1000° with oxygen over a plati-num gauze to CO_2, HCl, water, and other inorganic substances. The gas is bubbled directly into a titration cell and the HCl analyzed with silver ion coulometrically. If the combustion is followed by catalytic hydro-genation at high temperature, the sulfur oxides are converted to hydrogen sulfide so that both sulfide and chloride are detected.

Using a hydrogen carrier gas, Burchfield, Johnson, Rhoades, and Wheeler (108) passed pesticides or drug metabolites (separated by gas chromatog-raphy) through an empty quartz column at 950° and converted organic phosphorus, sulfur, and halogen to PH_3, H_2S, and HCl. The three inorganic gases could be measured simultaneously with a microcoulometric titration cell equipped with silver electrodes. Alternatively, the gases could be measured selectively by inserting appropriate subtracting agents in the line just prior to the titration cell or by modifications of the titration cell. For example, only phosphine was detected with aluminum oxide as the subtracting agent.

Coulson (109) recently described an electrolytic conductivity detector for determining carbon, sulfur, and/or halogens. The sample is oxidized in a furnace to carbon dioxide, sulfur oxides, and hydrogen halide, which are measured by their electrolytic conductivity in a stream of deionized water. Analysis in the low nanogram range is said to be possible. By using reductive conditions in the furnace, nitrogen may be determined as ammonia (88a,88b).

Sternberg and Jones (110) have described a simple detector which is sensitive to halogens and sulfur. The detector measures the electrolytic conductivity of a thin film of flowing electrolyte which extracts soluble combustion products from the exhaust gases of a conventional hydrogen flame detector. In this arrangement, the flame detector is really operating as a microcombustion chamber prior to electrolytic conductivity detection of the products. The limit of sensitivity of the detector is 10^{-10} g/sec of sulfur or halogen. Application of this device to the selective determination of pesticide residues has been made by Johns and Braithwaite (111).

The hydrogen flame detector, as modified by Karmen and Giuffrida (112–114) to include a sodium salt vapor, is highly specific for phosphorus determinations at the parts-per-billion level, and is also suitable for halogen detection at higher levels. In a recent version of this detector Giuffrida, Ives, and Bostwick (114a) employ a potassium chloride vapor which represses halogen response without significantly affecting the response to phosphorus. The detector has been further modified to give a selective response to nitrogen-containing compounds (114b).

J. Elemental Analysis of Radiolabeled Molecules

The measurement of radioactivity in compounds is often facilitated by breakdown of the compounds to simple gas molecules, as in elemental analysis, followed by detection of radioactivity. Radioactive carbon and tritium are generally determined by combustion of a chromatographic effluent to form labeled carbon dioxide and water. The ^{14}C may be counted directly as $^{14}CO_2$, possibly diluted with unlabeled carbon dioxide according to the method of James and Piper (115), or after conversion to methane as described by Mlinko and Szarvas (81) or by Drawert et al. (116). Tritium may be determined by converting the labeled water of combustion back to tritium, followed by passage in an appropriate carrier gas through a katharometer or radioactivity detector. Elemental analysis of radio-labeled molecules has been reviewed by Drawert and Bachmann (117) and by Bruzzi, Castelli, and Cervellati (118).

The analysis of radioactive carbon and tritium in gas chromatographic effluents was described recently by James and Hitchcock (119). With argon as carrier gas, the labeled organic effluent is passed through a heated combustion tube containing copper oxide and iron powder for conversion to carbon dioxide and tritium. The carbon dioxide is diluted with unlabeled carbon dioxide and determined with a proportional counting tube. Proportional counting tubes coupled with gas chromatographs have been utilized also by Wolfgang and Rowland (120), Lee et al. (121), and others. In addition, a continuous flow ionization chamber has been used to monitor the products of chromatographic effluents formed by ignition of the sample to CO_2 at 650°C (122) or conversion into methane (117) and hydrogen with zinc and metal oxide at 650°C.

K. Trends in Elemental Analysis

In the early 1960's, traditional combustion methods were coupled with gas chromatographs for separation and direct readout from chromatograms. Analysis times tended to be at least 30 min, and sample sizes were the traditional 3–5 mg. From this initial and widespread effort the goals for future elemental analyses have been steadily elevated. Automatic or nearly automatic procedures and instrumentation are being developed for the analysis of elements and combinations of elements. Time of analysis, now about 10–15 min, will continue to decrease, perhaps to a few minutes per analysis. The sample size minimum, presently ca. 0.2 mg for a CHN analysis, should also become smaller. There is the possibility of using, for elemental analysis, available detectors, which are more sensitive and more specific than thermal conductivity units (electron-capture, thermionic (113), electrolytic conductivity (109)).

V. Class Reactions

Class reactions are potentially valuable to the chemist in that they provide an analysis that may be useful for compounds containing a certain functional group or a specific structure. Class reactions may include alteration or degradation of a molecule to a related structure, formation of a derivative, or an analysis for the amount of a functional group in a compound. A few analyses bordering on reaction gas chromatography have been included as suggestive of determinations that may be adaptable to reaction gas chromatography.

Many of the class reactions are given in other sections of this chapter, where they seemed more appropriate. Thus, carbon-skeleton chromatography, which has been used to analyze many classes of compounds, is located under hydrogen reactions; hydrogenation, dehydrogenation, subtractive processes, and even elemental analyses have also been placed elsewhere and may likewise be considered class reactions.

A. Precolumn Analyses

1. *Amino Acids*

Zlatkis, Oro, and Kimball (123) passed a selected group of amino acids through a ninhydrin-containing precolumn which converted the compounds to aldehydes. Because the aldehydes could not be suitably dried for thermal conductivity detection, they were cracked and reduced to methane, which is easily dried, with a short column containing a nickel catalyst at 425°C placed just ahead of the detector.

2. Aldehydes and Ketones

Lower aldehydes and ketones are too volatile to recover from natural materials in free form, but as 2,4-dinitrophenylhydrazone derivatives, there is no problem. Jack Ralls (124) was able to regenerate the original compounds from micro amounts of 2,4-dinitrophenylhydrazones by heating the derivatives for 10 sec at 250°C with α-ketoglutaric acid in a capillary tube opening into the injection port. The regenerated compounds pour into the injection port and are chromatographed in the usual way. The determination is not quantitative. Modifications by Stephens and Teszler (125), Ralls (126), and most recently by Jones and Monroe (127), have improved yields of the carbonyl compounds.

3. Acids

Flash-exchange gas chromatography for the study of lower carboxylic acids was introduced by Ralls (128) and later improved and extended by Hunter (129) to the C_{18} level. An aliquot of a mixture of potassium (or sodium) salts or organic acids and potassium ethyl sulfate in water is drawn into a hypodermic needle containing diatomaceous earth. The water is removed by warming the mixture in the needle in a convection oven at 100°C. The needle is connected to a source of argon (15 psig) and then inserted into a preheated (275°C) section of the gas chromatography column. The exchange reaction forms ethyl esters of the organic acids, which are swept into the chromatograph by the argon gas stream. The resulting sharp, well-separated peaks can be used to confirm the identity of organic acids previously detected in free form by gas chromatography. No attempt was made to quantitate results as the exchange reaction does not go to completion.

Hoffman and White (129a) analyzed malonic acids by decarboxylating them in the injection port and separating the monocarboxylic acids on a column of 6% Carbowax 20M-terephthalic acid on Chromosorb W (acid washed).

Salts of fatty acids in aqueous solutions can be converted to the free acids in a forecolumn packed with an acid-coated support as described by Thompson and Smith (129b). In an analogous manner, a basic-packed forecolumn can liberate amines from their salts just prior to separation on an analytical column.

Drawert (130) used a heated injection port to complete the esterification of acids. After treating the potassium salts of fatty acids with sulfuric acid and boron trifluoride–methanol reagent and filtering, the partially esterified mixture was injected into the hot port to complete the esterification.

Hoffman, Barboriak, and Hardman (131) determined lactic acid in aqueous solution by depositing the solution plus periodic acid in an injection port at 100°. The reaction, which is very slow at room temperature, goes to completion almost instantly at 100°; the acetaldehyde produced is a measure of lactic acid content and is determined gas chromatographically. The procedure will be recognized as the classical Malprade reaction scaled down to gas chromatography size; it may be applicable to other compounds with vicinal carbonyl or hydroxyl groups.

Acids, such as HCl, can be determined (132) by passing them through a precolumn packed with sodium bicarbonate; the amount of carbon dioxide released is related to the acid concentration.

4. Alcohols

Drawert (133) was able to convert alcohols to three different derivatives which could be analyzed more readily than the alcohols themselves at the time that these methods were developed. In the C_1–C_3 range the alcohols could be converted with nitrous acid to their volatile alkyl nitrites; alcohols in the C_2–C_{10} range were dehydrated to olefins by passing them through a column containing phosphoric acid at temperatures between 200° and 300°C; the C_1–C_4 alcohols were also reduced to hydrocarbons with Raney nickel at 170°C.

5. Esters

For identification purposes Janák, Novák, and Sulovsky (133a) converted esters to alcohols by passing them through a wet potassium hydroxide column.

6. Organometallics

Leonhardt, Morrison, and Kamienski (133b) determined vinyllithium quantitatively by hydrolysis on a short precolumn containing a solid support coated with high-boiling polyol followed by measurement of the ethylene.

B. On-Column Derivative Formation

The technique of "peak shifting," whereby volatile compounds are converted to volatile derivatives on a gas chromatographic column, was introduced by Langer and Pantages (134). The sample to be analyzed is injected into the gas chromatograph, and after a short time interval a second injection is made of a compound that forms a volatile derivative of one or more of the compounds in the original sample. The technique was originally employed to convert alcohols to trimethylsilyl ether derivatives and later by Haken (135) to convert alcohols to acetates. Anders and Mannering (136) used the peak-shift technique to characterize alkaloids and steroids. They injected acetic or propionic anhydride to form acetyl or propionyl derivatives of compounds containing hydroxyl, phenolic, or primary and secondary amine groups. They also reported similar formation of trifluoroacetate and trimethylsilyl ether derivatives, the latter being formed by injection of hexamethyldisilazane.

Marmion, White, Bille, and Ferber (137) determined 2-naphthylamine in commercial 1-naphthylamine, as their acetamides, by consecutive injection of the amine mixture and acetic anhydride.

C. Functional Group Analysis

The following two functional group analyses utilize a reaction vessel ahead of the injection port rather than a flow-through tube reactor. The reaction requires several minutes to go to completion, and the gaseous products are then swept into the gas chromatograph by diverting the carrier gas through the vessel.

1. Active Hydrogen

Two groups of investigators advanced methods for determining active hydrogen. Chumachenko and Tverdyukova (138) reacted compounds with a tetrahydrofuran solution of lithium aluminum hydride in a small vessel. The evolved hydrogen is swept into the gas chromatograph with the nitrogen carrier gas and determined by thermal conductivity. Lysyj and Greenough (139) determined two kinds of hydrogen: the hydridic (hydrogen on boron) and the active hydrogen type (as in OH, NH_2, COOH). Hydrogen was liberated by acid from borane compounds and by lithium aluminum hydride from compounds with active hydrogen. Sample sizes were 1–6 mg, and 5–7 min were required for analysis.

Putnam and Myers (139a) measured the hydrogen formed when boron hydrides were hydrolyzed on a wet Molecular Sieve 5A column. The reaction appears to be useful for the analysis of hydridic hydrogen with a flow-through tubular system.

2. Primary Amino Group

The determination of primary amino group by reaction gas chromatography was introduced by Hoffmann and Lysyj (140). The sample (1–5 mg) is introduced into a reaction vessel with a sodium nitrite solution. After the vessel is purged with helium, acetic acid is added to generate nitrous acid, and 1 min is allowed for the reaction to take place; the evolved nitrogen is then flushed into the gas chromatograph and measured.

D. Methods Bordering on Reaction Gas Chromatography

a. Zeisel Determination. Mitsui and Kitamura (141) described the simultaneous separation and gravimetric determination of alkoxy groups by combining the Zeisel method with gas chromatography. The alkyl iodides that form are absorbed in a tube filled with silica gel and weighed. The iodides are then heated under nitrogen and released into a gas chromatograph to give a measure of the kinds and amounts of alkyl iodides. Although not reaction gas chromatography, the method appears to be adaptable to the process.

b. Carboxyl Group Determination. Ma, Shang, and Manche (142) determined the amount of carboxyl group in compounds gas chromatographically. The sample (0.05–0.15 meq carboxyl group), heated in a closed vessel with quinoline and cupric carbonate, decarboxylates and forms carbon dioxide which is driven into a gas chromatograph for measurement. Peak height of a particular acid, which varies linearly with sample size, must be calibrated with known amounts of sample. Analysis time is one hour.

c. Organic Sulfide Analysis. By the method of Franc, Dvoracek, and Kolouskova (143), alkyl or aryl organic sulfides are cleaved with Raney nickel by heating in a glass microreactor for 15 min; the resulting hydrocarbons are swept directly into the gas chromatograph for identification.

d. Syringe Reactions. A technique for functional group analysis, which utilizes gas chromatography (but cannot be classed as reaction gas chromatography because the reaction does not occur within the system), has been described by Hoff and Feit (144) and is called "syringe reaction." Dilute vapors of organic compounds in air or an inert gas are brought into contact with chemical classification reagents in a hypodermic syringe. The reagents, which may be bases, solids, or aqueous solutions, are used to detect carbonyl compounds, differentiate between aldehydes and ketones, convert alcohols to acetates or nitrites, detect unsaturation, hydrogenate unsaturated compounds, and differentiate ethers, olefins, aromatic hydrocarbons, and paraffins.

A useful variation of this technique has been introduced recently by Davison and Dutton (144a) for ozonolysis of fatty acid esters. Combined with the syringe is a microreactor apparatus in which a 5 μl sample can be ozonized, thermally cleaved, and injected directly into the gas chromatograph.

VI. Subtractive Processes

One of the simplest reaction gas chromatographic processes is the subtraction of a particular group of compounds through the inclusion of a chemical in the chromatographic system. The chemical reacts with certain types of compounds by chemical or physical means so that they do not reach the detector. Occasionally the compounds can be released at the desired moment by appropriate temperature or flow programming. A compound can be subtracted from the same gas stream by conversion to another with markedly different retention time or selectively retained. The subtractive reagents have been located at every point of the chromatographic pathway depending on the result desired.

The comparison of chromatograms with and without certain types of compounds aids in peak identification and can simplify considerably the evaluation of a complex analysis. The presence or absence of compounds with certain structures, e.g., alcohols, straight- or branched-chain hydrocarbons, or olefins, can be demonstrated through the use of subtractive reagents in the system. Even partial subtraction or retardation can yield valuable data on the structure of substances.

Identification of hydrocarbon peaks in gas chromatography by sequential application of subtractive reagents (also hydrogenation and dehydrogenation) has been employed by Rowan (7). The sample is passed through a column, through a reaction zone, and then into a cold trap. The products in the cold trap may then be returned to the column to see what changes have taken place. The operations are carried out rapidly and conveniently in a closed system with a series of 4-way valves. Peaks from a complex hydrocarbon mixture can be identified as n-olefins, isoolefins, n-paraffins, isoparaffins, naphthenes, or aromatics. All peaks of a synthetic and a commercial gasoline sample were identified by hydrocarbon class and over half by name.

A. Molecular Sieves

Probably the best known of the subtractive processes is the removal of normal alkanes from branched, cyclic, and aromatic hydrocarbons with Molecular Sieve 5A, as advanced originally by Brenner and Coates (145) in the subtraction of C_3-C_{11} n-alkanes, and as extended by Albert (146) for a more comprehensive analysis of gasolines. Whitham (147) applied the technique to a higher molecular weight range (C_7-C_{16}) and determined the n-paraffin content and distribution in kerosines and gas oils. Subtractive procedures of this type have been reviewed by Adlard and Whitham (148). Brenner and co-workers (149) revealed that low molecular weight compounds of the following types were completely adsorbed on a Molecular Sieve 5A column: normal paraffins (except methane), normal olefins, normal alcohols, aldehydes, and acids. In addition, Ettre and Brenner (150) found that a compound with carbonyl or hydroxyl groups may retard another such compound in passage through a molecular sieve column. Variations in adsorption properties of 5A sieves at extremely low concentrations (found in studying atmospheric pollutants) have been reported by Williams (150a). Adsorption characteristics of Molecular Sieves 4A and 5A as reported by Hersh (151) are shown in Table 9-4.

TABLE 9-4
Molecular Sieve Adsorption Characteristics

Adsorbed on 4A and 5A	Adsorbed on 5A but not 4A	Not adsorbed on 4A or 5A
Water	Propane and higher n-paraffin to C_{14}	Isobutane and all isoparaffins
Carbon dioxide		
Carbon monoxide[a]	Butene and higher n-olefins	Isopropanol and all iso, sec, and tert alcohols
Hydrogen sulfide		
Sulfur dioxide	n-Butanol and higher n-alcohols	
Ammonia		Benzene and all aromatics
Nitrogen[a]	Cyclopropane	
Oxygen[a]	Freon-12	Cyclohexane and all cyclics with at least 4-membered rings
Methane[a]		
Methanol		
Ethane		Carbon tetrachloride
Ethanol		
Ethylene		Hexachlorobutadiene
Acetylene		
Propylene		Freon 114
n-Propanol		Freon 11
Ethylene oxide		Sulfur hexafluoride
		Boron trifluoride
		Molecules larger than 50 Å

[a] Adsorbed at temperatures below $-30°C$.

Barrall and Baumann (152) investigated molecular sieve columns which would quantitatively retain all normal olefins and paraffins from C_7–C_{20} with minimum tailing of branched-chain, aromatic, and naphthenic substances. The accuracy of their normal hydrocarbon determination (difference between chromatograms of total and molecular-sieve-treated sample) is 2–3%.

B. Removal of Olefins

Although some olefins may be retained by molecular sieves, the usual means of removing olefins is with packings containing sulfuric acid or silver, mercuric, or cuprous salts. The technique of preparing the packings and a summary of packings that will permit the passage of alkanes but

TABLE 9-5

Absorption (%) of Hydrocarbon Classes by Chemical Absorbents

Gas	20% HgSO$_4$, 20% H$_2$SO$_4$	Mercuric acetate, sat. soln.	4% Ag$_2$SO$_4$, 95% H$_2$SO$_4$	H$_2$SO$_4$ 95%	80%	60%
Methane	0	0	0	0	0	0
Ethane	0	0	0	0	0	0
Propane	0	0	0	0	0	0
n-Butane	0	0	0	0	0	0
n-Hexane	0	0	0	11	7	0
n-Octane	0	0	0	0	0	0
Cyclohexane	0	0	8	31	0	0
Ethylene	100	94	100	11	6	0
Propylene	100	100	100	100	67	0
Isobutylene	100	100	100	100	100	100
2-Pentene	100	67	100	100	88	0
3-Heptene	100	60	100	100	85	0
4-Methylcyclohexene	100	70	100	100	70	0
Benzene	5	46	100	94	32	13
Toluene[a]	0	22	100	100	33	0
p-Xylene[a]	0	0	100	100	0	0
Acetylene	100	100	100	16	11	0

[a] Accuracy is only ca. ±10% because of hangup; otherwise estimated to be ±5%.

subtract alkenes (with or without aromatics and/or alkynes) has been given by Innes et al. (153,154). They developed a process of hydrocarbon gas analysis based on the use of chemical absorbents shown in Table 9-5. Subtractive techniques of this type have also been employed by Altshuller in air pollution studies (155). Janák and Novák (156) removed butadiene with a precolumn containing maleic anhydride on silica. Gil-Av and Herzberg-Minzly (157) used chloromaleic anhydride on the column to subtract partially aliphatic dienes. They were able to distinguish cis and trans isomers because the trans isomer is preferentially retained.

C. Removal of Aldehydes and Alcohols

Allen (157a) has recently demonstrated that freshly prepared column packing containing 20 % of the commercially available liquid phase FFAP (157b) will subtract aromatic or aliphatic aldehydes from complex mixtures during gas chromatography. Sharma, McLean, and Bardwell (157c) reported the removal of formaldehyde from a gaseous mixture when passed through a tube packed with glycerol on firebrick located between the injection point and the analytical column. Kerr and Trotman-Dickenson (157d) have described the removal of butyraldehyde with a mull of sodium bisulfite in ethylene glycol on firebrick.

Primary and secondary alcohols can be removed from complex mixtures by using boric acid on packing material. Ikeda, Simmons, and Grossman (158) studied the process in detail using known mixtures of primary, secondary, and tertiary alcohols as well as nonalcoholic compounds. They employed a dual column gas chromatograph with 10 ft $\times$ $\frac{1}{4}$ in. columns packed with 20 % Carbowax 20M, but one of the columns included a 6-in. section containing 3 % boric acid just ahead of the detector. In the latter column, primary and secondary alcohols were subtracted; tertiary alcohols, which generally dehydrated to olefins, were sometimes retained by the column depending upon the structure of the alcohol and chromatographic conditions employed. The technique was also used by Hefendehl (159) for the determination of terpene alcohols by comparison of chromatograms made with and without boric acid in the packing.

D. Removal of Halogenated Compounds

Rogozinski (160) found that Versamide 900 irreversibly retains α-bromo fatty acid esters, benzoyl chloride, and other compounds containing labile halogens. It does not retain ordinary halogen compounds, e.g., bromobenzene, bromoethane, chloroform, ethyl γ-bromo-butyrate.

Harris and McFadden (161) determined amounts of 2-bromobutane and 1-bromo-2-methylpropane by passing the compounds through two columns, one with a short precolumn of silver nitrate on firebrick and one without. Under the conditions employed secondary and tertiary alkyl halides dehydrohalogenate to olefins which are retained by the silver nitrate packing.

E. Removal of Water

Water has been removed from the chromatographic train by a variety of methods, some of which have already been mentioned. Kilner and Ratcliff (162) used a heated precolumn, 10 $\times$ $\frac{1}{2}$ in., filled with granular

6- to 12-mesh anhydrous calcium sulfate. In the course of the analysis of chlorine cell gas by gas chromatography, Neely (163) used a concentrated sulfuric acid scrubber, a glass-wool trap, and a magnesium perchlorate tube for final drying. To remove water interference in the gas chromatographic analysis of aqueous solutions of hydrocarbons and halocarbons, Jacobs (164) devised a precolumn trap consisting of a 16 × ¼ in. copper tube packed with a mixture of 9 parts phosphorus pentoxide powder to 1 part Desicote- and Siliclad-treated firebrick. Drawert (130) used a calcium hydride zone in front of his analytical column to react with water and acids from an esterification mixture. The hydrogen generated in the reaction was not detected because hydrogen was the carrier gas. Kung, Whitney, and Cavagnol (165) used a heated precolumn of calcium carbide to subtract the water (by conversion to acetylene) from an aqueous solution of organic materials. The same technique has been used by Knight and Weiss (166) to determine traces of water in hydrocarbons. Robbins, Bethea, and Wheelock (167) trapped water as well as H_2S, SO_2, and CO_2 on an 11-ft section of ¼-in. copper tubing filled with 25% potassium hydroxide on Chromosorb W. The column was one of three used with a single detector for the analysis of carbon dioxide, hydrogen sulfide, hydrogen, oxygen, nitrogen, methane, carbon monoxide, and sulfur dioxide from a single gas sample.

F. Selective Retardation of Compounds

The subtraction of compounds, whether by physical or chemical means, is a form of reaction gas chromatography which need not necessarily be complete, but may be more of a retardation process. This facet of the subtractive technique does not fall within the scope of this chapter; but it is worthy of mention as a means of resolving compounds which, although of different chemical makeup, are difficult to separate conventionally because they possess very similar retention times. For example, a compound with double bonds may be selectively retarded, as compared with a saturated one, by substrates containing silver nitrate in ethylene glycol, glycerol, triethylene glycol, or benzyl cyanide. Olefins are also retarded by polar liquid phases (168). Aromatics and picric acid–fluorene addition compounds may be retarded by polyalkylene glycol-type substrates. Amines and amino acid esters are detained by substrates containing heavy metal salts of fatty acids (168). Water can be selectively retained by such substrates as the hydrochloride of Quadrol (169). The use of a retardation technique is usually based on known differences in the structure of components. The differences may be utilized to select appropriate packings.

VII. Other Reaction Gas Chromatographic Processes

This section presents catalytic processes, reaction kinetics, and miscellaneous reactions (e.g. rearrangements, exchanges, and degradations). Also given are examples of procedures in which two or more sequential reactions are combined. In connection with reactions which take place directly on the column, several studies are of interest. Kallen and Heilbronner (170), have calculated the shapes of the chromatographic peaks resulting from the irreversible transformation on the column of one substance into another with different retention characteristics. Magee (171) has proposed a simplified model and mathematical description of the course of a reaction in a chromatographic column operated as a pulse reactor.

A. Catalytic Processes and Reaction Kinetics

The original use of the microreactor devised by Kokes, Tobin, and Emmett (2) was for studying vapor-phase catalytic processes. A small amount of substance or reaction mixture is injected into the carrier gas stream and transported through the heated precolumn or microreactor containing the catalyst; the products pour into the gas chromatograph for analysis. As reaction conditions and catalysts are varied, qualitative and quantitative changes in the products may be studied. A similar but more flexible microreactor was described by Ettre and Brenner (171a); it is also commercially available. Hall, MacIver, and Weber (172) devised a semiautomatic microreactor to make possible simple microscale evaluations of catalyst parameters. More recently, Harrison, Hall, and Rase (173) have devised a completely automatic precision microreactor to facilitate the acquisition of data on reaction kinetics, catalyst behavior, catalyst activity studies, and catalyst comparisons.

The microreactor of Kokes et al. (2) has been widely used. Norton (174) conducted over one hundred experiments to determine the catalytic activities of Molecular Sieves 5A and 10X for olefin isomerization, polymerization, and depolymerization at 300–400°C. Norton and Moss (175) evaluated metal oxides for selective dealkylation of alkyl aromatic hydrocarbons to lower homologs under oxidative conditions. Stein, Feenan, Hofer, and Anderson (176) checked catalysts for ability to oxidize methane and auto exhausts under various conditions. The de Mourgues group (177,178) studied the cracking of such compounds as isooctane and cumene with silica–alumina catalysts. For slow reactions they isolated a slug of reactant in the catalyst column for a time interval and swept the volatile contents into the gas chromatograph for analysis. Hartwig (179), with a similar microreactor, studied the isomerization and hydrogenolysis of n-paraffins at different temperatures in the presence of catalysts containing palladium at various concentrations. The work of Keulemans and Voge (6) and Okamoto and Onaka (20), described under Hydrogen Reactions, is worthy of note. Owens and Amberg (180) have studied the hydrodesulfurization of thiophene over chromic and supported cobalt molybdate catalysts. Although not reaction gas chromatography, the process of Martin and Grant (181) exposed sulfur-containing petroleum samples to alumina at 500°, producing hydrogen sulfide, aromatic thiols, and dealkylated thiophenic compounds, which are measured gas chromatographically.

As a means of studying the mechanism of surface catalysis, Tamaru (182) passed a gas through a catalyst-packed column and related absorbability to retention time. Piringer and Tataru (183) described a method for studying the chemisorption of hydrogen on metal surfaces by means of gas chromatographic techniques. The amounts of hydrogen adsorbed during specific time intervals are determined through subsequent desorption in an inert gas stream, and kinetic data are calculated.

Bassett and Habgood (184) examined in detail the first-order surface-catalyzed isomerization of cyclopropane when introduced as a reactant pulse in a catalyst column. They showed that it was possible to determine the activation energy for the rate based on gas-phase partial pressures, the heat of adsorption, and the activation energy for the surface steps.

The reaction gas chromatographic method for studying reaction kinetics has usually been limited to fast processes and low partial pressures of the reactants. The results obtained are seldom directly comparable to reactions in steady-flow reactors under practical work conditions. However, for studies of the mechanisms of catalytic reactions, the simplification of kinetics and the ability to measure the adsorption and reaction steps separately are real advantages (185).

B. Miscellaneous Reactions

In the course of conventional gas chromatography, unexpected chemical reactions are frequently encountered. Thus, Phillips, Pollard, and Soloway (186) found that the insecticide, endrin, isomerized on their chromatographic column to form a pentacyclic ketone and an isomeric aldehyde. Morris, Holman, and Fontell (187) observed dehydration, deacetylation, and cis-trans isomerization of methyl esters of fatty acids under certain conditions. Michel and Troyanowsky (188) found that their support material isomerized conjugated allene and diene compounds during gas chromatography. It is conceivable that some of these unexpected reactions may be developed into reaction gas chromatographic methods.

Terpenes and related compounds are susceptible to chemical change. Catalytic isomerization of terpenes on columns in which firebrick was used as support has been reported (189). The isomerization of β-pinene on various columns at 125° has been observed by Vilkas and Abraham (190). Kenney and Fisher (191) reported the complete isomerization of a terpene alcohol by 20% Carbowax 20M on alkaline Chromosorb W at temperatures of 180–200°C, and no isomerization under the same conditions using a nonalkaline column. Day and Miller (192) studied the decomposition of oxygenated terpenes that occurs at 205° in the injection heater; they found evidence of some decomposition even at 100°C. The catalytic effect of 11 supporting materials on gas–liquid chromatography of terpenes was described by Hayashi et al. (193).

Nigam and Levi (194) reported recently the rearrangement of the 9-membered ring of carophyllene oxide to an 8-membered ring when chromatographed with a column of 1% Reoplex 400 on acid washed Chromosorb W. The reaction does not occur if the support is treated with methanolic KOH.

The reaction between benzoin and quinone on a gas chromatographic column was studied by Bunbury and Osyany (195). They found that the evolved reaction products, hydroquinone, deoxybenzoin, and benzil, were formed not only by heat, but also by column catalysis (in the case of the self reaction of benzoin).

Minyard and Jackson (196) passed chlorinated pesticides through a precolumn containing a chemical reagent (sodium carbonate, cupric oxide, cadmium chloride, aluminum chloride, potassium dichromate) at 240°C followed by gas chromatography with electron-capture detection. The "fingerprint" chromatograms were used to identify pesticides. As a means of characterization, Scholz, Bednarczyk, and Yamauchi (196a) oxidized polymers in a short precolumn and separated the fragments on an analytical column.

Bastick, Baverez, and Castagne (196b) analyzed heavy and light water by reducing the water over iron to H_2, HD, and D_2. Senn, Richter, and Burlingame (197) reported that the enolizable hydrogen atoms of ketones exchanged quantitatively in a single pass through a gas chromatographic column pretreated with deuterium. Their column, which was 10 ft long, contained 100–120 mesh GasChrom Z coated with 10% Carbowax 6000 and 10% KOD, prepared from KOH and D_2O.

Tadmor (198) described isotopic exchange of radiolabeled ions in the stationary phase with nonradioactive ions during passage through a column. The technique was used to label inorganic compounds for analytical determinations of the compounds, and for study of interaction between solid stationary phase and solute in gas chromatography. Labeling of organic halides by isotopic exchange in gas chromatographic columns using ^{131}I, ^{82}Br, and ^{36}Cl has been described by Elias (198a). Tritium labeling of hydrocarbons and use of ^{18}F for labeling organic compounds by heterogeneous exchange reactions have been reported by Stoecklin (198b).

C. Combination of Two or More Reactions

Several examples incorporating more than one reaction in a chromatographic train have already been cited. For example, Zlatkis et al. (123) converted amino acids to aldehydes in a precolumn, separated them chromatographically, catalytically cracked them over nickel to methane, and removed water prior to detection in a thermal conductivity cell. The advantage that may be gained in combining a pyrolysis and hydrogenation unit prior to gas chromatography in the analysis of a polyethylene sample was recently illustrated by Kolb and co-workers (199,200). Figure 9-4 shows the chromatograms obtained with and without the catalytic hydrogenation unit. The complex pyrolyzate is simplified into a beautiful series of straight-chain hydrocarbons by hydrogenation, which is what you would expect from polyethylene.

VIII. Design of Reaction Gas Chromatographic Analyses and Apparatus

An examination of the many reaction gas chromatographic procedures that have been paraded before the reader reveals that most of them are based on straightforward reactions scaled down to gas chromatographic size. Apparatus for pyrolysis, elemental analysis, carbon-skeleton determinations, and a microcatalytic reactor are now commercially available; but for other analyses the investigator may have to adapt or modify available instrumentation, or build the equipment himself. As an aid in designing such equipment, the following discussion of reaction gas chromatographic parameters and apparatus may be helpful. The primary objective is to obtain sharp, well-defined peaks with retention times reliable enough for identification purposes.

A. Reaction Time Considerations

Inasmuch as the identifications of gas chromatographic peaks are usually made on the basis of retention time, it is most desirable that the reactions introduced into a system be instantaneous in order to obtain the normal retention times of the reaction products. Reactions occurring within 6–10 sec are usually considered satisfactory, although slower reactions may be admissible, depending on the compounds to be distinguished and

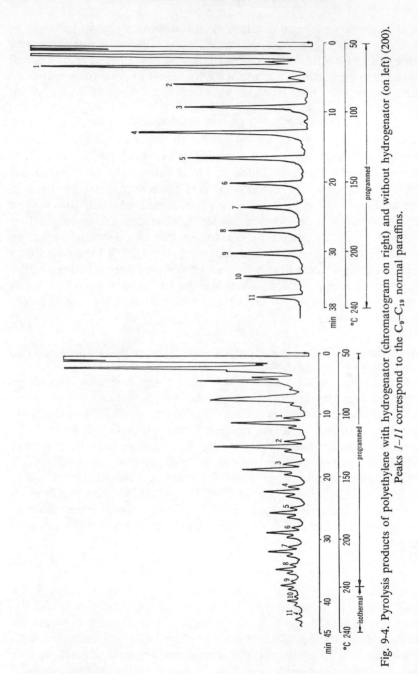

Fig. 9-4. Pyrolysis products of polyethylene with hydrogenator (chromatogram on right) and without hydrogenator (on left) (200). Peaks *1–11* correspond to the C_9–C_{19} normal paraffins.

the discriminating power of the gas chromatographic system. An increase in reaction time causes peaks to broaden and the normal retention times of products to be delayed; either of these confuses identifications and should be avoided.

B. Chemical Considerations

As has been noted, most of the early contributions in this field were made with low-molecular-weight, volatile compounds. The more volatile the compound, the less likely it is to be held up in the reaction tube. The temperature of a reaction is important, not only because it usually speeds up reactions, but because it makes compounds more volatile and thus increases their rate of flow through the reaction tube. The polarity of a molecule affects reaction time. Early investigations showed that polar molecules are significantly delayed by adsorption on a catalyst (or catalyst carrier) contained in a microreactor.

A significant aid in hastening the reaction rate is the small amount of compound injected per analysis. In the presence of a comparatively large amount of catalyst, the reaction of the minute amount of injected substance will, on the basis of law of mass action considerations, tend to go to completion rapidly.

In order to assure a uniform and high reaction rate when a packing, catalyst, or other particulate material is used in the reaction chamber, the particle size of the packing should be small and uniform in size, e.g., 60–80 mesh. A small particle size will provide enough area for complete reaction in a single pass. The reaction agent should be packed uniformly.

C. Apparatus Considerations

Many of the variables contributing to optimum performance in gas chromatographic separations are likewise applicable in reaction gas chromatography. Dead volume at any point in the system causes peak spreading and should be held to a minimum. The geometry of the tube or reaction vessel should permit travel of a compound in a minimum volume and the bore of a reaction tube should be small enough so that a uniform temperature exists in the tube. Fabricating the reaction tube of a good heat conductor or a heat-conducting sheath will help maintain a uniform reaction tube temperature. The use of a thick-walled reactor tube is advantageous; it has a high heat capacity and can offset small temperature changes due to sample vaporization or heat of reaction. The reaction tube or vessel wall should not inhibit the desired reaction, impede flow, or poison the catalyst (if one is used). Analyses of the products should be possible with a minimum of special equipment.

The length of a reactor tube, if a tube is used, will depend on the particular analysis. When the tube is too short, part of the sample may pass the reactor unchanged; when it is too long, undesirable side reactions may occur. It may be necessary to have reactor assemblies of several lengths to accommodate all of the desired analyses, or, as has been mentioned, the length of a reactor may be varied by inserting inert material in part of the tube. Alternatively, the carrier gas may be tapped or the sample injected at any point along the reactor tube length through suitably placed ports.

Reactor size will be gaged by sample size, which in turn will depend on the detector's range of sensitivity; e.g., a thermal conductivity apparatus requires a larger sample than one with a flame ionization detector.

In some analyses it is desirable or necessary to inject the compound directly onto or within the reactor bed because the products have a volatility greater than that of the sample. For example, in carbon-skeleton chromatography, dihexadecyl ether has to be placed directly on the catalyst bed to give quickly the more volatile C_{15} and C_{16} hydrocarbon products which move through the reactor with no significant delay in retention time. Were the compound placed ahead of the catalyst bed, its low volatility would result in slow migration to the bed and cause a delay in retention time of the products.

D. Trapping

Reactions that are not instantaneous (or nearly so) may still be incorporated into a gas chromatographic system. The products are trapped or otherwise retained (e.g., within a closed loop or reaction vessel) while the reaction goes to completion and then are released into the gas chromatograph for analysis. Trapping may be accomplished with a cold trap, a gas chromatographic packing in a tube, or a molecular sieve column, and the quick release of the trapped substance brought about by rapid heating.

To satisfy the need for fast reactions, the search for reaction gas chromatographic processes has centered mainly on low-molecular-weight compounds. If an instrument with temperature programming or one with a low-mass oven is available, this limitation need not apply to substances of low volatility, e.g., those of high molecular weight. Such substances may be stopped without a trap in the beginning of an analytical column that follows a reactor. The analytical column is kept cool or at room temperature to allow complete collection of the reaction products following sample injection; the temperature of the column is then programmed or raised quickly (low-mass oven necessary) to a given temperature; the substances emerge as sharp, well-defined peaks with accurate retention times (13).

IX. Concluding Remarks

The value of reaction gas chromatography has been amply demonstrated by its successful application in many fields of endeavor. It has greatly facilitated and extended the study of high-temperature and high-speed reactions and kinetics, the analysis and degradative studies of polymers, elemental analysis, and—most important—it is making possible the analysis and structure determination of remarkably small amounts of chemical, a development that should help identify minute amounts of potent, biologically active substances. Additionally, reaction gas chromatography opens up the possibility of introducing high-speed methodology in many analytical areas and offers the chemist the challenge and opportunity of utilizing his chemical skill to develop new and useful vapor-phase technology, some of which may be applicable for preparative purposes. Contributions to date represent little more than a beginning so that the potential for future development of reaction gas chromatography is bright.

References

1. F. Drawert, R. Felgenhauer, and G. Kupfer, *Angew. Chem.*, **72,** 555 (1960).
2. R. J. Kokes, H. Tobin, Jr., and P. H. Emmett, *J. Am. Chem. Soc.*, **77,** 5860 (1955).
3. M. Beroza and R. A. Coad, *J. Gas Chromatog.*, **4,** 199 (1966).
4. T. L. Mounts and H. J. Dutton, *Anal. Chem.*, **37,** 641 (1965).
5. H. J. Dutton and T. L. Mounts, *J. Catalysis*, **3,** 363 (1964).
5a. M. Beroza and R. Sarmiento, *Anal. Chem.*, **38,** 1042 (1966).
6. A. I. M. Keulemans and H. H. Voge, *J. Phys. Chem.*, **63,** 476 (1959).
7. R. Rowan, Jr., *Anal. Chem.*, **33,** 658 (1961).
8. C. J. Thompson, H. J. Coleman, R. L. Hopkins, and H. T. Rall, *U.S. Bur. Mines Rept. Invest.*, **6096,** 28 pp. (1962).
9. M. Beroza, *Nature*, **196,** 768 (1962).
10. M. Beroza, *Anal. Chem.*, **34,** 1801 (1962).
11. M. Beroza and R. Sarmiento, *Anal. Chem.*, **35,** 1353 (1963).
12. M. Beroza and F. Acree, Jr., *J. Assoc. Offic. Agr. Chemists*, **47,** 1 (1964).
13. M. Beroza and R. Sarmiento, *Anal. Chem.*, **37,** 1040 (1965).
14. M. Beroza, *J. Gas Chromatog.*, **2,** 330 (1964).
15. M. Beroza and R. Sarmiento, *Anal. Chem.*, **36,** 1744 (1964).
16. M. Beroza, *J. Org. Chem.*, **28,** 3562 (1963).
17. J. J. Broderick, *Am. Perfumer Cosmet.*, **80,** 39 (1965).
18. R. C. Crippen and C. E. Smith, *J. Gas Chromatog.*, **3,** 37 (1965).
19. G. Schomburg, *Z. Anal. Chem.*, **200,** 360 (1964).
20. T. Okamoto and T. Onaka, *Chem. Pharm. Bull.* (*Tokyo*), **11,** 1086 (1963).
21. J. Franc and V. Kolouskova, *J. Chromatog.*, **17,** 221 (1965).
22. S. G. Perry, *J. Gas Chromatog.*, **2,** 54 (1964).
23. J. Voigt and W. G. Fischer, *Chemiker Ztg.*, **88,** 919 (1964).
23a. W. M. Barbour, *J. Gas Chromatog.*, **3,** 228 (1965).

24. R. W. McKinney, *J. Gas Chromatog.*, **2,** 432 (1964).
25. Preston Gas Chromatography Abstract Cards, 909 Pitner Ave., Evanston, Ill., 60202.
26. G. M. Brauer, *J. Polymer Sci.*, **8,** 3 (1965).
26a. S. Dal Nogare and R. S. Juvet, Jr., *Anal. Chem.*, **38,** 72R (1966).
27. J. C. Sternberg and R. L. Little, *Anal. Chem.*, **38,** 321 (1966).
28. F. A. Lehmann and G. M. Brauer, *Anal. Chem.*, **33,** 673 (1961).
29. L. N. Winter and P. W. Albro, *J. Gas Chromatog.*, **2,** 1 (1964).
30. B. Groten, *Anal. Chem.*, **36,** 1206 (1964).
31. G. G. Esposito, *Anal. Chem.*, **36,** 2183 (1964).
32. H. Giacobbo and W. Simon, *Pharm. Acta Helv.*, **39,** 162 (1964).
33. E. W. Cieplinski, L. S. Ettre, B. Kolb, and G. Kemmner, *Z. Anal. Chem.*, **205,** 357 (1964).
33a. K. Ettre and P. F. Váradi, *Anal. Chem.*, **35,** 69 (1963).
34. B. C. Cox and B. Ellis, *Anal. Chem.*, **36,** 90 (1964).
35. L. Fortina, *Ann. Chim. (Rome)*, **54,** 945 (1964).
36. G. Garzó and T. Székely, in *Gas-Chromatographie 1963*, H. P. Angelé and H. G. Struppe, Eds., Akademie-Verlag, Berlin, 1963, pp. 48–70.
37. M. F. Burke and W. W. Brandt, *Pittsburgh Conf. Anal. Chem. Appl. Spectry.*, *March 1–5, 1965*, Abstr. No. 121, p. 82.
38. C. Ainsworth and N. R. Easton, *J. Org. Chem.*, **27,** 4118 (1962).
39. G. Grossi and R. Vece, *J, Gas Chromatog.*, **3,** 170 (1965).
40. E. W. Robb and J. J. Westbrook III, *Anal. Chem.*, **35,** 1644 (1963).
41. N. E. Hetman, H. G. Arlt, Jr., R. Paylor, and R. Feinland, *J. Am. Oil Chemists' Soc.*, **42,** 255 (1965).
42. W. W. Hanneman and R. S. Porter, *J. Org. Chem.*, **29,** 2996 (1964).
43. S. G. Perry, *J. Gas Chromatog.*, **2,** 93 (1964).
44. J. C. Craig, N. Y. Mary, and S. K. Roy, *Anal. Chem.*, **36,** 1142 (1964).
45. B. J. Gudzinowicz, H. F. Martin, and J. L. Driscoll, *J. Gas Chromatog.*, **2,** 265 (1964).
46. I. M. Goldman, *J. Org. Chem.*, **28,** 1921 (1963).
47. S. Hyden, *Anal. Chem.*, **35,** 113 (1963).
48. J. H. Dhont, *Analyst*, **89,** 71 (1964).
49. C. T. Greenwood, J. H. Knox, and E. Milne, *Chem. Ind. (London)*, **1961,** 1878.
50. S. Glassner and A. R. Pierce III, *Anal. Chem.*, **37,** 525 (1965).
51. W. Langenbeck and H. Dreyer, *Z. Anorg. Allgem. Chem.*, **329,** 179 (1964).
52. J. Voigt, *Kunststoffe*, **54,** 2 (1964).
53. D. F. Nelson, J. L. Yee, and P. L. Kirk, *Microchem. J.*, **6,** 225 (1962).
54. J. Voigt, *Kunststoffe*, **51,** 18 (1961).
55. H. Feuerberg and H. Weigel, *Kautschuk Gummi*, **15,** 276 WT (1962).
56. A. I. M. Keulemans and S. G. Perry, *Nature*, **193,** 1073 (1962).
57. J. H. Dhont, *Nature*, **200,** 882 (1963).
58. A. Karmen, T. Walker, and R. L. Bowman, *J. Lipid Res.*, **4,** 103 (1963).
59. J. G. Burr, R. A. Meyer, and J. D. Strong, *J. Am. Chem. Soc.*, **86,** 3846 (1964).
60. J. G. Burr and J. D. Strong, *J. Am. Chem. Soc.*, **86,** 5065 (1964).
61. J. Janák, *Nature*, **185,** 684 (1960).
62. K. J. Harkiss, *Nature*, **205,** 78 (1965).
63. R. L. Levy, H. Gesser, E. A. Halevi, and S. Saidman, *J. Gas Chromatog.*, **2,** 254 (1964).
64. L. Haraldson, *Mikrochim. Acta*, **4,** 650 (1962).

65. E. C. Jennings, Jr., and K. P. Dimick, *Anal. Chem.*, **34**, 1543 (1962).
66. H. J. O'Neill, R. E. Putscher, A. Dynako, and C. Boquist, *J. Gas Chromatog.*, **1** (2), 28 (1963).
67. K. Ettre and P. F. Váradi, in *Advances in Electron Tube Techniques*, Vol. 2 (Sixth Natl. Conf. Electron Tube Technol.), D. Slater, Ed., Pergamon Press, New York, 1963, pp. 179–183.
68. R. H. Waltz, J. V. Wisniewski, and S. F. Spencer, *F&M Sci. Corp. Tech. Paper* No. 21, 7 pp.
69. T. S. Ma and M. Gutterson, *Anal. Chem.*, **36**, 150R (1964).
70. H. J. Francis, Jr., *Anal. Chem.*, **36** (7), 31A (1964).
71. A. E. Martin and J. Smart, *Nature*, **175**, 422 (1955).
72. J. Juranek, *Tech. Digest*, **11**, 14 (1960).
73. A. Liberti, G. P. Cartoni, and U. Pallotta, *Ann. Chim. (Rome)*, **48**, 40 (1958).
74. A. Dijkstra, C. C. M. Fabrie, G. Kateman, C. J. Lamboo, and J. A. L. Thissen, *J. Gas Chromatog.*, **2**, 180 (1964).
75. O. Piringer, E. Tataru, and M. Pascalau, *J. Gas Chromatog.*, **2**, 104 (1964).
76. D. L. West, *Anal. Chem.*, **36**, 2194 (1964).
77. J. M. Walker and C. W. Kuo, *Anal. Chem.*, **35**, 2017 (1963).
78. A. Zlatkis and J. A. Ridgway, *Nature*, **182**, 130 (1958).
79. K. Porter and D. H. Volman, *Anal. Chem.*, **34**, 748 (1962).
80. U. Schwenk, H. Hachenberg, and M. Förderreuther, *Brennstoff-Chem.*, **42**, 295 (1961).
81. S. Mlinko and T. Szarvas, *Acta Chim. Acad. Sci. Hung.*, **33**, 118 (1962).
82. O. E. Sundberg and C. Maresh, *Anal. Chem.*, **32**, 274 (1960).
83. J. Franc and M. Wurst, *Collection Czech. Chem. Commun.*, **25**, 2290 (1960).
84. C. D. Miller, *Pittsburgh Conf. Anal. Chem. Appl. Spectry.*, *March 1–5, 1965*, Abstr. No. 122, p. 82.
85. Y. Mashiko, H. Konosu, and T. Morii, *Kogyo Kagaku Zasshi*, **67**, 555 (1964)
86. R. H. Reitsema and N. L. Allphin, *Anal. Chem.*, **33**, 355 (1961).
87. M. L. Parsons, S. N. Pennington, and J. M. Walker, *Anal. Chem.*, **35**, 842 (1963).
88. B. A. Stewart, L. K. Porter, and W. E. Beard, *Anal. Chem.*, **35**, 1331 (1963).
88a. D. M. Coulson, *J. Gas Chromatog.*, **4**, 285 (1966).
88b. R. L. Martin, *Anal. Chem.*, **38**, 1209 (1966).
89. L. Mikkelsen and S. F. Spencer, *F&M Sci. Corp. Tech. Paper* No. 15, p. 4.
90. S. A. Greene and H. Pust, *Anal. Chem.*, **30**, 1039 (1958).
91. R. R. Suchanec, *Dissertation Abstr.*, **22**, 719 (1961).
92. A. Götz, *Z. Anal. Chem.*, **181**, 92 (1961).
93. J. W. Swinnerton, V. J. Linnenbom, and C. H. Cheek, *Anal. Chem.*, **36**, 1669 (1964).
94. K. Abel, *Anal. Chem.*, **36**, 953 (1964).
95. I. Okuno, J. C. Morris, and W. E. Haines, *Anal. Chem.*, **34**, 1427 (1962).
96. O. Rochefort, *Anal. Chim. Acta*, **29**, 350 (1963).
97. A. A. Duswalt and W. W. Brandt, *Anal. Chem.*, **32**, 272 (1960).
97a. C. D. Miller and J. D. Winefordner, *Microchem. J.*, **8**, 334 (1964).
98. O. N. Hinsvark and R. H. Waltz, *F&M Sci. Corp. Tech. Paper* No. 31.
99. C. F. Nightingale and J. M. Walker, *Anal. Chem.*, **34**, 1435 (1962).
100. W. Walisch, *Trans. N.Y. Acad. Sci.*, **25**, 693 (1963).
101. D. R. Beuerman and C. E. Meloan, *Anal. Chem.*, **34**, 319 (1962).
102. W. K. Stuckey and J. M. Walker, *Anal. Chem.*, **35**, 2015 (1963).
103. J. C. Mamaril and C. E. Meloan, *J. Chromatog.*, **17**, 23 (1965).

104. A. P. Terent'ev, N. M. Turkel'taub, E. A. Bondarevskaya, and L. A. Domochkina, *Proc. Acad. Sci. USSR, Chem. Sect. English Transl.*, **148**, 167 (1963). (*Dokl. Akad. Nauk SSSR*, **148**, 1316 (1963).)
105. F. H. Huyten and G. W. A. Rijnders, *Z. Anal. Chem.*, **205**, 244 (1964).
106. W. J. Baker, R. J. Wheeler, and H. P. Burchfield, *Pittsburgh Conf. Anal. Chem. Appl. Spectry.*, *March 1–5, 1965*, Abstr. No. 185, p. 92.
107. D. M. Coulson, L. A. Cavanagh, J. E. De Vries, and B. Walther, *J. Agr. Food Chem.*, **8**, 399 (1960).
108. H. P. Burchfield, D. E. Johnson, J. W. Rhoades, and R. J. Wheeler, *J. Gas Chromatog.*, **3**, 28 (1965).
109. D. M. Coulson, *J. Gas Chromatog.*, **3**, 134 (1965).
110. J. C. Sternberg and D. T. L. Jones, U. S. Pat. 3,158,446 (1964).
111. T. Johns and C. H. Braithwaite, Jr., *Residue Rev.*, **5**, 45 (1964).
112. A. Karmen and L. Giuffrida, *Nature*, **201**, 1204 (1964).
113. L. Giuffrida, *J. Assoc. Offic. Agr. Chemists*, **47**, 293 (1964).
114. A. Karmen, *J. Gas Chromatog.*, **3**, 336 (1965).
114a. L. Giuffrida, F. Ives, and D. C. Bostwick, *J. Assoc. Offic. Agr. Chemists*, **49**, 12 (1966).
114b. R. C. Tindle, C. D. Ruyle, C. W. Gehrke, D. L. Stalling, and W. A. Aue, *152nd Am. Chem. Soc. Meeting, Sept. 11–16, 1966, New York*, Abstr. No. C-144.
115. A. T. James and E. A. Piper, *J. Chromatog.*, **5**, 265 (1961).
116. F. Drawert, A. Rapp, A. Ziegler, O. Bachmann, and H. Steffan, *Chem. Ingr.-Tech.*, **35**, 853 (1963).
117. F. Drawert and O. Bachmann, *Angew. Chem. Intern. Ed. Engl.*, **2**, 540 (1963).
118. L. Bruzzi, A. Castelli, and A. Cervellati, *Nucl. Instr. Methods*, **26**, 305 (1964).
119. A. T. James and C. Hitchcock, *Kerntechnik*, **7**, 5 (1965).
120. R. Wolfgang and F. S. Rowland, *Anal. Chem.*, **30**, 903 (1958).
121. J. K. Lee, E. K. C. Lee, B. Musgrave, Y.-N. Tang, J. W. Root, and F. S. Rowland, *Anal. Chem.*, **34**, 741 (1962).
122. F. Cacace, R. Cipollini, and G. Perez, *Anal. Chem.*, **35**, 1348 (1963).
123. A. Zlatkis, J. F. Oro, and A. P. Kimball, *Anal. Chem.*, **32**, 162 (1960).
124. J. W. Ralls, *Anal. Chem.*, **32**, 332 (1960).
125. R. L. Stephens and A. P. Teszler, *Anal. Chem.*, **32**, 1047 (1960).
126. J. W. Ralls, *Anal. Chem.*, **36**, 946 (1964).
127. L. A. Jones and R. J. Monroe, *Anal. Chem.*, **37**, 935 (1965).
128. J. W. Ralls, *J. Agr. Food Chem.*, **8**, 141 (1960).
129. I. R. Hunter, *J. Chromatog.*, **7**, 288 (1962).
129a. N. E. Hoffman and I. R. White, *Anal. Chem.*, **37**, 1541 (1965).
129b. G. F. Thompson and K. Smith, *Anal. Chem.*, **37**, 1591 (1965).
130. F. Drawert, in *Gas Chromatography 1962*, M. van Swaay, Ed., Butterworths, London, 1962, pp. 347–355.
131. N. E. Hoffman, J. J. Barboriak, and H. F. Hardman, *Anal. Biochem.*, **9**, 175 (1964).
132. G. F. Harrison, in *Vapour Phase Chromatography*, D. H. Desty, Ed., Butterworths, London, 1957, pp. 332–345.
133. F. Drawert, in *Gas-Chromatographie 1963*, H. P. Angelé and H. G. Struppe, Eds., Akademie-Verlag, Berlin, 1963, pp. 339–350.
133a. J. Janák, J. Novák, and J. Sulovsky, *Collection Czech. Chem. Commun.*, **27**, 2541 (1962).
133b. W. S. Leonhardt, R. C. Morrison, and C. W. Kamienski, *Anal. Chem.*, **38**, 466 (1966).

134. S. H. Langer and P. Pantages, *Nature*, **191**, 141 (1961).
135. J. K. Haken, *J. Gas Chromatog.*, **1** (10), 30 (1963).
136. M. W. Anders and G. J. Mannering, *Anal. Chem.*, **34**, 730 (1962).
137. D. M. Marmion, R. G. White, L. H. Bille, and K. H. Ferber, *J. Gas Chromatog.*, **4**, 190 (1966).
138. M. N. Chumachenko and L. B. Tverdyukova, *Proc. Acad. Sci. USSR, Chem. Sect. English Transl.*, **142**, 77 (1962). (*Dokl. Akad. Nauk SSSR*, **142**, 612 (1962).)
139. I. Lysyj and R. C. Greenough, *Anal. Chem.*, **35**, 1657 (1963).
139a. R. F. Putnam and H. W. Myers, *Anal. Chem.*, **34**, 486 (1962).
140. E. R. Hoffmann and I. Lysyj, *Microchem. J.*, **6**, 45 (1962).
141. T. Mitsui and Y. Kitamura, *Microchem. J.*, **7**, 141 (1963).
142. T. S. Ma, C. T. Shang, and E. Manche, *Mikrochim. Acta*, **1964**, 571.
143. J. Franc, J. Dvoracek, and V. Kolouskova, *Mikrochim. Acta*, **1965**, 4.
144. J. E. Hoff and E. D. Feit, *Anal. Chem.*, **36**, 1002 (1964).
144a. V. L. Davison and H. J. Dutton, *Anal. Chem.*, **38**, 1302 (1966).
145. N. Brenner and V. J. Coates, *Nature*, **181**, 1401 (1958).
146. D. K. Albert, *Anal. Chem.*, **35**, 1918 (1963).
147. B. T. Whitham, *Nature*, **182**, 391 (1958).
148. E. R. Adlard and B. T. Whitham, *Nature*, **192**, 966 (1961).
149. N. Brenner, E. Cieplinski, L. S. Ettre, and V. J. Coates, *J. Chromatog.*, **3**, 230 (1960).
150. L. S. Ettre and N. Brenner, *J. Chromatog.*, **3**, 235 (1960).
150a. I. H. Williams, *Anal. Chem.*, **37**, 1723 (1965).
151. C. K. Hersh, *Molecular Sieves*, Reinhold, New York, 1961, pp. 1–122.
152. E. M. Barrall II and F. Baumann, *J. Gas Chromatog.*, **2**, 256 (1964).
153. W. B. Innes, W. E. Bambrick, and A. J. Andreatch, *Anal. Chem.*, **35**, 1198 (1963).
154. W. B. Innes and W. E. Bambrick, *J. Gas Chromatog.*, **2**, 309 (1964).
155. A. P. Altshuller, *J. Gas Chromatog.*, **1** (7), 6 (1963).
156. J. Janák and J. Novák, *Chem. Listy*, **51**, 1832 (1957).
157. E. Gil-Av and Y. Herzberg-Minzly, *J. Chromatog.*, **13**, 1 (1964).
157a. R. R. Allen, *Anal. Chem.*, **38**, 1287 (1966).
157b. Varian Aerograph, Walnut Creek, Calif.
157c. R. K. Sharma, D. R. McLean, and J. Bardwell, *Indian J. Chem*, **3**, 282 (1965).
157d. J. A. Kerr and A. F. Trotman-Dickenson, *Nature*, **182**, 466 (1958).
158. R. M. Ikeda, D. E. Simmons, and J. D. Grossman, *Anal. Chem.*, **36**, 2188 (1964).
159. F. W. Hefendehl, *Naturwissenschaften*, **51**, 138 (1964).
160. M. Rogozinski, *J. Gas Chromatog.*, **2**, 163 (1964).
161. W. E. Harris and W. H. McFadden, *Anal. Chem.*, **31**, 114 (1959).
162. A. A. Kilner and G. A. Ratcliff, *Anal. Chem.*, **36**, 1615 (1964).
163. E. E. Neely, *Anal. Chem.*, **32**, 1382 (1960).
164. E. S. Jacobs, *Anal. Chem.*, **35**, 2035 (1963).
165. J. T. Kung, J. E. Whitney, and J. C. Cavagnol, *Anal. Chem.*, **33**, 1505 (1961).
166. H. S. Knight and F. T. Weiss, *Anal. Chem.*, **34**, 749 (1962).
167. L. A. Robbins, R. M. Bethea, and T. D. Wheelock, *J. Chromatog.*, **13**, 361 (1964).
168. S. Dal Nogare and R. S. Juvet, Jr., *Gas-Liquid Chromatography*, Interscience, New York, 1963, 450 pp.
169. T. J. Lemoine, R. H. Benson, and C. R. Herbeck, *J. Gas Chromatog.*, **3**, 189 (1965).
170. J. Kallen and E. Heilbronner, *Helv. Chim. Acta*, **43**, 489 (1960).
171. E. M. Magee, *Ind. Eng. Chem. Fundamentals*, **2**, 32 (1963).
171a. L. S. Ettre and N. Brenner, *J. Chromatog.*, **3**, 524 (1960).

172. W. K. Hall, D. S. MacIver, and H. P. Weber, *Ind. Eng. Chem.*, **52,** 421 (1960).
173. D. P. Harrison, J. W. Hall, and H. F. Rase, *Ind. Eng. Chem.*, **57,** 20 (1965).
174. C. J. Norton, *Chem Ind. (London)*, **1962,** 258.
175. C. J. Norton and T. E. Moss, *Ind. Eng. Chem. Process Design Develop.*, **3,** 23 (1964).
176. K. C. Stein, J. J. Feenan, L. J. E. Hofer, and R. B. Anderson, *U.S. Bur. Mines Bull.* **608,** 1962, 19 pp.
177. L. de Mourgues, M. Fichet, and G. Chassaing, *Bull. Soc. Chim. France*, **1962,** 1918.
178. L. de Mourgues, *Chim. Anal. (Paris)*, **45,** 103 (1963).
179. M. Hartwig, *Brennstoff-Chem.*, **45,** 234 (1964).
180. P. J. Owens and C. H. Amberg, *Advan. Chem. Ser.*, **33,** 182 (1961).
181. R. L. Martin and J. A. Grant, *Anal. Chem.*, **37,** 649 (1965).
182. K. Tamaru, *Nature*, **183,** 319 (1959).
183. O. Piringer and E. Tataru, *J. Gas Chromatog.*, **2,** 323 (1964).
184. D. W. Bassett and H. W. Habgood, *J. Phys. Chem.*, **64,** 769 (1960).
185. H. W. Habgood, *Ann. Rev. Phys. Chem.*, **13,** 259 (1962).
186. D. D. Phillips, G. E. Pollard, and S. B. Soloway, *J. Agr. Food Chem.*, **10,** 217 (1962).
187. L. J. Morris, R. T. Holman, and K. Fontell, *J. Lipid Res.*, **1,** 412 (1960).
188. E. Michel and C. Troyanowsky, *Compt. Rend.*, **260,** 1434 (1965).
189. See discussion in D. H. Desty, Ed., *Gas Chromatography 1958*, Butterworths, London, 1958, pp. 214–215.
190. M. Vilkas and N. A. Abraham, *Bull. Soc. Chim. France*, **1959,** 1651.
191. R. L. Kenney and G. S. Fisher, *J. Gas Chromatog.*, **1,** 19 (1963).
192. E. A. Day and P. H. Miller, *Anal. Chem.*, **34,** 869 (1962).
193. S. Hayashi, K. Yano, N. Yokoyama, and T. Matsura, *Bull. Chem. Soc. Japan*, **38,** 1824 (1965).
194. I. C. Nigam and L. Levi, *J. Org. Chem.*, **30,** 653 (1965).
195. D. L. Bunbury and M. S. Osyany, *J. Chromatog.*, **14,** 98 (1964).
196. J. P. Minyard and E. R. Jackson, *J. Agr. Food Chem.*, **13,** 50 (1965).
196a. R. G. Scholz, J. Bednarczyk, and T. Yamauchi, *Anal. Chem.*, **38,** 331 (1966).
196b. J. Bastick, M. Baverez, and M. Castagne, *Bull. Soc. Chim. France*, **1965,** 1292.
197. M. Senn, W. J. Richter, and A. L. Burlingame, *J. Am. Chem. Soc.*, **87,** 680 (1965).
198. J. Tadmor, *Anal. Chem.*, **36,** 1565 (1964); *Israel At. Energy Comm., Rept. IA-895,* Feb. 1964, 32 pp.
198a. H. Elias, *Nucl. Sci. Abstr.*, **19,** No. 17 (Sept. 15, 1965), Abstr. 32274.
198b. G. Stoecklin, *Nucl. Sci. Abstr.*, **19,** No. 17 (Sept. 15, 1965), Abstr. 32275.
199. B. Kolb and K. H. Kaiser, *J. Gas Chromatog.*, **2,** 233 (1964).
200. B. Kolb, G. Kemmner, K. H. Kaiser, E. W. Cieplinski, and L. S. Ettre, *Z. Anal. Chem.*, **209,** 302 (1965).

CHAPTER 10

Automatic Process Gas Chromatography

Eugene L. Szonntagh, *Leeds & Northrup Corporation, North Wales, Pennsylvania*

I. Introduction

The term "process gas chromatography" is used in describing industrial gas chromatographic methods which can be carried out on an automatically repetitive basis. Since the sample to be analyzed is in most cases a plant stream, the term "plant chromatograph" is sometimes used to denote instruments employed in process gas chromatography. A third term, "industrial gas chromatography," is used interchangeably with the other two designations.*

The requirements of process gas chromatography differ considerably from those of laboratory applications. Industrial or plant applications usually require automatic, repetitive sample-introducing cycles. Because of continuous day and night operation, process gas chromatographs must

---

* A now-obsolete term, "process vapor fractometry," was previously used quite frequently; however, it lost its popularity following a committee recommendation (3).

meet higher standards of reliability than laboratory gas chromatographs. Process gas chromatographs are expected to provide long, accurate, and trouble-free service with minimum maintenance, a difficult task considering the rather complicated, complex hardware. A large number of plants using process gas chromatographs are operated under rigid safety rules; the process gas chromatograph must also fulfill various federal (1,2), state, and local safety requirements.

A further important requirement of an industrial gas chromatograph is to provide meaningful data in the simplest possible way. The routine presentation of conventional laboratory-type gas chromatograms (sometimes called "spectra") is not practical for a process gas chromatograph. Trend-type readout, or other easy-to-read methods, are standard on most present-day industrial gas chromatographs. The recent tendency towards automated plants has produced the further requirement of adaptability to closed-loop control of process streams.

The environmental requirements of industrial chromatographs are quite different from those of laboratory models. A case in point is the explosion hazard to which many industrial chromatographs are exposed. Most industrial gas chromatographs are operated under unfavorable ambient temperature conditions. Other environmental disturbances, such as high humidity and moisture, the presence of dust, vibration, power line instability, and noise, can also be extremely irksome. The user of the process gas chromatograph should satisfy himself that his equipment will operate satisfactorily in the most hostile environment.

Most process gas chromatographs have separate analyzer and programmer–readout units. The environmental problems discussed in the preceding paragraph apply mostly to the analyzer, since this unit must be located close to the process stream. The rest of the equipment will ordinarily bè remotely located under more favorable environmental conditions, e.g. in control rooms. A frequently neglected component, the sample handling system, is usually not integrated with the analyzer, but is adjacent to it. Because of its basic importance, we shall begin our description with the sample handling system.

II. Sample Handling Systems

In process gas chromatography, the sample-handling procedure is entirely different from the customary manual methods used in the laboratory. The sample may be taken continuously from the process stream; it has to be cleaned, conditioned, and regulated for the process gas chromatograph. All the above operations may be carried out by a sample handling system sometimes called the sample conditioner. Although the sampling system should be custom engineered for each individual application, some companies offer preengineered sample systems, which may be arranged to meet special requirements. In many cases the user prefers to provide his own sampling system, but in every instance the sample should be properly regulated and cleaned. The type of system used for sample introduction and the composition of the sample aid the user in determining whether to keep the sample in the gas or liquid phase.

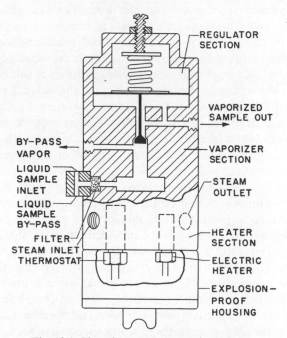

Fig. 10-1. Vaporizer–pressure regulator (3a).

If a gas sample introducing valve is employed in the analyzer, the sample temperature must be kept high enough to avoid condensation. This may be accomplished by insulating the sample line and associated equipment. When additional heating of the sample handling system is needed, electric heaters or steam tracing are most frequently used. Liquid samples may be used with an analyzer having a gas sample introducing valve provided the instrument is equipped with a vaporizer to make the necessary conversion from the liquid to the gas phase. Phillips Petroleum Co., for instance, developed a vaporizer utilizing either electric or steam heating. The Phillips model, which is marketed by Greenbrier Instruments Div. of the Bendix Corp. (3a) includes a pressure regulator and provides a regulated vapor flow for the analyzer (Fig. 10-1). The vapor discharge pressure is controlled to within 1 %. The capacity of the vaporizer is 50 milliliters to 2 liters per minute of vapor at pressures up to 450 psig.

If the process gas chromatographic analyzer employs a liquid sample introducing valve, the sample must be kept in the liquid phase. This can be accomplished by keeping the sample handling system at a sufficiently low temperature or, as is more frequently the case, at a high enough pressure to prevent partial or total vaporization.

Filtering devices are a prime consideration in process gas chromatography. When using gas samples, filters have to remove all solid and liquid contaminants; in the case of liquid samples all solid, undissolved liquid and gas contaminants have to be removed. Filters are especially important in the case of liquid samples because minute quantities of solids can change considerably the volume of the liquid in the sampling valve. Even if the gas chromatograph is equipped with filters, additional filters of sufficient capacity should be used in the sample handling system because most process streams require more careful filtering than is achieved with the built-in filters. Bypass-type filtering devices are very effective because the filter element is continuously cleaned by flushing (4). Gas contaminants may be removed by traps and undissolved liquids by special filters. For example, since hydrocarbons wet porous ceramic more readily than water, a ceramic filter may be used to prevent water globules from passing into the sample line. In many cases driers have to be provided especially if high moisture content exists and water will deteriorate the gas chromatographic column. The operator should use driers with discretion, however, since the desiccant may alter the composition of the stream. When other contaminants such as CO_2 or corrosive substances must be removed from the stream the operator should judiciously select a proper and specific adsorbent, absorber, or preferably chemisorber. Commercial scrubbers are readily available for a number of contaminants. It must be realized that if this technique is used before sample injection, it will alter the concentration of all constituents by the amount that is trapped.

If the concentration of the contaminants is not high, it may be made negligible by packing an additional column with the previously mentioned materials and placing it between the sample introducing valve and the regular column. The contaminants will be trapped by this additional column for a period of time which can be predetermined by knowing the chemisorber's capacity, the amount of contaminant in the sample, and the frequency of sample introduction. Small amounts of H_2O and CO_2, for example, may be trapped by a column about two feet long filled with Ascarite or soda lime. Normally, the lifetime of such a column will compare favorably with the lifetime of the regular column.

When using filtering or scrubbing techniques before sample introduction, we must always remember that they all introduce dead space into the sample line and increase the sample lag. This is especially true with high speed gas chromatographic techniques. Figure 10-2 shows the schematic diagram of a simple close-coupled application of a Leeds and Northrup high speed gas chromatograph using an appropriate sampling system. The application is monitoring a tail gas stream of a propane recovery unit.

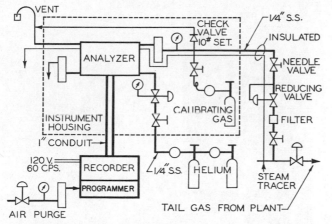

Fig. 10-2. Schematic diagram of the sampling system used in the installation shown in Figure 10-3 (5).

Filtering, pressure reduction, and flow control of the sample are done at the sample takeoff point, to minimize transport lag to the analyzer. Figure 10-3 shows the actual installation at the Philadelphia plant of the Atlantic Refining Co. For the convenience of personnel working on the chromatograph and sampling system, an inexpensive 4 × 6 × 6 ft aluminum tool shelter is used to house the analyzer. A bottled sample of standard gas is kept in the shelter and can be conveniently used to calibrate the instrument. The shelter is heated by a finned steam radiator, and the sample line is traced and insulated. The application is described in more detail in reference 5.

Regulation of pressure and flow is an important function of sample handling systems. If the sample stream is at high pressure, pressure regulators may be used to reduce the pressure to a useful level. In the case of liquid samples, a back pressure regulator is recommended to provide a pressurized sample line and to avoid vaporization.

If the sample stream is at or below atmospheric pressure, suitable pumps have to be used to introduce the sample into the plant stream analyzer. In

Fig. 10-3. Process gas chromatograph installation (5).

case of gas samples, if the pump is not a constant-delivery type, a pressure regulator should be used to control the pressure. The maximum amount of sample which can be removed from the stream without upsetting the process should be determined. Sometimes the sample line of the chromatograph cannot be used at full capacity without upsetting the process. This is the case in some of the heat treating furnace applications.

The amount of sample taken into the gas chromatographic column is a function not only of the analyzer sample volume, but also of the sample pressure. Frequently, it is customary to measure the sample flow instead of the sample pressure. In most cases, sample flow rates between 50 and 2000 ml/min (approx. 0.1–4 cu ft/hr) are adequate.

If the same gas chromatograph is to be used for the analysis of several streams of similar composition, stream selector units may be employed to

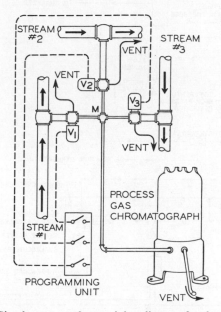

Fig. 10-4. Simple stream selector piping diagram for three streams.

switch from one stream to another. Additionally, they may be used to switch to calibrating gases. Stream selector units can be incorporated into the sample handling system or they can be of separate construction. The stream selector usually consists of a flow selecting unit (valve) and an electric controlling or programming unit. This last portion of the stream selectors will be described in the section on programmers.

Figure 10-4 shows the piping diagram of a simple stream selector for three streams. V_1, V_2 and V_3 are three-way solenoid valves which may be operated in sequence from a programming unit by energizing the solenoids one at a time. The dotted line indicates part of the electric wiring used to energize the solenoids. The outlets from the solenoid valves are connected to a manifold M having small internal volume.

Other types of valves, e.g. rotary valves, or pneumatically operated plug valves (4), can also be used for stream selection. Rotary valves can be driven by stepping solenoids or by motors. In this last case a switching mechanism can stop the valve in the desired positions. Continuous scanning may also be used.

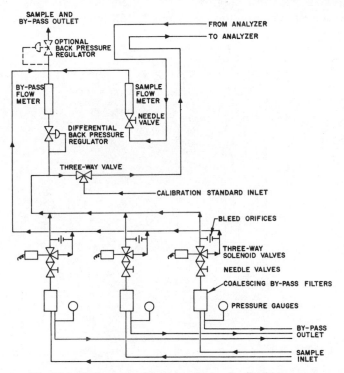

Fig. 10-5. Beckman multistream selector for liquid streams.

For special purposes, more elaborate stream selection devices can be built. Such a device is the Phillips Petroleum Co.'s system (6) incorporating means to provide a signal on the recorder chart which identifies the particular stream being analyzed.

A complete modular sample handling system being offered by Beckman Instruments, Inc., is shown schematically in Figure 10-5. This particular model is suitable for multiple liquid streams and can handle sample pressures up to 200 psig in 2 to 8 streams. Power requirements are 115 V dc, 10 W per stream; 115 V 60-cps ac, 10 W (for optional air operator).

The material of the sampling system has to be carefully selected and is usually determined by the service temperature range and the corrosiveness of the sample stream. In most cases corrosion resistive materials such as stainless steel, Hastelloy, Teflon, etc., have to be used. When in doubt, consult the appropriate literature (6a,7).

III. The Analyzer

A. General Requirements

The analyzer or sensor unit of a process gas chromatograph normally contains the sampling valve, the column, and the detector, in a temperature controlled zone. The analyzer is generally situated in close proximity to the

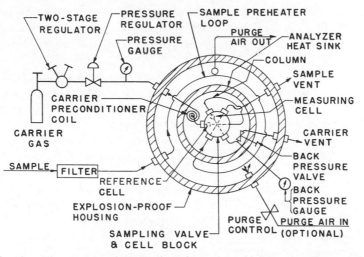

Fig. 10-6. Flow System of the Leeds and Northrup high speed analyzer (7a).

process stream with all ancillary equipment remotely located at a control station. Accessories such as the multiple column switching valve, the back pressure valve, etc., may be included in the temperature-controlled zone as part of the analyzer unit. Figure 10-6 is a schematic diagram illustrating a simple flow system of an actual gas chromatographic analyzer. Understandably, instruments vary from manufacturer to manufacturer but the basic schemes are similar. The essential parts and their relationship to one another can be readily studied from Figure 10-6.

Major differences between process analyzers and laboratory models are: process analyzers usually have explosion-proof housings (standard on most industrial models) and automatic sample introducing valves, whereas the laboratory models are seldom explosion-proof and generally use manual sampling valves. Automatic sample introduction requires a sample line for continuous flow of the sample stream. This is provided by the sample handling system described in Section II. In other respects, the process analyzer and the laboratory instrument are not significantly different. Basic principles concerning mobile phase, columns, detectors, and ancillary systems have been described in previous chapters and need not be repeated here; however, some major points should be mentioned.

All components of a process analyzer unit have to withstand the stress of repetitive cycling for a considerable length of time. Column liquid bleeding and other aging processes must be minimized. Column tubing material has to have high resistance to corrosion. For this reason, stainless steel and Teflon tubing are frequently used. Although Teflon offers considerable flexibility, in some cases, as in connection with molecular sieve packing, it should be replaced with porous tube materials such as Kel-F or stainless steel.

Because safety regulations are stringently enforced by most industrial users, a number of manufacturers as a matter of course supply analyzers that meet Class I, Group D, Division 1 requirements (1,2). Since the programmer and the recorder are usually remotely located in a control room, they normally do not have to meet the same safety requirements that the analyzer proper must meet. Occasionally, however, even the control room location may be contaminated, giving rise to hazardous conditions. To take care of such situations, the recorder and controller may be made to meet Class I, Group D, Division 2 requirements (2). Analyzer units that meet Class I, Group D, Division 1 requirements may be seen on Figures 10-3, 10-8, 10-9 and 10-10.

Four major parts of the process gas chromatographic analyzer deserve special attention.

B. Detectors

The detectors must operate well on a continuous basis if they are to provide maintenance-free service for extended periods. Drift should be small, not exceeding the capabilities of the automatic zeroing system, and detector noise should be within the accuracy requirements. Most process gas chromatographs use thermal conductivity detectors, despite their relatively low sensitivity, because they are very reliable, reasonably stable, and inexpensive. In trace component analysis, however, ionization detectors have to be used.

In process gas chromatography, most users of ionization detectors employ a flame ionization detector (FID). Argon and cross-section ionization detectors are also used.

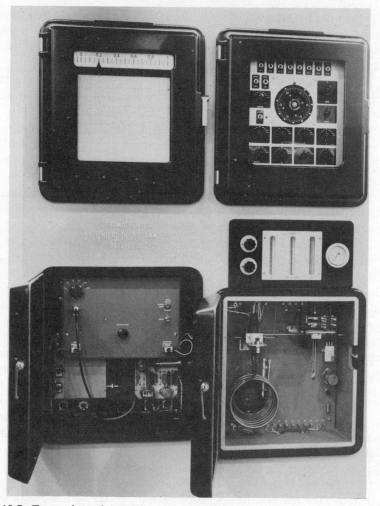

Fig. 10-7. Front view of MECI's process gas chromatography system with flame ionization detector (7b).

Figure 10-7 shows MECI's (France) type 68A FID process gas chromatograph. The analyzer proper is in the lower right-hand corner; the accessories for the FID are at the lower left. The photograph also shows the recorder and programmer in the upper half. Other companies marketing FID process gas chromatographs include Beckman Instruments, Inc., Greenbrier Instruments Div. (Bendix Corp.), and Mine Safety Appliances Co.

Although the FID has about 1000 times the sensitivity of a thermal conductivity bridge, and usually has satisfactory long-term stability it has a number of disadvantages from the standpoint of process gas chromatography:

1. It is generally not sensitive to fixed gases and water vapor. (In certain cases, however, this may be an advantage, e.g., when hydrocarbons are to be measured in aqueous media.)

2. The FID needs hydrogen for its operation. Some communities do not allow the storage of pressurized hydrogen tanks. If this is the case, hydrogen generators may be used; however, none of them is provided with an explosion-proof housing as yet.

3. A considerable amount of water vapor is generated in the FID as a byproduct. The safe and effective discharge of the water vapor is a serious problem when using analyzers in explosion-resistant housing.

4. The use of FID is limited to a certain flow range. The maximum allowable sample concentration is also limited unless stream splitters are employed.

5. Reliability is only good if properly filtered gases are used, otherwise the flame may go out at any time. Furthermore, condensation of water vapor in the gas lines may extinguish the flame. In laboratory-type chromatographs the operator may reignite the flame, but in the process gas chromatograph an automatic fail-safe ignition system has to be used. Even when using automatic ignition some information may be missed during the period of no flame.

6. The cost of the FID, including the high-impedance amplifier and other accessories, is rather high compared to thermal conductivity bridges.

The aforementioned difficulties have to be considered and checked before using the FID. In many instances, despite the problems listed, the FID is a useful tool for low-concentration analysis.

Among the less frequently used detectors is the gas density detector. In this detector, the sensor cells do not come into contact with the sample. It finds its greatest use in the case of serious corrosion problems.

C. Heat-Controlled Zones

There are two major types of heat control systems used in process gas chromatographs: the heat sink type and the air circulating type.

The heat-controlled zone in Figure 10-8 is a heat sink arrangement. The aluminum heat sink, which contains the components of the analyzer, can be seen in the top portion of the photograph with the insulation and the explosion resistant bell housing removed. Heat sink systems are employed, for example, by Teledyne Analytical Instruments Co., Consolidated

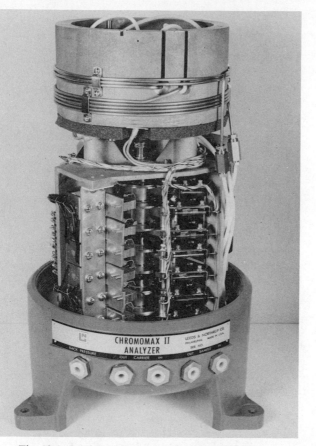

Fig. 10-8. Leeds and Northrup analyzer–timer unit.

Electrodynamics Corp.,* Foxboro Co., Leeds and Northrup Co. (Fig. 10-8), and Perkin-Elmer Corp. whose process instrumentation has been acquired by Mine Safety Appliances Co. Air circulating systems are used by a number of manufacturers including Beckman Instruments, Inc., Carlo Erba (Italy) (Fig. 10-9), Greenbrier Instruments Div. of Bendix Corp., Leeds and Northrup Co., MECI (France) (Fig. 10-7), Mine Safety Appliances Co. (Fig. 10-10) and Siemens and Halske (Germany).

An example of an air circulating system is shown in Figure 10-10. This analyzer has two heat-controlled zones. The inner one (in the lower left portion of the cabinet) may be refrigerated for low-temperature operation

* CEC's process gas chromatography instrumentation has been taken over by Process Analyzers, Inc., Houston, Texas.

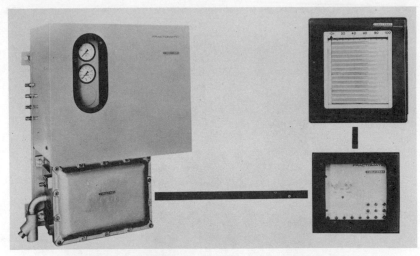

Fig. 10-9. Carlo Erba (Italy) process gas chromatograph.

Fig. 10-10. Mine Safety Appliances Co.'s dual-temperature zone analyzer.

and heated for high-temperature runs, or can be replaced with an oven for temperature-programmed analysis.

D. Sample Introducing Valves

The sample handling systems described in Section II prepare the sample for the sample introducing valve, commonly referred to as sampling valve. The sample introducing valve places a small, properly metered portion of the continuously flowing sample into the carrier gas stream. In

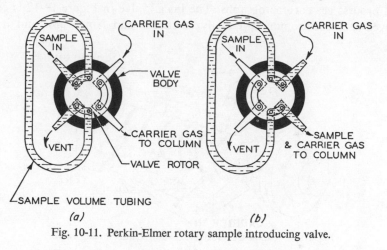

Fig. 10-11. Perkin-Elmer rotary sample introducing valve.

laboratory-type gas chromatography, this can be done by syringe injection, or by manually operated valves as described in Chapter 3. Since process gas chromatographs are required to operate continuously, their sample introducing valves must be automatic. Referring again to Figure 10-6, we see the sample introducing valve connected directly to the column. The figure shows the sample introducing valve located in the temperature-controlled zone of the analyzer, to ensure proper reproducibility of the sample size and sample temperature.

Several different principles are employed in automatic sample introducing valves for process gas chromatography. The two earliest developments, the rotary valve (8) and the linear valve (9), are still very popular, and several versions are used to handle various problems.

Figure 10-11 shows a function diagram of the Perkin-Elmer rotary valve which is used in both laboratory and process gas chromatographs. Figure 10-11a shows the valve in its sample taking position as the sample volume is being flushed with sample. After the sample volume has been completely filled with the fresh sample, the valve can be turned into the position shown in Figure 10-11*b*. This is the sample introducing position in which the carrier gas sweeps the sample slug into the column. The valve can be actuated manually in laboratory-type equipment. In process gas chromatographs, the automatic operation is accomplished by electric or pneumatic actuators. Electric actuators include electromotors and solenoids.

The same basic methods of actuation are employed when linear valves are used. Figure 10-12 shows such a valve which was first developed by the Union Carbide Corp. and is licenced to several manufacturers of commercial process gas chromatographs. The linear valve in Figure 10-12 is employed in the Chromomax I analyzer (Leeds and Northrup), and it is

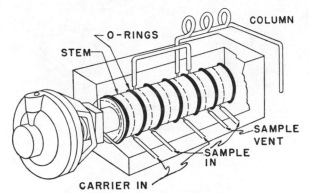

Fig. 10-12. Union Carbide linear sample introducing valve.

actuated by a pneumatic system. As can be seen in the figure, the movable stem has segments separated by O-rings. These segments interconnect the various inlets and outlets. The location of the O-rings for sample taking is represented by the heavy lines, and for sample introducing by the dotted lines. A spring is used to assure that the piston returns to the sample-introducing position after the pressure from the pneumatic actuator has been released. In the pressurized position (sample taking), the sample loop is being flushed by the sample stream.

There are many combinations of the valves described, including continuously rotating (10), linear sliding (11), and rotary linear (12) valves. The number of ports employed, the arrangement of interconnections, the shape and position of the sample volume, and the materials used add up to a very large number of possible combinations.

Another type of valve, the diaphragm sampling valve (13), can be seen in Figure 10-13. In operation, seating the diaphragm against the ports closes them, and releasing the diaphragm opens them. This operation can be accomplished by air pressure (14), rollers (15), and by pneumatically

(15a) or electrically (15b) operated pushrods. Greenbrier Instruments and Mine Safety Appliances Co. are among those who employ this principle in some of their process gas chromatography equipment.

Other kinds of valves which are or may be used for automatic sample introduction include poppet valves, needle valves, flapper valves, and tapered plug valves. With proper actuation, these valves are made to open and close a selected number of ports.

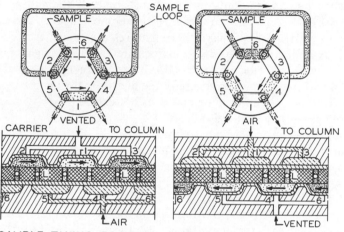

SAMPLE TAKING POSITION   SAMPLE INTRODUCING POSITION
Fig. 10-13. Phillips Petroleum Co.'s diaphragm valve (13).

Sample introducing valves have to fulfill several requirements for proper and trouble-free operation in process gas chromatographs. One of the most important of these is that the valves be free of leaks between ports, and between the inside channels and the outside atmosphere. The seal between the moving parts has to remain intact even after prolonged operation. Various lifetime figures may be regarded as satisfactory, depending on the cycle time of the process gas chromatograph. Using a 1-min cycle time, for instance, the valve of the process gas chromatograph when continuously used will operate more than half a million times per year. Under these circumstances, two to four years of operation may be considered satisfactory if, by simply changing some O-rings, rotors or the like, the lifetime can be extended a few years.

The sampling valve has to withstand operating temperatures and pressures and corrosive media. Deterioration of the seal causes leaks and makes the valve useless. In most cases, stainless steel or Hastelloy is used for metal parts exposed to the sample. This part of the problem is relatively simple, but the elastic member (diaphragm, O-ring, disc seal, etc.) in the valve poses a much more difficult problem. Teflon is excellent for most purposes as far as corrosion resistance is concerned. It is also useful at much higher temperatures than most plastics can tolerate. Its principal disadvantage, however, is that it "flows" under pressure. In certain instances this can be minimized by limiting the space where it can flow. The problem can also be mitigated by the use of filler materials, but this approach sometimes results in sacrificing some of the other excellent properties of Teflon. The problem is further complicated by Teflon's relatively low elasticity requiring rather high pressure to achieve good seals.

Various graphite-composition materials are also used in gas chromatographic sample introducing valves (10). If the impregnating agent is inert and can withstand the temperature of the analyzer, the materials are very useful. Graphite is self-priming and does not exhibit "flow"; however, it is more brittle than most other seals.

In valves which require more elastic materials, Viton, silicone rubber, etc., may be employed as sealing materials. Properties of the sample stream may also influence the choice of material. Teflon-coated elastic seals are sometimes ideal, providing both elasticity and resistance to corrosion.

These details have been described to help the buyer and user. The sample introducing valve is a very important part of the process gas chromatograph. The reliability of the whole equipment depends to a great extent on the valve. It is of the utmost importance that the selection of a gas chromatograph be made only after studying the valve structure and seal with a specific application in mind. The user of the gas chromatograph has to know his process stream and its temperature, pressure, and corrosiveness, and then select the materials in the sampling valve and elsewhere in the sample line accordingly.

So far we have not differentiated between gas and liquid sample introducing valves. It was mentioned in the previous section, however, that samples may be in either phase. This creates the problem of deciding which type of valve has to be used.

In general, any of the previously described valves can be used for introducing gas samples. For liquid samples, however, only certain types of valves are practical. This is due to the difference in specific volume between the gas and liquid. Assuming, for example, that a C_8 or C_9 hydrocarbon (molecular weight of about 110) is to be introduced into the column, then 5 μl of liquid sample will be required to produce about 1 ml of vapor. The following equation may be used in determining the liquid volume to be used to achieve a given volume of gas sample after vaporization:

$$V_l = MV_v/22.4D_l \tag{10-1}$$

where V_l = volume of the liquid sample in microliters
  D_l = density of the liquid sample
  M = average molecular weight of the sample
  V_v = The volume of the sample after vaporization in milliliters

The choice of V_v will be influenced by the degree of separation required and by the sensitivity expected without overloading the column. Using about 0.1-in. i.d. columns—the so-called ⅛-in. o.d. columns—(high-speed chromatography), the maximum value may be around 1 ml; using 0.18-in. i.d. columns (¼ in. o.d.), this value may be in the neighborhood of 5 ml.

In many cases, slider valves (11) are used for the introduction of liquid samples. The liquid sample volume may be as low as 0.2 μl; however, reproducibility decreases with decreasing sample volume. The problem of keeping gas and solid contaminants out of the liquid becomes more serious when small sample volumes are used.

The choice of using either a gas sampling valve with a vaporizer or a liquid valve has been mentioned before. Each method has advantages and disadvantages. Some of the basic objections to the vaporizer method are:

1. The whole sample line after the vaporizer should be heat traced.

2. Some users question the representativeness of the sample leaving the vaporizer.

3. Sample consumption is quite high.

One of the advantages is the vaporizers' ability to average a sample.

The direct liquid sample introduction method has the following disadvantages:

1. The sample line has to be pressurized in order to insure that the sample remains in the liquid state.

2. Minute quantities of gas bubbles, solids or immiscible liquids can cause great errors.

3. The extremely small sample cavity sometimes has very high flow resistance, causing flow upset when introducing the sample.

Since the liquid sample is directly introduced into the carrier stream when a liquid valve is used, it is necessary to use a small flash vaporizer or a heated column inlet. Keeping the entire analyzer at a temperature high enough to maintain vaporization will also achieve the same result. The relationship between the analyzer temperature and the boiling point of the constituents is discussed in reference 16.

E. Column Switching Procedures

When a sample contains a wide variety of components of different boiling points and the lighter components are of interest, it is often desirable to permit only the light gases to elute to the detector. The heavy end may be vented. Although the high-boiling-point components will not show up on the record, the time during the elution of the heavy constituents will be lost. Assuming that the heavy components did not travel too far along the column while the components of interest were eluted, back-flushing the column will be less time consuming than plain forward-flushing to a vent. This method is usually denoted as *single column backflush operation*.

If it is desirable to utilize the time spent on the backflush, to reduce further the analysis time, a dual-column system may be employed and the first column can be backflushed while the second one is performing useful separation. This mode is commonly known as *dual-column backflush operation*.

The *"backflush measure" mode* is used if the total amount of heavy components is to be measured. In this case the backflushed sample is passed through the detector instead of directly connecting it to a vent. This method has to be used with discretion since backflushing the heavy components into one single peak is not always successful.

The *dual-column (without backflush) method* usually employs two columns of different packings to obtain given separations in the second column not obtainable in the first. If the two columns for some reason cannot be operated in series during the entire chromatographic cycle, a switching valve is necessary to bypass temporarily one of the columns. Figure 10-14 illustrates the dual column switching principle for a specific application.

Let us suppose that our sample contains oxygen, nitrogen and carbon dioxide. In order to achieve complete separation of the oxygen and nitrogen, a molecular sieve column (C_2) is generally used. Molecular sieve columns, however, do not let the carbon dioxide through at ordinary temperatures. The problem can be solved by employing a silica gel column as the first column (C_1). V_1 and V_2 are rotary valves, and in the position shown they put the two columns in series. In this mode, the CO_2 will be separated from the O_2-N_2 in the silica gel column. As soon as the composite slug of O_2-N_2 leaves C_1, the rotary valves are turned clockwise 90°, thus trapping the O_2-N_2 slug in C_2 and allowing the CO_2 to bypass C_2 and reach the detector through a dummy column (C_D). The CO_2 then appears as a peak on the record. Now the column switching valves are turned back to their former positions allowing the carrier gas to flow through C_2 again. C_2 now performs the O_2-N_2 separation, and the two constituents produce two distinct peaks on the record.

The dummy column C_D may be filled with some inert material, which causes no appreciable retention of the constituents, but produces the same flow restriction as C_2. Maintaining the same rate of flow in both positions is important in order to maintain a stable baseline. As a packing material for C_D, Chromosorb, firebrick, or some other inert support material can be used. C_D may be replaced by an adjustable or fixed flow restriction such

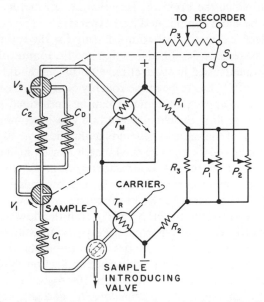

Fig. 10-14. Dual-column switching scheme with dual bridge balancing system (17).

as a needle valve, a capillary, etc. Most process gas chromatography equipment uses adjustable restrictions in place of C_D. Fine needle valves usually provide a satisfactory adjustment for doing this.

A simple method of determining whether or not the flow restrictions of C_2 and C_D are equal is to examine the baseline level at high sensitivity. If the flow rates (and the restrictions, of course) are equal, no change in the baseline level should occur when switching from one mode to another. There are several problems, however. First, the adjustment of these valves with the required accuracy is quite difficult. Furthermore, if the amount of flow restriction changes for some reason (e.g., column aging), readjustment is necessary. In many cases, when a Class 1, Group D, Division 1 explosion-resistant enclosure is used, this procedure may be quite difficult. The most serious problem, however, comes from the fact that process analyzers are nearly always remotely located from their recorders. This means that during the above-described flow matching procedure, adjustment is made in an analyzer which may be as far as 500 ft away from the recorder on which the result of the adjustment ought to be checked. Frequently no communication means are available between the two locations, but even if they were, to achieve a proper adjustment is very difficult and time consuming. Obviously, a remote flow adjusting device at the recorder location would solve the problem. However, a satisfactory remote servo system would be quite complicated and expensive.

A simple electrical method of compensating for the mismatch between the two flow systems is described in reference 17. Figure 10-14 shows the essential components used in connection with this method. First of all, the flow restriction of C_D has to be made roughly equivalent to the restriction shown by C_2. This approximate match can be performed by using flowmeters. This coarse flow matching procedure can be eliminated by using a dummy column of the same length and having the same support material (but no liquid coating) as C_2. The final match can be made by using two zero adjustments in the thermal conductivity bridge circuit instead of the usual one. Each potentiometer (P_1 and P_2) corresponds to a position of valves V_1 and V_2. For example, when the carrier gas flows through C_2, P_1 is selected by means of the switch S_1; if C_D is in the flow passage, then P_2 is selected. By properly adjusting P_1 and P_2, you can easily compensate for flow difference between the two modes. The automatic operation of the dual-bridge zeroing system will be described in Section IV-C.

Some of the other components in Figure 10-14 are: T_M, the measuring thermistor; T_R, the reference thermistor; R_1 and R_2, the bridge arm resistors; R_3, shunt for potentiometers P_1 and P_2.

Instead of rotary valves, other types of valves, described in the previous section, can be used. Depending on the complexity of the switching function, two to twelve port valves may be employed. Actuation, of course, has to be automatic for process gas chromatographs. Electric or pneumatic actuators can be employed as is the case with sample introducing valves.

Sometimes more than two columns are used to achieve certain separations within a given time and/or to improve accuracy (13). Figure 10-15 shows a three-column system which can be used in three different modes. Changing modes in this particular example is achieved by using three pneumatic diaphragm valves. Some companies use multiple column switching systems having more than three columns and a multiplicity of valves. Some of these systems are very complicated and their programming and maintenance is rather difficult. In many cases it would be more advisable to use two or more analyzers instead of a complicated column switching system. Even in relatively simple cases, sometimes two or more analyzers may mean less trouble for the user. With multiple analyzers, there is the added advantage of being able to use different carrier gases and

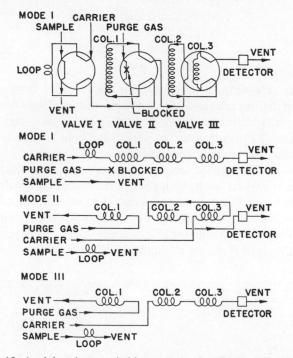

Fig. 10-15. A triple-column switching system using diaphragm valves (13).

different temperatures. In some cases, this method may be not only more reliable and simple, but the cost may be competitive with a single, complicated analyzer.

IV. The Programmer

A. General Requirements

A programming device is necessary when a gas chromatograph is being operated automatically. This is the case in process gas chromatographs and in certain automatically operated laboratory gas chromatographs. Preparative gas chromatographs may also employ programmer units. Instead of "programmer unit," sometimes the term "control unit" is used.

The programmer ordinarily contains a cycling timer or timers, which control certain functions such as:

> Sample introduction
> Zeroing
> Peak selection
> Attenuator selection
> Polarity reversal
> Auxiliary valve actuation
> Stream selection

In certain cases additional functions, namely recorder chart advance or slave timer initiation are also used. Another function (sometimes referred to as the "hold" function) is always included, when single-cycle (or manual) mode is desired. For automatic cycling this "hold" mode is bypassed, causing the timer to recycle automatically.

The above-listed operations require accessories, such as relays, potentiometers, electromotors, power supplies, etc., which are usually included in the programmer. The control panel may contain switches, adjustments, and visual indicators. An example of such a control panel showing function switches, indicator lights, and range adjustment dials can be seen in Figure 10-16. Another type is shown in Figure 10-17 with the timer cams visible

Fig. 10-16. Programmer control panel of the Leeds and Northrup Chromomax II process gas chromatograph (7a).

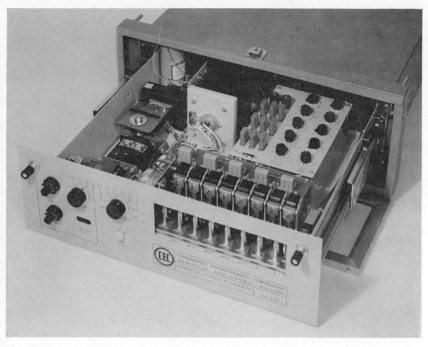

Fig. 10-17. Consolidated Electrodynamics Corp.'s process gas chromatography programmer.

on the front panel. The range adjustments and some of the function switches in this instrument are inside the chassis. This arrangement has the advantage that the settings cannot be changed accidentally or by unauthorized personnel. The equipment in Figure 10-16 is made tamper-proof by using a transparent window on the instrument door, which may be locked. The window enables the operator to check some of the settings without opening the programmer cabinet.

Figure 10-18 illustrates some of the programmer functions on a synthetic chromatogram. One of them is the sample introduction, which marks the beginning of the gas chromatographic cycle. The duration of the sampling depends on the valve construction, on the sample size, and on the carrier gas flow rate. In many cases a few seconds is enough to complete sample introduction. The automatic zeroing (to be described in more detail later) can be programmed to take place before sample introduction or immediately after it. In certain cases, when the timer construction allows it, zeroing may be performed several times during a cycle. This is especially useful when excessive drift is present (18).

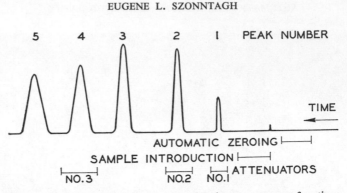

Fig. 10-18. Composite chromatogram showing programmer functions.

For recording or control purposes, the peaks of interest have to be selected from among the many peaks which may occur on a continuous chromatogram or spectrum. In Figure 10-18, for example, peaks number *1*, *2*, and *4* are selected and they are to be picked up through individual attenuators *1*, *2*, and *3*, respectively. The attenuators may provide continuous (Fig. 10-16) or stepwise control (Fig. 10-7). The two methods may be combined (Fig. 10-17).

A continuous type single attenuator arrangement can be seen in Figure 10-14 in connection with a thermal conductivity bridge. The attenuator P_3 is in most cases a 10-turn potentiometer.

Fig. 10-19. Greenbrier Instruments Division's (Bendix Corp.) multistream selector programmer.

The proper timing for the auxiliary valve (or auxiliary valves) depends on the type of separation desired, the type of columns used, etc. In each case the proper timing has to be determined as the function of certain peaks.

Stream selection was described in Section II. To program the selection of streams, the same types of programmers may be used as the ones used for the programming of other functions. Sometimes the programmer for the stream selector is included in the master programmer. In other cases a separate programmer is used for stream selection. Figure 10-19 shows such a programming unit for stream selection, manufactured by Greenbrier Instruments. The switches on the front panel enable the operator to select streams either manually or automatically. The automatic sequential selection of streams is accomplished by stepping switches.

Two major components of the gas chromatographic programmer, the timers and the automatic zeroing devices, will be described in more detail in the following sections.

B. Timers

Timers are used in process gas chromatographs to provide the automatic cycling operation. A wide variety of timers is used in gas chromatographs. Most frequently analog-type timers are employed, although there are a few instances in which digital systems are used. Most analog-type timing systems belong to the rotary cycling category and are driven by electric motors. Depending on the principle used for function actuation, the timers most commonly used may be classified as:

1. Electromechanical.
2. Electrooptical.
3. Electromagnetic.

The first group can use cams, endless tapes, or discs. The second group utilizes endless tapes or discs most frequently, and the third group is most practical when using endless tapes.

The simplest form of the electromechanical timer is the cam-type timer. The cam is a disc of varying radii and an abrupt slope or step perpendicular to the axis (18). The actuation of a function is accomplished by an electric switch (or switches) mechanically engaged with the periphery of the cam. The dwell time is determined by the length of the valley or the plateau on the cam (gating). The length of the valley can be adjusted by hand and has to be properly locked against slippage. Also, the position of the valley with respect to the cycle can be manually adjusted. Industrial Timer Corp., for instance, manufactures timers of this type, containing several individual cams on one shaft driven by a synchronous motor. A complete unit can

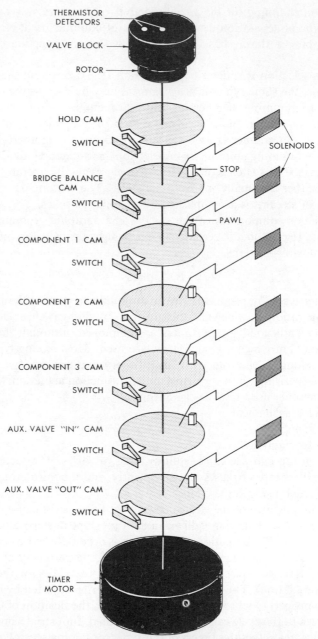

THERMISTOR
DETECTORS

VALVE BLOCK

ROTOR

HOLD CAM

SWITCH

SOLENOIDS

BRIDGE BALANCE
CAM

SWITCH

STOP

PAWL

COMPONENT 1 CAM

SWITCH

COMPONENT 2 CAM

SWITCH

COMPONENT 3 CAM

SWITCH

AUX. VALVE "IN" CAM

SWITCH

AUX. VALVE "OUT" CAM

SWITCH

TIMER
MOTOR

Fig. 10-20. Function diagram of a direct set cam programmer.

be seen on Figure 10-17 as part of a commercial programmer. Different manufacturers offer different methods of adjustment for speed change and other variables. Despite some evident disadvantages—such as the rather slow actuation when the follower arm climbs up the ramp—the cam-type timers are very popular because of their high reliability and low price. The most serious disadvantage of the cam-type timer is the length of time required to set up a program.

The setting of the cams to the proper position requires trial-and-error adjustment by loosening a holding device, moving the cam to a new position and retightening the holding device. Even when dials are used on the cams, the precision is not satisfactory and repeated runs and readjustments are necessary to achieve proper setting. The direct set method (19) developed at Leeds and Northrup Co. eliminates this disadvantage.

According to this method, each cam (see Fig. 10-20) is mounted on the main shaft by a slip clutch, and each cam has a stop on it mounted opposite the cam valley. A spring-loaded pawl which can be operated by a nearby solenoid is mounted next to each cam. When the solenoid is energized, the pawl moves toward the solenoid and stops the cam when the pawl engages the cam stop. Thus the cam is "grabbed" and held securely in this position, and the slip clutches allow the shaft to turn freely until all cams are grabbed and the timer finally comes to a stop. After initiating a new cycle, the program can be set directly within one chromatographic cycle, without tedious adjustments, calculations, or repeated runs. When a function is to be set on the program, the proper solenoid has to be deenergized to release the cam at the precise instant in the timing cycle. By watching the record, the same deenergizing procedure can be repeated for each additional function, thus setting them all.

In this method, the accuracy and reliability of setting has been greatly increased by eliminating operator error and uncertainty in the transfer of data from a chart record to a cam position. This direct setting feature eliminates preliminary runs and trial and error adjustments thus decreasing time and effort needed for programming. The accuracy of setting is high and is determined primarily by the ability of the operator to observe the record and to flip a switch at the appropriate time.

Other types of electromechanical timers include Beckman Instruments' timer with properly spaced pins around the circumference of a disc (Figs. 10-21 and 10-22), Foxboro Co.'s timer (Fig. 10-23) with small adjustable metal actuators along the two edges of a belt, and Mine Safety Appliances' disc ramp timer, introduced originally by Perkin-Elmer, employing rotatable follower springs (18).

Mine Safety Appliances' Model 525 programmer (Fig. 10-24) has an

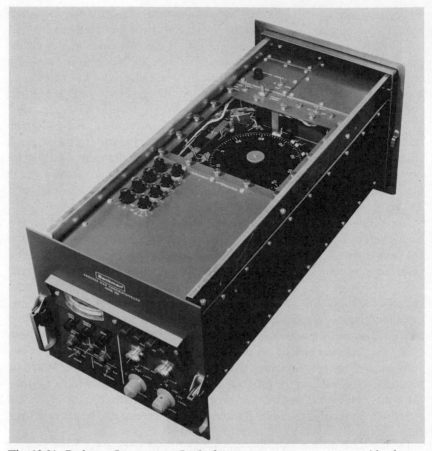

Fig. 10-21. Beckman Instruments, Inc.'s four-component programmer with electromechanical timer.

electrooptical timer which utilizes a transparent disc and opaque pencil
marks to set up a program. Erasing a pencil mark removes a function from
the program; extending the length of a mark gives the function a longer
duration.

The principle of an electromagnetic programmer can be seen in Figure
10-25. This particular arrangement utilizes a multichannel head system (up
to 14 channels) and an endless tape (19). Single-channel tape programmers
are also used. They usually employ sequential steppers to provide multiple
component selection. Beckman Instruments markets such a tape programmer (19b) that is interchangeable with their mechanical programmer
shown in Figure 10-21.

Fig. 10-22. Beckman 520 programmer with Leeds and Northrup Type H strip chart recorder.

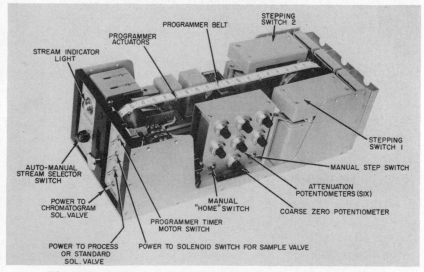

Fig. 10-23. Foxboro programmer for multistream application (19a).

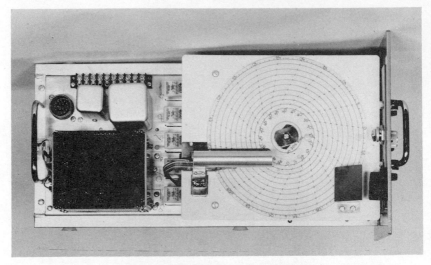

Fig. 10-24. Mine Safety Appliances Company electrooptical programmer.

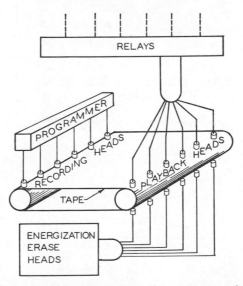

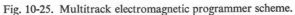

Fig. 10-25. Multitrack electromagnetic programmer scheme.

C. Automatic Zeroing Devices

The baseline of the gas chromatographic trace is the line recorded when only carrier gas is flowing through the detectors. For optimum interpretation of chromatograms, the baseline should be a continuous trace, parallel to the time axis, and in most applications it should be positioned at 0 mV on the recorder. Drift is a baseline instability which appears as a continuously and slowly increasing or decreasing baseline value. The

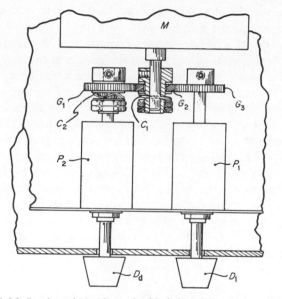

Fig. 10-26. Leeds and Northrup double bridge balancing system (17).

automatic zeroing devices are used to compensate for the drift and to adjust the baseline to the zero value, when only carrier gas is flowing through the detectors.

A conventional automatic zeroing device consists of an electromotor-driven potentiometer which is connected to the bridge or to the amplifier circuit in such a way that it can correct the output voltage to zero. Depending on the direction of rotation of the electromotor, the potentiometer can be driven to cause an "upscale" or "downscale" baseline change. Figure 10-26 shows such a system. M is a reversible motor which drives the potentiometer P_1 through gears G_2 and G_3. The potentiometer can also be manually driven at dial D_1; the slip clutch C_1 allows P_1 to turn independently of the motor.

P_2 is a second potentiometer and is only employed when multiple column switching methods are used (17). The clutch C_2 allows the setting of P_2 independently of P_1. In automatic mode, both potentiometers are driven by the balancing motor. The schematic wiring diagram of a double bridge balancing system can be seen in Figure 10-14.

The electromotor can be actuated by a control switch located in the recorder. When in the zeroing mode, the motor is energized, and, depending on the control switch position relative to the zero point of the recorder scale, the potentiometer will be driven either clockwise or counterclockwise causing the detector output to correct itself toward zero. If one switch is employed, the baseline will oscillate slightly around the zero point. When two properly adjusted switches are used, the base line will stay at zero after reaching it, unless further drift disturbs the output.

Instead of a recorder, an operational amplifier may be used to supply the polarity information to the zero balancing motor. Also, mechanical means (friction drive) can be used directly to operate the zero potentiometers from a recorder, thus eliminating the control switch and the additional zeroing motor.

Another type of zeroing system is electronic zeroing (20) which completely eliminates electromechanical devices by using a bucking voltage. In this zeroing mode, the feedback is removed from the amplifier thus greatly increasing its gain for use as an error detector. The output amplifier is bypassed, and the input amplifier is used as a detector circuit during zeroing. The signal is fed through a combination of a phase inverter and an amplifier to the manual zeroing potentiometer which is one leg of the bridge. This zeroing circuit provides an automatic correction capacity of ± 25 mV.

The capacity of zeroing devices is very important. Sometimes dials are employed on the zeroing potentiometer shaft (Fig. 10-16) to indicate the actual position of the potentiometer in regard to its total capacity. The maximum allowable drift, influences the capacity requirements and the time needed for zeroing. The maximum allowable rate of drift (D_{max}) can be expressed in millivolts per minute in the following manner:

$$D_{max} = [(a - b)m]/(100c), \qquad (10\text{-}2)$$

where a = the required accuracy of the analysis in percent
$\quad\quad b$ = the accuracy of the gas chromatographic equipment expressed in percent of recorder range
$\quad\quad c$ = cycle time of the analysis in minutes
$\quad\quad m$ = recorder range in millivolts

The factor b is a function of the accuracy of the recorder, power supplies, and temperature regulation of the gas chromatograph and a function of the sample injection method. The maximum allowable rate of drift can be greater than the figure given by the above equation if the bridge can be balanced more than once per cycle.

V. Data Handling and Processing

We can differentiate between two types of data handling in process chromatography: that required for recording and that required for process control. Recording is generally still a simpler procedure.

A. Recording

If we were to use continuous chromatograms (Fig. 10-27a) in process gas chromatography, the amount of chart paper needed would very quickly become prohibitively large. As an example, consider the case of a high-speed process gas chromatograph requiring a recorder chart speed of 12 inches per minute. In a 24-hr period the recorder would use a quarter of a mile of chart paper.

Several techniques have been developed to simplify the record and economize on paper. Perhaps the earliest method is the *bar graph* which is shown in Figure 10-27b. In the bar graph presentation, a selected peak is recorded during a period of no chart advance. The chart then moves a predetermined distance to a new position and stays there until the second selected peak has been recorded. This process continues in the same fashion until all the peaks of interest have been recorded. The bar graph may be used to present peak height or peak area values. In the latter case, an integrator must be used to provide signals proportional to the integrated areas under the curves of the selected constituents (21).

Figure 10-28 is a simplified diagram of an electronic integrator. The operational amplifier is shown inside the dashed lines. Switches S_1 and S_2, which are operated by the programmer of the chromatograph, are normally open. S_1 closes just before the chromatographic peak begins and remains closed until the peak ends. The output signal of the amplifier is proportional to the time integral of the signal received from the retransmitting slidewire. After the output signal has been read out by a recorder, data-logger, computer or other such device, switch S_2 is closed momentarily to discharge C_0 and thus resets the integrator to zero. A continuous output signal can be obtained by using the output of the integrator to drive an electropneumatic converter. When integration of a new peak is occurring, the output of the electropneumatic converter is held at the value of the last integral by deenergizing a solenoid valve. Figure 10-29 is the photograph of an actual integrator used in process gas chromatography.

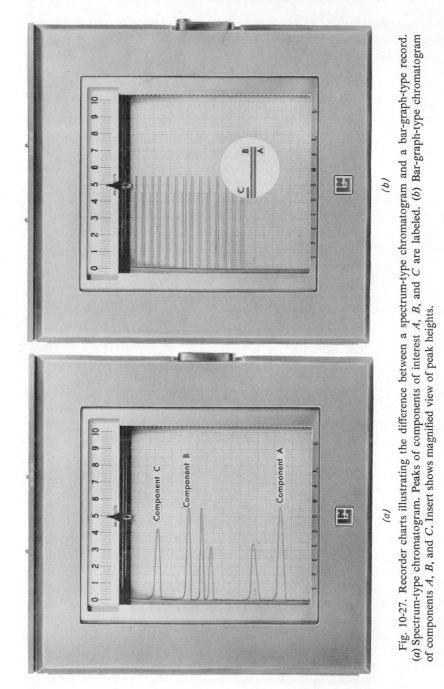

Fig. 10-27. Recorder charts illustrating the difference between a spectrum-type chromatogram and a bar-graph-type record. (a) Spectrum-type chromatogram. Peaks of components of interest A, B, and C are labeled. (b) Bar-graph-type chromatogram of components A, B, and C. Insert shows magnified view of peak heights.

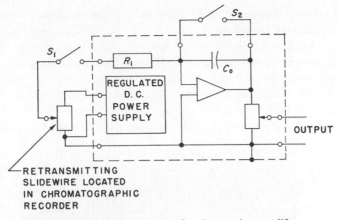

Fig. 10-28. Schematic diagram of an integrating amplifier.

There are several other types of integrators used in process gas chromatography, including voltage-to-frequency converter type, ball-and-disc type, and optical integrators (22). There are also many methods which provide means for transferring the integrated values to an analog or digital readout system.

In the past the bar graph method was used almost exclusively for the analog presentation of peaks for process gas chromatography. When properly programmed, the bar graph presents a simple, easily interpreted

Fig. 10-29. Leeds and Northrup electronic integrator.

record using a reasonably small amount of paper. It does, however, consume a relatively large amount of ink and it does not adequately portray trends. In case of multicomponent analyses, the bar-graph-type recording method can be quite confusing. To overcome these deficiencies *trend recording methods* have been developed. Figure 10-30 shows one such method. It is the dot-dash method, so called from the appearance of the printed record. One variation of this method uses an electromechanical one-way clutch as a peak height value reading device (7*a*). When energized,

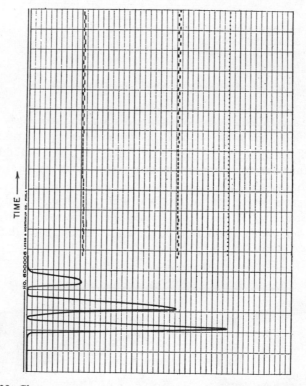

Fig. 10-30. Chromatogram and dot-dash trend record for three components (22*a*).

the clutch allows the pen which is lifted off the chart paper to move upscale only. When the highest point of the chromatographic peak is reached the pen is dropped to the paper. Now, depending upon the programming, the chart paper does not move at all, or moves either a small distance or a slightly longer distance, producing either a dot, a short dash, or a long dash, identifying three different constituents. The peak height values may be fed into a memory device for control purposes.

For more than three-point trend recording, multipoint recorders may

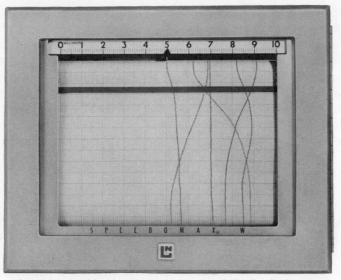

Fig. 10-31. Multicomponent record on a Speedomax W recorder.

be used. Figure 10-31 shows a multicomponent record using a Speedomax Type W recorder. Although Figure 10-31 shows only a six-point record, more complicated runs having up to 24 components can be realized with the W recorder.

For peak height value recording, electronic peak-pickers may be used instead of the electromechanical devices. Figure 10-32 shows an electronic peak height value reading and memory circuit. The system uses a diode-capacitor peak reader. Pneumatic-type peak readers and memory devices are employed by some manufacturers.

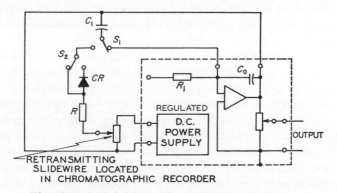

Fig. 10-32. Peak-height reading and memory device.

In addition to null-balance electronic recorders, pneumatic recorders and meter movements are also used for monitoring process gas chromatography data. In certain cases digital readout systems offer advantages.

There are differences of opinion as to whether peak height or peak area readings should be used in process gas chromatography. In practice, both are used, but peak height values are used in about 90% of the applications (23). The equipment needed for peak height recording is simpler, and the separation of peaks does not have to be as good for peak height as for peak area recording, although complete separation is still required for maximum accuracy.

B. Process Control

Not too long ago, the control of a process was carried out almost exclusively by manually sampling the plant stream, taking the sample to a control laboratory, analyzing it, and making the necessary changes in the process. The next step in the evolution of process control was to use continuous automatic analyzers and use the data for manual control. Finally, most recent practice is to have the sensing unit directly actuate control mechanisms such as valves, pumps, heaters, etc. In this way the operating conditions of the process are automatically kept at the desired levels. In addition, the analyzer can be made to actuate alarm systems, or it can even shut down a process when hazardous conditions exist (24).

As far as basic control theory and practice are concerned, the reader is referred to textbooks (25–26a) included in the list of references. In this section, only essential facts concerning process gas chromatographic control will be discussed.

The main components of a control system are: the process, the analyzer, the error detector, the controller, and the final control element (e.g., valve). These elements can be interconnected in one of two different ways: as an open loop or as a closed loop. In open-loop control, the output has no effect on the input. The open loop is inherently stable because there can be no self-excitation (27).

In closed-loop control, the output information is fed back to the input, so there is a possibility of instability through self-excitation. Even so, the advantages of the closed-loop control system far outweigh the disadvantages. A typical block diagram of a control loop using a gas chromatograph is shown in Figure 10-33. The process gas chromatograph performs the functions of the analyzer and the "signal hold" device. Since we usually want to run the process at some set value of the measured variable, a set point device has to be used. The set point is a reference. The error detector senses the difference between the set point and the measured variable. This difference actuates the controller which includes the final control element. This element can be a valve which changes the process input, thus completing the loop. Disturbances, as is shown, can enter at the input or output of the process.

Because material produced while the process is off control may have to be scrapped, a good control system must minimize time lags. C. W. Ross (28), among others, has studied the effect of different time lags and their influence on the control, with special emphasis on gas chromatography.

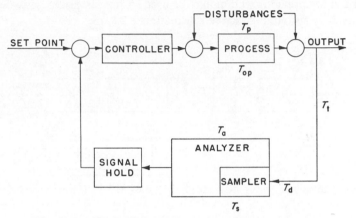

Fig. 10-33. Block diagram of a closed loop control system.

He used analog computer simulation to study, for example, disturbances appearing at the output for $T_p/T_0 > 1$. The results can be summarized by the following equation:

$$t_s \cong 0.7T_p + 2.38T_0 + 0.15T_S + T_D, \qquad (10\text{-}3)$$

where t_s = the settling time of the process under automatic control when subject to a step input; time required to reduce the output error to 10% of the step disturbance

T_p = the effective time constant of the process

T_0 = total system dead time, and it consists of the sum of T_a, T_t and T_{0p} (see Fig. 10-33). (T_{0p} is the dead time in the process, T_a is the dead time in the analyzer, and T_t is the sample transport delay.)

T_S = time interval between samplings

T_D = sampling dead time; time between the arrival of a disturbance at the sampler and the subsequent sampling

The choice of a particular method of control depends upon many factors. To a large extent, it will require ingenuity and experience to select that method which is optimum for the given specifications of accuracy, reliability, cost, control speed, characteristics of the signals and systems, etc.

In order to apply the output of a chromatographic process stream analyzer to a data-logger, computer, or controller, a device is required which will select and store the chromatographic signal of the desired component and make available a continuous electrical or pneumatic output signal proportional thereto. For signal holding, the memory devices described in the previous section may be used. A transistorized peak detector and memory system is described in reference 29.

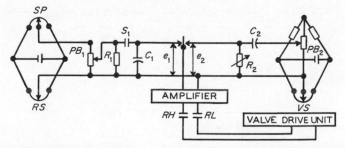

Fig. 10-34. Simplified wiring diagram of the Leeds and Northrup Series 60 control unit (30).

Figure 10-34 shows the simplified schematic wiring diagram of a complete control system using a position adjusting type (PAT) control (30). The retransmitting slidewire RS is located in a Speedomax H recorder-programmer, and the slidewire VS is in the valve drive unit. All the other elements are located in a control unit, which in its outside appearance is similar to the integrator shown in Figure 10-29. PB_1 and PB_2 are manually adjustable proportional band rheostats; the speed of reset is adjustable by means of variable resistor R_2.

As a component is being measured in the gas chromatograph, the programmer closes switch S_1. Any difference in the voltage drop (e_1) across RS and the set-point slidewire SP is placed on memory capacitor C_1. This emf is compared to e_2, the emf from the feedback bridge. The difference between e_1 and e_2 is detected by the amplifier, which in turn operates the valve drive unit through relay contact RH or RL. This control system operates on one component only. Multicomponent systems have also been developed and operated. In many cases, ratios or sums or differences of sample components are used for the controller.

At a sharply increasing rate, process gas chromatography equipment is being linked to computers to achieve fast, accurate, and highly reliable process control. The computer, through accurate analyses, can detect inaccuracies in the instrumentation, such as a drift in flowmeter calibration. Also, computers can compare the gas chromatographic analyses against preset high or low limits to detect off-spec conditions that warn of faulty product or hazardous situations (31). The computer can use gas chromatography analysis data for a variety of calculations, such as summing, taking ratios, etc. Reference 31 describes a method in which the computer is given complete control of the analyzer functions. It is claimed that this way the computer cannot misinterpret analyzer signals.

Unfortunately the nature of the gas chromatographic process does not lend itself to continuous control, since the separation on the column requires a definite increment of time. Although several patents have been obtained on continuous gas chromatographs (e.g. refs. 32, 33), no continuous commercial equipment was announced until recently.

The economic considerations of process control through analytical instrumentation are well described in reference 24. Reference 34 contains important practical data including payout time figures with special emphasis on the analyzer system itself.

A section on applications of process chromatography is beyond the scope of this book. New applications are being developed daily, and most present-day process streams are amenable to process gas chromatographic techniques. Several manufacturers have lists of applications and application data sheets which are available to the customer.

VI. Installation and Maintenance

The analyzer unit of a process gas chromatograph in general has to be mounted near the process stream in order to reduce time lag and to simplify sampling system problems. An actual installation was shown in Figure 10-3 on page 516. The explosion resistant housing of the analyzer in this particular example is a bell-type enclosure. The three lugs on the base (Fig. 10-8) offer a convenient method for mounting the analyzer. Rectangular cases can be similarly mounted either by lugs or by mounting holes.

Safety requirements should be determined prior to installation, and the actual set-up should satisfy these needs (see Section I of this chapter). For detailed information concerning power requirements, air and gas supply needs, and the like, consult the instruction book accompanying the equipment. The following general startup scheme may be helpful:

When all the connections have been made, turn on the equipment and let it warm up with the carrier gas flowing through the analyzer. Check for leaks and, if necessary, correct faulty plumbing. After a couple of hours, check for stabilization by examining the baseline. If the recorder pen can be adjusted to zero with the zeroing potentiometers provided and the baseline stays at zero, the equipment is in order and it is stabilized. If the pen cannot be brought to zero, something may be wrong with the detector, with the power supply, or with the amplifier in case of an ionization detector. The instruction book should serve as a guide for troubleshooting. If zeroing can be achieved only temporarily, the equipment is not yet warmed up. Excessive drift after a considerable waiting time may indicate a faulty detector or other defective components.

If no drift occurs, run a single cycle by introducing a sample of known composition (standard sample). Run a conventional chromatogram and check it for separation, for sensitivity, and for total analysis time. If any one of these is not satisfactory, a change of parameters (carrier gas flow, pressure, column temperature) or a change of column may be required. Since these operations are the same for laboratory gas chromatographs, the procedures will be omitted here.

If the chromatogram is satisfactory, run a cycle with the process stream. If the standard sample and the process stream were identical, the result should be the same. In practice, however, there may be differences between the two. If this is the case, you have to be sure that there is nothing interfering with those peaks that you want to program automatically, and that after the cycle time is over, no additional peaks are eluted from the column (heavy components). If further peak elution occurs, backflush methods may be employed.

If everything is satisfactory, you can start to program the process gas chromatograph.

Programming in general was described in Section IV and has to be done according to instructions supplied by the manufacturer. A considerable amount of time can be saved by using one of the direct set-programming methods. The trial-and-error adjustment of nondirect set timers is tedious and increases the operator's attendance time. If proper columns are employed, reprogramming every month or two will probably be satisfactory. In case of a severely aging column, however, reprogramming may be necessary every four or five days.

Calibration can be done in a number of different ways. To calibrate the recorder in terms of actual sample concentration, a standardizing mixture of known concentration must be run through the analyzer and the reading of the recorder must be adjusted by the attenuator potentiometer to the known value.

We will consider the case when peak height values are to be calibrated.

The adjustment of the attenuator during the brief period when the recorder pen is at the peak height value is very difficult. Trial-and-error adjustments can be made, but this procedure is very time consuming.

A more convenient and fast procedure is the following:

1. Make a run with the standardizing mixture by using the automatic attenuator selecting mode. The record then will show peak height values recorded through attenuators, one, two, etc. Take number one peak, for instance, and let us suppose that the peak height value shown on the recorder is 75 divisions. Suppose the concentration of the calibrating constituent is 85%. For convenience, we would like to change the attenuator setting so that 85% gas concentration will really read 85 divisions instead of 75.

2. Without running additional samples, offset the zero level of the recorder to read 75 divisions. This can be done by adjusting the zero potentiometers.

3. After reaching a stable reading (of 75 divisions), adjust the proper attenuator (attenuator number one, in this case) to the desired reading (85 divisions). The zero adjustment now can be readjusted to the previous zero level.

When running a new analysis of the calibrating gas with this corrected attenuator setting, the peak height on the recorder now should be the correct desired reading (85 divisions for 85% gas concentration, in this example).

The above-described procedure can be repeated for each additional component. The whole operation should not take longer than a minute or two per component. The initial run with the calibrating mixture, of course, is an additional 1–30 min, depending on the analysis time.

The peak height vs. concentration curve is basically a nonlinear curve. Although the above-described method provides calibration at one point only, in many cases this is still satisfactory, especially if the concentration of the component in the stream and the concentration of the same component in the calibration mixture are close and the stream component concentration does not vary much.

If peak areas are used, basically the same procedure can be followed. In this case the recorder deflection and the concentration will have a more linear relationship.

Other aspects of calibrating methods are described in reference 35. Some gas chromatographs use stepwise attenuator selection instead of a continuous one. In these cases calibration curves have to be made in order to interpret properly the recorder readings.

After the first calibration, recalibration may be necessary at appropriate

TABLE 10-1

List of Automatic Process Gas Chromatograph Manufacturers Mentioned
in Chapter 10

Teledyne Analytical Instruments Company 370 S. Fair Oaks Avenue Pasadena, California	MECI (Matériel Électrique de Controle et Industriel) 123, Bd de Grenelle Paris-XVe, France
Beckman Instruments, Inc. 2500 Harbor Blvd. Fullerton, California	Mine Safety Appliances Co. 201 North Braddock Avenue
Bendix Corporation Greenbrier Instruments Division P. O. Box 68 Ronceverte, West Virginia	Pittsburgh, Pennsylvania The Perkin-Elmer Corp.[a] Main Avenue Norwalk, Connecticut
Carlo Erba S.P.A. Casella Postale 3996 Milano, Italy	Process Analyzers, Inc. 5405 Griggs Road Houston, Texas
Consolidated Electrodynamics Corp.[b] 360 Sierra Madre Villa Pasadena, California	W. G. Pye & Co. Ltd. P. O. Box 60 York Street
The Foxboro Company Neponset Avenue Foxboro, Massachusetts	Cambridge, England Siemens & Halske A.G.
Leeds & Northrup Company 4109 Stenton Avenue Philadelphia, Pennsylvania	Rheinbrückenstrasse 50 Karlsruhe West Western Germany

[a] The Perkin-Elmer Corp.'s process instrumentation has been acquired by Mine Safety Appliances Co.

[b] Consolidated Electrodynamics Corporation's process gas chromatography instrumentation has been taken over by Process Analyzers, Inc.

time intervals e.g. every second week. The recalibration is necessary mainly because of the aging of the column and the detector.

Routine maintenance procedures should include (1) checking the proper operation of the gas chromatograph by running a spectrum of a standard gas sample at least once a week; (2) checking the carrier tank pressure and replacing the cylinder when necessary; and (3) regularly checking recorder chart paper and ink supply.

Other maintenance procedures may include care of the analyzer sampling valve and occasional replacement of detector cells. The chromatographic column has to be changed at certain intervals. In some cases the lifetime of the column may be as high as a year; in other cases it may be only a couple of months.

In general it can be said that a well-constructed process gas chromatograph on a proper application needs very little maintenance.

References

1. *Standard for Industrial Control Equipment for Use in Hazardous Locations*, Underwriters' Laboratories, Inc., 1954.
2. *Electrical Instruments in Hazardous Atmospheres. Recommended Practice* 12.1, Instrument Society of America, 1960.
3. D. H. Desty, Ed., *Vapor Phase Chromatography*, Butterworths, London, 1957, p. xi.
3a. *Greenbrier Technical Bulletin* PVR-59.
4. E. A. Houser, *The Analyzer*, Beckman Instruments, Inc., January 1961, p. 5.
5. T. A. Gray and J. Imber, in *Instrumentation in the Chemical and Petroleum Industries, 1964*, G. H. Robinson, Ed., Plenum Press, New York, 1964, p. 57.
6. D. M. Vesper, U.S. Pat. 3,069,898 (1962).
6a. I. Mellan, *Corrosion Resistant Metals Handbook*, Noyes, Park Ridge, N.J., 1966.
7. H. H. Uhlig, Ed., *Corrosion Handbook*, Wiley, New York, 1948.
7a. E. L. Szonntagh, *Instr. Soc. Am. Proc. Ann. Instr.–Autom. Conf. Exhibit*, **18**, 11-1-63 (1963).
7b. C. Schoedler, *Genie Chim.*, **89**, 146 (1963).
8. E. J. Watson, U.S. Pat. 2,757,541 (1956).
9. S. B. Spracklen, U.S. Pat. 3,041,869 (1962).
10. E. L. Szonntagh, in *Gas Chromatography*, L. Fowler, Ed., Academic Press, New York, 1963, pp. 233–241.
11. K. W. Charlton, C. T. Maxwell, and S. B. Spracklen, U.S. Pat. 3,160,015 (1964).
12. G. L. Pratt and J. H. Purnell, *Anal. Chem.*, **32**, 313 (1960).
13. F. W. Karasek and B. O. Ayers, *ISA J.*, **7** (3), 70 (1960).
14. Greenbrier Instruments Division of Bendix Corp. *Tech. Bull.* DS-59.
15. C. P. Rohmann, U.S. Pat., 2,989,076 (1961).
15a. A. B. Broerman, U.S. Pat. 3,140,615 (1964).
15b. A. B. Broerman, U.S. Pat. 3,198,018 (1965).
16. G. S. Turner and R. Villalobos, in *Gas Chromatography*, N. Brenner, J. E. Callen, and M. D. Weiss, Eds., Academic Press, New York, 1963, p. 363.
17. E. L. Szonntagh, French Pat. 1,406,369 (1965).
18. C. J. Bossart, H. Heller, H. J. Maier, and T. L. Zinn, *Instr. Control Systems*, **38** (3), 143 (1965).
19. E. L. Szonntagh, U.S. Pat. 3,205,701 (1965).
19a. The Foxboro Corp., *Technical Information* 37-10/e.
19b. Beckman Instruments, Inc., *Bulletin* GC-4036.
20. *Instruction Book for Model* 284 *High Speed Process Vapor Fractometer*, The Perkin-Elmer Corp.

21. J. U. Eynon, U.S. Pat. 3,051,989 (1962).
22. I. Halász and W. Schneider, in *Gas Chromatography 1960*, R. P. W. Scott, Ed., Butterworths, Washington, 1960, p. 104.
22a. W. T. Ott, U.S. Pat. 3,200,404 (1965).
23. C. D'Oyly-Watkins, *Nature*, **203**, 129 (1964).
24. S. Siggia, *Continuous Analysis of Chemical Process Systems*, Wiley, New York, 1959.
25. D. P. Eckman, *Automatic Process Control*, Wiley, New York, 1958.
26. L. M. Zoss and B. C. Delahooke, *Theory and Applications of Industrial Process Control*, Delmar Publishers, Albany, N.Y., 1961.
26a. D. M. Considine, *Process Instruments and Controls Handbook*, McGraw-Hill, New York, 1957.
27. L. M. Zoss and H. S. Wilson, *ISA J.*, **9** (1), 26 (1962).
28. C. W. Ross, *ISA Trans.*, **2**, 69 (1963).
29. D. N. Campbell, P. A. Michaels, and J. Mohan, *Bendix Report* RLDP-65-08.
30. Leeds & Northrup *Data Sheet C3.4441*, 1965.
31. J. B. Neblett and F. C. Mears, *ISA J.*, **9** (1), 44 (1962).
32. R. A. Findlay, U.S. Pat. 2,869,672 (1959).
33. L. H. Hall, U.S. Pat. 2,891,630 (1959).
34. D. J. Fraade, in *Analysis Instrumentation 1963*, L. Fowler, R. D. Eanes, and T. J. Kehoe, Eds., Plenum Press, New York, 1963, p. 83.
35. G. S. Turner and W. N. Crum, in *Analysis Instrumentation 1963*, L. Fowler, R. D. Eanes, and T. J. Kehoe, Eds., Plenum Press, New York, 1963, p. 77.
36. L. Fowler, R. D. Eanes, and T. J. Kehoe, Eds., *Analytical Instrumentation 1963*, Plenum Press, New York, 1963.

Author Index

Numbers in parentheses are reference numbers and indicate that the author's work is referred to although his name is not mentioned in the text. Numbers in italics show the pages on which the complete references are listed.

A

Abel, K., 97, *125*, 262, 324(257), *327*, *332*, 482, *507*

Abraham, N. A., 500, *510*

Abrams, S. T., 309(223), *331*

Acree, F., Jr., 466(12),467(12), 470(12), 471(12), *505*

Adlard, E. R., 493, *509*

Ahrens, E. H., Jr., 76, *125*

Ainsworth, C., 475, *506*

Aibert, D. K., 493, *509*

Albro, P. W., 474(29), 477, *506*

Alencar, J. W. de, 52(1), 67(1), *69*, 221(139), *238*

Allen, L. C., 446(98), *459*

Allen, R. R., 496, *509*

Allphin, N. L., 480(86), 481, *507*

Altenau, A. G., 176(62), *236*

Altshuller, A. P., 495, *509*

Amberg, C. H., 499, *510*

American Society for Testing and Materials, 415, *457*

Anders, F., 325, *332*

Anders, M. W., 490, *509*

Anderson, D. F., 426(63), *458*

Anderson, R. B., 498, *510*

Anderson, W. A., 444(95), *459*

Andreatch, A. J., 396(44), *406*, 495(153), *509*

Andrew, T. D., 279, *328*

Angelini, P., 218(132), *238*, 429, *458*

Annis, J. L., 315(232), 316, 317(232), *331*

Aoyagi, M., 249(16), *326*

Archer, E. D., 440(89a), *459*

Argabright, P. A., 250, *326*, 396(40), 397 (40), *406*

Arlt, H. G., Jr., 476, *506*

Atkinson, E. P., 192, 210(82), *236*, 409(6), *456*

Aue, W. A., 487(114b), *508*

Aul, F., 274, 275(101), *328*

Auricourt, F., 287(152,153a), 288, *329*, 399(54), *406*

Averill, W., 123(21b), *124*, 135(9), 181, 201, 202(98), 211, 228(150), *234*, *236*–*238*, 256(49), 265(49), *326*, 396(47), 397(47), 399(47), *406*

Ayers, B. O., 526(13), 527(13), 532(13), 533(13), *557*

B

Bachmann, O., 487, *508*

Bair, L. R., 284(137), *329*

Baker, W. J., 186(74), *236*, 486(106), *508*

Bambrick, W. E., 495(153,154), *509*

Banner, A. E., 319, *331*

Baraud, M. J., 79, *123*

Barber, R. M., 172(49), *235*

Barboriak, J. J., 489, *508*

Barbour, W. M., 473, *505*

Bardwell, J., 496, *509*

Barford, R. A., 97, *125*

Barr, J. K., 190(78), *236*

Barrall, E. M., II, 494, *509*

Bartlet, J. C., 393, *406*

Barton, G. W., Jr., 446(97), *459*

559

T

Tadmor, J., 500, *510*
Tákacs, J., 221(141), *238*
Takeuchi, T., 266, *327*
Tamaru, K., 499, *510*
Tanaka, I., 275, *328*
Tang, Y.-N., 487(121), *508*
Tataru, E., 303–305(211), *330*, 481(75), 499, *507, 510*
Tattrie, N. H., 99, *125*
Taylor, B. W., 228(151), 229(151), *238*
Technical Measurements Corp., 445(97*a*), 446(97*a*), *459*
Teitelbaum, P., 79, *123*
Tenney, H. M., 377, *405*
Teranishi, R., 221(136), *238*, 316(238–240), *331*, 407, 409(11,16), 410(16), 412(16), 414(32), 426(60,66,67), 427(66, 67), 430(71), 431(73), 432(73,74), 433(73), 440(89*a*,90), 446(90), 447(90), 450(101,103), 451–453(101), *456–459*
Terent'ev, A. P., 485, *508*
Terry, J. O., 229, *238*
Testerman, M. K., 322, 323, *331*
Teszler, A. P., 489, *508*
Teuwissen, B., 86, *126*
Thevelin, M., 280, *328*
Thiele, H., 4(13,14), 5, *48*
Thielemann, H., 292, *330*
Thissen, J. A. L., 305(214), *330*, 481(74), *507*
Thoburn, S., 288, 289(156), *329*
Thompson, A. E., 409(8), *456*
Thompson, C. J., 100, *126*, 466, *505*
Thompson, G. F., 489, *508*
Thompson, R. J., 252(34), *326*
Tilak, M. A., 89, *127*
Timms, P. L., 286(148), 288, *329*
Tindle, R. C., 487(114*b*), *508*
Tipotsch, D. G., 411(20), *456*
Tiselius, A., 4, 5, *49*
Tobin, H., Jr., 280(129), *329*, 463, 498, *505*
Tomida, I., 89, *127*
Tominaga, K., 249(16), *326*
Tornheim, L., 180(68), *236*
Tritch, H. R., 285, *329*
Trotman-Dickenson, A. F., 496, *509*
Trowell, J. M., 227(149), *238*

Troyanowsky, C., 499, *510*
Tschnikina, W. K., 171(45), *235*
Tsuge, S., 266(75,76), *327*
Tswett, M., 3, 5, *49*
Tucker, H. C., 274, *328*
Tudge, A. P., 213(121), *237*
Tuey, G. A. P., 192, 210(82), *236*, 409(6), *456*
Tulloch, A. P., 76, *124*
Turkel'taub, N. M., 213, *237*, 485, *508*
Turner, D. W., 297, *330*
Turner, G. S., 224(143), *238*, 529(16), 555(35), *557, 558*
Turner, N. C., 4, 5, *49*
Tverdyukova, L. B., 491, *509*

U

Uhlig, H. H., 519(7), *557*
Ulrich, W. F., 411(20), *456*
Underwriters' Laboratories, 512(1), 520(1), *557*
Upham, F. T., 266, *327*
Urone, P., 201, *237*

V

Vagelos, P. R., 100, *126*
Valega, T. M., 471
Van den Dool, H., 387(28), *406*
VandenHeuvel, W. J. A., 86, 92, 93, 95, 98, 100, 104, 105, *125, 126*, 193, *236*, 387, *405*
Van Middelem, C. H., 102, *126*
Van Tiggelen, A., 254(45), *326*
Váradi, P. F., 275, 320(102), 321, 322 (102), *328*, 474, 478, *506, 507*
Varian Associates, 121(123), *127*, 439(79, 87), *459*
Vaughan, G. A., 393, *406*
Vece, R., 476, *506*
Vernand, J. M., 34(43), *49*
Vesper, D. M., 518(6), *557*
Vessman, J., 175(61), *236*
Vetter, W., 87, *123*
Vilkas, M., 500, *510*
Villalobos, R., 224(143), 225, 226(145), 230(145), *238*, 529(16), *557*
Voge, H. H., 465, 499, *505*

Subject Index*

A

Acetylacetonates, detector for, 313–314
Acetylenes, 144, 288
Acids. See Carboxylic acids.
Activation energy, 499
Adjusted retention volume. See Retention volume, adjusted.
Adsorbent, 8, 35, 140. See also Gas–solid chromatography.
Adsorption, 149, 189–193, 389, 500
  effect on retention data, 149, 389
  reduction of, 189–193, 500
Adsorption chromatography. See Gas–solid chromatography.
Absorption columns, 9, 35. See also Gas–solid chromatography.
Aerosols, 409
Air, purification of, 55–56, 62
Air circulation system in process GC, 523–525
Air peak, 14, 36, 136–137, 148, 375
Alcohols and derivatives of, 32, 89–94, 100, 142–144, 173, 270, 376, 378, 380–385, 411, 468, 472, 476, 490, 492, 496
  carbon skeletal analysis of, 472
  conversion to hydrocarbons, 91
  dinitrobenzoates of, 91
  esters of, 90
  nitrite esters from, 91
  olefins from, 91
  pyrolysis of, 476
  removal of, 496
  separations of, 142, 144, 173, 376, 378, 380–385
  trimethylsilyl ethers of, 490
Aldehydes, 92–94, 144, 295, 380–385, 411, 468, 489, 492, 496
  acetals from, 92–93

derivatives of, 92–93
esters from, 92
removal of, 496
Schiff bases from, 92
separations of, 144, 380–385
Alkaloids, 429, 477, 490
  carbon skeletal analysis of, 471
Alkanes. See Hydrocarbons.
Alkaterge T, 453
Alkoxy groups, Zeisel determination of, 491
Alkylbenzenes. See Hydrocarbons, aromatic.
Alkyl halides. See Halogens.
Alteration before injection, 413
Alumina, 8, 151, 171, 182–183, 199
Amides, 468
Amines, 79, 93–98, 173, 292, 295, 411, 468, 491
  derivatives of, 93–98
  detection of primary, 491
  fatty aldehyde derivatives of, 94
  low level detection of, 95
  TFA derivatives of, 93
Amine oxides, pyrolysis of, 476
Amine salts, 475–476
Amino acid analyzer, 355
Amino acids and derivatives, 72–87, 377, 477, 488, 501
  N-acetyl N-amyl esters of, 82
  N-acetyl N-butyl esters of, 82
  N-acetyl N-propyl esters of, 81
  ammonia in separation of, 86
  butyl ester hydrochlorides of, 86
  chloromethyl esters of, 80
  conversion to amines, 79
  decarboxylation of, 79
  2,4-dinitrophenylmethyl esters of, 86
  dipeptides, methyl esters of, 89
  hydroxymethyl esters of, 80

* Prepared by Robert J. Olson, Shell Oil Company, Deer Park, Texas.